MODULATION OF CELLULAR INTERACTIONS BY VITAMIN A AND DERIVATIVES (RETINOIDS)

ANNALS OF THE NEW YORK ACADEMY OF SCIENCES

Volume 359

MODULATION OF CELLULAR INTERACTIONS BY VITAMIN A AND DERIVATIVES (RETINOIDS)

Edited by Luigi M. De Luca and Stanley S. Shapiro

The New York Academy of Sciences
New York, New York
1981

Second printing, June, 1982.

The cover shows the atomic model of mannosylretinylphosphate.

Library of Congress Cataloging in Publication Data

Main entry under title:

Modulation of cellular interactions by vitamin A and derivatives (retinoids)

(Annals of the New York Academy of Sciences; v. 359)
"This series of papers is the result of a conference . . . held on March 10–12, 1980 in New York and sponsored by the New York Academy of Sciences."
    1. Vitamin A – Metabolism – Congresses. 2. Vitamin A – Physiological effect – Congresses. 3. Cell interaction – Congresses. I. De Luca, Luigi M., 1940-   . II. Shapiro, Stanley S., 1940-   . III. New York Academy of Sciences. IV. Series: New York Academy of Sciences. Annals; v. 359. [DNLM: 1. Vitamin A – Metabolism – Congresses. 2. Vitamin A – Analogs and derivatives – Congresses. 3. Tretinoin – Metabolism – Congresses. 4. Models, Biological – Congresses. W1 AN626YL v. 359 / QU 167 M692 1980] Q11.N5 vol. 359 [QP772.V5] 500s [599.01'33] 80-28082

CCP
Printed in the United States of America.
ISBN 0-89766-107-9 (cloth)
ISBN 0-89766-108-7 (paper)

ANNALS OF THE NEW YORK ACADEMY OF SCIENCES

VOLUME 359

February 27, 1981

MODULATION OF CELLULAR INTERACTIONS BY VITAMIN A AND DERIVATIVES (RETINOIDS)*

Editors and Conference Chairmen
LUIGI M. DE LUCA and STANLEY S. SHAPIRO

———————————————◆———————————————

* This series of papers is the result of a conference entitled Modulation of Cellular Interactions by Vitamin A and Derivatives (Retinoids), held by The New York Academy of Sciences on March 10–12, 1980.

Part IV. Cellular Interactions

Part V. Biochemical Models

Financial assistance was received from:

- BASF AKTIENGESELLSCHAFT
- FOGARTY INTERNATIONAL CENTER, NIH
- HOFFMANN-LA ROCHE, INC.
- JOHNSON & JOHNSON PRODUCTS, INC.
- McNEIL LABORATORIES
- NATIONAL CANCER INSTITUTE
- NATIONAL INSTITUTE OF DENTAL RESEARCH
- NATIONAL SCIENCE FOUNDATION
- REVLON HEALTH CARE GROUP
- USV PHARMACEUTICAL CORPORATION

INTRODUCTION

Our knowledge in the field of vitamin A has undergone considerable expansion since George Wolf convened the International Symposium on Vitamin A in 1968. On that occasion, Umberto Saffiotti discussed his observations on an inhibitory effect of retinylpalmitate on the development of benzo[a]pyrene-induced carcinogenesis in the hamster respiratory tract. Werner Bollag's and Michael Sporn's laboratories extended this area of research to include a variety of synthetic derivatives of retinol, collectively termed "retinoids."

The rationale for this research derived from the observation that one of the physiological roles of vitamin A is to maintain normal phenotypic expression of epithelial tissues, which, in deficiency, undergo squamous metaplasia and keratinization, processes that also occur as a result of treatment with chemical carcinogens. As a result of these investigations some retinoids have been shown to be effective preventive agents of chemical carcinogenesis in some biological systems.

In another development, retinoids have been found to alter cell surface properties of neoplastically transformed cells. Administration of retinoids to cultured cells profoundly alters their ability to adhere to the growth surface and to each other, thus suggesting a role for these compounds in modulating cellular interactions.

All these observations are the result of the work of chemists and biological scientists of different background and specialization. Therefore, we thought it appropriate to convene a conference to discuss and analyze recent data on the action of retinoids at biochemical and cellular levels.

The presentations are organized to fall into four main research areas:

- metabolism of retinoids;
- binding proteins for retinol and retinoic acid;
- cellular interactions;
- biochemical models.

The documentation of our thoughts at this time on these subjects will provide a useful resource for future research at the interface between the classical vitamin A research approaches and the new ones in the realm of cell biology. The study of cellular interactions is a highly promising area of research for it may offer interesting leads as to how neoplastically transformed cells escape contact inhibition and anchorage dependence of growth.

ACKNOWLEDGMENTS

During the organization and duration of this conference we received advice, encouragement, and support from the staff of the New York Academy of Sciences. We also acknowledge the help of our colleagues at the National Cancer Institute and Hoffmann-La Roche during the organization of this meeting.

We wish to thank Dr. Tobias D. Yellin (Wilmington, Delaware) for his hospitality and for providing us with a halfway house for our organizational meetings.

Finally, we are grateful to the financial supporters of the Conference, and most indebted to the chairmen, speakers, and participants for their contributions.

LUIGI M. DE LUCA
STANLEY S. SHAPIRO

A HISTORICAL INTRODUCTION TO THE CHEMISTRY OF VITAMIN A AND ITS ANALOGS (RETINOIDS)

Beverly A. Pawson

Hoffmann-La Roche Inc.
Nutley, New Jersey 07110

The discovery,[1,2] in 1909, of a fat-soluble extract from egg yolk, which was essential for life, marked the beginning of the now more than 70 years of chemical and biological research with Vitamin A and its derivatives (retinoids). This substance, termed fat-soluble A,[3] was also found in animal fats and fish oils and was subsequently named Vitamin A.[4] In 1931, Karrer[5] obtained highly purified material and proposed the structural formula for vitamin A, which is also termed retinol (FIG. 1).

The history of the carotenoids predates that of vitamin A. Carotene was isolated in 1831, and other carotenoid pigments were described in the 19th century.[6] It was not until 1928, however, that the high vitamin A activity of carotene was discovered.[7] In 1930, its metabolism to vitamin A and storage in the liver were demonstrated.[8] The structural assignment for β-carotene was also made by Karrer[9] in 1930.

A further demonstration of the importance of the vitamin A derivatives came from the research of Wald[10] in 1935, when he carried out his elegant studies on the visual process. The identity of the retinal isolated from these visual experiments and vitamin A aldehyde was shown by Morton in 1944[11,12] (FIG. 1).

Another vitamin A derivative, vitamin A acid (FIG. 1), was synthesized by van Dorp and Arens[13] in 1946 and was shown to be important to growth.

The structural assignments of Karrer in 1931 and the isolation of crystalline retinol in 1942[14] spawned synthetic efforts by many groups. The first recorded synthesis of vitamin A, as a 7.5% concentrate with biological activity, appeared in 1937,[15] but the report was doubted until the work could be repeated by Arens and van Dorp in 1948.[16]

Several industrial processes of vitamin A have been developed.[17] Many of these produced vitamin A aldehyde or an ester of vitamin A acid, which must be reduced to the alcohol and esterified to give vitamin A acetate or palmitate. Two of the commercially more important ones were those by F. Hoffmann-La Roche & Co. Ltd., Basel, Switzerland, and by Badische Anilin und Sodafabrik [BASF], Ludwigshafen, West Germany.

In 1947, Isler *et al.*[18] of the Roche group reported the synthesis of pure vitamin A alcohol as shown in FIGURE 2. Pseudoionone (**1**), containing thirteen carbon atoms, was obtained ultimately from three molecules of acetone and two molecules of acetylene.[19-21] Cyclization of pseudoionone with acid gives β-ionone (**2**), a key intermediate in all the syntheses of vitamin A. In the Roche process, one carbon is added to β-ionone *via* a Darzens glycidic ester condensation to give β-C_{14} aldehyde (**3**). This substance was reacted in a Grignard reaction with "*cis*-pentol," *cis*-3-methyl-2-penten-4-yn-l-ol, an intermediate prepared by addition of acetylene to methyl vinyl ketone, subsequent rearrangement and fractionation. The resulting C_{20} acetylenic diol **5**, a crystalline intermediate, was partially hydrogenated over Lindlar catalyst to give the diol **6**. After acetylation of the pri-

0077–8923/81/0359–0001 $01.75/0 © 1981, NYAS

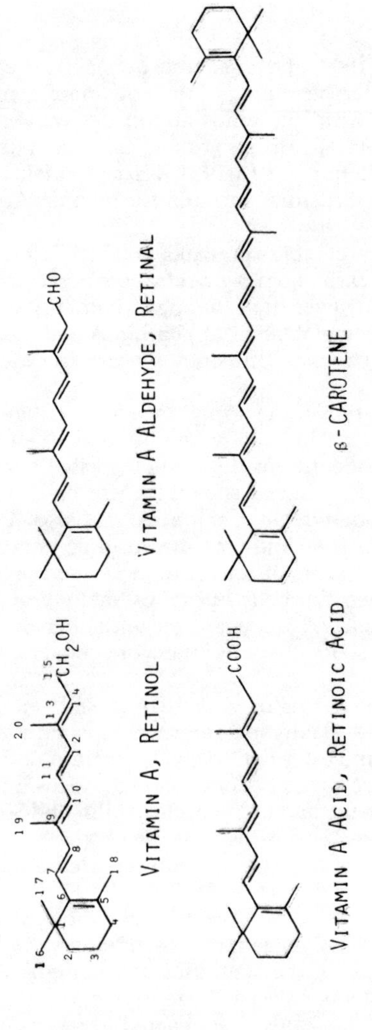

FIGURE 1. Chemical structures of vitamin A and related molecules.

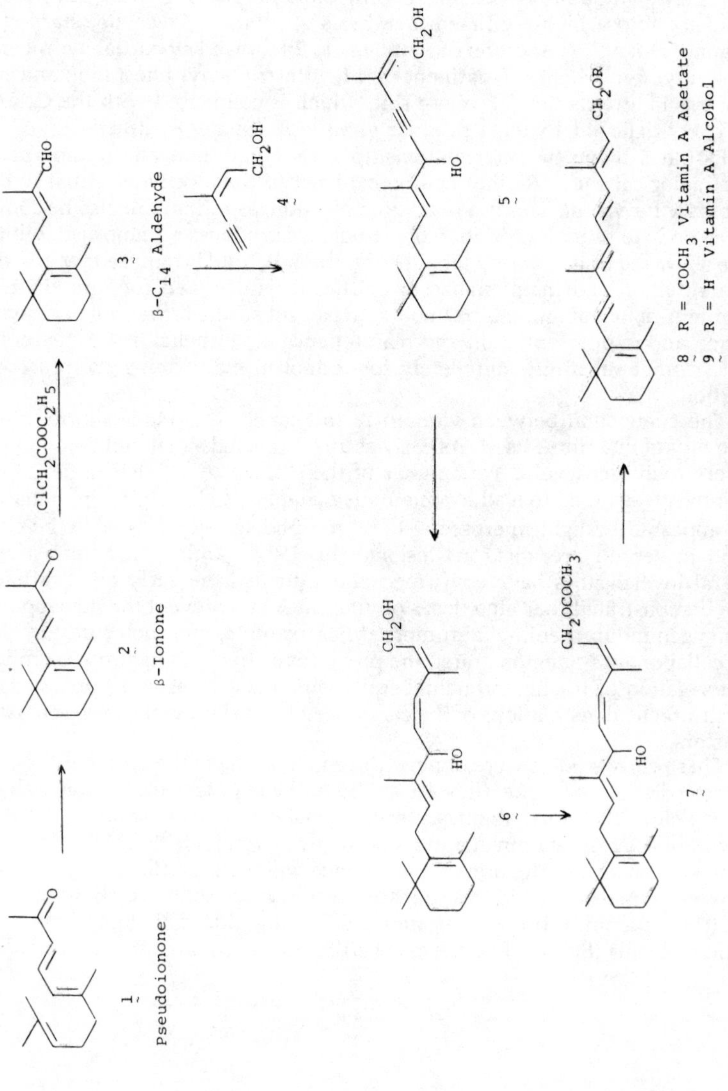

FIGURE 2. Roche industrial synthesis of vitamin A.

mary alcohol, final dehydration and rearrangement led to crystalline vitamin A acetate, which is saponified and purified to obtain crystalline retinol (9).

The discovery of the Wittig reaction,[22,23] a highly specific synthetic method for olefin formation (FIG. 3) for which Professor Georg Wittig received the 1979 Nobel Prize in Chemistry, opened the door to many other synthetic routes to vitamin A, retinoids, and carotenoids. Pommer and his group at BASF developed this chemistry into a highly efficient synthesis of vitamin A acetate, starting from β-ionone (FIG. 4).[24,25] Addition of acetylene to 2 followed by partial hydrogenation gives vinyl β-ionol (11). Treatment of 11 with triphenyl phosphine and hydrochloric acid affords the C_{15} Wittig salt, which is condensed with the C_5 unit 13 (γ-acetoxy tiglic aldehyde) to produce vitamin A acetate (8) directly.

FIGURE 5 shows the interrelationship of retinol, retinal, and retinoic acid and their biological roles. Retinol can be oxidized to the aldehyde retinal, which is necessary for vision. This is a reversible reaction, as retinal can also be converted by the body to retinol. Oxidation of retinol also produces retinoic acid, which has been shown to be a major metabolite of retinol. Retinol is required for growth, for differentiation and maintenance of epithelial tissues, and for reproduction. In vitamin A-deficient animals, retinoic acid can substitute for retinol in growth promotion and in differentiation and maintenance of epithelial tissue. Retinoic acid alone cannot substitute completely for retinol in maintaining the reproductive function.

The connection between vitamin A and cancer was made shortly after the discovery of vitamin A itself. As early as 1926, rats fed a diet deficient in vitamin A were found to develop carcinomas of the stomach.[26] Further, a deficiency of vitamin A was found to lead to squamous metaplastic changes in epithelial tissue that appeared by light microscopy to be morphologically similar to the changes found in certain precancerous lesions caused by carcinogen administration.[27] Several investigators have confirmed and extended the early observations and have demonstrated that high doses of vitamin A can prevent the development of carcinogen-induced epithelial tumors.[28] For example, one such study by Saffioti and collaborators[29] demonstrated the preventive effect of vitamin A palmitate on the formation of tracheo-bronchial squamous metaplasias and tumors, induced by intratracheal instillations of the carcinogen benzo [a]-pyrene and iron oxide, in hamsters.

These early studies were done with retinol or one of the retinyl esters, which have the disadvantage that they are stored in the liver and are toxic at high doses. Nevertheless, they form the basis for the renaissance in the study of the chemistry and biology of vitamin A and its derivatives (retinoids)[30] which has occurred in the last ten years. The present conference will focus on these recent biological discoveries, many of which were made with new retinoids which differ in structure from vitamin A through variations in the ring, side chain and terminal group of the molecule (FIG. 6). The chemical structures of some of these retinoids, con-

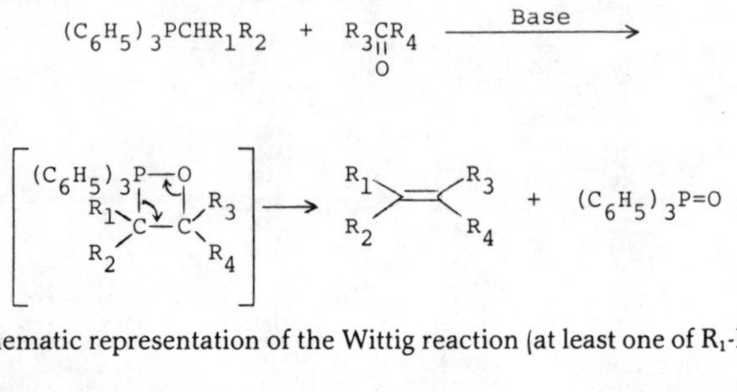

$$(C_6H_5)_3PCHR_1R_2 \quad + \quad R_3\underset{\underset{O}{||}}{C}R_4 \quad \xrightarrow{\text{Base}}$$

$$\left[\begin{array}{c} (C_6H_5)_3P-O \\ R_1 \diagdown | \diagup R_3 \\ C-C \\ R_2 \diagup \diagdown R_4 \end{array} \right] \longrightarrow \begin{array}{c} R_1 \diagdown \diagup R_3 \\ >\!\!=\!\!< \\ R_2 \diagup \diagdown R_4 \end{array} \quad + \quad (C_6H_5)_3P\!\!=\!\!O$$

FIGURE 3. Schematic representation of the Wittig reaction (at least one of R_1-R_4 must be H).

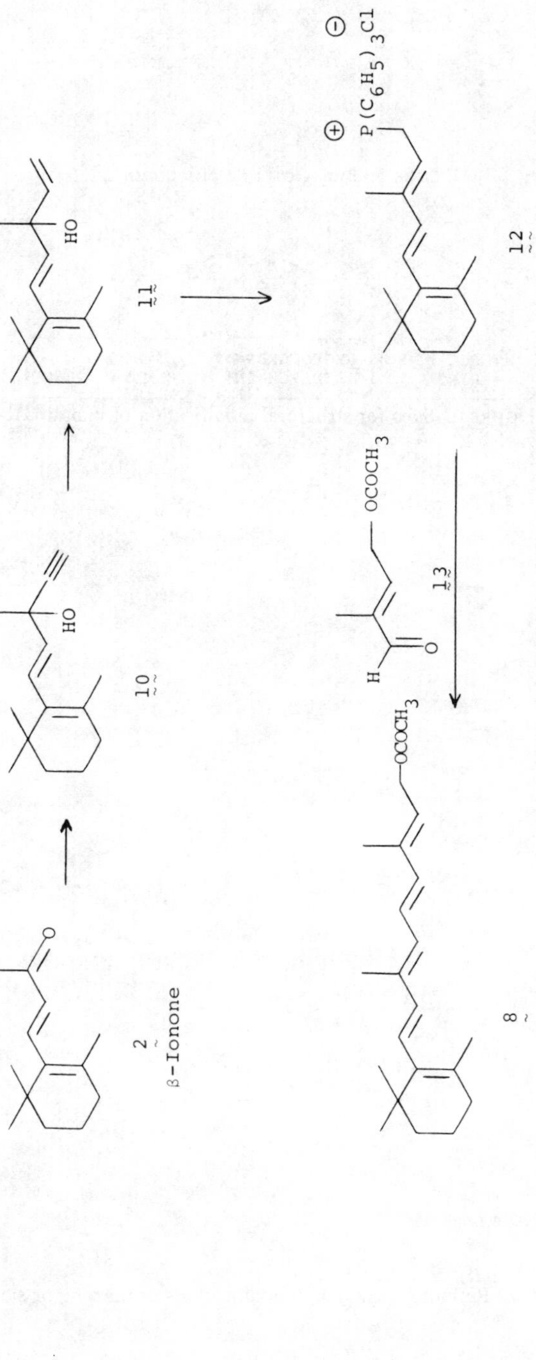

FIGURE 4. BASF process for vitamin A acetate.

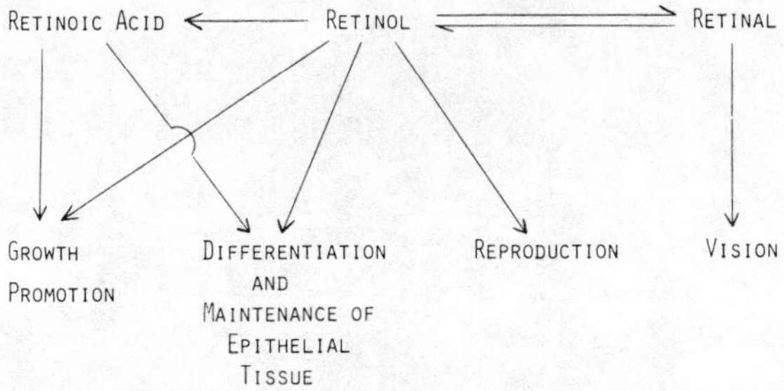

FIGURE 5. Biological role of vitamin A.

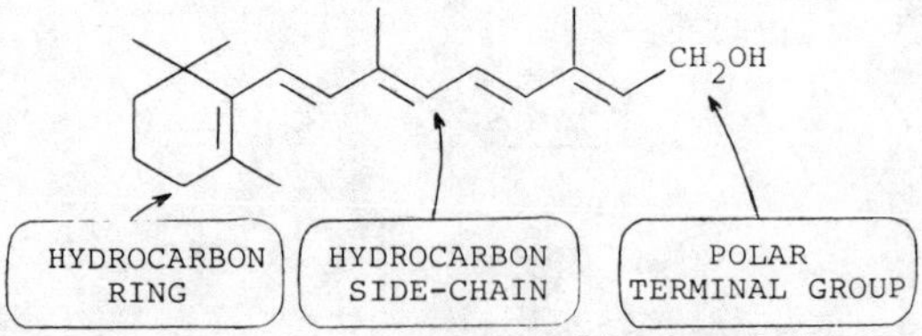

FIGURE 6. Sites for structural modification of vitamin A.

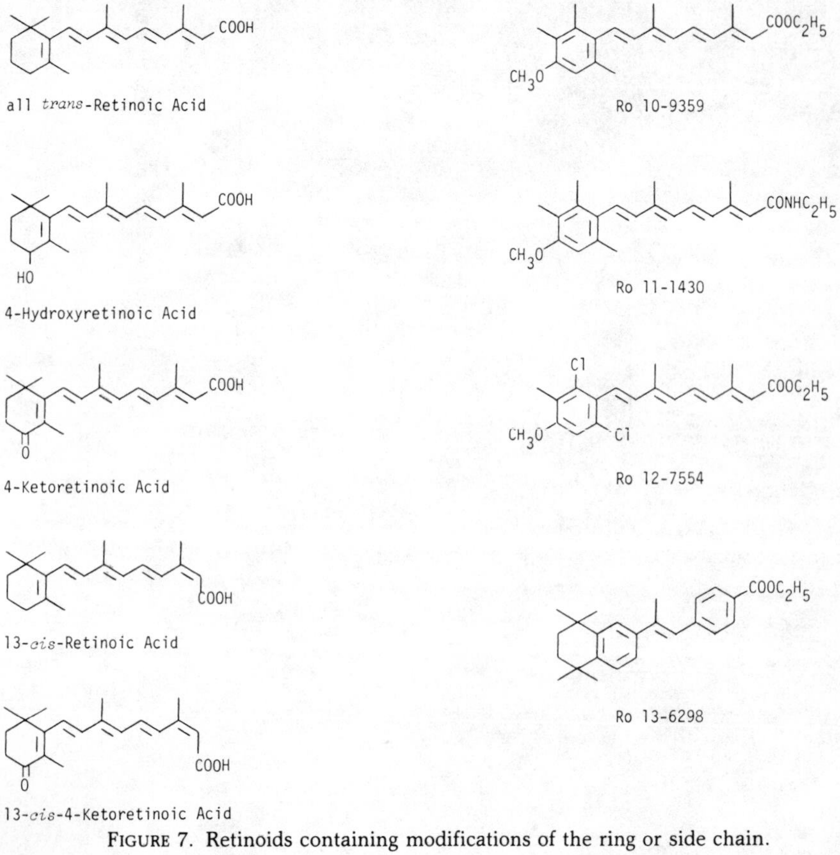

FIGURE 7. Retinoids containing modifications of the ring or side chain.

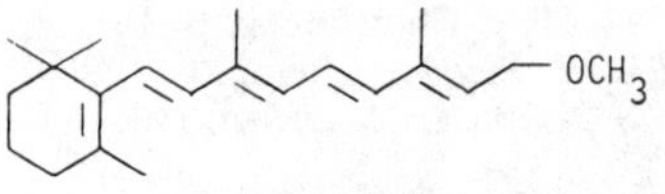

Retinyl Methyl Ether

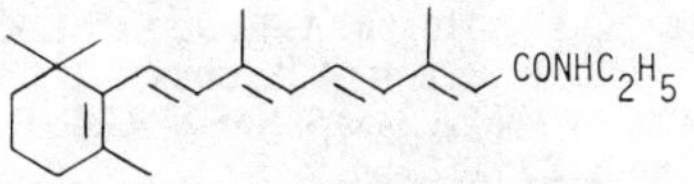

Retinoic Acid Ethyl Amide

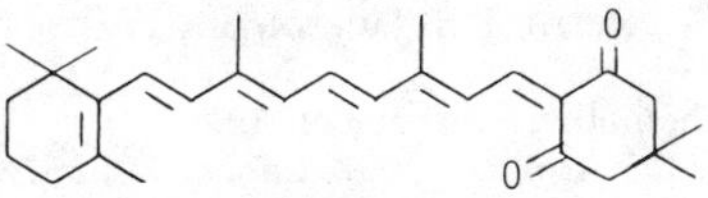

Retinylidene Dimedone

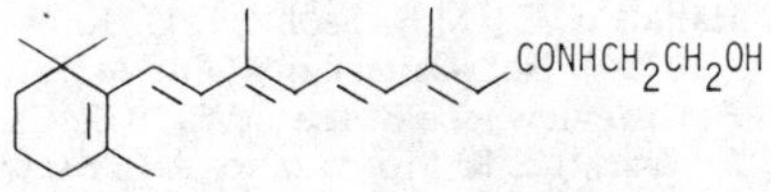

Retinoic Acid 2-Hydroxyethyl Amide

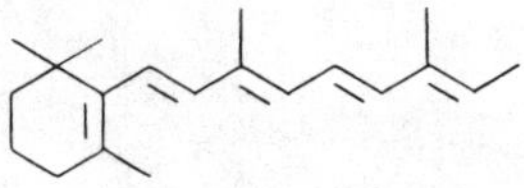

Axerophthene

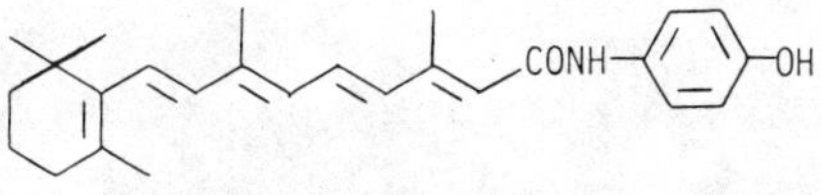

Retinoic Acid p-Hydroxyphenyl Amide

FIGURE 8. Retinoids with variations in the polar terminal group.

taining modifications in the ring or side chain, are shown in FIGURE 7. Others with variations in the polar terminal group are shown in FIGURE 8. Many of these compounds will be the subjects of investigations to be described in the forthcoming papers and posters.

REFERENCES

1. STEPP, W. 1909. Biochem. Z. 22: 452.
2. STEPP, W. 1911. Z. Biol. 57: 135.
3. McCOLLUM, E.V. & C. KENNEDY. 1916. J. Biol. Chem. 24: 491.
4. DRUMMOND, J.C. 1920. Biochem. J. 14: 660.
5. KARRER, P., R. MORF & K. SCHÖPP, 1931. Helv. Chim. Acta 14: 1036, 1431.
6. ISLER, O. Carotenoids. O. ISLER, Ed.: 13. BIRKHAUSER VERLAG. Basel.
7. V. EULER, B., H.V. EULER & H. HELLSTRÖM. 1928. Biochem Z. 203: 370.
8. MOORE, T. 1930. Biochem. J. 24: 692.
9. KARRER, P., A. HELFENSTEIN, H. WEHRLI & A. WETTSTEIN. 1930. Helv. Chim. Acta 13: 1084.
10. WALD, G. 1935. J. Gen. Physiol. 18: 905.
11. MORTON, R.A. 1944. Nature. 153: 69.
12. MORTON, R.A. & T.W. GOODWIN. 1944. Nature. 153: 405.
13. VAN DORP, D.A. & J.F. ARENS. 1946. Rec. Trav. Chim. 65: 338.
14. BAXTER, J.G. & C.D. ROBESON. 1942. J. Am. Chem. Soc. 64: 2407, 2411.
15. KUHN, R. & C.J.O.R. MORRIS. 1937. Chem. Ber. 70: 853.
16. ARENS, J.F. & D.A. VAN DORP. 1948. Rec. Trav. Chim. 67: 973.
17. ISLER, O. 1979. Pure Appl. Chem. 51: 447.

18. ISLER, O., W. HUBER, A. RONCO & M. KOFLER. 1947. Helv. Chim. Acta **30:** 1911.
19. ISLER, O., R. RUEGG, A. STUDER & R. JÜRGENS. 1953. Z. Physiol. Chem. **295:** 290.
20. KIMEL, W., N.W. SAX, S. KAISER, G.G. EICHMANN, G.O. CHASE & A. OFNER. 1958. J. Org. Chem. **23:** 153.
21. SAUCY, G. & R. MARBET. 1967. Helv. Chim. Acta. **50:** 1158, 2091, 2095.
22. WITTIG, G. & G. GEISSLER. 1953. Annalen **580:** 44.
23. WITTIG, G. & U. SCHÖLLKOPF. 1954. Chem. Ber. **87:** 1318.
24. POMMER, H. 1960. Angew. Chem. **72:** 811.
25. POMMER, H. 1977. Angew. Chem. **89:** 437.
26. FUJIMAKI, Y. 1926. J. Cancer Res. **10:** 469.
27. HARRIS, C.C., M.B. SPORN, D.G. KAUFMAN, J.M. SMITH, F.E. JACKSON & U. SAFFIOTI. 1972. J. Nat. Cancer Inst. **48:** 743.
28. For a review, see BOLLAG, W. 1979. Cancer Chemother. Pharmacol. **3:** 207.
29. SAFFIOTI, U., R. MONTESANO, A.R. SALLAKUMAR & S.A. BORG. 1967. Cancer **20:** 857.
30. SPORN, M.B., N.M. DUNLOP, D.L. NEWTON & J.M. SMITH. 1976. Fed. Proc. **35:** 1332.

FROM VITAMIN A TO RETINOIDS IN EXPERIMENTAL AND CLINICAL ONCOLOGY: ACHIEVEMENTS, FAILURES, AND OUTLOOK

W. Bollag and A. Matter

Department of Pharmaceutical Research
F. Hoffmann-La Roche & Co. AG
4002 Basel, Switzerland

The problems of prevention and therapy of cancer are far from being solved. Regarding therapy, it is beyond doubt that surgery and radiotherapy cure a certain percentage of cancer patients. Cancer chemotherapy with the conventional cytostatic agents is a further means by which oncologists can help patients. Immunotherapy, including the newest methods of treatment with thymosin, and particularly interferon, may bring further progress. In the field of prevention of cancer mortality, early detection of precancerous and cancerous lesions and elimination of carcinogenic agents are up to now the most successful means. The continuing high mortality of cancer, even in the most developed countries, underlines the still unsatisfactory medical methods at our disposal. New approaches to the cancer problem are badly needed. It is the purpose of this conference to acquaint us with the basic research work done in the field of retinoids. The retinoids (vitamin A and analogs) represent a fairly new development in the cancer field, offering a new approach differing markedly in their more physiological mode of action from the hitherto existing approaches in prevention and therapy of cancer.

HISTORY OF THE RELATIONSHIP BETWEEN VITAMIN A AND CANCER

Vitamin A is vital for promotion of general growth, differentiation of epithelial tissues, visual function and reproduction. A connection between vitamin A and cancer was detected as early as 1926 when it was found that carcinomas of the stomach appeared in rats fed a vitamin A-deficient diet.[1] Between 1922 and 1928 it was discovered that a deficiency of vitamin A leads to metaplastic changes in the epithelia of the respiratory, gastrointestinal and genito-urinary tracts.[2-4] These metaplasias may be considered as the first step in the transformation from normal to preneoplastic and finally to neoplastic tissue. The similarity between the histological features of epithelial tissues of vitamin A-deficient animals and certain precancerous lesions of skin and mucous membranes was the starting point for interesting new investigations. Several authors[5-7] showed a prophylactic effect of vitamin A *in vivo* on the induction of such precancerous conditions as benign epithelial tumors and metaplasias as well as carcinomas. In a carefully planned study it was demonstrated that vitamin A had a preventive effect on the appearance of squamous metaplasias of trachea and bronchus induced in hamsters by intratracheal instillations of benzpyrene, a carcinogenic hydrocarbon.[8] By prevention of the metaplasias the development of carcinomas was actually delayed or avoided. Furthermore, in organ culture work, vitamin A was shown to prevent hyperplasia, dysplasia, and metaplasia in various tissues, produced either by a vitamin A-deficient medium or by carcinogenic hydrocarbons.[9] All the early experiments were carried out with natural vitamin A compounds such as

9

0077-8923/81/0359-0009 $01.75/0 © 1981, NYAS

retinol and retinyl esters, and only in prevention tests; in more recent investigations, however, analogs of vitamin A were also used. Such compounds were tested for prevention as well as for therapy of cancer.

THE SHIFT FROM VITAMIN A TO RETINOIC ACID AND OTHER ANALOGS

The reason for not confining our experiments to vitamin A alone, was the fact that high doses of vitamin A were toxic to animals and man and induced the so-called hypervitaminosis A syndrome. Therefore, a search for less toxic and more potent analogs of vitamin A was undertaken. The first compound which was investigated intensively was all-*trans*-retinoic acid.[10-12]

Experimental Results

Successful preventive and therapeutic experiments with retinoic acid were carried out on chemically induced papillomas and carcinomas of the skin of mice.[11,12] The initiator used was 7,12-dimethyl-benz (a) anthracene, painted on the back skin of female Swiss albino mice (2 × 150 μg) on days 1 and 15; croton oil (500 μg, 2 × weekly) was then applied as promoter. Papillomas usually appeared after 3-8 months, whereas carcinomas were not induced until after 5-12 months.

In a typical therapeutic experiment carried out with well-established papillomas the control animals showed an increase in the mean papilloma diameter per animal of 22.7% within 14 days, whereas in the animals treated with all-*trans*-retinoic acid a dose-dependent regression of up to 51.4% was observed. Furthermore, even chemically induced skin carcinomas regressed to a certain degree. In prophylactic experiments with the same model system, all-*trans*-retinoic acid given during the promotion phase delayed the appearance and retarded the growth of papillomas and also inhibited the induction of carcinomas. With these experiments it was proven that all-*trans*-retinoic acid had a chemopreventive (antipromoting) as well as a chemotherapeutic effect on benign and malignant epithelial tumors. These experimental results encouraged us to carry out clinical trials with retinioic acid.

Clinical Results

In the treatment of actinic keratoses (a precancerous condition) and basal cell carcinomas of the skin positive results were obtained by topical application of retinoic acid.[13] Of the patients with actinic keratoses, 40% responded with complete regression and 45% with partial regression. In patients with basal cell carcinomas, the corresponding figures amounted to 31% and 63%, respectively. Positive clinical results were also achieved by oral treatment with retinoic acid in preneoplastic and neoplastic lesions of the skin and mucous membranes.[14,15] Actinic keratoses, basal cell carcinomas, leukoplakias of the mouth, tongue and larynx, and papillomas of the urinary bladder were favorably influenced. However, carcinomas — except for basal cell carcinomas — did not respond to retinoic acid.

HYPERVITAMINOSIS A AND THE THERAPEUTIC INDEX

From a scientific point of view the results reported appeared encouraging. However, this treatment could not be recommended for practical purposes because the regression rate was too low and side effects too pronounced. Also retinoic acid induced the toxic effects of the hypervitaminosis A syndrome both in animals and in man. In man, the main signs and symptoms were changes in the skin (e.g. erythema, desquamation, hair loss) and mucous membranes (e.g. cheilitis, stomatitis, conjunctivitis etc.), hepatic dysfunction and headache. All these signs and symptoms prohibited use of the higher doses which may be required for the successful prevention and treatment of precancerous conditions and particularly of carcinomas. Therefore, as early as 1968 we initiated the synthesis of retinoic acid analogs with the aim of producing compounds which would, it was hoped, possess high activity and high tumor specificity linked with low toxicity. To this end, a new screening system was developed and applied, which made it possible to detect a dissociation *in vivo* between the antitumor effect and the toxic syndrome of hypervitaminosis A.[16] The therapeutic index* was defined as the ratio between the lowest daily i.p. dose causing in a 14-day study a defined degree of hypervitaminosis A and the dose given i.p. once a week for 2 weeks causing a 50% regression of papillomas. In mice, hypervitaminosis A manifests itself in the form of weight loss, desquamation of the skin, hair loss, and bone fractures. A grading system of 0–4 (none to very marked) for each of the above-mentioned signs and symptoms was used. The points scored for each one of the four parameters were added, and hypervitaminosis A defined as the dose provoking at least three points. Thus, the therapeutic index enabled us to compare retinoids one against the other.

THE SEARCH FOR NEW RETINOIDS

All previous experimental and clinical trials demonstrated that the toxic signs and symptoms of so-called hypervitaminosis A syndrome were a serious handicap to the administration of the rather high doses of retinoids that are probably necessary for the successful prevention and therapy of cancer. The aim of the chemical program was therefore directed towards finding compounds with better therapeutic margins. In the Roche laboratories alone, about 1000 retinoids were synthesized and tested biologically. Molecular modifications were made to all three building units of the vitamin A molecule: the cyclic end group, the polyene chain, and the polar end group.[17] TABLE 1 lists a series of compounds that were active at extremely different doses and possessed different therapeutic indices. The three aromatic retinoids Motretinid, Etretinate and its dichloro analog (DCMMP), as well as two new analogs with a second aromatic ring in the side chain, the arotinoid ethyl ester and the arotinoid methyl ether, each possessed a therapeutic index of 2.0; this was 10 times more favorable than that of retinoic acid, which was 0.2. Considering only potency, the arotinoid ethyl ester was 8000 times more ac-

---

* In previous publications the inverse relationship had been defined as a "therapeutic ratio." For practical reasons this is now abandoned in favor of the more widely used "therapeutic index." Thus, lower toxicity and higher therapeutic efficacy will yield *higher* therapeutic indices. The importance of measuring both parameters *in vivo* should be stressed if clinical applications are envisaged. *In vitro* measurements may be misleading.

TABLE 1

List of Series of Retinoids with Very Different Chemical Structures
(The Therapeutic Index, As Well As the Dose Necessary for an Antipapilloma Effect, Varies Markedly Among the Various Retinoids*)

Chemical structure	Hypervitaminosis A (mg/kg)	Antipapilloma Effect (mg/kg)	Therapeutic Index
all-trans-Retinoic acid (Tretinoin)	80	400	$\frac{80}{400} = 0.2$
1-Methoxyethyl-cyclopentenyl analog of retinoic acid	6	24	$\frac{6}{24} = 0.25$
13-cis-Retinoic acid (Isotretinoin)	400	800	$\frac{400}{800} = 0.5$
Trimethylmethoxyphenyl (TMMP) analog of retinoic acid ethyl amide (Motretinid)	100	50	$\frac{100}{50} = 2.0$
Trimethylmethoxyphenyl (TMMP) analog of retinoic acid ethyl ester (Etretinate)	50	25	$\frac{50}{25} = 2.0$
Dichloromethylmethoxyphenyl (DCMMP) analog of retinoic acid ethyl ester	12	6	$\frac{12}{6} = 2.0$
Arotinoid ethyl ester	0.1	0.05	$\frac{0.1}{0.05} = 2.0$
Arotinoid methyl ether	0.1	0.05	$\frac{0.1}{0.05} = 2.0$

* The therapeutic index was defined as the ratio between the lowest daily i.p. dose causing in a 14-day study a defined degree of hypervitaminosis A and the dose given i.p. once a week for 2 weeks causing a 50% regression of papillomas.

tive than all-*trans*-retinoic acid in the antipapilloma test. The minute dose of 0.05 mg/kg given once a week led in a 2-week experiment to 50% regression of established papillomas. It is our opinion, however, that the usefulness of a retinoid is mainly dependent on a marked dissociation between activity and toxicity. Very many compounds were tested by many investigators in various *in vitro* and *in vivo* model systems. The most frequently investigated retinoids include retinyl esters such as retinylacetate and retinylpalmitate, retinyl methyl ether, all-*trans*-retinoic acid, 13-*cis*-retinoic acid and the aromatic retinoids.

RESULTS OF THE EFFECTS OF AN AROMATIC RETINOID IN DIFFERENT MODELS

To avoid giving a complete review on all retinoids tested up to now in a large variety of model systems, we will restrict ourselves to one retinoid, the aromatic retinoid Etretinate = Ro 10–9359 = ethyl all-*trans*-9-(4-methoxy-2, 3, 6-trimethyl-phenyl)-3, 7-dimethyl-2, 4, 6, 8-nonatetraenoate. This does not mean that this retinoid is superior to other retinoids in all respects. It has its own spectrum of activities, and these will now be described.

Organ Cultures

Organ cultures of prostate, trachea or fetal lung, when cultivated in a medium deficient in vitamin A or treated with carcinogens or hormones develop hyperplasia, dysplasia and squamous metaplasia, phenomena attributed to a preneoplastic state. It has been shown that hyperplasia and metaplasia do not develop when Etretinate is added prophylactically to the medium.[18-21] When hyperplasia had already developed after a previous treatment with methylcholanthrene or testosterone in prostate culture or with benzpyrene in trachea or in fetal lung culture, Etretinate was even able to reverse the hyperplasia.[19-21] The extent of hyperplasia was measured by the morphometric method or by determination of the number of colcemid-arrested mitotic figures.

Transplantable Tumors

Almost all the agents used in present-day cancer chemotherapy have been detected in screening programs with transplantable tumors. This applies to alkylating agents, antimetabolites, plant extracts, antibiotics and various other anticancer drugs. With retinoids the situation is quite different. Most of the conventionally used transplantable tumors did not respond to retinoids. Thus, Etretinate had not the slightest growth-inhibitory effect on the following tumors: Leukemia L 1210, Ehrlich ascites carcinoma, Ehrlich carcinoma, solid form, Crocker sarcoma S 180, Lewis lung carcinoma, melanoma B-16, Walker carcinoma.[16] On the other hand, in the rat chondrosarcoma, Etretinate, depending on the dose, not only retarded growth, but well-established tumors even underwent striking regressions.[22] An inhibitory effect of Etretinate on the growth of a human bronchial carcinoma serially transplanted in athymic nude mice has also been found.[23]

CHEMICALLY INDUCED TUMORS

Most of the experimental work on the influence of retinoids in *in vivo* model systems has been carried out with chemically induced tumors. Dimethylbenz-anthracene (DMBA), benzypyrene (BP), methylcholanthrene (MCA) or nitroso compounds have been used as carcinogenic agents. A large number of investigations followed the earlier ones, various carcinogens being used to induce all sorts of tumors at different organ sites in the body. In some experiments not only initiating agents but also promoting agents were administered. Etretinate was found to possess a marked preventive effect on the development of skin papillomas and carcinomas of mice induced by DMBA and croton oil.[24] The daily oral administration of 30 mg/kg Etretinate – given during the promotion phase of carcinogenesis – delayed the appearance and retarded the growth of papillomas and reduced the incidence of carcinomas. At day 293 after the beginning of the experiment Etretinate – in comparison with controls – reduced the mean number of papillomas per mouse from 12.4 to 1.1, the mean volume of papillomas per mouse from 426.3 to 6.8 mm,[3] and the incidence of carcinomas from 46 to 4 (FIGS. 1, 2, and 3). Similar results were found by other investigators using 12-O-tetra-decanoyl-phorbol-13-acetate (TPA) instead of croton oil. In these studies with mice the topical application of Etretinate counteracted the papilloma-promoting effect of TPA.[25] The DMBA-induced keratoacanthoma on the skin of the rabbit's ear was completely prevented by administering Etretinate orally during the induction phase.[26] A large number of chemopreventive experiments have been done with many retinoids in various kinds of chemically induced tumors.[27-32] Usually a retinoid has an influence on a particular spectrum of tumors. This may be dependent on many factors such as species, organ site, pharmacokinetics, distribution pattern, metabolism, and binding to receptors etc.

Etretinate was not only effective in the prevention of tumors but had also a clear-cut therapeutic activity on chemically induced tumors.[16] In a 14-day thera-

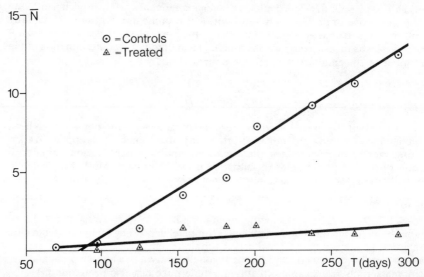

FIGURE 1. Prevention of chemically induced papillomas and carcinomas by the aromatic retinoid Etretinate, 30 mg/kg daily orally, given during the promotion phase. Mean number of papillomas per animal in controls [O] and Etretinate-treated mice [Δ]. $\bar{N}$ = Mean number of papillomas per animal; T = Days after first application of carcinogen. (From Bollag.[24] By permission of *Eur. J. Cancer.*)

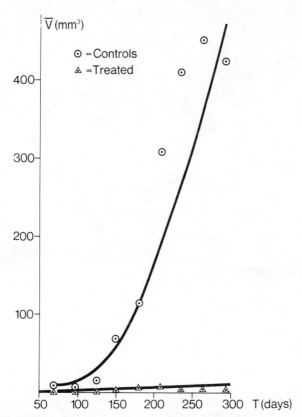

FIGURE 2. Prevention of chemically induced papillomas and carcinomas by the aromatic retinoid Etretinate, 30 mg/kg daily orally, given during the promotion phase. Mean volume of papillomas per animal in controls [O] and Etretinate-treated mice [Δ]. V̄ = Mean volume of papillomas per animal (mm³); T = Days after first application of carcinogen. (From Bollag.[24] By permission of *Eur. J. Cancer.*)

peutic experiment with established papillomas the controls showed a progression of growth by 23.2%, whereas in the animals treated with Etretinate once a week the papillomas regressed; this regression was dose-dependent: 200 mg/kg i.p. led to a regression of 74.1% and even 25 mg/kg still reduced the papilloma diameters by 48.8% (TABLE 2). The therapeutic effect on chemically induced squamous cell carcinomas of the skin was also pronounced. Whereas the mean carcinoma volume of the controls increased by 92.7%, the carcinoma volumes of the animals treated with 200 mg/kg daily i.p. during 14 days regressed by 53.4% and with 400 mg/kg even by 72.2%. These high doses, however, provoked marked toxic symptoms of hypervitaminosis A.

Virus-induced Tumors

Some of these tumors also responded to retinoids.[33,34] In rabbits inoculated

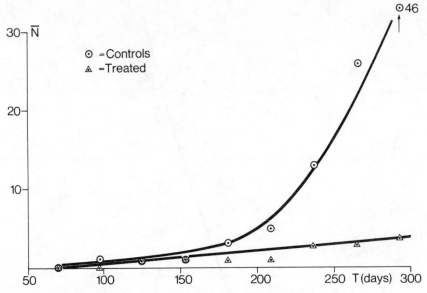

FIGURE 3. Prevention of chemically induced papillomas and carcinomas by the aromatic retinoid Etretinate, 30 mg/kg daily orally, given during the promotion phase. Incidence of carcinomas (cumulative number) in controls [O] and Etretinate-treated mice [Δ]. N = Number of carcinomas; T = Days after first application of carcinogen. (From Bollag.[24] By permission of *Eur. J. Cancer.*)

with Shope papilloma virus a dose-dependent growth inhibition was observed with Etretinate.[33,34] A 200 mg/kg i.m. dose, once a week completely prevented the appearance of papillomas, whereas 50 mg/kg still exerted marked inhibition of the growth of these tumors. Also, established Shope papillomas could be influenced therapeutically by Etretinate, which provoked regressions of these virus-induced tumors. Until recently the opinion prevailed that retinoids possess a preventive effect only on the induction of epithelial tumors. An experiment with Etretinate on the induction of the virus-induced Rous sarcoma in chickens revealed a preventive effect of this compound on the induction of this tumor, which is of mesenchymal origin. Of 20 control animals inoculated with Rous sarcoma virus all developed large sarcomas, whereas in the group treated with Etretinate only one small tumor was observed.[34] Furthermore, sarcomas in hamsters induced by the Schmidt-Ruppin strain of Rous sarcoma virus could be prevented by Etretinate.[33,34] Thus, not only chemical but also viral carcinogenesis can be inhibited by retinoids, including tumors both of epithelial and mesenchymal origin.

CLINICAL TRIALS WITH RETINOIDS FOR THE PREVENTION AND THERAPY OF CANCER

Our intention in providing experimental data was to offer the clinician the chance of choosing one or the other retinoid for clinical trials, either for prevention or for therapy of cancer. Everybody is aware that this is always a difficult task in view of the fact that it is usually impossible to foresee whether the results of a certain animal experiment can be transferred to clinical practice. So many factors are involved, such as toxicology, pharmacokinetics, metabolism, species- and tissue- and organ-specificity etc., that the outcome of every new clinical trial is unpredictable. Furthermore, trials dealing with the therapy of precancerous and cancerous lesions can be planned and carried out quite accurately, whereas the organization and realization of a well-designed preventive study is an overwhelmingly difficult task, with many obstacles. It should suffice here to mention the usually long duration of such trials and the large populations required because of low incidence rates. Furthermore, the high drop-out rate due to toxicity and the difficult ethical questions that arise, particularly when setting up prospective controls, are further hindrances. Therefore, most clinical trials so far have been therapeutic. The successful therapy of actinic keratoses and basal cell carcinomas of the skin with topical application of retinoic acid[13] was a first step in this direction. Further positive results were obtained by oral administration of all-*trans*-retinoic acid,[14,15,35] 13-*cis*-retinoic acid[35,36] and Etretinate[35] in leukoplakias, bladder papillomas, and basal cell carcinomas. Besides these published results, many more clinical trials have been done in Europe with Etretinate in which positive, but not optimal, therapeutic results have been achieved in actinic keratoses, basal cell carcinomas, and Gorlin's syndrome; in leukoplakias of the oral cavity, of the tongue and of the larynx; in oral papillomatosis and in urinary bladder papillomas. The results of clinical trials with Etretinate in monotherapy of carcinomas, particularly squamous cell carcinomas of different organs, were unsatisfactory since only partial remissions could be achieved and only with

TABLE 2

THERAPY OF CHEMICALLY INDUCED PAPILLOMAS;
RESULTS OF TREATMENT OF ESTABLISHED SKIN PAPILLOMAS DURING 2 WEEKS WITH
DIFFERENT DOSAGE SCHEDULES OF THE RETINOID ETRETINATE

Dose (mg/kg)	Average Sum of the Papilloma Diameter/Animal (mm)		Percent Change in the Average Sum of the Papilloma Diameter/Animal
	Day 0	Day 14	
Controls	21.1	26.0	+23.2%
Etretinate			
200 1 × weekly i.p.	25.5	6.6	−74.1%
100	28.0	8.5	−69.6%
50	20.4	9.1	−55.4%
25	24.4	12.5	−48.8%
12.5	24.8	17.3	−30.2%
400 1 × weekly p.o.	22.0	4.8	−78.2%
200	23.7	9.8	−58.6%
100	21.5	14.3	−33.5%
50	21.0	16.5	−21.4%
25	16.0	14.2	−11.3%
40 daily p.o.	19.5	4.6	−76.4%
20	16.6	7.4	−55.4%
10	18.4	9.8	−46.7%
5	16.5	13.7	−17.0%

From Bollag.[16] By permission of *Eur. J. Cancer.*

doses inducing intolerable side effects. Therefore, therapeutic trials with Etretinate are now under way combining Etretinate with cytostatic agents or x-rays. In the field of prevention several trials are being carried out: prevention of relapses of bladder papillomas after electroresection, prevention of relapses of bronchial carcinomas after surgery, and prevention of lung cancer in high-risk patients (heavy smokers). The great difficulties of such trials have been mentioned.

What Can We Gain from an Understanding of Basic Mechanisms?

Retinoids are – besides steroid hormones and some growth factors – among the few defined substances that govern growth and differentiation of tissues. Thus, they offer a convenient means for the study of mechanisms that are of utmost importance to present-day biologists. It is likely that a solution of the cancer problem will become much closer if we can but understand the basic control mechanisms which drive a cell from the proliferative to the nonproliferative, differentiated state. In addition, if we can unravel the chain of events that lead to the transformation of a cell, the solution will come still closer.

The fact that retinoids are not only able to maintain a normal level of differentiation in untransformed epithelia, but are also capable of preventing and reversing carcinogenesis in quite a number of systems, has prompted an increasing amount of studies directly aimed at elucidating the underlying mechanisms. With more and more data available, the following tentative conclusions can be drawn: It seems at this moment impossible to outline a single hypothesis concerning retinoid action. Epithelial tissues, as well as tissues of mesenchymal origin, are influenced by retinoids. Every target cell reacts in its own typical way to retinoids, often simultaneously at different levels of cellular organization. This is documented in the case of glycosaminoglycan and glycoprotein biosynthesis, where a retinoid-induced increase can have opposite biological effects: decreased adhesion of skin and other epithelial cells by mucous metaplasia,[37] and on the other hand increased adhesion with shape change and restoration of anchorage dependence in transformed fibroblasts[38-40] and other cells.[41] The work of De Luca's group[42] certainly has given us a framework which provides the basis for an understanding of retinoid-induced increased glycosylation: availability of retinyl-phosphate intermediates and specificity of glycosyl transferases appear to be responsible for the nature and amount of glycosaminoglycans and proteoglycans appearing at the cell surface and in the extracellular space. It is now well documented – at least for in vitro tests – that such products of carbohydrate metabolism can have profound consequences for the differentiation level and growth rate of cells, fibronectin being the best known example so far.[40,43] Such epigenetic control mechanisms are certainly fascinating, despite the implication that retinoids will probably be inactive on fully dedifferentiated cells, since it is likely that such cells will have shed the biochemical structures that are necessary for retinoid action. An example for this is the SV 40-transformed 3T3 cell, which does not respond – as does the untransformed 3T3 cell – to retinoic acid with an increase in glycosaminoglycan synthesis.[40,44]

What are the biochemical structures necessary for a cell to respond to retinoids? The cellular binding proteins are certainly likely candidates. At present, it is probably safe to state the following: In some instances (e.g. chondro-sarcoma,[45] embryonal carcinoma[46]) presence of cellular retinoic acid binding protein (cRABP) seems to correlate well with retinoid sensitivity. In others, where it is absent despite retinoid sensitivity, it can be postulated that presently available detection methods for cRABP are still too crude.[47] Affinity studies[48,49] of various retinoids to cRABP have shown that the polar end group must be an unsubstituted carboxylic group and that strong binding is limited to a group of closely related molecular structures. However, quantitative correlations between biological activities and affinities are not very good. Arotinoids in particular, although of extreme potency, show only binding affinities which are in the range of retinoic acid. However, we know of no retinoid with high activity and nil binding to cRABP, if it is assumed that end-group-substituted retinoids are split by the corresponding enzymes to yield free carboxyl radicals. Metabolic studies seem to confirm this. Binding proteins also hold promise as diagnostic, and perhaps, prognostic markers for diseases such as preneoplastic and neoplastic changes of mammary tissue.[50] All in all, it can be said that binding proteins probably are necessary, but not sufficient, prerequisites for retinoid action.

The hypothesis has been proposed[51] that retinoids act similarly to steroid hormones via a receptor protein (the binding proteins) and be translocated as a complex into the nucleus, this leading to altered gene expression via protein kinase activities. It is probably too early to draw final conclusions, but some of the work published seems to confirm such an hypothesis.[47,52,53] Altered gene expression by retinoids has been documented in the case of interferon production where a repressor protein has been found.[54] Also the depressed ODC activity by retinoic acid is in favor of this hypothesis.[25] Besides the altered glycosylation and gene expression, there is a mechanism, discovered long ago, but which still merits our interest: the labilization of lysosomal membranes and the release of lysosomal enzymes,[55] best illustrated by the destruction of normal cartilage,[56] by the inhibition of chondrogenesis[57] and the regression of chondro-sarcomas,[22] may have important consequences: firstly, it is probably one of the mechanisms by which retinoids manifest their toxicity and is therefore clinically important; secondly, the release of sialidases[58] has numerous consequences, not least of all the changing of the pattern of metastasis and immune recognition of tumor cells; thirdly, macrophage activation may also be brought about by lysosomal activation, thus providing a clue for the understanding of the manifold effects of retinoids on immune functions such as activation of T killer cells.[59] Last but not least, the direct detergent effect of retinoids on most cellular membranes should be mentioned,[60-62] this possibly contributing to tumor regression in experimental situations. However, in clinical situations this could give rise to unacceptable toxic effects.

To answer the title question: what can be gained from all this research? It is our opinion that basic research has provided and will continue to provide still more insight into the mechanisms of action of retinoids. Also these compounds will be useful tools for understanding some of the most basic problems of biology. It is also hoped that basic research will show us the precise relations between toxicity and efficacy and that structure–activity relationships will become apparent in terms of molecular biology. This in turn will facilitate the use of retinoids in therapy and–one hopes–in the prevention of cancer.

CONCLUSIONS AND OUTLOOK

In this article we have reviewed early and recent investigations with retinoids in experimental and clinical oncology. The retinoids, including vitamin A compounds and synthetic structural analogs, represent a new class of compounds with remarkable prophylactic and therapeutic activities in oncology. In various *in vitro* and *in vivo* models retinoids have proved to be capable of retarding or preventing the transformation of a normal to a neoplastic cell. Moreover, reversion of transformed cells and regression of certain tumors have been observed. The activity of retinoids depend on their chemical structure. Different cells, tissues, or organs react to the various retinoids in different ways. Epithelial tissues are the most prominent target of this class of compounds, but other tissues also show profound alterations under the influence of retinoids. In spite of the many achievements, we are still far from having reached a point where we can be satisfied with the practical clinical progress. One of the main handicaps to the practical use of retinoids is their toxicity, this being manifested as the hypervitaminosis A syndrome. New synthetic retinoids have already been shown to possess a better therapeutic index than natural vitamin A compounds. We still hope that further chemical manipulations of the molecule will lead to compounds possessing even more favorable therapeutic margins. New ideas, perhaps originating rather from rational basic research than from empirical work, may bring us the desired progress.

There is still much speculation about the mechanism of action of retinoids on normal and neoplastic cells. At the moment it seems almost impossible to give a simple explanation for the manifold effects of retinoids on such different processes as proliferation, differentiation and malignant transformation. It will be an important function of this symposium to present a large series of basic research investigations in order to throw more light on the many unexplained properties of the retinoids, which at the moment constitute a veritable jungle. It is hoped that thanks to the results in basic research it will one day be possible to use retinoids as an effective weapon against cancer.

REFERENCES

1. FUJIMAKI, Y. 1926. Formation of carcinoma in albino rats fed on deficient diets. J. Cancer Res. **10**: 469–477.
2. MORI, S. 1922. The changes in the para-ocular glands which follow the administration of diets low in fat-soluble A; with notes on the effect of the same diets on the salivary glands and the mucosa of the larynx and trachea. Bull. Johns Hopkins Hosp. **33**: 357–359.
3. WOLBACH, S.B. & P.R. HOWE. 1925. Tissue changes following deprivation of fat-soluble A-vitamin. J. Exp. Med. **42**: 753–778.
4. WOLBACH, S.B. & P.R. HOWE. 1928. Vitamin A deficiency in the guinea-pig. Arch. Pathol. **5**: 239–253.
5. ROWE, N.A. & R.J. GORLIN. 1959. The effect of vitamin A deficiency upon experimental oral carcinogenesis. J. Dent. Res. **38**: 72–83.
6. CHU, E.W. & R.A. MALMGREN. 1965. An inhibitory effect of vitamin A on the induction of tumors of forestomach and cervix in the Syrian hamster by carcinogenic polycyclic hydrocarbons. Cancer Res. **25**: 884–895.
7. DAVIES, R.E. 1967. Effect of vitamin A on 7,12-dimethyl-benz(a)anthracene-induced papillomas in Rhino mouse skin. Cancer Res. **27**: 237–241.
8. SAFFIOTTI, U., R. MONTESANO, A.R. SELLAKUMAR & S.A. BORG. 1967. Experimental cancer of the lung. Inhibition by vitamin A of the induction of tracheobronchial squamous metaplasia and squamous cell tumors. Cancer **20**: 857–864.
9. LASNITZKI, I. 1963. Growth pattern of the mouse prostate gland in organ culture and its response to sex hormones, vitamin A and 3-methylcholanthrene. Nat. Cancer Inst. Monogr. **12**: 381–403.
10. BOLLAG, W. 1970. Vitamin A and vitamin A acid in the prophylaxis and therapy of epithelial tumors. Int. J. Vitam. Nutr. Res. **40**: 299–314.
11. BOLLAG, W. 1971. Effects of vitamin A acid on transplantable and chemically induced tumors. Cancer Chemother. Rep. **55**: 53–58.

12. BOLLAG, W. 1972. Prophylaxis of chemically induced benign and malignant epithelial tumors by vitamin A acid (retinoic acid). Eur. J. Cancer 8: 689–693.
13. BOLLAG, W. & F. OTT. 1971. Therapy of actinic keratoses and basal cell carcinomas with local application of vitamin A acid. Cancer Chemother. Rep. 55: 59–60.
14. RYSSEL, H.J., K.W. BRUNNER & W. BOLLAG. 1971. Die perorale Anwendung von Vitamin-A-Säure bei Leukoplakien, Hyperkeratosen und Plattenepithelkarzinomen: Ergebnisse und Verträglichkeit. Schweiz. Med. Wochenschr. 101: 1027–1030.
15. EVARD, J.P. & W. BOLLAG. 1972. Konservative Behandlung der rezidivierenden Harnblasenpapillomatose mit Vitamin-A-Säure. Schweiz. Med. Wochenschr. 102: 1880–1883.
16. BOLLAG, W. 1974. Therapeutic effects of an aromatic retinoic acid analog on chemically induced skin papillomas and carcinomas of mice. Eur. J. Cancer 10: 731–737.
17. MAYER, H., W. BOLLAG, R. HAENNI & R. RUEGG. 1978. Retinoids, a new class of compounds with prophylactic and therapeutic activities in oncology and dermatology. Experientia 34: 1105–1119.
18. SPORN, M.B., N.M. DUNLOP, D.L. NEWTON & W.R. HENDERSON. 1976. Relationships between structure and activity of retinoids. Nature 263: 110–113.
19. LASNITZKI, I. 1976. Reversal of methylcholanthrene-induced changes in mouse prostates in vitro by retinoic acid and its analogues. Br. J. Cancer 34: 239–248.
20. CHOPRA, D.P. & L.J. WILKOFF. 1979. Effect of retinoids and estrogens on testosterone-induced hyperplasia of mouse prostate explants in organ culture. Proc. Soc. Exp. Biol. Med. 162: 229–234.
21. LASNITZKI, I. Personal communication.
22. TROWN, P.W., M.J. BUCK & R. HANSEN. 1976. Inhibition of growth and regression of a transplantable rat chondrosarcoma by three retinoids. Cancer Treat. Rep. 60: 1647–1653.
23. KISTLER, G.S. & H.J. PETER. 1979. Wirkung von zwei Retinoiden auf menschliche Bronchuskarzinome in vivo (nu/nu-Maus) und in vitro. Schweiz. Med. Wochenschr. 109: 847–850.
24. BOLLAG, W. 1975. Prophylaxis of chemically induced epithelial tumors with an aromatic retinoic acid analog. (Ro 10-9359). Eur. J. Cancer 11: 721–724.
25. VERMA, A.K., B.G. SHAPAS, H.M. RICE & R.K. BOUTWELL. 1979. Correlation of the inhibition by retinoids of tumor promoter-induced mouse epidermal ornithine decarboxylase activity and of skin tumor promotion. Cancer Res. 39: 419–425.
26. MAHRLE, G. & H. BERGER. 1978. Protective effect of an aromatic retinoic acid analog on skin tumor. J. Invest. Dermatol. 70: 235.
27. PORT, C.D., M.B. SPORN & D.G. KAUFMAN. 1975. Prevention of lung cancer in hamsters by 13-cis-retinoic acid. Proc. Am. Assoc. Cancer Res. 16: 21.
28. CONE, M.V. & P. NETTESHEIM. 1976. Effects of vitamin A on 3-methyl-cholanthrene-induced squamous metaplasia and early tumors in the respiratory tract of rats. J. Nat. Cancer Inst. 50: 1599–1606.
29. MOON, R.C., C.J. GRUBBS & M.B. SPORN. 1976. Inhibition of 7,12-dimethyl-benz(a)-anthracene-induced mammary carcinogenesis by retinyl acetate. Cancer Res. 36: 2626–2630.
30. GRUBBS, C.J., R.C. MOON, M.B. SPORN & D.L. NEWTON. 1977. Inhibition of mammay cancer by retinyl methyl ether. Cancer Res. 37: 599–602.
31. NEWBERNE, P.M., & V. SUPHAKARN. 1977. Preventive role of vitamin A in colon carcinogenesis in rats. Cancer 40: 2553–2556.
32. SPORN, M.B., R.A. SQUIRE, C.C. BROWN, J.M. SMITH, M.L. WENK & S. SPRINGER. 1977. 13-cis-retinoic acid: Inhibition of bladder carcinogenesis in the rat. Science 195: 487–489.
33. FRANKEL, J.W., E.J. HORTON, A.L. WINTERS, H.V. SAMIS & Y. ITO. 1979. Inhibition of viral tumorigenesis by a retinoic acid analog. XI. Internatl. Congress of Chemotherapy, Boston, Abstract No. 850.
34. FRANKEL, J.W., E.J. HORTON, A.L. WINTERS, H.V. SAMIS & Y. ITO. 1979. IX. Internatl. Symposium on Comparative Leukemia and Related Diseases. Pitsunda, USSR.
35. KOCH, H. 1978. Biochemical treatment of precancerous oral lesions: The effectiveness of various analogs of retionic acid. J. Maxillofac. Surg. 6: 59–63.

36. PECK, G.L., T.G. OLSEN, D. BUTKUS, M. PANDYA, J. ARNAUD-BATTANDIER, F. YODER & W.R. LEVIS. 1979. Treatment of basal cell carcinomas with 13-cis-retinoic acid. Proc. Am. Assoc. Cancer Res. 20: 56.

37. MATTER, A. & W. BOLLAG. 1977. A fine structural study on the therapeutic effect of an aromatic retinoid on chemically-induced skin papillomas of the mouse. Eur. J. Cancer 13: 831–838.

38. DE LUCA, L.M., S. ADAMO, P.V. BHAT, W. SASAK, C.S. SILVERMAN-JONES, I. AKALOVSKY, J.P. FROT-COUTAZ, T.R. FLETCHER & G.J. CHADER. 1979. Recent developments in studies on biological functions of Vitamin A in normal and transformed tissues. Pure Appl. Chem. 51: 581–591.

39. ADAMO, S., I. AKALOVSKY & L.M. DE LUCA. 1978. Retinoic acid induced changes in saturation density and adhesion of transformed mouse fibroblasts. Proc. Am. Assoc. Cancer Res. 19: 27.

40. JETTEN, A.M., M.E.R. JETTEN, S.S. SHAPIRO & J.P. POON. 1979. Characterization of the action of retinoids on mouse fibroblast cell lines. Exp. Cell Res. 119: 289–299.

41. LOTAN, R. 1979. Different susceptibilities of human melanoma and breast carcinoma cell lines to retinoic acid-induced growth inhibition. Cancer Res. 39: 1014–1019.

42. DE LUCA, L.M. 1977. The direct involvement of vitamin A in glycosyl transfer reactions of mammalian membranes. Vitamins and Hormones 35: 1–57.

43. JETTEN, A.M., M.E.R. JETTEN & M.I. SHERMAN. 1979. Stimulation of differentiation of several murine embryonal carcinoma cell lines by retinoic acid. Exp. Cell Res. 124: 381–391.

44. KEVIN, J. & S. ROTH. 1974. The effect of polyprenols on cell surface galactosyltransferase activity. In Control of Proliferation in Animal Cells. B. Clarkson & R. Baserga, Eds. Vol. 1: 533–539. Cold Spring Harbor Laboratory. New York.

45. SHAPIRO, S.S., M. BISHOP, J.P. POON & P.W. TROWN. 1976. Effect of aromatic retinoids on rat chondrosarcoma glycosaminoglycan biosynthesis. Cancer Res. 36: 3702–3706.

46. JETTEN, A.M. & M.E.R. JETTEN. 1979. Possible role of retinoic acid binding protein in retinoid stimulation of embryonal carcinoma cell differentiation. Nature 278: 180–182.

47. CHYTIL, F. & D.E. ONG. 1978. Cellular vitamin A binding proteins. In Vitamins and Hormones. P.L. Munson et al., Eds. Vol. 36: 1–29. Academic Press. New York.

48. TROWN, P.W., A.V. PATTERONI, O. BOHOSLAWEC, B.N. RICHELO, J.M. HALPERN, N. GIZZI, R. GEIGER, C. LEWINSKI, L.J. MACHLIN, A. JETTEN & M.E.R. JETTEN. 1980. Relationship between binding affinities to cellular retinoic acid binding protein and in vivo and in vitro properties for 18 retinoids. Cancer Res. 40:212–220.

49. HUBER, P.R., W. KUENG, E. GEYER & A. MATTER. Structure dependence of retinoid binding to retinoic acid binding protein (cRABP) from rat testis. Submitted.

50. HUBER, P.R., E. GEYER, W. KUENG, A. MATTER, J. TORHORST & U. EPPENBERGER. 1978. Retinoic acid-binding protein in human breast cancer and dysplasia. J. Nat. Cancer Inst. 61: 1375–1378.

51. PRUTKIN, L. & B. BOGART. 1970. The uptake of labeled vitamin A acid in keratoacanthoma. An electron microscopic radioautography study. J. Invest. Dermatol. 55: 249–255.

52. SANI, B.P. 1977. Localization of retinoic acid-binding protein in nuclei. Biochem. Biophys. Res. Commun. 75: 7–12.

53. WIGGERT, B., P. RUSSELL, M. LEWIS & G. CHADER. 1977. Differential binding to soluble nuclear receptors and effects on cell viability of retinol and retinoic acid in cultured retinoblastoma cells. Biochem. Biophys. Res. Commun. 79: 218–225.

54. BLALOCK, J.E. & G.E. GIFFORD. 1977. Retinoic acid (vitamin A acid) induced transcriptional control of interferon production. Proc. Natl. Acad. Sci. USA 74: 5382–5386.

55. DINGLE, J.T. & J.A. LUCY. 1965. Vitamin A, carotenoids and cell function. Biol. Rev. 40: 422–461.

56. KISTLER, A. 1978. Inhibition of vitamin A action in rat bone cultures by inhibitors of RNA and protein synthesis. Experientia 34: 1159–1161.

57. PENNYPACKER, J.P., C.A. LEWIS & J.R. HASSELL. 1978. Altered proteoglycan metabolism in mouse limb mesenchyme cell cultures treated with vitamin A. Arch. Biochem. Biophys. 186: 351–358.

58. HONGAN-RYAN, A. & J.J. FENNELLY. 1978. Neuraminidase-like effect of vitamin A on cell surface. Eur. J. Cancer **14:** 113–116.

59. DENNERT, G. & R. LOTAN. 1978. Effects of retinoic acid on the immune system: Stimulation of T killer cell induction. Eur. J. Immunol. **8:** 23–29.

60. GLAUERT, A.M., M.R. DANIEL, J.A. LUCY & J.T. DINGLE. 1963. Studies on the mode of action of excess of vitamin A. VII. Changes in the fine structure of erythrocytes during haemolysis by vitamin A. J. Cell Biol. **17:** 111–121.

61. MURPHY, M.J. 1973. Effects of vitamin A on the erythrocyte membrane surface. Blood **42:** 893–899.

62. WENZEL, D.G. & D. ACOSTA. 1973. Permeability of lysosomes and mitochondria in cultured rat heart muscle and endothelioid cells as affected by vitamin A, chlorpromazine, amphotericin B, and clofibrate. Res. Commun. Chem. Pathol. Pharmacol. **6:** 689–700.

THE METABOLISM OF RETINOIC ACID TO 5,6-EPOXYRETINOIC ACID, RETINOYL-β-GLUCURONIDE, AND OTHER POLAR METABOLITES*

Hector F. DeLuca, Maija Zile, and William K. Sietsema

Department of Biochemistry
College of Agricultural and Life Sciences
University of Wisconsin-Madison
Madison, Wisconsin 53706

INTRODUCTION

Although vitamin A has been known since 1913, its overall metabolism remains to be elucidated in detail. The conversion of β-carotene to retinal and subsequent reduction to retinol in the intestine has been clearly established.[1,2] It has also been established that retinol (vitamin A) is transported in the plasma bound to a specific transport protein called RBP. Retinol is stored in the liver as retinyl palmitate and is mobilized under conditions of need.[3] Further metabolism of retinol is known to occur in the target tissues, especially the eye where it is converted to retinal. Many tissues possess the capability of carrying out this conversion. It is an NAD-requiring reaction and its biochemistry is well known. Beyond these known facts, considerable uncertainty remains.

In 1946 Arens and van Dorp[4] synthesized retinoic acid as a curious analog of retinol. This compound possessed marked biological activity in stimulating growth of vitamin A-deficient rats but it failed to satisfy the visual and reproductive requirements for vitamin A.[4,5] Presumably, therefore, retinoic acid could not be reduced *in vivo* to retinal or retinol, a belief which was easily confirmed by the measurement of retinyl palmitate of the livers of vitamin A-deficient rats given retinoic acid.[6,7] For many years it was believed that retinoic acid is not a metabolite of retinol. In fact, some investigators may still hold that belief. The basis of this is the fact that retinoic acid could not be detected in animals given retinol.[8] However, with the synthesis of radioactive retinol compounds of sufficient radioactivity and the development of chromatographic methods suitable for separation without the generation of artifacts, it became clear that retinoic acid is a bonafide metabolite of retinol.[9,10] Moreover, in some target tissues such as intestine, retinoic acid could be detected in major amounts as compared to retinol and retinal, in animals given a radiolabeled dose of retinol. An argument against retinoic acid as a metabolically active form of retinol is the fact that retinoic acid given as a single daily dose did not equal retinol in supporting growth of vitamin A-deficient rats. However, because retinoic acid is very rapidly metabolized as compared to retinol,[12] it appeared likely that the turnover of this form of vitamin A was responsible for its poor growth promoting activity when given as a single daily dose. Multiple small doses given to vitamin A-deficient rats daily resulted in marked growth stimulation superior to that of retinol, providing strong evidence that retinoic acid is a further activation form of retinol.[13] This is clearly supported

* This work was supported by National Institutes of Health Program-Project Grant AM-14881 and the Harry Steenbock Research Fund of the Wisconsin Alumni Research Foundation.

0077-8923/81/0359-0025 $01.75/0 © 1981, NYAS

by the work with tracheal organ cultures in which it was shown that retinoic acid is more active than retinol in stimulating the differentiation of mucus-secreting epithelial cells.[14] Thus there is little doubt that retinoic acid is a metabolite of retinol and that it can possibly be considered an active form of vitamin A. Moreover, it is likely that it is generated in the tissues where it carries out its function.

Because retinoic acid is rapidly metabolized to other compounds, it seemed possible that it could be converted even further to active forms. This possibility has continued to stimulate interest in studying metabolism of retinoic acid. Dunagin et al.[15] pioneered the study of retinoic acid metabolism and demonstrated the conversion of retinoic acid to a compound believed to be retinoyl-β-glucuronide. Lippel and Olson[16] concluded that this represents the major excretory form of retinoic acid accounting for 90% of its metabolism. However, with retinoic acids labeled in the 14, 15, and 6, 7 positions with C^{14} (Hoffmann-La Roche, Inc., Nutley, NJ) Roberts and DeLuca demonstrated the existence of at least three metabolic pathways for retinoic acid in which various fragments of the side chain are oxidized to carbon dioxide and water.[12] This, therefore, argued strongly against the conclusion of Lippel and Olson,[16] demonstrating that much remained to be learned concerning the metabolism of retinoic acid. The work of Roberts and DeLuca was confirmed by others.[17] In support of the complexity of retinoic acid metabolism, Hänni and his coworkers[18,19] and Rietz and coworkers[20] have published the struc-

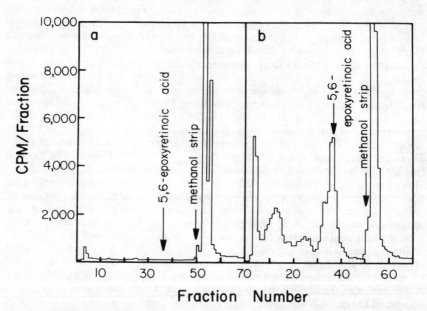

FIGURE 1. The production of 5,6-epoxyretinoic acid from retinoic acid by kidney homogenates. The incubation mixture contained 24 mM magnesium, 100 mM potassium chloride, 2 U/ml glucose-6-phosphate dehydrogenase, 1 U/ml alcohol dehydrogenase, glucose-6-phosphate 25 mM, ATP 20 mM, NADP 0.5 mM, NAD 0.5 mM, nicotinamide 150 mM, and disodium succinate 5 mM, pH 7.4; atmosphere air; incubation time 3 min.

Panel A represents an HPLC tracing in which the 1% kidney homogenate has been heated to 100°C for 15 min, whereas Panel B represents the fresh kidney homogenate incubation. The HPLC column was a reversed-phase μBondapak C_{18} column using a solvent system of methanol:water 55:45 containing 10 mM ammonium acetate.

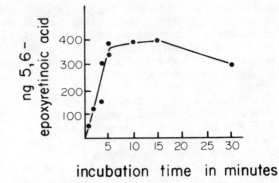

FIGURE 2. Time course of intestinal homogenate production of 5,6-epoxyretinoic acid from retinoic acid. Incubation conditions are as described in FIGURE 1. Separation and measurement of the 5,6-epoxyretinoic acid was by high pressure liquid chromatography.

tures of several metabolites of retinoic acid in urine and feces of rats given large amounts of retinoic acid. These compounds which were well characterized, may or may not represent metabolites observed when physiologic amounts of retinoic acid are administered.

Since these lines of evidence suggested the possiblity that metabolism of retinoic acid could yield further active forms, Ito and coworkers developed gentle methods of extraction of tissues from rats given labeled retinoic acid and demonstrated in several tissues the appearance of three polar metabolite fractions termed "Peaks 8, 9, 10."[10, 21] These peaks possessed biological activity in the tracheal organ culture system of Sporn and coworkers (unpublished results).

RETINOIC ACID 5,6-EPOXIDASE

During the past 3 years we isolated and identified the 5,6-epoxyretinoic acid as a polar metabolite of retinoic acid generated *in vivo* in intestine.[21-23] The amount of the 5,6-epoxide present in the tissues did not exceed 90 pg/g of tissue and appeared transient in nature.[24] Furthermore, in animals given predoses of retinoic

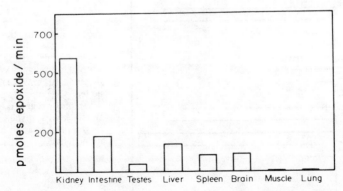

FIGURE 3. Retinoic acid 5,6-epoxidase of various rat tissues. Incubation was as described in FIGURE 1, except kidney homogenate was replaced by the indicated tissue homogenate. Incubation was for 3 min.

acid we were unable to detect the 5,6-epoxide *in vivo*. Therefore, the importance of the 5,6-epoxide both in the metabolism and function of retinoic acid remained uncertain. To confirm that the 5,6-epoxidation was a meaningful biological reaction *in vivo*, we began to search for the enzymatic system that carries out the conversion. Homogenates of kidney from either normal or vitamin A-deficient rats are able to convert all-*trans*-retinoic acid to the 5,6-epoxyretinoic acid as shown in FIGURE 1.[25] Identity of the 5,6-epoxide produced by this reaction was proved by cochromatography with synthetic epoxide, by mass spectrometry and by ultraviolet spectrophotometry. In this system homogenates are supported with ATP, NADPH, NADH, succinate and magnesium ions. Boiling the homogenate for 10 min eliminates the conversion, and 5,6-epoxidation does not take place in the medium under the conditions used if tissue is not added. Epoxidation is extremely rapid as shown in the time course experiment of intestinal homogenates in FIGURE 2. Within minutes following incubation with [11, 12-³H]retinoic acid the epoxide is generated, reaches a maximum at 10 min, and thereafter diminishes. In some experiments, the epoxide reaches extremely low levels following 30 min of incubation. This disappearance of the product during long incubations (30 min) may account for failure of certain investigators to detect the 5,6-epoxidase *in vitro*. To learn whether the 5,6-epoxidase is a general property of all tissues, we studied the epoxidation reaction in a variety of tissues as shown in FIGURE 3. Among the tissues, kidney is the most active followed by the intestine, liver, spleen. No activity was detected in muscle and lung.

In additional studies, we examined the components of the reaction mixture required for 5,6-epoxidation. FIGURE 4 demonstrates that NADPH, magnesium ions, and ATP are required for this reaction whereas the presence of succinate is actually inhibitory and NADH is not required. In addition, note that there is an oxygen requirement for this epoxidation, as might be expected. Of considerable interest is the requirement for magnesium ions. We also observed that the re-

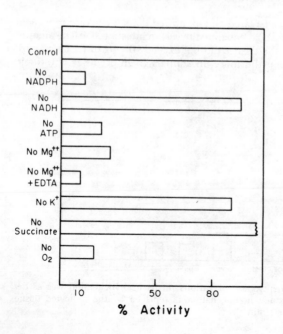

FIGURE 4. A study of the requirements of the kidney 5,6-epoxidase. The complete reaction mixture is as described in FIGURE 1. Where indicated, 10 mM EDTA was added. In the experiment where no oxygen is present, the flask was flushed with nitrogen prior to addition of the homogenate.

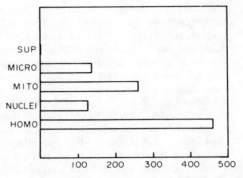

FIGURE 5. Epoxidase activity of cell fractions of rat kidney. Subcellular localization of the 5,6-retinoic acid epoxidase.

quirement for magnesium ions could be intensified by the addition of EDTA thereby reducing the activity of the epoxidase.

A subcellular fractionation was carried out using standard differential centrifugation methods and the kidney as a source of the enzyme (FIG. 5). The results show that both mitochondrial and microsomal components possess significant amounts of activity although the mitochondrial fraction appears to be highest in total amount. However, when expressed on a per mg protein basis mitochondrial and microsomal fractions were equal in activity. It is not clear whether both frac-

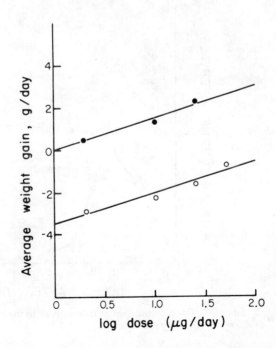

FIGURE 6. Biological potency of synthetic 5,6-epoxyretinoic acid in support of growth of vitamin A-deficient rats. Rats were made vitamin A-deficient by feeding an appropriate diet for a period of 28–32 days until they ceased to gain weight. At that time they received the indicated dose of retinoic acid (•) or 5,6-epoxyretinoic acid (O) as a daily subcutaneous injection. The effect on weight gain over the next 21 days was measured and plotted.

tions carry out the epoxidation or whether these fractions have not been satisfac-
torily separated. Cytosol had no activity whatsoever and while the nuclear fraction had some activity, this is possibly the result of mitochondrial contamination.
Additional work will be required to pinpoint the subcellular site of the epoxidase.

We have also carried out an experiment with 13-*cis*-retinoic acid as the substrate. The 5,6-epoxidase is equally active on the 13-*cis*-isomer as it is on the all-
trans-isomer. The apparent Michaelis constant for all-*trans*-retinoic acid is 3.7 ×
10^{-6}M comparable to 3.2 × 10^{-6}M for 13-*cis*-retinoic acid. The apparent K_m for
all-*trans*-retinoic acid is unchanged by the prior administration of any form of
vitamin A to the animals. Thus there is no doubt that an enzymatic system does
exist for the production of 5,6-epoxyretinoic acid and it is likely that it does represent a true metabolic pathway for retinoic acid. The major question, of course, is
whether it possesses any functional significance.

The 5,6-epoxyretinoic acid had been prepared prior to our work on metabolism.[26] The synthetic 5,6-epoxide, which would represent two isomers, has been
studied in terms of biological activity. One report claims that it is 150% as active
as all-*trans*-retinyl acetate in supporting growth of vitamin A-deficient rats.[27]
This was later revised to 80% of all-*trans*-retinyl acetate activity.[28] In the ornithine decarboxylase suppression assay of skin the 5,6-epoxide had about equal
activity to all-*trans*-retinoic acid (McCormick, Napoli and DeLuca, unpublished
results). However, in the organ culture assay the 5,6-epoxide appeared to be
about one-tenth as active as all-*trans*-retinoic acid. It therefore became important
to evaluate more precisely the biological activity of the 5,6-epoxide. In a number
of tests we have examined its growth-promoting activity in vitamin A-deficient
rats. The 5,6-epoxide was generously supplied to us by Dr. Pawson of Hoffmann-

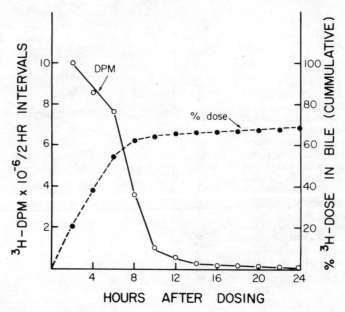

FIGURE 7. The accumulation of radioactivity in the bile of rats given a single injection
of 2.2 mg of tritiated retinoic acid.

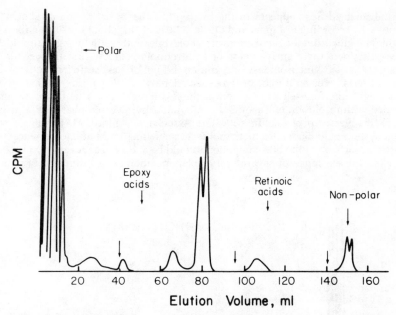

FIGURE 8. The HPLC profile of the labeled compounds found in rat bile following injection of the animals with radioactive retinoic acid. Following butanol extraction, the biliary sample was placed on a reversed-phase μBondapak column using a solvent system of 55% methanol/45% water containing 10 mM ammonium acetate. The last arrow indicates a methanol strip.

La Roche, Inc. It was shown to be pure by high-pressure liquid chromatography (HPLC). The compound was administered in a variety of ways, primarily subcutaneously or intraperitoneally. The results shown in FIGURE 6 illustrate that the 5, 6-epoxide is considerably less active than all-*trans*-retinoic acid in promoting growth of vitamin A-deficient rats. The results of several experiments revealed that the 5,6-epoxyretinoic acid is only 0.5% as active as all-*trans*-retinoic acid. These findings agree with the tracheal organ culture assay of its activity performed in the laboratory of Dr. Michael Sporn. The results, however, do not eliminate 5, 6-epoxyretinoic acid as a possible active form or intermediate thereof. For example, the epoxide could be generated within the very same cell in which it acts. It is indeed possible that administration of such a compound to a whole animal may result in its rapid degradation and elimination or alternatively, it is possible that it may not penetrate the cells as well as all-*trans*-retinoic acid. However, the most likely explanation is that 5,6-epoxidation does not represent an activation metabolic pathway for retinoic acid.

BILIARY METABOLITES OF RETINOIC ACID

In continuing our investigation of the metabolism of retinoic acid, we have given attention to the excretory routes of physiologic and pharmacological doses of retinoic acid. Following injection of tritiated retinoic acid (11,12 position), 80%

of the injected dose appears in the bile within the 24-hr. period as shown in
FIGURE 7. According to Lippel and Olson,[16] 90% of this should be in the form of
retinoyl-β-glucuronide. Incubation of whole bile with retinoyl-β-glucuronidase
gave disappointingly small yields of free retinoic acid. At first this led us to
suspect that our glucuronidase preparation did not possess sufficient activity, although tests revealed it to be of the expected activity. We considered that whole
bile might interfere with the action of the β-glucuronidase. We, therefore, proceeded with resolution of the biliary components by reversed-phase HPLC using
a μC-18 reversed-phase column (Waters Associates, Milford, MA). Using a solvent system of 45:55, water:methanol together with 10 mM ammonium acetate,
partial resolution of the bile components could be achieved as revealed in FIGURE
8. Note the existence of several very polar metabolites of retinoic acid poorly

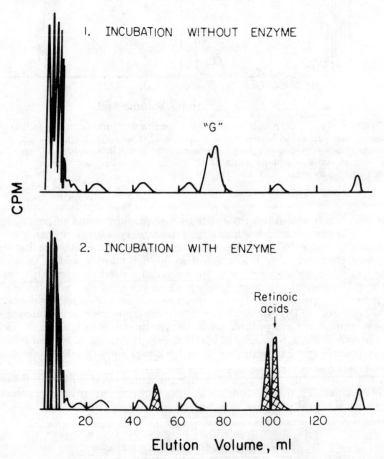

FIGURE 9. The HPLC profile of radioactivity from bile as in FIGURE 8, either following
incubation without β-glucuronidase (1) or with β-glucuronidase (2). Note the disappearance
of Peak G following incubation with glucuronidase and the appearance of retinoic acids.
Solvent system is as in FIGURE 8.

resolved in this system and the presence of a peak designated G. Incubation of this bile sample with β-glucuronidase did not significantly alter the polar region of the chromatogram as shown in FIGURE 9, but led to a disappearance of the Peak G region and the appearance of compounds that cochromatographed with authentic 13-*cis*- and all-*trans*-retinoic acids. The polar metabolites of bile were each isolated and individually incubated with retinoyl-β-glucuronidase. Only Peak G yielded retinoic acids. Peak G was, therefore, suspected to be the retinoyl-β-glucuronide originally isolated and identified by Olson an his coworkers.[16] Of considerable interest is the fact that Peak G is not appreciably more polar in this chromatographic system than is free retinoic acid. This raised the question of whether in fact the suspected compound really is a retinoyl-β-glucuronide. Furthermore, glucuronidase is not highly specific especially when used in the available partially purified form. The Peak G was isolated from the bile of five rats by a procedure involving butanol extraction as originally suggested by Lippel and Olson[16] followed by Sephadex LH-20 chromatography using a solvent system of 65:35:3, chloroform:hexane:methanol.[21] This column was then stripped with acetone:methanol, 1:1, to give the polar metabolite fraction. The polar fraction was then subjected to reversed-phase HPLC as described above. This gave several polar peaks and Peak G. Peak G was purified further to homogeneity by rechromatography on reversed-phase HPLC. It had an absorption spectrum with a λ_{max} 358 nm, similar to that of retinoic acid esters. This compound was then methylated with diazomethane. The silylated derivative of the methylated metabolite gave the mass spectrum revealed in FIGURE 10. It had a molecular ion of 706 and had important fragments at 407 representing cleavage of the glycosidic bond. The 407 fragmentation also gave a m/e 372 or a m/e 300 representing retinoyl-TMS fragment and retinoic acid respectively. The methylated metabolite was then subjected to acetylation. This product had a molecular ion of 616 that gave rise to a 317 fragment and had the expected fragmentation consistent with methyl retinoyl-β-glucuronide triacetate. High resolution mass spectra confirmed the structural assignments to the fragments of both derivatives. Thus peak G proved to be the retinoyl-β-glucuronide of all-*trans* and 13-*cis*-retinoic acid. This was confirmed by incubation of Peak G with the β-glucuronidase, the isolation of the retinoic acid and cochromatography with a mixture of 13-*cis* and all-*trans*-retinoic acid. Thus the original structure proposed by Dunagin *et al.* was confirmed. However, the amount of retinoyl-β-glucuronide in bile of rats given tritiated retinoic acid is considerably less than had been proposed by Olson and his collaborators.[16] We, therefore, carried out a quantitative measurement of the amount of retinoyl-β-glucuronide and the percent of the radioactivity found in the bile which cochromatographs with this substance. The results show that in a 24-hr period less than 20% of the biliary radioactivity is found as the retinoyl-β-glucuronide. In fact, it is likely that not more than 12% of the total radioactivity found in bile from rats given tritiated retinoic acid is in the form of retinoyl-β-glucuronide, the remaining radioactivity being distributed among other polar metabolites. Thus, it is clear that a great deal remains to be learned concerning the biliary excretion products of retinoic acid. Retinoyl-β-glucuronide was not identified by Rietz *et al.*[20] or Hänni *et al.*[18,19] as a metabolite of retinoic acid when large amounts (20-40 mg) of retinoic acid are administered. It is highly questionable as to whether the metabolites of retinoic acid identified under these circumstances will be found under more physiological circumstances.

FIGURE 11 illustrates the proven pathways of retinol metabolism including the only proven physiological excretion product of retinoic acid, retinoyl-β-glucuronide.

Obviously much remains to be learned concerning the total pathway of

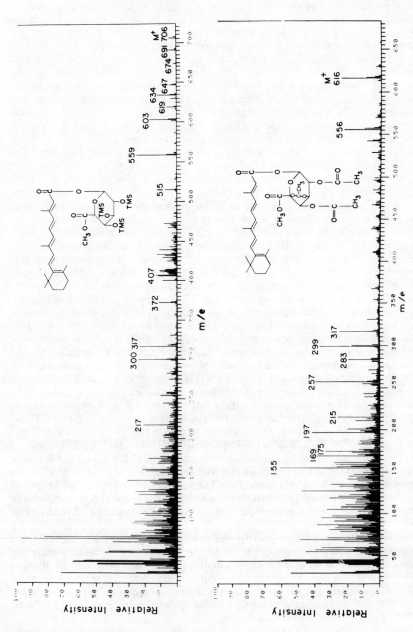

FIGURE 10. Mass spectrum of the TMS ether derivative of methylated Peak G (*top panel*) or acetylated and methylated Peak G (*lower panel*).

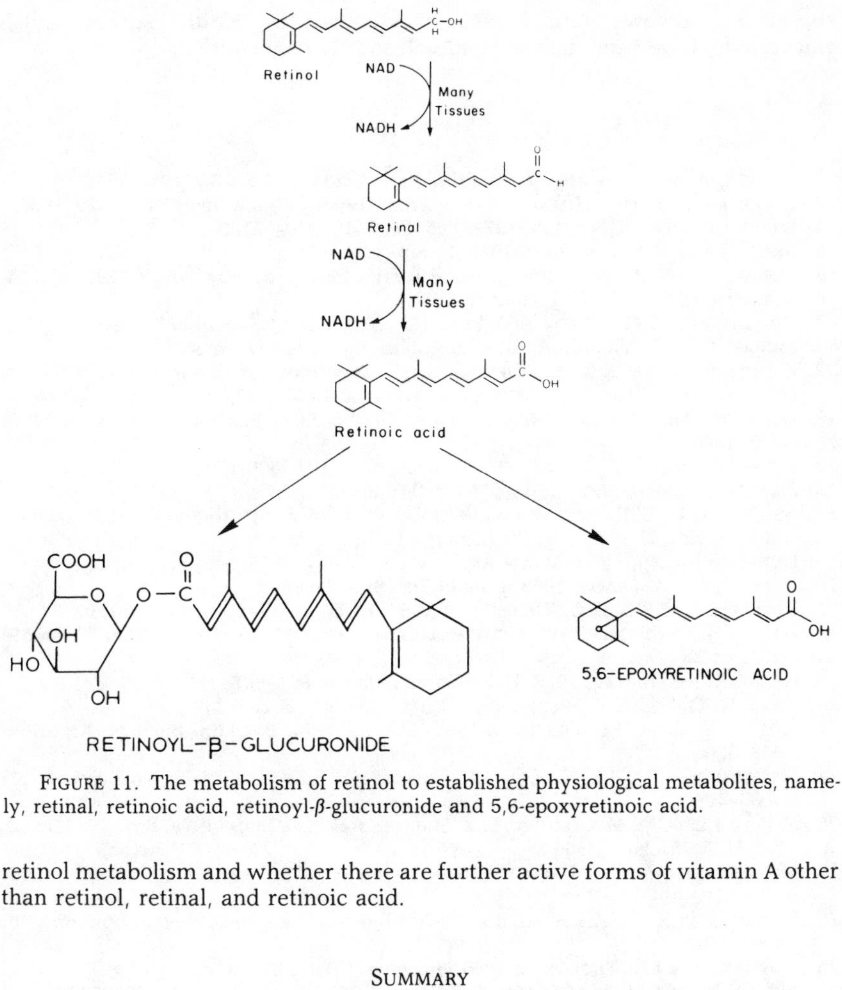

FIGURE 11. The metabolism of retinol to established physiological metabolites, namely, retinal, retinoic acid, retinoyl-β-glucuronide and 5,6-epoxyretinoic acid.

retinol metabolism and whether there are further active forms of vitamin A other than retinol, retinal, and retinoic acid.

SUMMARY

A description of the enzyme that produces 5,6-epoxyretinoic acid from all-*trans*-retinoic acid has been presented. This enzyme system is found in highest concentrations in the kidney followed by intestine, liver and spleen. The enzyme requires molecular oxygen, magnesium ions, ATP, and NADPH. In the kidney, it is found in the mitochondrial and microsomal fractions and has a Michaelis constant of 3.2×10^{-6} M and 3.7×10^{-6} M for 13-*cis* and all-*trans*-retinoic acid, respectively. The resultant product, 5,6-epoxyretinoic acid, has minimal activity in supporting growth of vitamin A-deficient rats, its activity estimated to be 0.5% that of retinoic acid. An investigation of the biliary excretion products of tritiated retinoic acid has revealed several unknown metabolites. A glucuronidase sensitive metabolite from these products has been isolated and identified as retinoyl-β-glucuronide by ultraviolet absorption spectrometry and mass spectrometry. The retinoyl-β-glucuronide originally discovered by Olson and collaborators accounts for only 12% of the total excreted biliary products of retinoic acid. At least four to six major unknown retinoic acid metabolites, in addition to retinoyl-β-glucuronide, have been detected and will shortly be identified.

REFERENCES

1. OLSON, J.A. & O. HAYAISHI. 1965. Proc. Natl. Acad. Sci. USA **54:** 1364-1370.
2. GOODMAN, D.S., H.S. HUANG & T. SHIRATORI. 1966. J. Biol. Chem. **241:** 1929-1932.
3. SMITH, J.E. & D.S. GOODMAN. 1979. Fed. Proc. **38:** 2504-2509.
4. ARENS, J.F. & D.A. VAN DORP. 1946. Nature **158:** 622-623.
5. THOMPSON, J.N., J. McC. HOWELL & G.A.J. PITT. 1964. Proc. Roy. Soc. B **159:** 510-535.
6. SHARMAN, I.M. 1949. Br. J. Nutr. **3:** viii.
7. DOWLING, J.E. & G. WALD. 1960. Proc. Natl. Acad. Sci. USA **46:** 587-608.
8. MOORE, T. 1957. Vitamin A. Elsevier Publishing Company. Amsterdam.
9. KLEINER-BÖSSALER, A. & H.F. DELUCA. 1971. Arch. Biochem. Biophys. **142:** 371-377.
10. ITO, Y.L., M.H. ZILE, H. AHRENS & H.F. DELUCA. 1974. J. Lipid Res. **15:** 517-524.
11. DUNAGIN, P.E., JR., R.D. ZACHMAN & J.A. OLSON. 1964. Biochim. Biophys. Acta **90:** 432-434.
12. ROBERTS, A.B. & H.F. DELUCA. 1967. Biochem. J. **102:** 600-611.
13. ZILE, M. & H.F. DELUCA. 1968. J. Nutr. **94:** 302-308.
14. NEWTON, D.L., W.R. HENDERSON & M.B. SPORN. 1978. Structure-Activity Relationships of Retinoids. National Cancer Institute, Bethesda, MD.
15. DUNAGIN, P.E., JR., E.H. MEADOWS, JR. & J.A. OLSON. 1965. Science **148:** 86-87.
16. LIPPEL, K. & J.A. OLSON. 1968. J. Lipid Res. **9:** 580-586.
17. SUNDARESAN, P.R. & D.G. THERRIAULT. 1968. Biochim. Biophys. Acta **158:** 92-97.
18. HÄNNI, R., F. BIGLER, W. MEISTER & G. ENGLERT. 1976. Helv. Chim. Acta **59:** 2221-2228.
19. HÄNNI, R. & F. BIGLER. 1977. Helv. Chim. Acta **60:** 881-887.
20. RIETZ, P., O. WISS & F. WEBER. 1974. Vitam. Horm. **32:** 237-249.
21. ITO, Y., M. ZILE, H.F. DELUCA & H.M. AHRENS. 1974. Biochim. Biophys. Acta **369:** 338-350.
22. McCORMICK, A.M., J.L. NAPOLI, H.K. SCHNOES & H.F. DELUCA. 1978. Biochemistry **17:** 4085-4090.
23. NAPOLI, J.L., A.M. McCORMICK, H.K. SCHNOES & H.F. DELUCA. 1978. Proc. Natl. Acad. Sci. USA **75:** 2603-2605.
24. McCORMICK, A.M., J.L. NAPOLI, S. YOSHIZAWA & H.F. DELUCA. 1980. Biochem. J. **186:** 475-481.
25. SIETSEMA, W.K. & H.F. DELUCA. 1979. Biochem. Biophys. Res. Commun. **90:** 1091-1097.
26. MORGAN, B. & J.N. THOMPSON. 1966. Biochem. J. **101:** 835-842.
27. JOHN, K.V., M.R. LAKSHMANAN & H.R. CAMA. 1967. Biochem. J. **103:** 539-543.
28. MALLIA, A.K., J. JOHN, K.V. JOHN, M.R. LAKSHMANAN, F.B. JUNGALWALA & H.R. CAMA. 1970. Ind. J. Biochem. **7:** 102-103.

IN VITRO AND *IN VIVO* METABOLISM OF ALL-*trans*- AND 13-*cis*-RETINOIC ACID IN THE HAMSTER

Charles A. Frolik

Laboratory of Chemoprevention
National Cancer Institute
National Institutes of Health
Bethesda, Maryland 20205

INTRODUCTION

Although, the metabolism of vitamin A has been under investigation for over 30 years, only a few metabolites have actually been structurally characterized. One of the first metabolites of retinol to be identified was all-*trans*-retinoic acid (RA). Interestingly, this compound was chemically synthesized[1] many years before it was shown to occur *in vivo.*[2-7] Since then, major natural metabolites of retinol or RA that have been physically characterized include retinyl esters (predominately the palmitate[8-10] and stearate[10] esters), 11-*cis*-retinal,[11] retinyl β-glucosiduronate,[12] retinoyl β-glucuronide,[12-14] 4-oxoretinol,[15] and retinyl phosphate.[16] 13-*cis*-RA has also been postulated to occur in nature,[17] although the extraction methods employed in the isolation procedure caused extension isomerization therefore leaving the physiological significance of this observation open to further investigation. More recently, through the use of high-pressure liquid chromatography (HPLC), further metabolites of RA have been identified as all-*trans*-4-oxoRA,[18] all-*trans* and 9-*cis* isomers of 5′hydroxyRA,[18] 5,6-epoxyRA,[19] as well as several decarboxylated metabolites in the urine of rats.[20]

A principal motivation behind this search for new metabolites of retinol and RA is the possibility that these compounds may have to be converted to an active form prior to their biological action in controlling epithelial differentiation. Indeed there are numerous reports indicating the possibility of finding a metabolite of RA that displays a greater biological activity than the parent compound.[17,19,21-25] Nevertheless, in all but one case, the metabolites of interest have remained uncharacterized. The exception is the identification of 5,6-epoxyRA.[19] The biological activity of this compound, however, is open to question. Initial reports indicated this compound may be as active as retinyl acetate in promoting growth when administered to vitamin A-deficient rats.[26] However, later reports from the same group,[27] as well as investigations from other laboratories,[28,29] concluded that epoxidation at the 5,6-double bond markedly lowers the biological activity of vitamin A. In addition, the obligatory formation of the 5,6-epoxide for biological activity is questionable in light of the high activity in reversing epithelial keratinization in tracheal organ culture observed for 5,6-dihydroRA[30] from which biosynthesis of 5,6-epoxyRA would be difficult. Therefore further investigations are warranted before a firm conclusion concerning the physiological significance of the 5,6-epoxyRA can be made.

IN VITRO METABOLISM OF RETINOIC ACID

In the present search for possible active metabolites of RA, a tracheal organ

37

culture system that is responsive to nanomolar concentrations of retinoids[31,32] is being utilized. In this system, the tracheal epithelium, in the absence of retinoids, forms a keratinized squamous metaplasia similar to that observed in the vitamin A-deficient animal. Addition of RA to the culture medium after such lesions have developed causes a reversal of keratinization with a return to the normal epithelial ciliated and mucus-secreting cells. It was felt that if RA must first be converted to an active metabolite prior to exerting its effects on the epithelium that this *in vitro* target tissue system would be useful in the attempts to identify such a compound. Using this method, all-*trans*-[³H]RA was found to undergo a tissue-dependent metabolism to a number of more polar metabolites[33] (FIG. 1). These metabolites formed *in vitro* behaved similarly in several different chromatographic

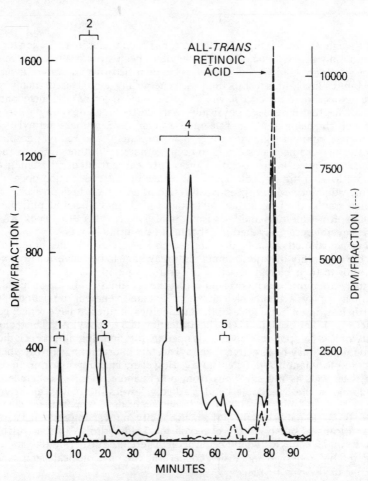

FIGURE 1. HPLC of the radioactive material present in the methanol extract of culture medium after a 24-hr incubation of 5.3 × 10⁻⁹ M all-*trans*-retinoic acid in the presence (————) or in the absence (- - - - - - -) of hamster trachea. Chromatography was performed on a reverse-phase column using an acetonitrile: 1% ammonium acetate gradient.[33,43]

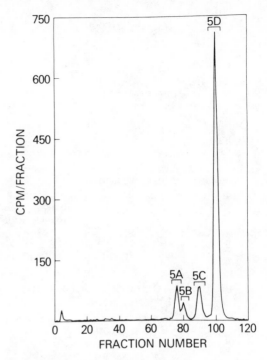

FIGURE 2. Chromatography of *in vitro* synthesized hamster liver peak 5 on an ODS 5 μm HPLC column eluted with acetonitrile: 0.1% acetic acid (42:58). (From Roberts & Frolik.[37] Reprinted with permission of *Federation Proceedings*).

systems to intestinal and urinary metabolites of retinoic acid formed *in vivo*, thereby demonstrating that the metabolism observed in the tracheal organ culture system was indeed following a pathway similar to that observed in the animal. Because only one of these metabolite regions, termed peak 5 (FIG. 1), retained the ability to reverse keratinization when tested in a tracheal organ culture assay,[33] it was decided to concentrate on this region in initial identification efforts.

In order to generate sufficient quantities of peak 5 metabolites for characterization, a hamster liver 10,000 × *g* supernatant system was utilized.[34,35] The production of peak 5 metabolites in this cell-free system was demonstrated to be enzymatic in nature[34] and to produce the identical peak 5 metabolites observed in the trachea.[35] The peak 5 region could be separated into four components designated peaks 5A through 5D[35] (FIGURE 2). Peak 5A has recently been identified as all-*trans*-4-hydroxyRA and peak 5D as all-*trans*-4-oxoRA (FIG. 3) based on ultraviolet and mass spectral characteristics as well as on their comigration with synthetic standards in two different reverse-phase HPLC systems.[35]

RELATIONSHIP BETWEEN *IN VITRO* AND *IN VIVO* METABOLISM OF RETINOIC ACID

Although initial work suggested that all-*trans*-4-hydroxy- and 4-oxoRA were also metabolites of all-*trans*-RA *in vivo*,[33-35] chromatographic techniques with greater resolving power have now indicated that this may not be the case. Administration of either 13-*cis*-[³H]RA or all-*trans*[¹⁴C]RA to normal hamsters yielded peak 5C as the major metabolite[36] (FIG. 4) rather than all-*trans*-4-oxoRA (peak 5D).

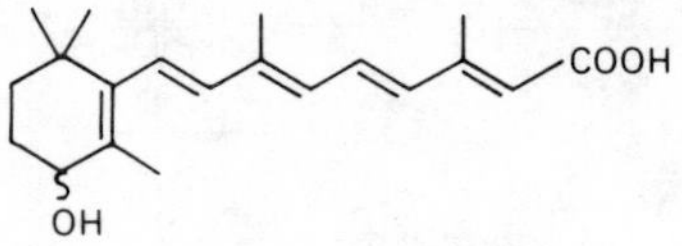

all-trans-4-HYDROXYRETINOIC ACID
(peak 5A)

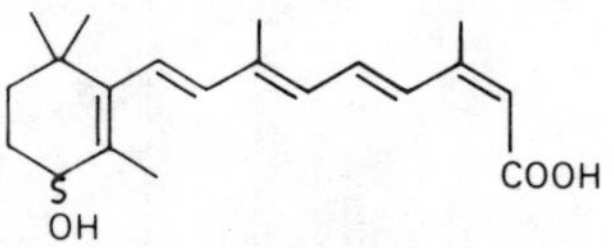

13-cis-4-HYDROXYRETINOIC ACID
(peak 5A-1)

FIGURE 3. Structures of *in vivo* and *in vitro* peak 5 metabolites from all-*trans*- and 13-*cis*-retinoic acid.

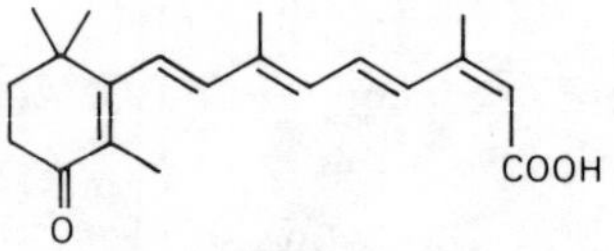

13-cis-4-OXORETINOIC ACID
(peak 5C)

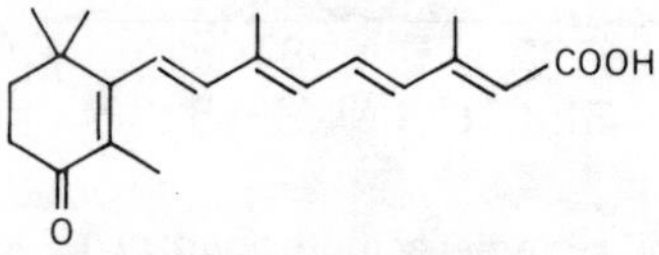

all-trans-4-OXORETINOIC ACID
(peak 5D)

Peak 5C is also the major metabolite observed after incubation of 13-*cis*-[³H]RA with hamster liver 10,000 × g supernatant.[36] This metabolite has now been identified as 13-*cis*-4-oxoRA (FIG. 3) by its mass spectral, ultraviolet absorption, and proton nuclear magnetic resonance characteristics.[36] It has also been shown to comigrate with synthetic 13-*cis*-4-oxoRA in two different HPLC systems. In addition, the metabolic precursor to the 4-oxo-compound, 13-*cis*-4-hydroxyRA, has been tentatively identified.[36]

Further investigation into the *in vitro* hamster liver incubation system revealed that the metabolism of all-*trans*-RA is concentration dependent.[37] As the concentration of all-*trans*-RA is reduced, the ratio of 13-*cis* to all-*trans*-4-oxoRA increases. That this may also occur *in vivo* is demonstrated by the identification of all-*trans*-4-oxoRA in feces after a massive 27.2mg dose of all-*trans*-RA to rats.[18] It is also interesting to note that in two target tissues of vitamin A action, the intestine and testis, 13-*cis*-4-oxoRA is the major peak 5 metabolite present after *in vitro* incubation of all-*trans*-RA.[37]

CONCLUSIONS

The observation that the formation of 4-hydroxy- and 4-oxoRA is maximal in RA-induced and in vitamin A-normal animals[38] leads to the idea that these metabolites are products of an elimination pathway for RA (FIG. 5). This postulation is further supported by evidence suggesting a decreased biological activity of these compounds in a tracheal organ culture assay[35] and in vitamin A-deficient rats.[39] Finally, all-*trans*-4-oxoRA has been identified as a fecal excretion product in rats administered a massive dose of all-*trans*-RA.[18] Similarly, more extensively modified metabolites found in the urine of rats[20] as well as in an *in vitro* horseradish peroxidase system[40] each contain the 4-oxo moiety. Therefore, attack at the 4-position of the cyclohexenyl ring of RA is suggested as being an early step in a series of reactions that lead to elimination of RA from the body. As depicted in FIGURE 5, it is further postulated that, under physiological conditions, both 13-*cis*-RA and all-*trans*-RA share a common metabolite, 13-*cis*-4-oxoRA. It is perhaps only as the concentration of all-*trans*-RA increases in the body that the levels of all-*trans*-4-oxoRA become significant. The importance of this pathway as compared to the glucuronidation pathway for the elimination of RA from the body is currently under investigation.

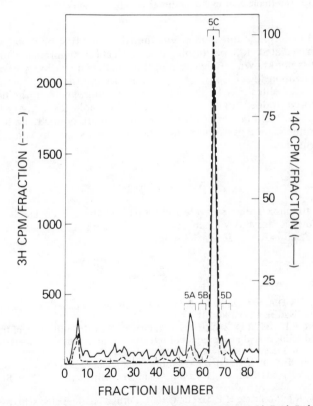

FIGURE 4. *In vivo* metabolism of all-*trans*- and 13-*cis*-retinoic acid. Peak 5 obtained from the extraction and chromatography of plasma removed from hamsters 2 hr after an intravenous dose of either 5.3 μg 13-*cis*-[11-³H]retinoic acid or 5.1 μg of all-*trans*-[15-¹⁴C] retinoic acid was combined and chromatographed as described in FIGURE 2. [¹⁴C] metabolites from all-*trans*-retinoic acid-dosed hamsters ———; [³H] metabolites from 13-*cis*-retinoic acid-dosed hamsters - - - - - - - -.[36]

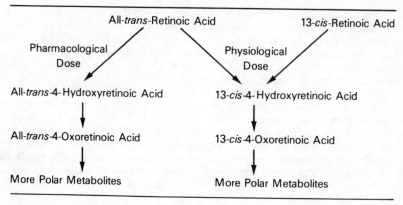

FIGURE 5. Proposed reaction pathway for the *in vivo* and *in vitro* metabolism of all-*trans*- and 13-*cis*-retinoic acid to 4-oxoretinoic acid in hamsters.

Unfortunately, the question of whether RA must first be metabolized to an active intermediate before performing its biological function remains unanswered. Because it is not known at what step in the metabolism pathway of all-*trans*-RA that isomerization to the 13-*cis* configuration occurs, the idea that 13-*cis*-RA or one of its metabolites may be the active form of all-*trans*-RA in the hamster can not be ignored. Indeed, 13-*cis*-RA is equivalent in biological activity to all-*trans*-RA both *in vivo*[41] and *in vitro*.[42] More work must therefore be done to determine whether isomerization of RA is an important mechanism in the control of epithelial differentiation.

ACKNOWLEDGMENTS

I wish to thank Thomas Tavela and Linda Dart for technical assistance, Anita Roberts, Peter Roller and Michael Sporn for their supportive roles, and Sari Tenn and Ellen Friedman for secretarial help.

REFERENCES

1. ARENS, J.F. & D.A. VAN DORP. 1946. Synthesis of some compounds possessing vitamin A activity. Nature **157:** 190–191.
2. DUNAGIN, P.E., JR., R.D. ZACHMAN & J.A. OLSON. 1964. Identification of free and conjugated retinoic acid as a product of retinal (vitamin A aldehyde) metabolism in the rat *in vivo*. Biochim. Biophys. Acta **90:** 432–434.
3. DESHMUKH, D.S., P. MALATHI & J. GANGULY. 1965. Rapid conversion of retinal (vitamin A aldehyde) to retinoic acid (vitamin A acid) in the living rat. Biochim. Biophys. Acta **107:** 120–122.
4. EMERICK, R.J., M. ZILE & H.F. DELUCA. 1967. Formation of retinoic acid from retinol in the rat. Biochem. J. **102:** 606–611.
5. CRAIN, F.D., F.J. LOTSPEICH & R.F. KRAUSE. 1967. Biosynthesis of retinoic acid by intestinal enzymes of the rat. J. Lipid Res. **8:** 249–254.
6. KLEINER-BÖSSALER, A. & H.F. DELUCA. 1971. Formation of retinoic acid from retinol in the kidney. Arch. Biochem. Biophys. **142:** 371–377.
7. ITO, Y.T., M. ZILE, H. AHRENS & H.F. DELUCA. 1974. Liquid-gel partition chromato-

graphy of vitamin A compounds; formation of retinoic acid from retinyl acetate *in vivo* J. Lipid Res. **15:** 517-524.

8. MAHADEVAN, S. & J. GANGULY. 1961. Further studies on the absorption of vitamin A. Biochem. J. **81:** 53-58.

9. MAHADEVAN, S., P. SESHADRI SASTRY & J. GANGULY. 1963. Studies on metabolism of vitamin A. The mode of absorption of vitamin A esters in the living rat. Biochem. J. **83:** 531-534.

10. HUANG, H.S. & DeW.S. GOODMAN. 1965. Vitamin A and carotenoids. I. Intestinal absorption and metabolism of ^{14}C-labeled vitamin A alcohol and β-carotene in the rat. J. Biol. Chem. **240:** 2839-2844.

11. HUBBARD, R. & G. WALD. 1952. Cis-trans isomers of vitamin A and retinene in the rhodopsin system. J. Gen. Physiol. **36:** 269-315.

12. LIPPEL, K. & J.A. OLSON. Biosynthesis of β-glucuronides of retinol and of retnoic acid *in vivo* and *in vitro*. J. Lipid Res. **9:** 168-175.

13. DUNAGIN, P.E., E.H. MEADOWS & J.A. OLSON. 1965. Retinoyl beta-glucuronic acid: A major metabolite of vitamin A in rat bile. Science **148:** 86-87.

14. LIPPEL, K. & J.A. OLSON. 1968. Origin of some derivatives of retinoic acid found in rat bile. J. Lipid Res. **9:** 580-586.

15. DMITROVSKII, A.A., N.B. SOLOV'EVA, T.A. DMITROVSKAYA, L.K. VERMILOVA & B.V. ROZYNOV. 1977. Vitamin A keto-metabolite, its structure and enzymatic transformation. Priki. Biokhim. Mikrobiol. **13:** 205-212.

16. FROT-COUTAZ, J.P., C.S. SILVERMAN-JONES & L.M. DeLUCA. 1976. Isolation, characterization and biological activity of retinyl phosphate from hamster intestinal epithelium. J. Lipid Res. **17:** 220-230.

17. ZILE, M.H., R.J. EMERICK & H.F. DeLUCA. 1967. Identification of 13-*cis*-retinoic acid in tissue extracts and its biological activity in rats. Biochim. Biophys. Acta **141:** 639-641.

18. HÄNNI, R. & F. BIGLER. 1977. Isolation and identification of three major metabolites of retinoic acid from rat feces. Helv. Chim. Acta **60:** 881-887.

19. McCORMICK, A.M., J.L. NAPOLI, H.K. SCHNOES & H.F. DeLUCA. 1978. Isolation and identification of 5,6-epoxyretinoic acid: A biologically active metabolite of retinoic acid. Biochemistry **17:** 4085-4090.

20. HÄNNI, R., F. BIGLER, W. MEISTER & G. ENGLERT. 1976. Isolation and identification of three urinary metabolites of retinoic acid in the rat. Helv. Chim. Acta **59:** 2221-2227.

21. KRISHNAMURTHY, S., J.G. BIERI & E.L. ANDREWS. 1963. Metabolism and biological activity of vitamin A acid in the chick. J. Nutr. **79:** 503-510.

22. WOLF, G., J.G. BERGAN & P.R. SUNDARESAN. 1963. Vitamin A and mucopolysaccharide biosynthesis by cell-free particle suspensions. Biochim. Biophys. Acta **69:** 524-532.

23. YAGISHITA, K., P.R. SUNDARESAN & G. WOLF. 1964. A biologically active metabolite of vitamin A and vitamin A acid. Nature **203:** 410-412.

24. ZILE, M. & H.F. DeLUCA. 1965. A biologically active metabolite of retinoic acid from rat liver. Biochem. J. **97:** 180-186.

25. SUNDARESAN, P.R. 1966. Vitamin A and the sulfate-activating enzymes. Biochim. Biophys. Acta **113:** 95-109.

26. JOHN, K.V., M.R. LAKSHMANAN & H.R. CAMA. 1967. Preparation, properties, and metabolism of 5, 6-monoepoxyretinoic acid. Biochem. J. **103:** 539-543.

27. KRISHNA MALLIA, A., J. JOHN, K.V. JOHN, M.R. LAKSHMANAN, F.B. JUNGALWALA & H.R. CAMA. 1970. Biological activity of epoxides of vitamin A. Ind. J. Biochem. **7:** 102-103.

28. PITT, G.A.J. 1969. Discussion Summary. Am. J. Clin. Nutr. **22:** 967-968.

29. KARRER, P. & E. JUCKER. 1947. Über vitamin A-epoxyd (Hepaxanthin) II. Helv. Chim. Acta **30:** 559-565.

30. PAWSON, B.A., H.C. CHEUNG, R.J.L. HAN, P.W. TROWN, M. BUCK, R. HANSEN, W. BOLLAG, U. INEICHEN, H. PHEIL, R. RUEGG, N.M. DUNLOP, D.L. NEWTON & M.B. SPORN. 1977. Dihydroretinoic acids and their derivatives. Synthesis and biological activity. J. Med. Chem. **20:** 918-925.

31. CLAMON, G.H., M.B. SPORN, J.M. SMITH & U. SAFFIOTTI. 1974. α- and β-Retinyl acetate

reverse metaplasias of vitamin A-deficiency in hamster trachea in culture. Nature **250:** 64–66.

32. SPORN, M.B., G.H. CLAMON, J.M. SMITH, N.M. DUNLOP, D.L. NEWTON & U. SAFFIOTTI. 1974. The reversal of keratinized squamous metaplastic lesions of vitamin A-deficiency in tracheobronchial epithelium by vitamin A and vitamin A analogs in organ culture: A model system for anti-carcinogenesis studies in experimental lung cancer. Carcinogenesis and Bioassays. E. Karbe & J.F. Park, Eds. 575–582. Springer-Verlag. Berlin.

33. FROLIK, C.A., T.E. TAVELA, D.L. NEWTON & M.B. SPORN. 1978. *In vitro* metabolism and biological activity of all-*trans*- retinoic acid and its metabolites in hamster trachea. J. Biol. Chem. **253:** 7319–7324.

34. ROBERTS, A.B., M.D. NICHOLS, D.L. NEWTON & M.B. SPORN. 1979. *In vitro* metabolism of retinoic acid in hamster intestine and liver. J. Biol. Chem. **254:** 6296–6302.

35. FROLIK, C.A., A.B. ROBERTS, T.E. TAVELA, P.P. ROLLER, D.L. NEWTON & M.B. SPORN. 1979. Isolation and identification of 4-hydroxy- and 4-oxoretinoic acid. *In vitro* metabolites of all-*trans*-retinoic acid in hamster liver and trachea. Biochemistry **18:** 2092–2097.

36. FROLIK, C.A., P.P. ROLLER, A.B. ROBERTS & M.B. SPORN. 1980. *In vitro* and *in vivo* metabolism of all-*trans*- and 13-*cis*-retinoic acid in hamsters. Identification of 13-*cis*-4-oxoretinoic acid. J. Biol. Chem. **255:** 8057–8062.

37. ROBERTS, A.B. & C.A. FROLIK. 1979. Recent advances in the *in vivo* and *in vitro* metabolism of retinoic acid. Fed. Proc. **38:** 2524–2527.

38. ROBERTS, A.B., C.A. FROLIK, M.D. NICHOLS & M.B. SPORN. 1979. Retinoid-dependent induction of the *in vivo* and *in vitro* metabolism of retinoic acid in tissues of the vitamin A-deficient hamster. J. Biol. Chem. **254:** 6303–6309.

39. Surekha Rao, M.S., J. John & H.R. Cama. 1972. Studies on vitamin A_2: Preparation, properties, metabolism and biological activity of 4-oxoretinoic acid. Int. J. Vit. Nutr. Res. **42:** 368–378.

40. ROCKLEY, N.L., B.A. HALLEY & E.C. NELSON. 1979. Identification of a decarboxylated product of retinoic acid. Fed. Proc. **38:** 281 (abstract).

41. ZILE, M. & H.F. DELUCA. 1968. Retinoic acid: Some aspects of growth-promoting activity in the albino rat. J. Nutr. **94:** 302–308.

42. NEWTON, D.L. Unpublished results.

43. FROLIK, C.A., T.E. TAVELA & M.B. SPORN. 1978. Separation of the natural retinoids by high pressure liquid chromatography. J. Lipid Res. **19:** 32–37.

MICROSOMAL OXIDATION OF RETINOIC ACID IN HAMSTER LIVER, INTESTINE, AND TESTIS

Anita B. Roberts

Laboratory of Chemoprevention
National Cancer Institute
National Institutes of Health
Bethesda, Maryland 20205

INTRODUCTION

Just as the 1930s and 1940s heralded breakthroughs in establishing the cofactor nature of the water-soluble B vitamin-complex,[1] so the 1970s have greatly increased our understanding of the metabolism and the biochemical mechanism of action of the fat-soluble vitamins. However, compared to the wealth of information now available regarding the metabolic activation and biochemical targets of vitamins D[2] and K,[3] our understanding of the members of the vitamin A family of compounds is still at an elementary level. The role of retinal in the visual cycle has been clearly defined,[4] but little is known concerning the mechanisms of action of the vitamin or the specific metabolites necessary for the more generalized functions of vitamin A in the support of growth and epithelial cell differentiation.

Central to any investigation aimed at the identification of the molecular species of the vitamin essential for the control of growth and epithelial cell differentiation must be a study of the biochemistry of retinoic acid (RA). Formed irreversibly from retinal,[5] RA has been identified as a natural metabolite of retinol in the rat.[6] Unlike retinol and retinal, however, RA cannot be stored and is rapidly metabolized.[7-9] These properties, along with its ability to support the growth of vitamin A-deficient animals,[10-12] to promote differentiation of epithelial tissues *in vivo*[10,13] and of tracheal epithelium[14] and chick embryo skin explants[15] *in vitro*, and to suppress neoplastic development both *in vivo* and *in vitro*,[16] have intensified interest in RA metabolism.

In the last three years, methodological advances such as milder extraction procedures[17] and high-pressure liquid chromatography (HPLC)[18,19] have resulted in the identification of several metabolites of RA from feces[20] and urine,[21] from intestinal mucosa,[22] and from liver.[23] It remains, however, to elucidate the pathways involved in the formation of these metabolites and to identify which reactions, if any, lead to biochemical activation and which are of a catabolic nature. It is equally important to understand the controls operating on each of these pathways as well as their relationships to each other. Finally, tissue-dependent differences in the metabolism, particularly in epithelial target tissues as compared to other tissues, may need to be considered. This report summarizes experiments designed to address these issues concerning the metabolism of RA.

PATHWAY OF RETINOIC ACID METABOLISM

FIGURE 1 shows a typical HPLC profile found following incubation of RA with liver microsomes of vitamin A-normal hamsters. Subcellular distribution

0077-8923/81/0359-0045 $01.75/0 © 1981, NYAS

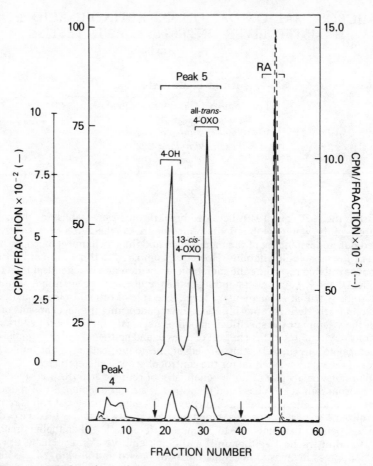

FIGURE 1. HPLC analysis of the metabolism of RA in liver microsomes of vitamin A-normal hamsters. The extract of a 25 min incubation of 1×10^{-7}M [^{3}H]RA in the absence of cofactors (- - - - -) or in the presence of NADPH (————) was eluted isocratically from a Chromanetics spherical ODS column using acetonitrile:0.1% acetic acid (45:55).[26] The fractions inbetween the arrows represent 0.5-min samples, the remainder being 1-min samples. RA was eluted with 100% methanol beginning at the second arrow.

studies had shown the enzymatic activity to be localized in the microsomal fraction and to require NADPH and oxygen.[24] The peak 5 metabolites in FIGURE 1 have been identified as the 13-*cis*[25] and the all-*trans* isomers[23] of 4-hydroxyRA and 4-oxoRA. Each of these metabolites has been shown to have reduced biological activity compared to RA in the reversal of keratinization in the tracheal epithelium.[23] The peak 4 metabolites have been shown to be products of further oxidation of 4-oxoRA.[24,26] Although the identity of these products is unknown, the nature of the reactions would indicate that further hydroxylation has taken place. Examination of the urinary metabolites identified by Hänni *et al.*[21] suggests that carbons 9, 14, or 16 might be likely positions for additional hydroxylation.

Investigations of the metabolism of 4-hydroxyRA and of 4-oxoRA support the reaction sequence shown in FIGURE 2 for the metabolism of RA in hamster liver microsomes.[26] Both the hydroxylation of RA to 4-hydroxyRA and the further oxidation of 4-oxoRA are NADPH-dependent, require oxygen, and are strongly inhibited by carbon monoxide. The reactions are inhibited by several classic inhibitors of P-450-mediated metabolism, but not by inhibitors of peroxidation.[24] These similarities to cytochrome P-450-mediated monooxygenase systems can be further extended by comparing the metabolism of RA in liver microsomes of vitamin A-deficient hamsters with that of preparations from vitamin A-normal or RA-pretreated animals. The metabolism was found to be highly dependent upon retinoid pretreatment of the animals,[27] but was not significantly increased by pretreatment with either phenobarbitol or 3-methylcholanthrene.[24]

The oxidation of 4-hydroxy- to 4-oxoRA requires NAD^+, is independent of the vitamin A-status of the animal, and is insensitive to carbon monoxide.[26] It is strongly inhibited by NADH, but there is no product inhibition by 4-oxoRA and the reaction is not reversible. The kinetic constants for this dehydrogenase reaction are significantly greater than for either of the NADPH-dependent steps, resulting in a very low ratio of 4-hydroxyto 4-oxoRA when RA is metabolized in the presence of both NADPH and NAD^+.[26]

RETINOID-DEPENDENT INDUCTION OF RETINOIC ACID METABOLISM

The effect of RA pretreatment of vitamin A-deficient hamsters on the metabolism of RA, either *in vivo* or *in vitro*, has been shown to be tissue dependent.[27] As shown in FIGURE 3, there is little RA metabolism in the intestinal mucosa and liver of the vitamin A-deficient hamster, but the activity is markedly elevated following pretreatment of the animals with RA. The inducing effect of RA pretreatment approaches its maximum after 2 to 3 consecutive days of treatment and is reduced to baseline levels 2 days following cessation of RA treatment.[27] In both of these tissues, the rate of the *in vitro* and *in vivo* metabolism of RA increases with

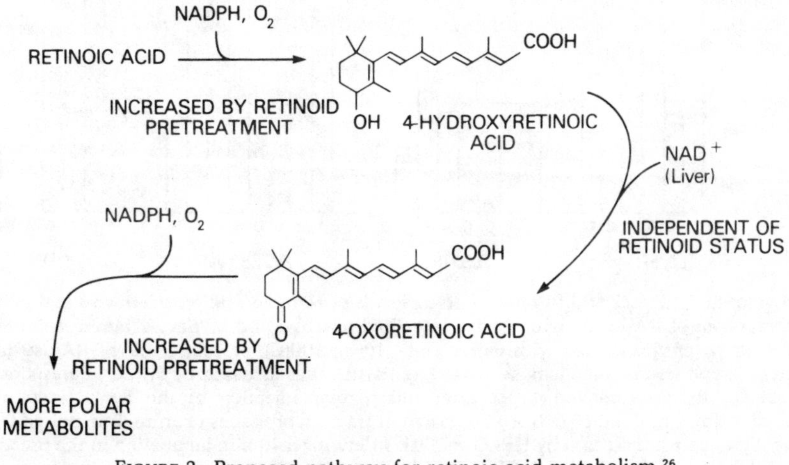

FIGURE 2. Proposed pathway for retinoic acid metabolism.[26]

increasing levels of RA pretreatment. An identical effect is seen in intestinal mucosa of vitamin A-normal animals; in the liver of these animals, on the other hand, a high level of RA-metabolizing activity is found in the uninduced state.[27] This suggests that the stores of retinyl esters in the livers of vitamin A-normal animals might provide a high local concentration of inducer. In contrast to the above, the *in vitro* metabolism of RA in the testis and in the trachea in organ culture is not significantly affected by the vitamin A status of the animal.[27] For all of these tissues, a parallel effect was seen on the *in vivo* metabolism of RA, even though it cannot be said with certainty that the metabolites found in a tissue following *in vivo* dosing originate in that tissue. The kidney does not metabolize retinoic acid *in vitro*, regardless of the inducing level of RA employed.

Of a series of retinoids tested for their ability to induce the *in vitro* metabolism of RA in intestinal mucosa of vitamin A-deficient hamsters, 13-*cis*-RA was the best inducer (FIG. 4).[27] This is probably related to the greater extent to which orally administered 13-*cis*-RA is absorbed in the plasma relative to the all-*trans* isomer.[28] In general, RA itself or compounds that might be considered to be capable of metabolism to RA are the best inducers. Their effectiveness is also in the same relative order as the activity of these compounds in controlling epithelial cell differentiation as measured in the tracheal organ culture assay system.[29] In regard to the stimulatory effect of retinyl acetate on intestinal RA metabolism, it should be pointed out that although RA metabolism in intestinal mucosa of vitamin A-normal hamsters is not significantly different from that of vitamin A-deficient hamsters, daily exposure of the mucosa to 0.75 moles of retinyl acetate is

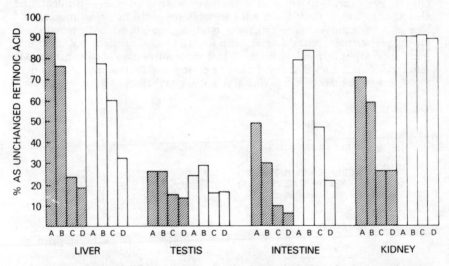

FIGURE 3. Effect of different inducing levels of retinoic acid on the *in vivo* and *in vitro* metabolism of RA in the liver, testis, intestinal mucosa, and kidney. Vitamin A-deficient hamsters were pretreated with either O(A), 10(B), 100(C), or 1000 μg(D) of RA/day for 3 days. The *in vivo* metabolism, ▨, of 0.9 μg [³H]RA was assessed by HPLC analysis of extracts of tissues removed 4 hrs after intrajugular injection of the RA. The *in vitro* metabolism, □, of the 10,000 × g supernatant fraction of tissues of animals in paired treatment groups was assessed by HPLC analysis following a 40-min incubation in the presence of NADPH and 1 × 10⁻⁷M [³H]RA. Results are reported as the percent of the recovered radioactivity associated with the RA peak following HPLC.[27]

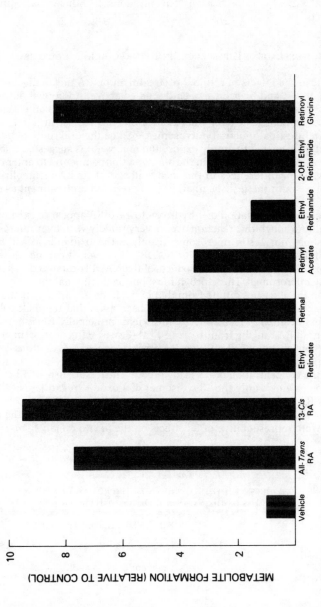

FIGURE 4. The effect of pretreatment with different retinoids on the induction of the *in vitro* metabolism of RA in intestinal mucosa of vitamin A-deficient hamsters. Each retinoid was administered by stomach tube at a level of 225 μg/day for 3 days. The assay was based on HPLC analysis of the metabolism of [^{3}H]RA, 5×10^{-8}M, in the presence of NADPH as described.[27]

able to weakly stimulate retinoic acid metabolism (FIG. 4). Thus it would appear that continual exposure to high local concentrations of inducers is required to elicit an effect.

TISSUE-DEPENDENT DIFFERENCES IN RETINOIC ACID METABOLISM

Variations in the effects of retinoid pretreatment on RA metabolism in intestinal mucosa, testis, and liver have been discussed above. Additional differences are shown in TABLE 1, where it can be seen that 4-hydroxyRA is an efficient inducer of RA metabolism in liver microsomes but has almost no effect on RA metabolism in intestinal mucosal microsomes.[26] Since the oral route of administration would be expected to amply expose the mucosa, it is suggested that these opposite effects reflect differences in the ability of this compound to enter cells of these two tissues or differences in the specificities of their RA-metabolizing enzymes. Metabolism in the testis is unaffected by retinoid pretreatment as shown before.

Differences in the oxidation of 4-hydroxy- to 4-oxoRA appear to exist in these tissues as well. Although this reaction occurs very rapidly with liver microsomes, neither intestinal nor testis microsomes catalyze the oxidation of all-*trans*-4-hydroxyRA in the presence of NAD^+ or $NADP^+$. However, it can be shown that both 4-hydroxyRA and 4-oxoRA are products of the NADPH-catalyzed metabolism of RA in these microsomes. Therefore, it must be concluded that the dehydrogenase reaction in these tissues differs from that of the liver. A partial explanation of these differences may come from the recent observation that the metabolism of all-*trans*-RA in intestinal or testis microsomes yields principally 13-*cis*-4-oxoRA at concentrations of RA ranging from 10^{-8} to 10^{-6}M (FIG. 5).[30] In contrast, in liver microsomes, at concentrations of all-*trans*-RA greater than 10^{-8}M, all-*trans*-4-oxoRA is the principal product, though increasing proportions of the 13-*cis* isomer are produced as the concentration of RA is lowered.[30] The metabolism of 13-*cis*-RA in liver microsomes yields only the 13-*cis*-isomer of 4-oxoRA, regardless of the concentration of RA employed.

Thus, just as it could be shown that the inductive effects of RA on the *in vitro* metabolism were representative of its effects on the *in vivo* metabolism, so it ap-

TABLE 1

COMPARISON OF THE INDUCTIVE EFFECTS OF RA AND 4-HYDROXY RA ON RA METABOLISM IN TISSUES OF THE VITAMIN A-DEFICIENT HAMSTER

Inducing Retinoid (150 µg/day × 3)	10,000 × g Supernatant Fraction		
	Liver	Intestine	Testis
	percent peaks 4 and 5*		
Vehicle	6	4	46
4-hydroxyRA	33	6	47
RA	46	32	40

* The metabolism of RA was assessed by the recovery of [³H] in peaks 4 and 5 following a 15-min incubation of 1×10^{-7}M [10-³H]RA in the presence of NADPH. The percent peaks 4 and 5 refers to the percent of the total [³H] recovered in those fractions following HPLC.

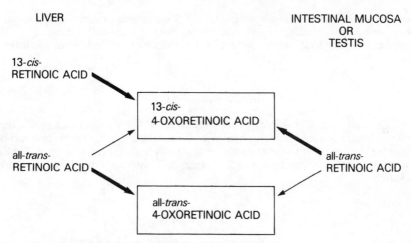

FIGURE 5. Summary of differences in isomeric routes of metabolism of RA in the microsomal fraction of the liver, intestinal mucosa, and testis.

pears that the isomeric forms of the *in vitro* metabolites of RA are also representative of the metabolism as it occurs *in vivo*. Frolik *et al.*[25] have recently shown that the *in vivo* metabolism of physiological doses of all-*trans*-RA yields 13-*cis*-4-oxoRA and not the all-*trans* isomer. It could be proposed then, that following the administration of pharmacological doses of RA, the intracellular concentration of RA in the liver might exceed 10^{-8}M, whereupon liver enzymes could function to rapidly deactivate excess retinoic acid via the *trans*-isomeric route in keeping with the detoxifying role of that tissue. In support of this is the identification of all-*trans*-4-oxoRA as a fecal elimination product of RA following the administration of mg quantities of RA to rats.[20] In addition it has been shown that the K_m for retinoic acid metabolism in the liver is approximately 10-fold higher than that of the intestinal mucosa or testis,[24] possibly indicating that a different set of enzymes is responsible for deactivation via the all-*trans* isomeric route. It could further be proposed from the *in vitro* data that epithelial target tissues of vitamin A, of which the intestinal mucosa and testis are representative, may have protective mechanisms for regulating intracellular RA concentrations, such as specific cell membrane receptors, and may therefore process all RA through the 13-*cis* isomeric route. This isomerization, which both the *in vivo* and *in vitro* data suggest can occur in the liver as well under physiological conditions, could be postulated to have significance in the activation of RA much in the same way as isomerization of retinal to the 11-*cis* isomer is essential in the visual process.[4]

CONCLUSIONS

Data from *in vitro* studies support the scheme presented in FIGURE 2 for the metabolism of RA. The decreased biological activity of the metabolites 4-hydroxyRA and 4-oxoRA compared to the parent compound as well as the demonstrated ability of RA to induce its own metabolism, suggest that this pathway represents the initial steps in the deactivation of RA. This is further supported by the fact that several of the urinary and fecal excretion products of RA have been shown to contain the 4-oxo moiety.[20,21] Observations concerning the metabolism of RA in epithelial target tissues leave open the possibility that 13-*cis* RA may be the biologically active form of RA in the control of epithelial cell differentiation.

ACKNOWLEDGMENTS

We thank Lois C. Lamb and Margaret D. Nichols for expert technical assistance, William B. Henderson for help with the dosing of the hamsters, and Sari B. Tenn for the typing of this manuscript. I also wish to thank Dr. Charles A. Frolik for many helpful discussions and Dr. Michael B. Sporn for his support of this research.

REFERENCES

1. WAGNER, A.F. & K. FOLKERS. 1964. Vitamins and Coenzymes. John Wiley & Sons. New York.
2. DELUCA, H.F. 1978. Vitamin D. *In* Handbook of Lipid Research, Vol. 2. The Fat-Soluble Vitamins. H.F. DeLuca, Ed.:69-132. Plenum Press. New York.
3. SUTTIE, J.W. 1978. Vitamin K. *In* Handbook of Lipid Research, Vol. 2. The Fat-Soluble Vitamins. H.F. DeLuca, Ed.:211-277. Plenum Press. New York.
4. WALD, G. 1968. Molecular basis of visual excitation. Science **162:** 230-239.
5. FUTTERMAN, S. 1962. Enzymatic oxidation of vitamin A aldehyde to vitamin A acid. J. Biol. Chem. **237:** 677-680.
6. EMERICK, R.J., M. ZILE & H.F. DELUCA. 1967. Formation of retinoic acid from retinol in the rat. Biochem. J. **102:** 606-611.
7. ROBERTS, A.B. & H.F. DELUCA. 1967. Pathways of retinol and retinoic acid metabolism in the rat. Biochem. J. **102:** 600-605.
8. ZACHMAN, R.D., P.E. DUNAGIN & J.A. OLSON. 1966. Formation and enterohepatic circulation of metabolites of retinol and retinoic acid in bile duct-cannulated rats. J. Lipid Res. **7:** 3-9.
9. ITO, Y., M. ZILE, H.F. DELUCA & H.M. AHERNS. 1974. Metabolism of retinoic acid in vitamin A-deficient rats. Biochim. Biophys. Acta **369:** 338-350.
10. ARENS, J.F. & D.A. VAN DORP. 1946. Synthesis of some compounds possessing vitamin A activity. Nature (London) **157:** 190-191.
11. DOWLING, J.E. & G. WALD. 1960. The biological function of vitamin A acid. Proc. Natl. Acad. Sci. USA **46:** 587-608.
12. ZILE, M. & H.F. DELUCA. 1968. Retinoic acid: Some aspects of growth-promoting activity in the albino rat. J. Nutr. **94:** 302-308.
13. WOLBACH, S.B. & P.R. HOWE. 1925. Tissue changes following deprivation of fat soluble A vitamin. J. Exp. Med. **42:** 753-777.
14. CLAMON, G.H., M.B. SPORN, J.M. SMITH & U. SAFFIOTTI. 1974. Alpha- and beta-retinyl acetate reverse metaplasia of vitamin A deficiency in hamster trachea in organ culture. Nature (London) **250:** 64-66.
15. WILKOFF, L.J., J.C. PECKHAM, E.A. DULMADGE, R.W. MOWRY & D.P. CHOPRA. 1976. Evaluation of vitamin A analogs in modulating epithelial differentiation of 13-day chick embryo metatarsal skin explants. Cancer Res. **36:** 964-972.
16. SPORN, M.B. & D.L. NEWTON. 1979. Chemoprevention of cancer with retinoids. Fed. Proc. **38:** 2528-2534.
17. ITO, Y.L., M. ZILE, H. AHERNS & H.F. DELUCA. 1974. Liquid-gel partition chromatography of vitamin A compounds: Formation of retinoic acid from retinyl acetate *in vivo*. J. Lipid Res. **15:** 517-524.
18. FROLIK, C.A., T.E. TAVELA & M.B. SPORN. 1978. Separation of the natural retinoids by high-pressure liquid chromatography. J. Lipid Res. **19:** 32-37.

19. McCormick, A.M., J.L. Napoli & H.F. DeLuca. 1978. High-pressure liquid chromatographic resolution of vitamin A compounds. Anal. Biochem. **86:** 25–33.
20. Hänni, R. & F. Bigler. 1977. Isolation and identification of three major metabolites of retinoic acid from rat feces. Helv. Chim. Acta **60:** 881–887.
21. Hänni, R., F. Bigler, W. Meister & G. Englert. 1976. Isolation and identification of three urinary metabolites of retinoic acid in the rat. Helv. Chim. Acta **59:** 2221–2227.
22. McCormick, A.M., J.L. Napoli, H.K. Schnoes & H.F. DeLuca. 1978. Isolation and identification of 5, 6-epoxyretinoic acid: A biologically active metabolite of retinoic acid. Biochemistry **17:** 4085–4090.
23. Frolik, C.A., A.B. Roberts, T.E. Tavela, P.P. Roller, D.L. Newton & M.B. Sporn. 1979. Isolation and identification of 4-hydroxy- and 4-oxoretinoic acid. In vitro metabolites of all-*trans*-retinoic acid in hamster trachea and liver. Biochemistry **18:** 2092–2097.
24. Roberts, A.B., M.D. Nichols, D.L. Newton & M.B. Sporn. 1979. In vitro metabolism of retinoic acid in hamster intestine and liver. J. Biol. Chem. **254:** 6296–6302.
25. Frolik, C.A., P.P. Roller, A.B. Roberts & M.B. Sporn. 1980. In vitro and in vivo metabolism of all-*trans*- and 13-*cis*-retinoic acid in hamsters. Identification of 13-*cis*-oxoretinoic acid J. Biol. Chem. **255:** 8057–8062.
26. Roberts, A.B., L.C. Lamb, & M.B. Sporn. 1980. Metabolism of all-*trans*-retinoic acid in hamster liver microsomes: Oxidation of 4-hydroxy- to 4-keto retinoic acid. Arch. Biochem. Biophys. **199:** 374–383.
27. Roberts, A.B., C.A. Frolik, M.D. Nichols & M.B. Sporn. 1979. Retinoid-dependent induction of the in vivo and in vitro metabolism of retinoic acid in tissues of the vitamin A-deficient hamster. J. Biol. Chem. **254:** 6303–6309.
28. Wang, C.C., R.E. Hodges & D.L. Hill. 1978. Colormetric determination of all-*trans*-retinoic acid and 13-*cis*-retinoic acid. Anal. Biochem. **89:** 220–224.
29. Sporn, M.B., N.M. Dunlop, D.L. Newton & W.R. Henderson. 1976. Relationships between structure and activity of retinoids. Nature (London) **263:** 110–113.
30. Roberts, A.B. & C.A. Frolik. 1979. Recent advances in the in vivo and in vitro metabolism of retinoic acid. Fed. Proc. **38:** 2524–2527.

ON METABOLISM AND PHARMACOKINETICS OF AN AROMATIC RETINOID

U. Paravicini, K. Stöckel, P.J. MacNamara,
R. Hänni, and A. Busslinger

F. Hoffmann-La Roche & Co. AG
4002 Basel, Switzerland

INTRODUCTION

Vitamin A and several of its analogs are able to prevent, to a certain extent, the induction of precancerous conditions *in vivo*.[1-4] In addition, these compounds have therapeutic effects on chemically induced skin papillomas and squamous cell carcinomas.[5,6]

One of the most potent vitamin A analogs in terms of its antipapilloma therapeutic ratio[7,8] is the ethyl-ester of an aromatic analog of the retinoic acid with the generic name Etretinate (ET) (FIG. 1).

In this overview of ET two topics will be discussed. First we will deal with metabolism of the substance (both in rats and humans) and second we will examine some pharmacokinetic aspects.

METABOLISM OF ETRETINATE

A large amount of information has been accumulated concerning the metabolic pathways and biotransformation products of retinol and retinoic acid in different *in vivo* and *in vitro* systems.[9-13] It was therefore interesting and important to see if there were any similarities to retinol or retinoic acid in certain biotransformation steps of ET both in rats and in humans.

PROTOCOL AND METHODS

In the first experiment, a single oral dose of 100 mg ^{3}H-ET (labeled at the 10 and 11 position) was given to two psoriatic patients. Appropriate venous blood samples were taken up to 48 hours after administration. Urine and feces were quantitatively collected during the first five days. An intravenous (i.v.) administration, though desirable, could not be performed, because no corresponding galenical formulation was at our disposition at that time. Earlier studies had established, that enterohepatic circulation of retinoic acid takes place in rats. This compound is rapidly conjugated with β-glucuronic acid in the liver, excreted in the bile and reabsorbed after cleavage of the glucuronide from the intestinal mucosa.[14-16] Unfortunately, to date no bile has been available from a patient undergoing therapy with ET. Therefore in another group of experiments, enterohepatic circulation was examined in rats. Bile duct cannulated rats were administered a single dose ^{3}H-ET both i.v. and oral. Urine and feces were collected during the first eight days, whereas bile was collected for only 48 hours.

The isolation and identification of ET-metabolites as described by Hänni[18] was carried out by means of high performance liquid chromatography (HPLC),

0077-8923/81/0359-0054 $01.75/0 © 1981, NYAS

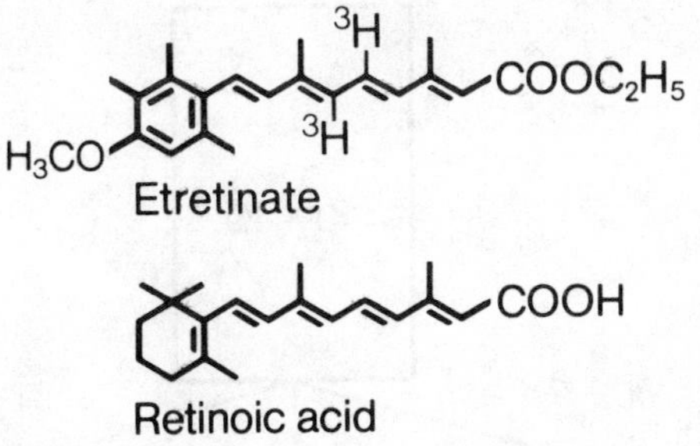

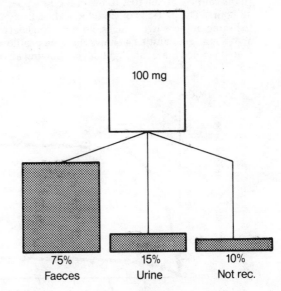

FIGURE 1. Chemical structure of the retinoic acid compared with that of the aromatic analog "Etretinate" in its labeled form, which has mainly been used in the experiments discussed in this paper.

thin-layer chromatography (TC) and subsequent mass-spectrometry as well as H-NMR-spectrometry. For quantitative determination of ET and its main metabolite in biological samples, an HPLC system was developed by Hänni.[17]

This method, which we have slightly modified (unpublished), allows both compounds to be separated simultaneously. In addition, one is able to identify the formation of isomers, an advantage that should not be underestimated when considering the light-sensitivity of the compound.

RESULTS AND DISCUSSION

Turnover of Total Radioactivity

Comparing input-output balance of total radioactivity 5 days (8 days for rats) after single oral doses of ³H-ET (FIGS. 2 & 3) in rats as well as in man, 70 to 80% of

FIGURE 2. Recovery of total radioactivity during 5 days following a single dose of 100 mg [³H]Etretinate to psoriatic patients.

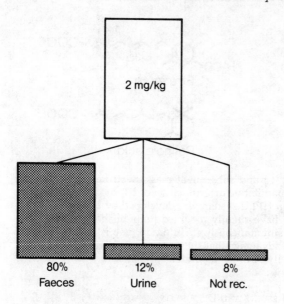

FIGURE 3. Recovery of total radioactivity during 8 days following a single oral dose of 2 mg/kg [³H]Etretinate to rats.

Cumulated amounts [³H]
after 8 days

total administered radioactivity appear in the feces and 10 to 20% in the urine. In the rat bile, about 10% of the oral dose appears during the collection period of 48 hours. The patterns of excreted radioactivity as a function of time look much the same in these two species, without considering the composition of this radioactive material. FIGURE 4 shows the time profile of the cumulated amounts of excreted labeled material. Eight days following an oral dose to rats, 90% of the total

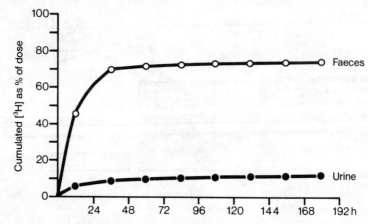

FIGURE 4. Cumulated amounts of recovered total radioactivity following a single oral dose of 2 mg/kg [³H]Etretinate to rats as a function of time.

radioactivity could be recovered from urine and feces. The extent to which this high fecal radioactivity consisted of unabsorbed drug will be discussed later.

Excretion in Rat Bile

In the bile, which was collected during 48 hours after an i.v. bolus of 3H-ET to a rat, 70% of the administered radioactivity was found. If this bile was infused (FIG. 5) into the duodenum of another bile duct cannulated rat, which had received no drug, 17% of that infused radioactivity was excreted in the bile within 48 hours (FIG. 6) with this experiment, an enterohepatic circulation of drug or of some of its biotransformation products could definitely be established.

Metabolites in Human Plasma

The extracts of plasma samples were fractionated in the aforementioned HPLC – procedure. Only two labeled fractions could be collected: The parent drug (ET) and its main metabolite, the corresponding acid (FIG. 7). An additional metabolite was identified in human plasma, but only in patients who were exposed to repeated doses. This compound was identified as the 13-*cis* isomer of the main metabolites.

Metabolites in Human Feces

In the feces of those same patients, 80% of the radioactivity (which accounts

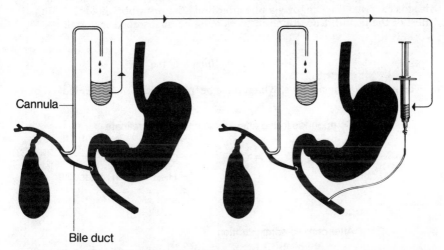

FIGURE 5. Scheme of the experiments for the investigation of biliary excretion and enterohepatic circulation of Etretinate in rats. Rats were bile-duct-cannulated and subsequently given both single oral and i.v. doses of [³H]Etretinate. Bile was collected during 48 hours and after samples for assaying radioactivity and metabolites had been taken, was infused into the duodenum of bile-duct-cannulated rats that had not received the drug. Bile was collected during 48 hours as well and assayed for total radioactivity.

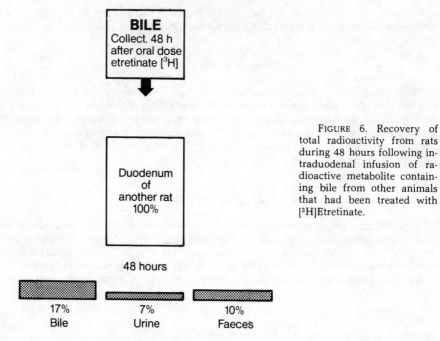

FIGURE 6. Recovery of total radioactivity from rats during 48 hours following intraduodenal infusion of radioactive metabolite containing bile from other animals that had been treated with [³H]Etretinate.

for 60% of the single oral dose) was unchanged drug ET and the remaining radioactivity was unidentified. If the finding from rat experiments, that virtually no drug is excreted unchanged via bile after oral administration, holds for humans, most of the parent drug, found in feces must be unabsorbed material.

Metabolites in Human Urine

The pattern of metabolites, which have been isolated from urine, looked quite

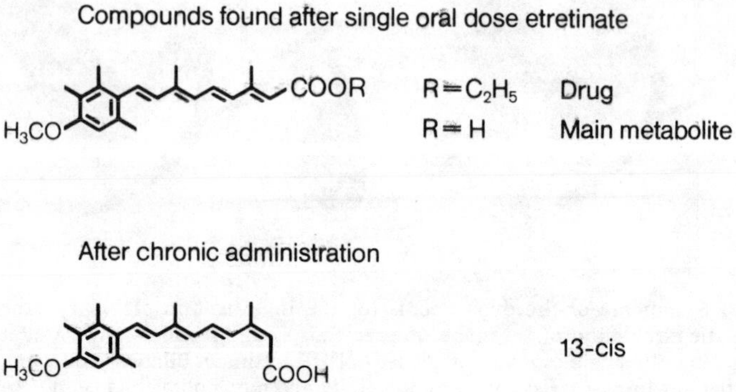

FIGURE 7. Structures of compounds that could be identified in *human plasma* after single and multiple oral administration of Etretinate.

different. Though only a relatively small part of the absorbed material was renally excreted, a large number of different biotransformation products could be isolated from urine; these are shown in FIGURE 8.

Metabolites in Rats

The metabolic pattern of ET is identical to that in humans as far as feces and plasma are concerned. In the urine of rats a smaller number of metabolites has been identified, but the structures identified thus far are essentially the same as in humans. In rat bile, the majority of biotransformation products is represented by the glucuronide of the corresponding acid. Two other minor fractions could be identified as glucuronides with still intact tetraen side chains (FIG. 9), but no unchanged drug was detectable.

These studies have shown, that ET undergoes essentially the same metabolic degradation both in humans and rats. The first step is the rapid hydrolysis of the ester ET. The acid is then biotransformed in three different kinds of metabolic reactions:

Compounds collected during 5 days after single oral dose		
11% of oral dose	**73**% of total urine radioactivity	
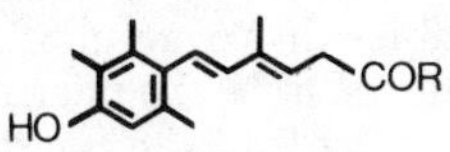 (structure: HO-aryl–CH=CH–C(CH$_3$)=CH–CH$_2$–COR) R=OH, R=OH conjugate, R=NH-CH$_2$-COOH	10%	17%
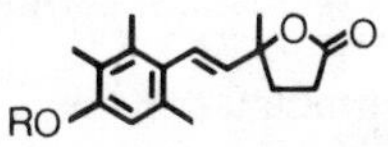 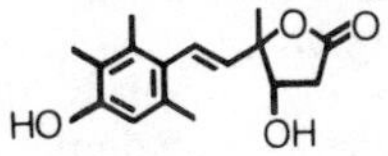 (structure: RO-aryl–CH=CH–CH$_2$–lactone ring O=O) R=CH$_3$, R=H, R=H conjugate; and (HO-aryl–CH=CH–CH$_2$–lactone, OH)	10%	**20**%
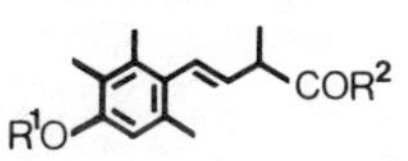 (structure: R^{1}O-aryl–CH=CH–CH$_2$–CH(CH$_3$)–COR^2) R^1=CH$_3$ R^2=OH; R^1=H R^2=OH; R^1=H R^2=OH conjugate; R^1=H R^2=NH-CH$_2$-COOH	10%	**20**%
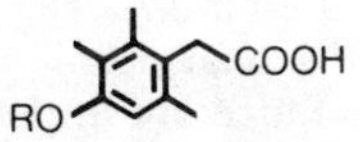 (structure: RO-aryl–CH$_2$–COOH) R=CH$_3$ conjugate, R=H, R=H conjugate	10%	**16**%

FIGURE 8. Structures of compounds that could be identified in *human urine* after single oral administration of Etretinate.

Compounds isolated after oral and i.v. dose

		% Total radioactivity
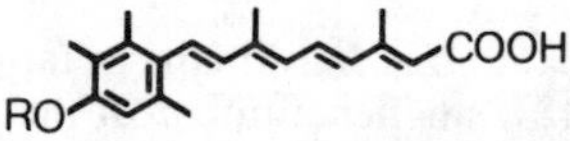	R=CH₃ conjugate R=H conjugate	70 10
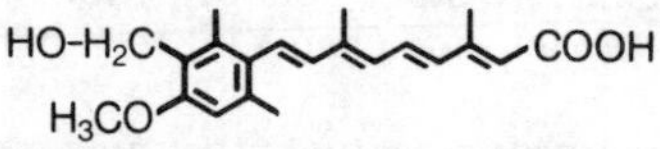	Conjugate	10

FIGURE 9. Structures of compounds that could be identified in *rat bile* after both oral and i.v. administration of Etretinate.

1. Formation of the β-glucuronide, leaving the tetraen side chain intact, with subsequent excretion exclusively in the bile;
2. Cleavage of the side chain; and
3. Demethylation of the methoxy group at the aromatic ring.

Metabolites with shortened side chain are exclusively eliminated renally.

The mechanism of cleavage of the tetraen side chain of retinoic acid has been widely discussed[19,20] and there are good reasons to accept this mechanism (the β-oxydative decarboxylation) for ET as well.[18] Further comparisons lead to the conclusion that the metabolic fate of ET resembles that of retinol in many ways. In both cases, the corresponding acids are believed to be the pharmacologically active compounds. Retinoic acid, which is now regarded as an essential product within the metabolic fate of vitamin A (retinol), guarantees the organism its growth-promoting effects. If ET is administered to the organism, it is rapidly hydrolized and the free acid is available.

Both, retinoic acid and the acid of ET are rapidly eliminated by glucuronidation in the liver and subsequent excretion in the bile, as well as by shortening of the side chain, partial glucuronidation, and renal excretion.

However, as far as the metabolic changes in the ring moiety of the compounds are concerned, it can not yet be established, whether the demethylation of ET is as an important deactivation step as the formation of the 4-keto retinoic acid seems to be.[29]

PHARMACOKINETIC ASPECTS OF ETRETINATE

Identifying the metabolic fate of a compound yields no information concerning the time course of distribution and elimination of the parent drug and its metabolite. Hence it becomes necessary to investigate the pharmacokinetics of ET. Pharmacokinetic parameters such as total body clearance are important as guidelines in establishing a rational dosing regimen. Pharmacokinetic analysis is usually accomplished by developing a mathematical model based on the drug concentration versus time profile of a single i.v. bolus administration.

Such an approach is valid provided that sufficient data are available (demanding a specific and sensitive analytical method) for a complete mathematical model description of the single-dose concentration time curve. Moreover, the prediction of other concentration time profiles of different dosing regimens (e.g. higher or multiple doses) by this model assumes that all processes governing the distribution and elimination of the drug are independent of drug concentration and time.

For the mathematical description of ET, substantial amounts of analytical data from volunteer and patient studies have been generated. Their acquisition and evaluation will be described and discussed in the following section.

PROTOCOL OF THE HUMAN VOLUNTEER STUDY

In order to maximize the information gained from the study, the following dosing regimen was used (FIG. 10):

1. The 5 volunteers initially received an i.v. bolus of 10 mg ^{3}H-ET. Venous blood samples were collected at appropriate time intervals through 96 hours. Urine and feces was quantitatively collected up to 10 days.

2. Two weeks following the i.v. bolus the volunteers received a single oral dose of 100 mg of nonradioactive ET. Venous blood samples were collected through 32 hours.

3. Three weeks after the single oral dose the subjects received a multiple oral dosing regimen that consisted of 25 mg ET administered every 12 hours, except for the first three doses (τ = 8 hours). Blood samples were collected every other day, prior to, and 3 hours after the morning dose.

4. Twelve hours following the last oral dose another i.v. bolus of 10 mg ^{3}H-ET was administered and blood samples were collected through 246 hours.

The plasma samples were assayed for the unchanged drug (ester) and its main metabolite (corresponding acid) using a slight modification of the HPLC-method described by Hänni.[17] In addition, the plasma samples and excreta obtained from the first i.v. bolus were assayed for total radioactivity.

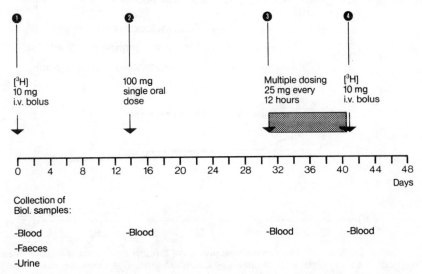

FIGURE 10. Protocol for pharmacokinetic studies with healthy male volunteers.

RESULTS AND DISCUSSION

According to the protocol, FIGURE 11 shows three different data sets of concentration time profiles of unchanged drug (ET) and its main metabolite (corresponding acid) in the plasma of one volunteer. The graphical method of residuals showed three phases of decline of the drug concentrations following the single i.v. dose were apparent (half-life of the phases: 5–10 minutes, 30–60 minutes, 6–12 hours). Although there were indications of at least one other longer phase, the sensitivity limit of the assay did not allow it to be visualized. However, fitting the data of four volunteers was performed with a three-compartment model using a nonlinear regression analysis program (NONLIN[30]). The goodness of fit (FIG. 12) as established by the correlation coefficient and visual asessment was

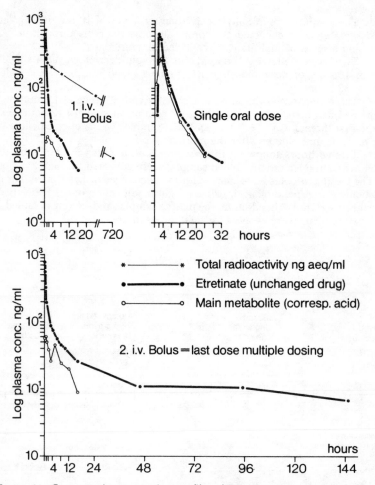

FIGURE 11. Concentration versus time profiles of Etretinate and main metabolite (corresponding acid) in plasma of volunteers to whom Etretinate was administered according to the protocol shown in FIGURE 10. The scale for all 3 graphs is identical.

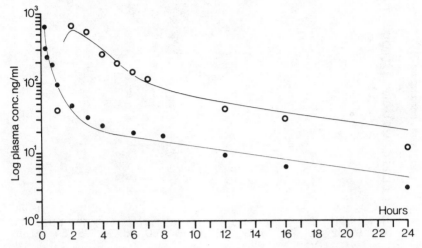

FIGURE 12. NONLIN fit of the plasmaconcentrations of parent drug following i.v. (. – .) and oral (O – O) administration to a volunteer, according to the protocol shown in FIGURE 10.

good for all subjects. However the large coefficient of variation for several of the parameters of two of the subjects was large and those estimates deviated from the same parameters in the other two subjects.

Although there was erratic absorption in one subject, the oral data could be adequately described using NONLIN[30] with the parameters generated from the i.v. data. The parameters describing the time lag of one hour as well as the extent of absorption equal to 40% were acceptable since similar values were obtained by alternate methods, such as visual assessment and comparisons of area under the concentration time curves (AUC).

Through 24 hours, the time course of concentrations in plasma following the i.v. bolus after the 10-day oral multiple dose regimen has the same general shape as after single i.v. bolus. The profile after 24 hours differs in that another pronounced elimination phase with a half-life of 4–8 days is observed. This is suggestive of the existence of another compartment that is "filled up" after multiple dosing to such an extent that analytically detectable concentrations are built up in the plasma (FIG. 13).

The cumulated amounts of excreted radioactivity as a function of time after the i.v. bolus to a volunteer are shown in (FIG. 14). The extremely slow elimination of the compound is obvious, which speaks in addition for a deep compartment.

Further evidence for an existing deep compartment derives from a trial study in psoriatic patients undergoing chronic therapy with 10–25 mg/day ET for more than a year. The protocol called for the measurement of three trough levels during the last week of therapy and the collection of venous blood samples up to 140 days. The parent drug was measured by the same analytical method (HPLC) as mentioned above. As seen in FIGURE 15 the minimum concentrations of unchanged drug at steady state were between 100 and 150 ng/ml plasma, which is roughly an order of magnitude higher than that which is observed 24 hours after a single oral dose of 100 mg. Concentration values of 20–50 ng/ml were still observed even

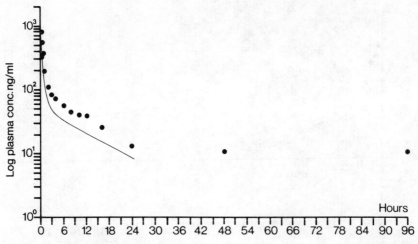

FIGURE 13. Decline of plasmaconcentrations of Etretinate following an i.v. bolus at the end of a multiple dosing regime (protocol FIGURE 10). Comparison of observed values with a simulation curve, which was generated from single dose (oral and i.v.) data, fitted to a three compartment model. The discrepancy between observed and simulated curve beyond 24 hours indicates the existence of another deep compartment.

140 days after cessation of the therapy. The persistence of elevated ET levels was associated with a *very* long elimination half-life of about 100 days.

Plasma Levels of the Main Metabolites

Significant plasma levels of the main metabolite (corresponding acid) are observed after oral administration of ET, whereas metabolite concentrations after an i.v. bolus are relatively low. Following oral administration, the metabolite rapidly appears in the plasma in parallel with the parent drug and subsequently declines in parallel as well.

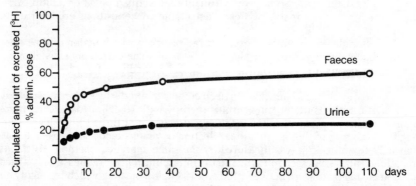

FIGURE 14. Cumulated amounts of totally excreted radioactivity as a function of time following an i.v. bolus (protocol FIGURE 10) of [³H]Etretinate to a healthy volunteer.

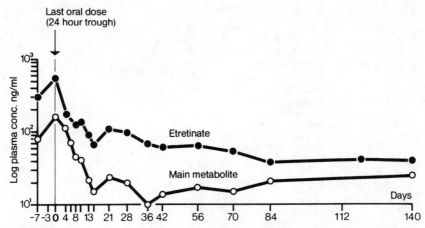

FIGURE 15. Plasma concentration time course of parent drug (. - .) and main metabolite (O − O) in a psoriatic patient following cessation of a chronic therapy (> 1 year) with Etretinate (50 mg/day).

This kind of behavior is suggestive of substantial presystemic hydrolysis of ET.

The following conclusions were reached on the basis of the human pharmacokinetic data:

1. The single-dose data (i.v. and oral) can be described by a three-compartment model.

2. Prolonged multiple dosing yields a drug concentration time profile that is significantly different from that which is predicted from the single-dose data.

3. The discrepancy encountered with the compartmental analysis could also

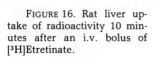

FIGURE 16. Rat liver uptake of radioactivity 10 minutes after an i.v. bolus of [³H]Etretinate.

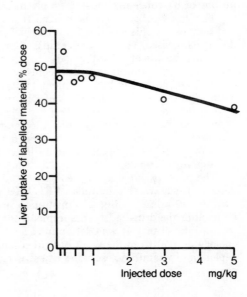

TABLE 1

TISSUE CONCENTRATIONS OF RADIOACTIVITY
IN RATS 6 HOURS FOLLOWING A SINGLE
ORAL DOSE OF [^{3}H]ETRETINATE

Tissue	dpm x 10^4/g tissue
Liver	**370**
Adipose tissue	15
Adrenals	75
Skin	13
Ovaries	27
Salivary glands	12
Kidneys	28
Lungs	16
Brain	7
Spleen	10
Heart	19
Skeletal muscle	6
Blood (per ml)	12

not be overcome by a noncompartmental approach because of the large errors in the AUC calculations, hence large differences in the clearance values.

4. The nonpredictability might either be a result of the limits of the analytical method used or a result of a nonlinear process involved in the distribution or elimination of ET.

5. Substantial plasma levels of the main metabolite (acid) are observed after oral administration, which is suggestive of presystemic hydrolysis of ET.

The presence of significant plasma levels of ET 140 days after the cessation of chronic therapy demands special attention. The extremely slow "elimination" is characteristic of the transfer rate back into the sampling (plasma) compartment from some deep storage compartment. Whether this long elimination phase defined in these studies (t½ ≅ 100 days) is representative of the final phase in the decline of ET concentrations in the plasma can not at this time be established.

This transfer back into the plasma is analogous to an infusion input process and therefore yields sustained levels of ET (and its main metabolite) long after dosing has ceased. This storage compartment plays such an important role in determining the fate of ET in the body that speculation concerning the identity and characteristics of this storage site seems warranted.

Although to date little experimental information is available about the type of tissue able to store large amounts of ET, one is compelled to compare ET with vitamin A and its storage site, the liver. Many studies have been carried out in order to determine normal vitamin A liver contents in humans,[21-25] liver storage capacities,[26] and storage sites in the liver tissue.[28]

Some hints in this direction can be drawn from preliminary experiments with radioactive ET in rats.

The primary outcome of these pilot studies indicated, that the liver was indeed the tissue which accumulated ET. Briefly, the liver took up about 50% of an i.v. dose 10 minutes after administration (unpublished data, FIG. 16) and at 6 hours after the drug had been administered, the highest tissue-to-blood concentration ratio (TABLE 1) was determined for the liver (r = 30.8[31]). An additional analogy derives from the work of Sauberlich et al.,[27] which has shown that the depletion of vitamin A reservoirs takes years because of the tremendous storage capacity of the liver.

Concluding Remarks

In the preceding overview, the analogy between vitamin A and an aromatic analog ET has been stressed. Since the similarities between the two compounds as far as metabolism is concerned have been established, further experimental data will show whether pharmacokinetic analogies are valid.

References

1. Rowe, N.A. & R.J. Gorlin. 1959. J. Dent. Res. **38:** 72-82.
2. Chu, E.W. & R.A. Malmgren. 1965. Cancer Res. **25:** 884-895.
3. Davies, R.E. 1967. Cancer Res. **27:** 237-241.
4. Bollag, W. 1972. Eur. J. Cancer **8:** 689-693.
5. Bollag, W. 1971. Cancer Chemother. Rep. **55:** 53-58.
6. Bollag, W. 1971. Experientia **27:** 90-92.
7. Bollag, W. 1974. Eur. J. Cancer **10:** 731-737.
8. Bollag, W. 1975. Eur. J. Cancer **11:** 721-724.
9. Dunagin, P.E., E.H. Meadows & J.A. Olson. 1965. Science **148:** 86-87.
10. Hänni, R., F. Bigler, W. Meister, & G. Englert. 1976. Helv. Chim. Acta **59:** 2221.
11. Hänni, R. & F. Bigler. 1977. Helv. Chim. Acta **60:** 881.
12. Ito, Y., M. Zile, H.F. De Luca & H.M. Ahrens. Biochim. Biophys, Acta **369:** 338-350.
13. Ott, D.B., P.A. Lachance & M.S. Lachance. 1979. Am. J. Clin. Nutr. **32:** 2522-2531.
14. Zachman, R.D. & J.A. Olson. 1964. Nature **201:** 1222.
15. Dunagin, P.E., R.D. Zachman & J.A. Olson. 1964. Biochim. Biophys. Acta **90:** 432.
16. Zachman R.D., P.E. Dunagin & J.A. Olson. 1966. J. Lipid Res. **7:** 3.
17. Hänni, R., D. Hervouet & A. Busslinger. 1979. J. Chromatogr. **162:** 615-621.
18. Hänni, R., F. Bigler, W. Vetter, G. Englert, & P. Loeliger. 1977. Helv. Chim. Acta **60:** 2309-2325.
19. De Luca, H.F. & A.B. Roberts. 1969. Am. J. Clin. Nutr. **22:** 945-952.
20. De Luca, H.F. & M. Zile. 1975. Acta Dermatovener. Suppl. **74:** 13-20.
21. Underwood, B.A., H. Siegel, R.C. Weisell & M. Dolinski. 1970. Am. J. Clin. Nutr. **23:** 1037-1042.
22. Mitchell, G.V., M. Young & C.R. Seward. 1973. Am. J. Clin. Nutr. **26:** 992-997.
23. Raica, N., Jr., J. Scott, L. Lowry & H.E. Sauberlich. 1972. Am J. Clin. Nutr. **25:** 291-296.
24. Hoppner, J., W.E.J. Phillips, T.K. Murray & J.S. Campbell. 1968. Can. Med. Assoc. J. **99:** 983-986.
25. Smith, B.M. & E.M. Malthus. 1962. Br. J. Nutr. **16:** 213-218.
26. Körner, W.F. & J. Völlm. 1975. Int. J. Vit. Nutr. Res. **45:** 363-372.
27. Sauberlich, H.E., R.E. Hodges, D.L. Wallace, H. Kolder, J.E. Canham, J. Hood, N. Raica, Jr. & K.L. Lowry. 1975. Vitamines and Hormones, Advances in Research and Applications. Vol. **32:** 251-275.
28. Inouye, T., O. Minick, C. Grubbs, R. Moon & G. Kent. 1978. Federation Proceedings **37:** 299.
29. Roberts, A.B., L.C. Lamb & M.B. Sporn. 1980. Arch. Biochem. Biophys. **199,** No. 2: 374-383.
30. Metzler, C.M., G.L. Elfring & A.J. Mc Ewen. 1974. A user's manual for NONLIN and associated programs. The Upjohn Company. Kalamazoo, MI.
31. Hänni, R. Workshop on "Retinoids in Dermatology." Int. Congress of Dermatology, 1977.

RETINOID-BINDING PROTEINS IN PLASMA AND IN CELLS*

DeWitt S. Goodman

Division of Metabolism and Nutrition, Department of Medicine
Columbia University College of Physicians and Surgeons
New York, New York 10032

It is now well established that specific retinoid-binding proteins exist in plasma and in the intracellular compartment in a number of tissues. The present review will attempt to summarize briefly our current state of knowledge about these proteins and to comment upon some of the major unanswered questions that are presently under investigation or that need to be addressed. For more detailed discussions of these subjects, and more extensive lists of references, the reader should consult other recent reviews of plasma retinol-binding protein (RBP)[1,2] and of the intracellular retinoid-binding proteins.[3,4]

PLASMA RETINOL-BINDING PROTEIN

Vitamin A is transported in plasma as the lipid alcohol retinol, which is bound to a specific transport protein, plasma RBP. Since the initial isolation of human RBP in 1968,[5] extensive studies in many laboratories have provided a considerable amount of information about the structure, metabolism, and biological roles of this protein. RBP is a single polypeptide chain with a molecular weight close to 20,000, α_1-mobility on electrophoresis, and a single binding site for one molecule of retinol. In plasma, most of RBP normally circulates as the retinol-RBP complex (holo-RBP).

RBP interacts strongly with another protein, plasma prealbumin, and normally circulates as a 1:1 molar RBP-prealbumin complex. The usual level of RBP in plasma is about 40–50 μg/ml and that of prealbumin is about 200–300 μg/ml.[6] In addition to its role in vitamin A transport, prealbumin plays a role in the binding and plasma transport of thyroid hormones. The formation of the RBP-prealbumin complex serves to reduce the glomerular filtration and renal catabolism of RBP.

During the past decade RBP has been isolated from serum of many species other than man, including the rat, monkey, pig, dog, rabbit, cattle, and chicken (see references[1,7–9] for earlier reviews and for references). In all of these species, RBP has been found to be a small protein of approximately 20,000 daltons which binds one molecule of retinol per molecule of RBP. In spite of occasional reports to the contrary, the RBP of all of these species appears to circulate in plasma as a protein-protein complex together with a larger protein. In the cases where the larger protein has been isolated, it has been found to generally resemble human prealbumin.

On the other hand, RBP isolated from fish (yellowtails) was somewhat smaller (16,000 daltons) and lacked binding affinity for prealbumin.[10] The

* The studies from the author's laboratory reported and commented upon here were supported by Grants HL 21006 and AM 05968 from the National Institutes of Health.

0077-8923/81/0359-0069 $01.75/0 © 1981, NYAS

vitamin A transport system of the tadpole resembled that found in fish, but, interestingly, the adult frog was found to transport vitamin A as the RBP-prealbumin complex.[10]

The vitamin A transport system provides an interesting model for the study of protein-protein and protein-ligand interactions and of the characteristics of a specific lipid-binding and transport system.

PREALBUMIN STRUCTURE

Prealbumin is one of the most completely characterized human proteins. The prealbumin molecule is a stable and symmetrical tetramer, composed of four identical subunits, with a molecular weight of 54,980.[11] The complete amino acid sequence of human prealbumin is known, and the full three-dimensional structure of the molecule has been determined by high resolution x-ray crystallography.[12,13] These studies have shown that the subunits have extensive β-sheet structure and are linked into stable dimers, each comprising two of the four subunits. A channel runs through the center of the prealbumin molecule, in which are located two symmetry-related binding sites for iodothyronine molecules. Only one molecule of thyroxine binds to prealbumin with high affinity, however, because of negative cooperativity.[12,14]

Recent x-ray crystallographic studies have shown that the prealbumin molecule contains two surface sites with structural complementarity to double-helical DNA.[15] Although the binding of prealbumin to DNA has not been reported, it has been suggested that the prealbumin molecule may serve as a model for the kind of structure that may be involved in hormone receptors with nuclear effects on DNA transcription.[15]

RBP STRUCTURE

Less detailed structural information is available about RBP. Studies employing circular dichroism and optical rotary dispersion have shown that human RBP appears to have a relatively high content of unordered conformation, a significant but small complement of β-conformation, and little or no α-helix.[16,17] The RBP molecule contains no bound lipid (other than retinol) and no carbohydrate.

The complete primary structure of human RBP has been reported recently.[18] RBP is cleaved by cyanogen bromide into five fragments; of these, the carboxy-terminal fragment represents slightly more than half the molecule. In another recent study,[19] the five cyanogen bromide fragments were isolated and aligned, the amino acid sequences of four of the fragments were determined, and the sequence of the amino-terminal two-thirds of the RBP molecule was reported. Information was sought concerning the possible existence of sequence homologies between the RBP partial sequence and the amino acid sequences of other proteins whose primary structures are known. A computer search with appropriate programs failed to reveal homologies in sequence between RBP and any other known sequenced protein.[19] The reported complete sequence[18] consists of 182 amino acids, with the carboxy-terminal sequence: -Gly-Arg-Ser-Glu-Arg-Asn-Leu-COOH.

RBP-Prealbumin Interaction

More information is needed about the structures and the characteristics of the binding sites on prealbumin and on RBP that are involved in the interaction between these two proteins. It is known that the interaction of RBP with prealbumin is very sensitive to ionic strength, with dissociation of the protein-protein complex occurring at low ionic strength.[20,21] The interaction of RBP with prealbumin is also strongly pH dependent; maximum binding occurs near physiological pH and falls gradually at lower and at higher pH values.[21] It has also been found that the binding of retinol to RBP appears to be stabilized by the formation of the RBP-prealbumin complex.[22,23] In contrast, there is no interdependence of the binding of thyroxine and of RBP to prealbumin.

The results of several studies strongly suggest that prealbumin contains four binding sites for human RBP.[21,24,25] It has been suggested[25] that prealbumin possesses four identical binding sites for RBP, but that the binding (for the human proteins) is of a negative cooperative nature, largely resulting from steric hindrance by already bound RBP molecules. With the information on hand, it seems reasonable to assume that each prealbumin subunit might contain one binding site for RBP. More data are, however, needed to confirm this hypothesis.

The structures that characterize the protein-protein binding sites on RBP and prealbumin appear to be very similar across a range of species. Thus, RBPs and prealbumins of human and chicken cross-interact, and show inter-species affinities similar to those displayed by the proteins of the same species.[25] Rat RBP has been isolated by affinity chromatography on human prealbumin coupled to agarose,[26] and conversely rat prealbumin has been isolated by affinity chromatography on human RBP coupled to agarose.[27] It appears that the structural features responsible for the protein-protein interaction were maintained during much of vertebrate evolution.

RBP-Retinol Interaction

A large number of studies have explored the binding of a variety of retinoids and related compounds to apo-RBP (see ref. 2 for review and references). The structural features required for the binding of all-*trans*-retinol to RBP appear to be fairly, but far from absolutely, specific. A number of retinoids can bind to apo-RBP with varying degrees of effectiveness. Some of these (including all-*trans* retinoic acid) bind to RBP with an affinity similar to that of retinol. Compounds unrelated to vitamin A in structure bind minimally to RBP or not at all.

Clinical Studies

Many clinical studies have examined the effects of a variety of diseases on the plasma levels of RBP and prealbumin in humans. This topic is discussed in more detailed in other reviews (refs. 1, 2, 7–9). No disease has yet been found where RBP was totally absent or had abnormal immunological properties. Plasma RBP levels are low in patients with liver disease and are high in patients with chronic renal disease.[6] These findings reflect the facts that RBP is produced in the liver and mainly catabolized in the kidneys. Several studies have examined the retinol transport system in patients with protein-calorie malnutrition. Such patients have decreased concentrations of plasma RBP, prealbumin, and vitamin A. Low intake of dietary protein and calories is frequently accompanied by an inadequate intake of vitamin A. However, even in cases where there is adequate vitamin A intake, the plasma RBP and vitamin A levels are low, reflecting a functional impairment in the hepatic release of vitamin A because of defective production of RBP.

RETINOL DELIVERY: RBP RECEPTORS

RBP is responsible for the delivery of retinol from the liver to the extrahepatic sites of action of the vitamin. Evidence is available that this delivery process may involve cell surface receptors for RBP. Thus, studies have been reported that suggest that there are specific cell surface receptors for RBP on monkey small intestine mucosal cells,[28] on bovine pigment epithelial cells,[29,30] and on chicken testicular cell membranes.[31] In these studies, retinol appeared to be taken up (from holo-RBP) by the cells without a concomitant uptake of RBP. Retinol was not taken up by the pigment epithelial cells when it was presented nonspecifically bound to bovine serum albumin.[30] Hence, RBP appears to deliver retinol to specific cell surface sites that "recognize" RBP, and to release retinol at these locations. The retinol then enters the cell for subsequent metabolism and action. The apo-RBP does not appear to enter the cell, but returns to the circulation, where it shows a reduced affinity for prealbumin and is selectively filtered by the renal glomeruli.

Studies in the rat[32] and in humans[33] have suggested that vitamin A toxicity occurs *in vivo* when the level of vitamin A in the body is such that retinol begins to circulate in plasma, and to be presented to membranes, in a form other than bound to RBP. It has been suggested that the nonspecific and unregulated delivery of vitamin A to biological membranes, in contrast to the specific and regulated delivery via RBP, leads to vitamin A toxicity.

Many questions exist about the nature of the retinol delivery process and about its regulation. Information is needed about the putative "RBP receptor," including answers to questions about its structure, metabolism, and regulation, and about its role in the release of retinol from RBP and in the uptake of retinol into the cell.

REGULATION OF RBP PRODUCTION AND SECRETION BY THE LIVER

Vitamin A mobilization from the liver, and its delivery to peripheral tissues, is highly regulated by factors that control the rates of RBP production and secretion by the liver. A major goal of our laboratory has been to try to elucidate the cellular and molecular mechanisms involved in the regulation of RBP production and secretion. These studies have employed the rat as an animal model, and a sensitive and specific radioimmunoassay for rat RBP.[34]

One factor that specifically regulates RBP secretion from the liver is the nutritional vitamin A status of the animal.[34-36] Thus, retinol deficiency specifically blocks the secretion of RBP from the liver, so that plasma RBP levels fall and liver RBP levels rise. Conversely, repletion of vitamin A-deficient rats intravenously with retinol stimulates the rapid secretion of RBP from the expanded liver pool (in the deficient rat) into the plasma. This release of RBP is not blocked by inhibitors of protein synthesis, indicating that it comes from the expanded liver pool of RBP rather than from *de novo* protein synthesis.

The block in RBP secretion seen after vitamin A depletion is highly specific for RBP. Thus, neither vitamin A depletion and deficiency, nor retinol repletion of deficient rats, significantly altered plasma levels of prealbumin.[37] The secretion of RBP and prealbumin appear to be independently regulated processes, with formation of the RBP-prealbumin complex occurring in plasma, after secretion of the two proteins from the liver cell.

Studies are in progress to explore the roles of various subcellular organelles and structures in the secretion of RBP. RBP in the liver is mainly found associated with the liver microsomes, and is particularly enriched in the rough microsomal fraction.[1] The Golgi apparatus was found to contain a maximum of 23% of RBP in the liver in normal rats, and a maximum of less than 10% of the expanded pool of liver RBP in vitamin A-deficient rats.[38] Presumptive evidence that the microtubules are involved in the secretion of RBP has been obtained in studies with the drug colchicine.[39] These recent studies[38, 39] suggest that the Golgi apparatus and secretory vesicles are involved in the pathway of RBP secretion from the liver, but also demonstrate that the Golgi is not the major subcellular locus for RBP in either normal or vitamin A-deficient rats. These studies, on the subcellular organelles and pathways involved in RBP secretion, are continuing with the goal of identifying and characterizing the rate-limiting steps in this overall process.

Recently, we have found two lines of differentiated rat hepatoma cells that synthesize RBP during culture *in vitro*.[40] When the cells were incubated in a vitamin A-free serumless medium, a relatively large proportion of the RBP synthesized was retained within the cells. Addition of retinol to the medium (at levels of 0.1 or 1 μg/ml) stimulated the release of RBP from the cells into the medium and also increased the net synthesis of RBP. In contrast, retinol had no effect on either the synthesis or secretion of rat serum albumin by these cells. Thus, these cell lines appear to respond to vitamin A depletion and repletion in a manner similar to the intact rat liver cell *in vivo*. We believe that these cells provide a good model to study many of the factors involved in the regulation of RBP synthesis and secretion. Our more recent studies utilizing these cells, and addressing questions about the regulation of RBP synthesis and secretion, will be reported by Dr. John E. Smith in a later presentation in this volume.

Information is needed about a number of key questions relating to RBP secretion. For example, we do not know the subcellular locus when retinol normally interacts and forms a complex with RBP in the liver cell. Since RBP secretion is specifically blocked in the absence of retinol, the possibility exists that one or more of the events involved in making retinol available to RBP for complex formation may normally play a key role in the regulation of RBP secretion. Nothing is known about the manner in which retinol is transported within the cell from the site(s) of retinyl ester hydrolysis[41] to a molecule of apo-RBP; the intracellular binding protein for retinol (CRBP, see below) may play a role in this process. An important general question which we eventually hope to address is: What are the molecular signals from peripheral tissues that normally stimulate or depress the synthesis and secretion of RBP?

FIGURE 1 schematically summarizes the information available about the processes involved in vitamin A mobilization from the liver, transport in the plasma, and delivery to and uptake into a peripheral target tissue. Retinol, taken up by the target cell at the cell surface receptor for RBP, probably interacts with CRBP within the cell, prior to subsequent translocation within the cell, metabolism, and/or initiation of a biological effect.

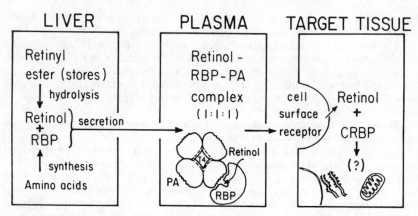

FIGURE 1. Schematic summary of the processes involved in vitamin A mobilization from the liver, transport in plasma, delivery to a target tissue, and uptake into the target cell. Plasma transport involves the protein-protein complex of holo-RBP with prealbumin (PA). After uptake of retinol from holo-RBP into the target cell, it is likely that the retinol interacts with CRBP before the occurrence of subsequent metabolic events. Only a very small fraction of prealbumin molecules normally contain a molecule of bound thyroxine (T4).

INTRACELLULAR BINDING PROTEINS FOR RETINOL AND RETINOIC ACID

During the past 5 years, there has been expanding interest in the properties and the possible functions of intracellular binding proteins for retinoids. Evidence for the existence of a specific, soluble binding protein for retinol in rat tissues was first reported by Bashor et al. in 1973.[42] Subsequently, the existence of a similar but distinct cytosolic protein with binding specificity for retinoic acid was also demonstrated. Since then, it has been clearly established that a number of tissues in rats, humans, and other species contain soluble proteins with binding specificity for retinol or for retinoic acid. The information available about these intracellular retinoid-binding proteins has been reviewed recently;[3,4] these reviews should be consulted for more extensive references than the limited number cited here.

The intracellular binding proteins for retinol (CRBP) and for retinoic acid (CRABP) have been purified to homogeneity from rat liver, rat testis, and bovine retina.[43-47] CRABP has also been purified from chick embryo skin.[48] The major properties of the purified preparations, for each protein from different sources, were quite similar to each other. Both CRBP and CRABP have molecular weights close to 14,600 and single binding sites for one molecule of retinoid ligand. The intracellular binding proteins differ from serum RBP with regard to molecular weight (the intracellular proteins are smaller), immunoreactivity (they are unreactive in the serum RBP radioimmunoassay), binding affinity for prealbumin (they show no affinity for prealbumin), and ultraviolet and fluorescence spectral characteristics. The ultraviolet absorption spectra of CRBP and CRABP are almost identical, despite differences in the nature of the ligands bound by these two proteins. The explanation for this phenomenon is not clear, but must reflect in large part the configuration of the ligand when bound to the protein.

Specific antibodies against CRBP isolated from rat liver were raised in rabbits and a radioimmunoassay for pure CRBP was developed.[49] CRABP was found to be immunologically distinct from CRBP. CRBP from rat testis showed identical immunoreactivity as that from liver, suggesting that the same CRBP molecule is found in different tissues. These observations have been confirmed recently in our laboratory (Adachi, Smith, Sklan and Goodman, unpublished observations), using CRBP isolated from rat testis cytosol and antibodies against CRBP raised in a turkey.

Distinct differences in the absorption spectra of CRBP and of serum RBP raised the question of the identity of the endogenous ligand bound to CRBP inside the cell. Qualitatively identical spectra were found with preparations of CRBP that had been incubated with exogenous all-*trans* retinol prior to isolation, and with other preparations of CRBP that contained only bound endogenous ligand (i.e., isolated without addition of any retinol).[4,44] The endogenous ligand was extracted from a sample of one of the latter preparations, and was analyzed by high performance liquid chromatography (HPLC) on a C_{18} reverse phase column, using 1% NH_4 acetate:methanol, 1:4 (v/v) as mobile phase (Gawinowicz and Goodman, unpublished observations). Identical retention times were found for pure all-*trans* retinol and for the endogenous ligand extracted from CRBP. Furthermore, only a single eluted peak was observed with a mixture of all-*trans* retinol and the CRBP extract. These data strongly suggest that the endogenous ligand bound to CRBP inside the cell is indeed all-*trans* retinol.

Interest in these intracellular retinoid-binding proteins has been stimulated by reports suggesting a relationship between the binding affinity of the proteins for various vitamin A-related compounds and the biological activity of the compounds.[3] Furthermore, a number of retinoids with anticarcinogenic activity can associate with the tissue binding proteins, and it has been reported that the binding ability tends to correlate with the biological activity for given compounds.[50] Accordingly, it has been suggested that the binding proteins might be involved in some way in the biological expression of vitamin A activity within the cell.

Many basic questions exist about the intracellular binding proteins. Information is needed about the identity of the retinoid ligand bound to CRABP *in vivo*. Much more data are needed on the binding specificities of these proteins for both natural and synthetic retinoids, in relationship to retinoid biological activity in various test systems. What are the functions of these proteins inside the cell? It has been suggested that these proteins may play a direct role in the biological expression of vitamin A activity (e.g., analogous to steroid hormone receptors), and that CRBP may be involved in facilitating the specific interaction of retinol with binding sites in the cell nucleus.[3,51] Another possibility is that these proteins mainly serve as intracellular transport proteins, and act to transport specific retinoids in a directed way from one locus to another within the cell. Future studies are needed in order to explore these and other possibilities.

SUMMARY

Much has been learned during the past decade about the specific retinoid-binding proteins that exist in plasma, and in the intracellular compartment in a number of tissues. Vitamin A is mobilized from liver stores and transported in plasma in the form of the lipid alcohol retinol, bound to a specific transport protein, retinol-binding protein (RBP). A great deal is now known about the chemical structure, metabolism, and biological roles of RBP. Vitamin A mobilization from the liver is highly regulated by factors that control the rates of RBP production and secretion. Retinol deficiency specifically blocks the secretion of RBP, which can then be rapidly stimulated by intravenous retinol repletion. The cellular and molecular mechanisms that mediate these phenomena are under investigation. Delivery of retinol to peripheral tissues appears to involve specific cell surface receptors for RBP. The retinol so delivered enters the target cell, where it may become associated with the intracellular binding protein for retinol (CRBP). A number of tissues of rats, humans, and other species contain soluble proteins with binding specificity for retinol (CRBP) or for retinoic acid (CRABP). These proteins have been purified from several tissues and partly characterized. They differ in a number of ways from plasma RBP, and differ from each other in regard to binding specificity and immunoreactivity. It has been suggested that these intracellular proteins may play a direct role in the biological expression of vitamin A activity in the cell. Studies are in progress to explore this and other possibilities.

REFERENCES

1. SMITH, J.E. & DeW.S. GOODMAN. 1979. Retinol-binding protein and the regulation of vitamin A transport. Fed. Proc. **38:** 2504–2509.
2. GOODMAN, DeW.S. 1980. Plasma retinol-binding protein. Ann. N.Y. Acad. Sci. In press.
3. CHYTIL, F. & D.E. ONG. 1979. Cellular retinol- and retinoic acid-binding proteins in vitamin A action. Fed. Proc. **38:** 2510–2514.
4. ROSS, A.C. & DeW.S. GOODMAN. 1979. Intracellular binding proteins for retinol and retinoic acid: Comparison with each other and with serum retinol-binding protein. Fed. Proc. **38:** 2515–2518.
5. KANAI, M., A. RAZ & DeW.S. GOODMAN. 1968. Retinol-binding protein: The transport protein for vitamin A in human plasma. J. Clin. Invest. **47:** 2025–2044.
6. SMITH, F.R. & DeW.S. GOODMAN. 1971. The effects of diseases of the liver, thyroid, and kidneys on the transport of vitamin A in human plasma. J. Clin. Invest. **50:** 2426–2436.
7. GOODMAN, DeW.S. 1976. Retinol-binding protein, prealbumin, and vitamin A transport. *In* Trace Components of Plasma: Isolation and Clinical Significance. G.A. Jamieson & T.J. Greenwalt, Eds.: 313–330. Alan R. Liss. New York.
8. GOODMAN, DeW.S. 1974. Vitamin A transport and retinol-binding protein metabolism. Vitam. Horm. **32:** 167–180.
9. GLOVER, J. 1973. Retinol-binding proteins. Vitam. Horm. **31:** 1–42.
10. SHIDOJI, Y. & Y. MUTO. 1977. Vitamin A transport in plasma of the nonmammalian vertebrates: Isolation and partial characterization of piscine retinol-binding protein. J. Lipid Res. **18:** 679–691.
11. KANDA, Y., DeW.S. GOODMAN, R.E. CANFIELD & F.J. MORGAN. 1974. The amino acid sequence of human plasma prealbumin. J. Biol. Chem. **249:** 6796–6805.
12. BLAKE, C.C.F., M.J. GEISOW, I.D.A. SWAN, C. RERAT & B. RERAT. 1974. Structure of human plasma prealbumin at 2.5 Å resolution. A preliminary report on the polypeptide chain conformation, quaternary structure and thyroxine binding. J. Mol. Biol. **88:** 1–12.
13. BLAKE, C.C.F., M.J. GIESOW, S.J. OATLEY, B. RÉRAT & C. RÉRAT. 1978. Structure of prealbumin: Secondary, tertiary, and quaternary interactions determined by Fourier refinement at 1.8 Å. J. Mol. Biol. **121:** 339–356.
14. FERGUSON, R.N., H. EDELHOCH, H.A. SAROFF & J. ROBBINS. 1975. Negative cooperativity in the binding of thyroxine to human serum prealbumin. Biochemistry **14:** 282–289.
15. BLAKE, C.C.F. & S.J. OATLEY. 1977. Protein-DNA and protein-hormone interactions in prealbumin: A model of the thyroid hormone nuclear receptor? Nature **268:** 115–120.
16. RASK, L., P.A. PETERSON & I. BJÖRK. 1972. Conformational studies of the human vitamin A-transporting protein complex. Biochemistry **11:** 264–268.
17. GOTTO, A.M., S.E. LUX & DeW.S. GOODMAN. 1972. Circular dichroic studies of human

plasma retinol-binding protein and prealbumin. Biochim. Biophys. Acta **271:** 429–435.

18. RASK, L., H. ANUNDI & P.A. PETERSON. 1979. The primary structure of the human retinol-binding protein. FEBS Letts. **104:** 55–58.
19. KANDA, Y. & DEW.S. GOODMAN. 1979. Partial amino acid sequence of human retinol-binding protein. Isolation and alignment of the five cyanogen bromide fragments and the amino acid sequences of four of the fragments. J. Lipid Res. **20:** 865–878.
20. PETERSON, P.A. 1971. Studies on the interaction between prealbumin, retinol-binding protein, and vitamin A. J. Biol. Chem. **246:** 44–49.
21. VAN JAARSVELD, P.P., H. EDELHOCH, DEW.S. GOODMAN & J. ROBBINS. 1973. The interaction of human plasma retinol-binding protein with prealbumim. J. Biol. Chem. **248:** 4698–4705.
22. GOODMAN, DEW.S. & A. RAZ. 1972. Extraction and recombination studies of the interaction of retinol with human plasma retinol-binding protein. J. Lipid Res. **13:** 338–347.
23. GOODMAN, DEW.S. & R.B. LESLIE. 1972. Fluorescence studies of human plasma retinol-binding protein and of the retinol-binding protein-prealbumin complex. Biochim. Biophys. Acta **260:** 670–678.
24. NILSSON, S., L. RASK & P.A. PETERSON. 1975. Studies on thyroid hormone binding proteins. II. Binding of thyroid hormones, retinol-binding protein, and fluorescent probes to prealbumin and effects of thyroxine on prealbumin subunit self-association. J. Biol. Chem. **250:** 8554–8563.
25. KOPELMAN, M., U. COGAN, S.MOKADY & M. SHINITZKY. 1976. The interaction between retinol-binding proteins and prealbumins studied by fluorescence polarization. Biochim. Biophys. Acta. **439:** 449–460.
26. POOLE, A.R., J.T. DINGLE, A.K. MALLIA & DEW.S. GOODMAN. 1975. The localization of retinol-binding protein in rat liver by immunofluorescence microscopy. J. Cell Sci. **19:** 379–394.
27. NAVAB, M., A.K. MALLIA, Y. KANDA & DEW.S. GOODMAN. 1977. Rat plasma prealbumin. Isolation and partial characterization. J. Biol. Chem. **252:** 5100–5106.
28. RASK, L. & P.A. PETERSON. 1976. *In vitro* uptake of vitamin A from the retinol-binding plasma protein to mucosal epithelial cells from the monkey's small intestine. J. Biol. Chem. **251:** 6360–6366.
29. HELLER, J. 1975. Interactions of plasma retinol-binding protein with its receptor. Specific binding of bovine and human retinol-binding protein to pigment epithelium cells from bovine eyes. J. Biol. Chem. **250:** 3613–3619.
30. CHEN, C.-C. & J. HELLER. 1977. Uptake of retinol and retinoic acid from serum retinol-binding protein by retinal pigment epithelial cells. J. Biol. Chem. **252:** 5216–5221.
31. BHAT, M.K. & H.R. CAMA. 1979. Gonadal cell surface receptor for plasma retinol-binding protein. A method for its radioassay and studies on its level during spermatogenesis. Biochim. Biophys. Acta **587:** 273–281.
32. MALLIA, A.K., J.E. SMITH & DEW.S. GOODMAN. 1975. Metabolism of retinol-binding protein and vitamin A during hypervitaminosis A in the rat. J. Lipid Res. **16:** 180–188.
33. SMITH, F.R. & DEW.S. GOODMAN. 1976. Vitamin A transport in human vitamin A toxicity. N. Engl. J. Med. **294:** 805–808.
34. MUTO, Y., J.E. SMITH, P.O. MILCH & DEW.S. GOODMAN. 1972. Regulation of retinol-binding protein metabolism by vitamin A status in the rat. J. Biol. Chem. **247:** 2542–2550.
35. SMITH, J.E., Y. MUTO, P.O. MILCH & DEW.S. GOODMAN. 1973. The effects of chylomicron vitamin A on the metabolism of retinol-binding protein in the rat. J. Biol. Chem. **248:** 1544–1549.
36. PETERSON, P.A., L. RASK, L. ÖSTEBERG, L. ANDERSSON, F. KAMWENDO & H. PERTOFT. 1973. Studies on the transport and cellular distribution of vitamin A in normal and vitamin A-deficient rats with special reference to the vitamin A-binding plasma protein. J. Biol. Chem. **248:** 4009–4022.
37. NAVAB, M., J.E. SMITH & DEW.S. GOODMAN. 1977. Rat plasma prealbumin. Metabolic studies on effects of vitamin A status and on tissue distribution. J. Biol. Chem. **252:** 5107–5114.

38. HARRISON, E.H., J.E. SMITH & DEW.S. GOODMAN. 1980. Effects of vitamin A deficiency on the levels and distribution of retinol-binding protein and marker enzymes in homogenates and Golgi-rich fractions of rat liver. Biochim. Biophys. Acta **628:** 489–497.

39. SMITH, J.E., D.D. DEEN, JR., D. SKLAN & DEW.S. GOODMAN. 1980. Colchicine inhibition of retinol-binding protein secretion by rat liver. J. Lipid Res. **21:** 229–237.

40. SMITH, J.E., C. BOREK & DEW.S. GOODMAN. 1978. Regulation of retinol-binding protein metabolism in cultured rat liver cell lines. Cell **15:** 865–873.

41. HARRISON, E.H., J.E. SMITH & DEW.S. GOODMAN. 1979. Unusual properties of retinyl palmitate hydrolase activity in rat liver. J. Lipid Res. **20:**760–771.

42. BASHOR, M.M., D.O. TOFT & F. CHYTIL. 1973. In vitro binding of retinol to rat-tissue components. Proc. Natl. Acad. Sci. USA **70:** 3483–3487.

43. ONG, D.E. & F. CHYTIL. 1978. Cellular retinol-binding protein from rat liver. Purification and characterization. J. Biol. Chem. **253:** 828–832.

44. ROSS, A.C., Y.I. TAKAHASHI & DEW.S. GOODMAN. 1978. The binding protein for retinol from rat testis cytosol. Isolation and partial characterization. J. Biol. Chem. **253:** 6591–6598.

45. SAARI, J.C., S. FUTTERMAN & L. BREDBERG. 1978. Cellular retinol- and retinoic acid-binding proteins of bovine retina. Purification and properties. J. Biol. Chem. **253:** 6432–6436.

46. ONG, D.E. & F. CHYTIL. 1978. Cellular retinoic acid-binding protein from rat testis. Purification and characterization. J. Biol. Chem. **253:** 4551–4554.

47. ROSS, A.C., N. ADACHI & DEW.S. GOODMAN. 1980. The binding protein for retinoic acid from rat testis cytosol: Isolation and partial charcterization. J. Lipid Res. **21:** 100–109.

48. SANI, B.P. & C.K. BANERJEE. 1978. Purification and properties of retinoic acid-binding protein from chick-embryo skin. Biochem. J. **173:** 643–649.

49. ONG, D.E. & F. CHYTIL. 1979. Immunochemical comparison of vitamin A binding proteins of rat. J. Biol. Chem. **254:** 8733–8735.

50. JETTEN, A.N. & M.E.R. JETTEN. 1979. Possible role of retinoic acid binding protein in retinoid stimulation of embryonal carcinoma cell differentiation. Nature **278:** 180–182.

51. TAKASE, S., D.E. ONG & F. CHYTIL. 1979. Cellular retinol-binding protein allows specific interaction of retinol with the nucleus in vitro. Proc. Natl. Acad. Sci. USA **76:** 2204–2208.

STRUCTURAL AND FUNCTIONAL STUDIES
OF VITAMIN A-BINDING PROTEINS*

Lars Rask, Helena Anundi, Jan Böhme,
Ulf Eriksson, Hans Ronne, Karin Sege,
and Per A. Peterson

The Department of Cell Research
The Wallenberg Laboratories
University of Uppsala
S-751 22 Uppsala, Sweden

In contrast to the water-soluble vitamins the fat-soluble vitamins are poorly soluble in plasma and other biological fluids. Thus, vitamins like the retinoids need vehicles to reach their sites of action. This was realized almost three decades ago,[1,2] but it was not until the last decade that details of the transport system for vitamin A were elucidated in any detail. DeWitt Goodman and his collaborators, in a remarkable series of papers, traced vitamin A from the intestine, via the chylomicrons to the liver.[3-6] As a consequence of these studies they were able to identify and purify the vitamin A-binding protein in plasma.[7] Independent work in this laboratory, aimed at identifying low molecular weight plasma proteins, allowed the isolation of large quantities of a low molecular weight protein, which turned out to be the retinol-binding protein (RBP).[8] The subsequent years witnessed a rapid accumulation of data as regards the properties and biological characteristics of the vitamin A-transporting plasma protein system.[9] Highlights were the determination of the primary structure of prealbumin,[10] the protein which forms a complex with RBP in plasma, and the elucidation of the tertiary structure of prealbumin.[11]

AMINO ACID SEQUENCE OF PLASMA RBP

The primary structure of human RBP was not determined until recently.[12] FIGURE 1 shows that RBP consists of a single polypeptide chain comprising 182 amino acid residues and three disulfide bridges. No apparent sequence homology exists between RBP and prealbumin. Moreover, in a computer search comparing the amino acid sequence of human RBP with the amino acid sequence of other proteins we did not obtain any evidence suggesting that RBP is similar to any previously sequenced protein.[13] Accordingly, RBP seems to be the first member of a new protein superfamily.

To try to get information about evolutionary constraints that have affected RBP we are currently examining the primary structure of rabbit RBP. FIGURE 2 shows that out of the 170 positions available for comparison 160 are identical. This extensive homology suggests that RBP may have been more highly conserved during evolution than cytochrome C and hemoglobin α- and β-chains.[14] Although some 10 amino acid residues of rabbit RBP have not yet been determined, it seems reasonable to conclude that the NH_2-terminal half of RBP is more

* This work was supported by grants from the National Institutes of Health (5 ROI EY 02417-02) and the Swedish Medical Research Council.

0077-8923/81/0359-0079 $01.75/0 © 1981, NYAS

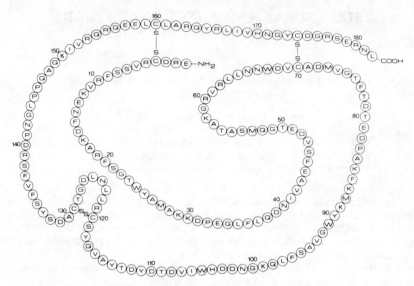

FIGURE 1. Amino acid sequence of human RBP.

conserved than the COOH-terminal portion. Thus, only a single amino acid substitution has been identified among the NH$_2$-terminal 96 residues while 9 substitutions are evident in the COOH-terminal region. It is not surprising that RBP has accumulated few mutations during evolution, since RBP participates in three molecular interactions.[9] All these interactions will, of course, severely limit the possibility for RBP to acquire amino acid substitutions since simultaneous and complementary mutations may have to occur in prealbumin and/or the cell surface receptor to allow for a maintained function of RBP. Likewise, most amino acid substitutions affecting the hydrophobic pouch containing retinol should also be abortive.

Although the NH$_2$-terminal region of RBP appears more conserved than the COOH-terminal portion, no information about which parts of RBP are engaged in the various molecular interactions can be deduced. However, recent progress in work aiming at elucidating the three-dimensional structure of RBP promises to clarify these points. Such structural analyses will also reveal whether the amino acid substitutions demonstated here will be of conseqeunce for the conformation of RBP.

Previous work on cytochrome C has shown that a single amino acid substitution is sufficient to give rise to antibody production.[15] Despite this information it is somewhat astonishing that human RBP, injected into rabbits, gives rise to high-titered antisera containing antibodies directed against five different epitopes.[16] As yet, it is too early to ascribe any one of the amino acid replacements to anyone of the antigenic sites, but it seems unlikely that replacements like Ile for Val, Phe for Tyr and Phe for Leu should greatly contribute to the antigenicity of human RBP. This can be inferred from the hydrophobic nature of these amino acid residues, which would suggest that they are not exposed on the surface of RBP. However, sequence information about RBP from other species is required to analyze its antigenicity in detail.

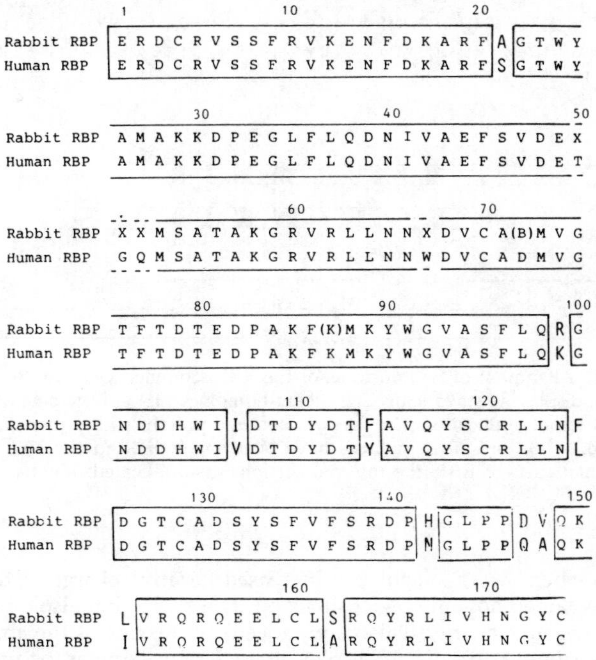

```
             1              10                  20
Rabbit RBP  E R D C R V S S F R V K E N F D K A R F│A│G T W Y
Human RBP   E R D C R V S S F R V K E N F D K A R F│S│G T W Y


             30             40                  50
Rabbit RBP  A M A K K D P E G L F L Q D N I V A E F S V D E X
Human RBP   A M A K K D P E G L F L Q D N I V A E F S V D E T


                            60             70
Rabbit RBP  X X M S A T A K G R V R L L N N X D V C A(B)M V G
Human RBP   G Q M S A T A K G R V R L L N N W D V C A D M V G


             80             90                 100
Rabbit RBP  T F T D T E D P A K F(K)M K Y W G V A S F L Q│R│G
Human RBP   T F T D T E D P A K F K M K Y W G V A S F L Q│K│G


                            110            120
Rabbit RBP  N D D H W I│I│D T D Y D T│F│A V Q Y S C R L L N│F
Human RBP   N D D H W I│V│D T D Y D T│Y│A V Q Y S C R L L N│L


             130            140                150
Rabbit RBP  D G T C A D S Y S F V F S R D P│H│G L P P│D V│Q K
Human RBP   D G T C A D S Y S F V F S R D P│N│G L P P│Q A│Q K


                            160            170
Rabbit RBP  L│V R Q R Q E E L C L│S│R Q Y R L I V H N G Y C
Human RBP   I│V R Q R Q E E L C L│A│R Q Y R L I V H N G Y C
```

FIGURE 2. Comparison of the amino acid sequences of rabbit and human RBP. Residues within boxes are identical.

As discussed above, RBP does not display any obvious structural homology with previously sequenced proteins. However, RBP seems to have arisen by an internal duplication of its primordial gene. FIGURE 3 demonstrates that residues 36-83 and 96-141 of human RBP display statistically significant homology.[13] This internal homology would suggest that the primordial gene for RBP once coded for a protein with a molecular weight of about 14,000. This is the molecular weight of the intracellular retinol-binding protein,[17] but the amino acid sequence of that protein is not homologous to that of serum RBP (see below). However, piscine serum RBP has a molecular weight of about 16,000,[18] which raises the possibility that the gene for serum RBP underwent a partial duplication after the divergence of fish and mammals.

In previous studies from this laboratory,[14] evidence was obtained demonstrating that RBP, on giving up vitamin A to target cells, becomes modified. This was ascertained by an increased electrophoretic mobility at pH 8.9, by a changed reactivity against anti-RBP antibodies, by a distinctly different CD spectrum, and by a greatly reduced affinity for prealbumin. All these changes were ascribed to the release of a COOH-terminal arginine. However, as can be seen in FIGURE 1, arginine is not the COOH-terminal residue. The erroneous result previously obtained was probably due to trypsin-like activity present in the commercial carboxypeptidase B preparations.

Since the amino acid sequence determination of human RBP ruled out a COOH-terminal arginine as being responsible for the modified form of RBP,

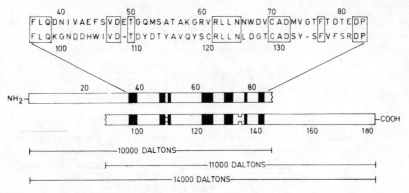

FIGURE 3. Alignment of two portions of the RBP sequence (residues 36–83 with residues 96–141) displaying statistically significant homology (33% of the positions are identical). Thus, internal duplication may have arisen in a protein with a molecular weight of about 14,000. While unique sequences have been maintained in the NH₂-terminal and COOH-terminal parts of RBP, the internal section was duplicated. Identical residues are black.

other explanations were sought. An increased negative charge of RBP may, of course, be obtained not only by loosing a positive charge but also by the addition of an extra negative charge. This may, indeed, be the case as the amino acid sequence in positions 5 to 9 of RBP display characteristics similar to those of several phosphorylated proteins (TABLE 1). It can be seen in the TABLE that the crucial amino acids for protein kinase-mediated phosphorylation are present in the RBP sequence. Recently, we showed that human RBP can become phosphorylated *in vitro* by γ-³²P-ATP and the catalytic subunit of cAMP-stimulated protein kinase. As yet, no evidence for an *in vivo* phosphorylation of RBP is available. However, examination of the possibility that RBP may become phosphorylated seems to be of interest inasmuch as a regulatory phosphorylation conceivably might control the uptake of retinol from RBP by the cell receptor.

TABLE 1

AMINO ACID SEQUENCES OF PHOSPHORYLATION SITES OF VARIOUS
PROTEINS COMPARED WITH RESIDUES 5 TO 9 OF RBP

5 9		References
-Arg-Val-Ser-Ser(P)-Phe-	Retinol-binding protein	
-Arg-Ser-Gly-Ser(P)-Val-	Phosphorylas kinase (β-subunit)	46, 47
-Arg-Arg-Leu-Ser(P)-Ile-	Phosphorylas kinase (α-subunit)	46, 47
-Arg-Arg-Ala-Ser(P)-Val-	Pyruvate kinase (rat liver)	47, 48
-Arg-Lys-Ala-Ser(P)-Gly-	Histone H1 (rat liver)	49
$\begin{matrix}\text{Arg}\\\text{(Lys)}\end{matrix}$-x₁-x₂-Ser-y	Essential residues	

x – uncharged or positively charged amino acid residue.
y – hydrophobic amino acid residue.

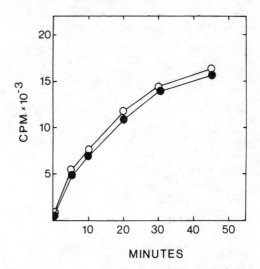

FIGURE 4. Uptake of [³H] retinol by small intestine epithelial cells from normal (O) and vitamin A-deficient rats (●). The cells were incubated together with [³H]retinol-containing RBP for the indicated periods of time. The experimental details are largely as described.[22]

CELL SURFACE RECEPTOR FOR PLASMA RBP

It is well established that several cell surface hormone receptors are modulated, i.e. the surface expression of the receptors are "down-shifted" in the presence of the ligand.[20] Thus, the receptor concentration represents one of the variable parameters which may be used to control the action of a peptide hormone. Since epithelial cells express a receptor recognizing RBP,[21,22] it appeared of interest to examine whether the RBP-receptor concentration varied with the nutritional status of the animal. To examine this, small intestine epithelial cells were isolated from vitamin A-deficient rats and control rats. The uptake of [³H]retinol from RBP by these cells was measured. As can be seen in FIGURE 4, there is no significant difference between the two sets of cells as regards accumulation of retinol. Kinetic analyses and blocking experiments with use of RBP containing unlabeled retinol (not shown) confirmed this conclusion. Moreover, analyses of the cell surface glycoprotein and glycolipid patterns of the two sets of cells did not reveal any apparent qualitative or quantitative differences. Therefore, it seems that the vitamin A uptake by epithelial cells from small intestine is not greatly affected by the vitamin A status of the animal. To learn more about the cell surface receptor for RBP measurements of the physical binding of RBP to the receptor would be required. However, on small intestine epithelial cells,[22] cornea cells,[23] and testicular cells (unpublished observation) the interaction between RBP and the receptor seems to be transient. After delivery of the retinol molecule to the cells, RBP seems to be released immedialy from the receptor.[22] To circumvent the problem of the transient interaction another approach was taken. This is explained in FIGURE 5. In the universe of antibodies there may exist some antibodies (C in FIG. 5) that recognize a protein similarly as the cell surface receptor A for that protein. However, most antibodies raised against B, like antibodies D and E, do not display antigen-combining sites similar to the protein-binding site of receptor A. If antibodies against B, i.e., C, D, and E are injected into a new animal the anti-idiotypic antibodies C' D' and E' will arise.

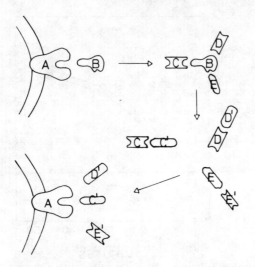

FIGURE 5. Schematic representation of the rationale behind the experiments. See text for explanation.

Some of the anti-idiotypic antibodies, C', could possibly react with the cell surface receptor A in a manner similar to B. That this principle may work was ascertained by raising antibodies against insulin and anti-idiotypic antibodies against the anti-insulin antibodies. In that system anti-idiotypic antibodies reacted with the insulin receptor and simulated an insulin-like action in diabetic mice.[24,25] Similarly, antibodies against RBP and anti-idiotypic antibodies against anti-RBP antibodies recognized the RBP-binding sites of prealbumin[26] as well as the RBP-receptor on intestine epithelial cells.[24] FIGURE 6 shows that the anti-idiotypic antibodies, raised against anti-RBP antibodies, blocked the uptake by intestine epithelial cells of [³H]retinol from RBP. Normal IgG and anti-idiotypic antibodies against anti-β_2-microglobulin antibodies had no effect on the uptake process.

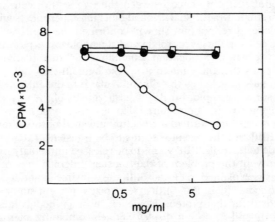

FIGURE 6. Blocking effect of anti-idiotypic antibodies raised against anti-RBP antibodies (O) on the uptake of [³H]retinol from RBP by rat small intestine epithelial cells. Anti-idiotypic antibodies against anti-β_2-microglobulin antibodies (●) and normal IgG (□) had no effect on the uptake process. The experimental details are given elsewhere.[24]

Control experiments ascertained that the anti-idiotypic antibodies raised against anti-RBP antibodies were completely devoid of reactivity towards RBP. The conclusion of these studies is that the anti-idiotypic antibodies reacted with the cell surface receptor for RBP. This was, in fact, directly demonstrated by showing that the anti-idiotypic antibodies bound to the surface of intestine epithelial cells. Also testicular cells bound the anti-idiotypic in much the same way. Therefore it seems reasonable to conclude that testicular cells display an RBP-cell surface receptor similar to that of small intestine epithelial cells.

As outlined in FIGURE 5, one would not expect that anti-idiotypic antibodies of the desired specificity would be of high titer. This was also the case, and despite numerous attempts we have not been able to extract the RBP receptor from radioactively labeled membranes with use of the antidiotypic antibodies. Therefore, we explored another approach, which may eventually lead to the isolation of the RBP receptor. We argued that the transient interaction between RBP and its receptor may be obligatory in the functional sense in that a conformational change of RBP may have to occur to allow the release of the retinol molecule from RBP to the cell. The conformationally changed RBP may not any longer be recognized by the receptor but is released and degraded in the kidney.[27,28] Thus, it seemed advantageous to establish a system where cells in active differentiation, which require vitamin A, should have a functional receptor whereas end cells of the same lineage may not depend on the vitamin and may not express a functional receptor. Epidermis seemed to provide a suitable system.

Keratinocytes of the epidermis require vitamin A for proper functioning, as evidenced by the skin lesions encountered in vitamin A deficiency.[29] In normal epidermis all mitoses occur in the innermost layer of *stratum germinativum*. Concomitantly with their moving towards *stratum corneum*, the keratinocytes differentiate and when they reach *stratum granulosum* they start to keratinize and extrude cell organelles. It is noteworthy that vitamin A deficiency causes keratinization of several types of epithelia. Although the two types of keratinization, i.e., that of normal epidermis and that of vitamin A-deficient epithelia, may be quite different at the molecular level, it seemed reasonable to us to ask whether the keratinization in epidermis was correlated with a "physiological vitamin A deficiency." The rationale behind this idea was that keratinocytes early on may need vitamin A whereas at terminal differentiation that need may be abrogated. Since RBP containing retinol should be available in skin, the terminal differentiation step should lead to alterations of the receptor in such a way that it does not take up retinol from RBP.

To address the hypothesis outlined above, we initially examined the distribution of RBP in thin, fixed sections of epidermis. Fluorescein-labeled antibodies against RBP stained intensively cells in *stratum glanulosum*, whereas weak or no fluorescence was evident in the deeper layers of the epidermis.[30,31] The reason for the accumulation of RBP on the surface of highly differentiated keratinocytes is not known, but it is tempting to suggest that it is due to the presence of a "defective" RBP receptor. Thus, during differentiation, when cross-linked keratin is to appear, keratinocytes may not need vitamin A any longer. FIGURE 7 depicts a hypothetical scheme of the events that may be involved. In lower layers of the epidermis, the keratinocytes accumulate retinol from the RBP-prealbumin complex. The receptor structure on the keratinocytes may be composed of two entities; one that recognizes RBP and one that may have an enzymatic function, like a protein kinase. After binding to the receptor, RBP becomes modified, retinol is taken up by the cell, and RBP is released from the receptor. However, on differentiating the keratinocytes may loose part of the receptor, perhaps as a result

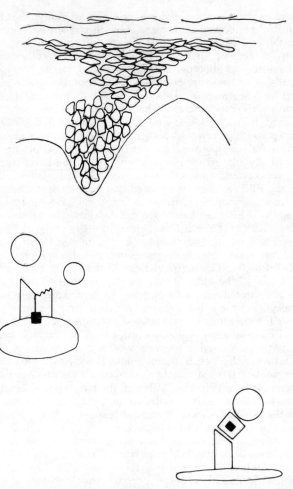

FIGURE 7. On differentiating keratinocytes in epidermis, generated at the basal layer, move upwards, become flattened and cross-linked keratin occurs (*top*). Cells in the lower layers have a requirement for retinol. Such cells may contain an RBP receptor composed of two entities. One part binds the RBP (*small circle*) prealbumin (*large circle*) complex and the other part modifies RBP so that its conformation changes and retinol (*black square*) is taken up by the cells (*middle left*). Flattened keratinocytes may have lost the "modifying component" of the receptor. Consequently, RBP (*square*) will bind but retinol will not be taken up by the cells (*lower right*).

of loss of transcription and translation in combination with a high turnover, which may only leave the binding entity of the receptor intact. If such a "defective" receptor exists, RBP will bind but it will not become modified and released, and retinol will not be taken up by the cells. If this reasoning is correct, vitamin A may have a direct effect on the cross-linking of keratin. This was examined by staining thin sections of epidermis obtained from psoriatic plaques with fluorescein-labeled antibodies against RBP. In keeping with the hypothesis presented above no RBP was bound to the cells. However, epidermis from unaffected regions of the patients as well as from healed plaques displayed the normal pattern, i.e. RBP was localized in abundance in *stratum granulosum*. These observations are entirely in keeping with the ideas presented above, and the prediction that epidermis from psoriatic plaques should contain more vitamin A than normal epidermis seems to be fulfilled (A. Vahlquist, personal communication).

Moreover, in *in vitro* cultures of explanted mouse epidermis it has been demonstrated that the accumulation of [^{3}H]retinol delivered by RBP is progressively diminished with time as the keratinocytes differentiate. This differentiation is greatly impeded if retinol is added to the culture medium. Apart from a lack of morphological change, the cultivated keratinocytes in the presence of retinol synthesize significantly reduced quantities of the most high molecular weight keratin polypeptide chain, as can be seen in FIGURE 8. Interestingly, the relative quantities of the newly synthesized keratin chains (cf. FIG. 8B) are very similar to those of keratin chains in psoriasis plaques (not shown). Thus, epidermis may provide a good experimental system for analyzing the cell surface receptor of RBP and may, in addition, provide a system to measure the effect of vitamin A on a defined gene product.

INTRACELLULAR RETINOL-BINDING PROTEIN

The fate of the retinol molecule, after it has been taken up by cells from plasma RBP, is far from understood. Several lines of evidence suggest that retinol may become phosphorylated and subsequently glycosylated.[32,33] This would suggest that retinol and its derivatives play a role in glycosylation reactions, since the monosaccharide can be transferred from retinol to endogeneous acceptors.[33] A function for retinol similar to that of dolichol has been postulated.[34] However, as

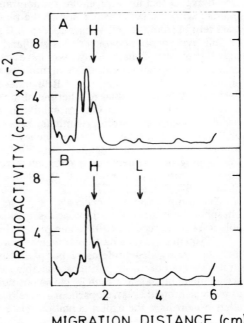

FIGURE 8. Single cells prepared from the epidermis of newborn mice were pulse-labeled with tyrosine after 10 days of cultivation in the absence (A) and presence (B) of retinol. Keratin was isolated and analyzed by Na-dodecyl-SO$_4$ polyacrylamide gel electrophoresis. The radioactivity in the keratin polypeptide chains was measured after completed electrophoresis. IgG heavy (H) and light (L) chains were run on a parallel gel.

yet no data are available which unequivocally demonstrate that any given glycoprotein or glycolipid is directly dependent on vitamin A for its glycosylation. Therefore, the possibility exists that small amounts of vitamin A may fortuitously become phosphorylated and glycosylated by enzyme systems which preferentially use dolichol as substrate under physiological conditions. Until distinct acceptor proteins or lipids and distinct enzymes with specificity for vitamin A have been unraveled the role of vitamin A in glycosylation reactions must be entertained only as an interesting and provoking possibility.

Quite another approach to elucidate the molecular function of vitamin A is to study the intracellular binding proteins[35,36] cellular retinol-binding protein (CRBP) and cellular retinoic acid-binding protein (CRAB). The discovery of these proteins provoked the idea that the function of vitamin A is analogous to that of steroid hormones.[37] If so, the extensive biochemical disturbances encountered in vitamin A-deficient epithelial cells may easily be explained. However, it should be pointed out that no data are available rigorously demonstrating that vitamin A may interact with the genome. It should also be pointed out that the above-mentioned, different theories to define a molecular function for vitamin A are by no means mutually exclusive. Therefore, it may be worthwhile to keep an open mind and consider the possibility that vitamin A may have more than one general function.

To approach the question of a molecular function for vitamin A it appears mandatory to learn more about the intracellular binding proteins and try to define their physiological role. Like many other laboratories, we have isolated rat liver CRBP to homogeneity. This protein, which has an apparent molecular weight of about 15,000, was isolated from liver cytosol. That cytosol serves as a source for CRBP is somewhat surprising since retinol is so hydrophobic that it should not occur free in an aqueous milieu. As outlined above, retinol enters the cell *via* a cell surface receptor and if vitamin A has to reach intracellular organelles one would expect that an intracellular retinol-transporting protein should be able to interact with the cytoplasmic side of the plasma membrane to successfully extract retinol from the cell surface receptor. If so, the transporting protein should exhibit hydrophobic characteristics similar to those of other peripheral membrane proteins. Consequently, we have examined whether CRBP displays characteristics shared with other membrane proteins. Analyses by charge-shift electrophoresis[40] ascertain that CRPB indeed does, i.e. CRBP interacts with detergents in a way similar to other membrane proteins. That this most probably is not a result merely of CRBP's exhibiting a hydrophobic vitamin A-binding pouch was suggested from preliminary experiments demonstrating that plasma RBP does not display the same behavior on charge-shift electrophoresis. Moreover, the amino acid sequence of CRBP, which apart from amibiguity in the overlapping of two peptides is completed, revealed that this protein is highly homologous to myelin protein P_2,[41] but does not display any homology with plasma RBP (FIG. 9).

The amino acid sequence also suggests that CRBP may be regulatorily phosphorylated since the amino acid sequence in positions 9 to 13 seems to be able to become recognized by some protein kinases (cf. TABLE 1).

Protein P_2, with a molecular weight of about 14,000[42] is one of the two major, nonglycosylated proteins of peripheral nerve myelin.[43] FIGURE 9 demonstrates that out of the 46 positions available for comparison CRBP and protein P_2 are identical in no fewer than 21 (46%) positions. This is exciting information inasmuch as protein P_2 is that particular myelin protein which elicits experimental allergic neuritis,[44] the experimental correlate to the Guillain-Barré syndrome.[45]

```
                              5              10              15                 20
P2   N-Ac   -Ser Asn Lys |Phe| Leu |Gly| Thr |Trp Lys| Leu Val |Ser| Ser |Glu Asn Phe| Asp Asp |Tyr| Met

cRBP         Pro Val Asp |Phe| Asn |Gly| Tyr |Trp Lys| Met Leu |Ser| Asn |Glu Asn Phe| Glu Glu |Tyr| Leu


            21           25              30                 35                 40
P2          Lys |Ala Leu| Gly |Val| Gly Leu |Ala| Thr |Arg Lys| Leu Gly |Asn Leu| Ala |Lys Pro| Asn Val

cRBP        Arg |Ala Leu| Asp |Val| Asn Val |Ala| Leu |Arg Lys| Ile Ala |Asn Leu| Leu |Lys Pro| Asp Lys


            41           45
P2          Ile |Ile| Ser Lys Lys Gly

cRBP        Glu |Ile| Val Gln Asp Gly
```

FIGURE 9. Comparison of the NH_2-terminal amino acid sequences of rat liver cRBP and myelin protein P_2.[41]

Protein P_2, which is usually solubilized with detergents like Triton X-100, seems to be a peripheral membrane protein. This can be inferred from the fact that after detergent solubilization protein P_2 is readily soluble in aqueous buffers.

The amino acid sequence homology between CRBP and myelin protein P_2, the possibility that both proteins are peripheral membrane proteins, and the fact that both proteins seem to contain a large proportion of β-structure (unpublished result) raise several interesting questions. Thus, is the poor antigenicity of CRBP only expressed at the humoral level of the immune system? In several laboratories, including our own, it has been difficult to raise antibodies against CRBP. This also seems to be the case for protein P_2.[46] However, protein P_2 gives rise to an avid cell-mediated immunity causing allergic peripheral neuritis.[44] The occurrence of cytolytic immune cells recognizing CRBP should accordingly be looked for after immunization.

Since CRBP contains endogeneous retinol does protein P_2 also contain a physiological ligand? If so, the amino acid sequence homology between the two proteins may suggest that a putative ligand of protein P_2 may be similar in structure to retinol. Whatever the evolutionary relationship between CRBP and the myelin protein P_2 means, the similarities in primary and secondary structure between the two proteins may open up an unexpected approach to define the function of CRBP and retinol.

ACKNOWLEDGMENTS

The expert technical assistance of Mr. Kjell Andersson, Ms. Inga Sjöquist, and Ms. Yvonne Tillman is gratefully acknowledged.

REFERENCES

1. GANGULY, J., N.I. KRINSKY, J.W. MEHL & H.J. DEVEL, JR. 1952. Arch. Biochem. Biophys. **38:** 275–282.
2. KRINSKY, N.I., D.G. CORNWELL & J.C. ONCLEY. 1958. Arch. Biochem. Biophys. **73:** 233–246.
3. GOODMAN, D.S., H.S. HUANG, M. KANAI & T. SHIRATORI. 1967. J. Biol. Chem. **242:** 3543–3554.
4. HUANG, H.S. & D.S. GOODMAN. 1965. J. Biol. Chem. **240:** 2839–2844.
5. GOODMAN, D.S., H.S. HUANG & T. SHIRATORI. 1965. J. Lipid. Res. **6:** 390–396.
6. LAWRENCE, C.W., F.D. CRAIN, F.J. LOTSPEICH & R.F. KRAUSE. 1966. J. Lipid. Res. **7:** 226–229.

7. KANAI, M., A. RAZ & D.S. GOODMAN. 1968. J. Clin. Invest. **47:** 2025-2044.
8. PETERSON, P.A. 1969. Abstr. Uppsala Diss. Med. **75:** 1-12.
9. RASK, L., H. ANUNDI, J. BÖHME, U. ERIKSSON, A. FREDRIKSSON, S.F. NILSSON, H. RONNE., A. VAHLQVIST & P.A. PETERSON. 1980. Scand. J. Lab. Invest. In press.
10. KANDA, Y., D.S. GOODMAN, R.S. CANFIELD & F.J. MORGAN. 1974. J. Biol. Chem. **249:** 6796-6805.
11. BLAKE, C.C.F., M.J. GEISOW, S.J. OATLEY, B. RÉRAT & C.J. RÉRAT. 1978. J. Mol. Biol. **121:** 339-356.
12. RASK, L., H. ANUNDI & P.A. PETERSON. 1979. FEBS Lett. **104:** 55-58.
13. DAYHOFF, M.O., Vol. 5. (1972) and supplements. Atlas of Protein sequence and structure. National Biomedical Research Foundation, Washington.
14. DAYHOFF, M.O., Vol. 5, suppl. 2 (1976) Atlas of Protein Sequence and structure. National Biomedical Research Foundation, Washington.
15. NISONOFF, A., M. REICHLIN & E. MARGOLIASH. 1970. J. Biol. Chem. **245:** 940-946.
16. VAHLQVIST, A. & P.A. PETERSON. 1973. J. Biol. Chem. **248:** 4040-4046.
17. BASHOR, M.M., D.O. TOFT & F. CHYTIL. 1973. Proc. Natl. Acad. Sci. USA **70:** 3483-3487.
18. MUTO, Y. M. NAKANISHI & Y. SHIDOJI. 1976. J. Biochem. **79:** 775-785.
19. RASK, L., A. VAHLQVIST & P.A. PETERSON. 1971. J. Biol. Chem. **246:** 6638-6646.
20. KAHN, C.R. 1976. J. Cell Biol. **70:** 261-286.
21. PETERSON, P.A., S.F. NILSSON, L. ÖSTBERG, L. RASK & A. VAHLQVIST. 1974. Vitam. Horm. **32:** 181-214.
22. RASK, L. & P.A. PETERSON. 1976. J. Biol. Chem. **251:** 6360-6366.
23. RASK, L., C. GEIJER, A. BILL & P.A. PETERSON. 1980. Exp. Eye Res. In press.
24. SEGE, K. & P.A. PETERSON. 1978. Proc. Natl. Acad. Sci. USA **75:** 2443-2447.
25. SEGE, K. & P.A. PETERSON. 1980. *In* Immunology of Diabetes. W.J. Irvine, Ed. In Press.
26. SEGE, K. & P.A. PETERSON. 1978. Nature. **271:** 167-168.
27. PETERSON, P.A. 1971. Eur. J. Clin. Invest. **1:** 437-444.
28. VAHLQVIST, A., P.A. PETERSON & L. WIBELL. 1973. Eur. J. Clin. Invest. **3:** 352-362.
29. OLSON, J.A. 1969. Fed. Proc. **28:** 1670-1678.
30. FORSUM, U., L. RASK, U. MALMNÄS-TJERNLUND & P.A. PETERSON. 1977.
31. RASK, L., H. ANUNDI, U. FORSUM, E. LARSSON, U. MALMNÄS-TJERNLUND, P. NORÉN, A. VAHLQVIST & P.A. PETERSON. 1980. Manuscript.
32. DeLUCA, S., G. ROSSO & G. WOLF. 1970. Biochem. Biophys. Res. Commun. **41:** 615-620.
33. HELTING, T. & P.A. PETERSON. 1972. Biochem. Biophys. Res. Commun. **46:** 429-436.
34. DeLUCA, L. 1977. Vitam. Horm. **34:** 1-57.
35. ONG, D.E. & F. CHYTIL. 1978. J. Biol. Chem. **253:** 828-832.
36. ONG, D.E. & F. CHYTIL. 1975. J. Biol. Chem. **250:** 6113-6117.
37. ONG, D.E. & F. CHYTIL. 1979. Vitam. Horm. **36:** 1-32.
38. ROSS, A.C., Y.I. TAKAHASHI & D.S. GOODMAN. 1978. J. Biol. Chem. **253:** 6591-6598.
39. SAARI, J.C., S. FUTTERMAN & L. BREDBERG. 1978. J. Biol. Chem. **253:** 6432-6436.
40. HELENIUS, A. & K. SIMMONS. 1977. Proc. Natl. Acad. Sci. USA **74:** 529-532.
41. ISHAQVE, A., T. HOFMANN, S. RHEE & E.H. EYLAR. 1980. J. Biol. Chem. **255:** 1058-1063.
42. ISHAQVE, A., M.W. ROOMI, N.R. KHAN & E.H. EYLAR. 1977. Biochem. Biophys. Acta **495:** 77-86.
43. SARVAS, H.D., D.J. MILEK, M.J. WEISE, T.B. CARNOW, H.H. FUDENBERG & S.W. BROSTOFF. 1980. J. Immunol. **124:** 557-561.
44. KADLUBOWSKI, M. & R.A.C. HUGHES. 1979. Nature. **277:** 140-141.
45. ARNASON, B.G.Q. 1971. *In* Immunological Disorders of the Nervous System. 1971. L. Rowland, Ed.: 156-177. Williams & Wilkins. Baltimore.
46. YEAMAN, S.J., P. COHEN, D.C. WATSON & G.H. DIXON. 1976. Biochem. Soc. Trans. **4:** 1027-1030.
47. YEAMAN, S.J., P. COHEN, D.C. WATSON & G.H. DIXON. 1977. Biochem. J. **162:** 411-421.
48. EDLUND, B., J. ANDERSSON, V.L. TITANJI, U. DAHLQVIST, P. EKMAN, Ö. ZETTERQVIST & L. ENGSTRÖM. 1975. Biochem. Biophys. Res. Commun. **67:** 1516-1521.
49. LANGAN, R.A. 1971. Ann. NY. Acad. Sci. **185:** 166-180.

A NOVEL CELLULAR RETINOID-BINDING PROTEIN, F-TYPE, IN HEPATOCELLULAR CARCINOMA*

Yasutoshi Muto and Masahide Omori

First Department of Internal Medicine
Gifu University School of Medicine
Gifu City, Japan

Department of Nutrition, School of Health Sciences
Faculty of Medicine
University of Tokyo
Tokyo, Japan

INTRODUCTION

Vitamin A (retinol) is essential for the support of growth in higher animals and for the maintenance of normal cell differentiation in epithelial tissue.[1] In addition, since the observation of Fujimaki[2] in 1926, it has become well known that there is a keen relationship between vitamin A and carcinogenesis; i.e., vitamin A and its analogs (collectively termed retinoids) are useful for prevention of the development of various cancers, particularly bladder and breast cancer, in experimental animals.[3,4]

Recently, it has been also established that many tissues contain two distinct binding proteins for retinol and its acid derivative (retinoic acid) in the cytosol: cellular retinol-binding protein (CRBP)[5] and cellular retinoic acid-binding protein (CRABP).[6,7] Moreover, it has been reported that both CRBP[8,9] and CRABP,[10,11] extensively purified to a homogeneous component, have similar molecular weights (about 14,600), whereas they are distinguished by a strict binding specificity either for retinol or for retinoic acid, respectively. In addition, CRABP has been shown to be present in several human tumors, including breast and lung cancer,[12] and hepatocellular carcinoma[13,14] and in experimental tumors.[15,16] These findings now raise the interesting possibility that the preventive effects on cancers with exogenous retinoids may be mediated through the cellular binding protein.[17]

During the course of comparative studies on retinol transport in plasma, Shidoji and Muto[18] have recently reported that retinol-binding protein (RBP), purified from the fish plasma to a homogeneous component, is distinctly different from that in other classes of the vertebrates higher than postmetamorphic *Amphibia*: i.e., it is a smaller protein with a molecular weight of 16,000, has a greater mobility on gel electrophoresis (in the prealbumin region, due to a lower isoelectric point of 4.3), and most importantly, has no binding affinity for the other plasma protein, prealbumin (PA) (and hence circulates in plasma exclusively as a monomeric form). Thus, the piscine RBP apparently lacks a binding site for PA, and seems to be similar in many ways to CRBP isolated from mammalian tissues. These similarities prompted us to investigate further the specific binding proteins for retinoids in the fish-eye cytosol. The studies showed that fish-eye

* This work was supported in part by Grant-in-Aid for Scientific Research (No. 157068) and for Cancer Research (No. 401536) from the Ministry of Education, Science and Culture in Japan.

0077-8923/81/0359-0091 $01.75/0 © 1981, NYAS

cytosol contains two specific binding proteins with low capacity: one, CRABP itself with a strict ligand-specificity for retinoic acid, the other, CRBP with affinity for both retinol and retinoic acid.[19] Furthermore, a binding protein similar to the fish-type CRBP has been also detected in the brain cytosol of developing chick embryos.[20] We have designated this cellular retinoid-binding protein, F-type or CRBP(F) as abbreviated.

The present paper mainly deals with changes in cellular retinoid-binding proteins in hepatocellular carcinoma tissue obtained from patients on surgery, in human fetal liver, in regenerating rat liver, and in rat hyperplastic liver nodules (a precancerous state of hepatocellular carcinoma) induced by chemical carcinogen. These studies suggest that CRBP(F) is a novel onco-fetal protein. The additional finding that vitamin A is locally depleted in hepatocellular carcinoma tissue is also described in this paper.

MATERIALS AND METHODS

Malignant, Fetal, and Regenerating Liver Specimens

Malignant and surrounding (noncancerous) tissue were obtained from specimens that were removed from 10 patients with hepatocellular carcinoma by Dr. K. Sugawara, First Department of Surgery, University of Tokyo Hospital. Liver cirrhosis was also present in nine of these cases and the serum hepatitis B surface antigen test was positive in three cases. Three human fetal livers from the second trimester (20 to 24 weeks) of pregnancy were kindly supplied by Dr. Y. Amenomori, Japan Red Cross Medical Center, Tokyo.

Hepatic regeneration was produced by about 70% hepatectomy according to the method of Higgins and Anderson.[21] Sixty weanling male rats, Sprague-Dawley (Japan Charles River Co., Atsugi City, Kanagawa) were fed either a vitamin A-deficient diet that was prepared in our laboratory[22] or a normal balanced stock diet (Japan Clea Inc., Tokyo) for 27 days prior to hepatectomy. Hyperplastic nodules were obtained from liver specimens produced in rats fed a normal diet containing 0.05% 2-acetylaminofluorene for 13 weeks,[23] which were kindly supplied by Dr. K. Okita, First Department of Internal Medicine, Yamaguchi University School of Medicine, Ube City. All the specimens were immediately frozen and stored at −20°C until needed.

Determination of Cellular Retinoid-binding Proteins

The assay system was essentially same as previously described[14]: liver cytosol (from homogenates centrifuged at 105,000 × g for 60 min) was incubated in the dark for 16 hr with either all-*trans* [15-^{3}H] retinol (2.66 Ci/mmol; New England Nuclear, Boston, MA) or all-*trans* [11, 12-^{3}H]retinoic acid (11.1 Ci/mmol; Hoffmann-LaRoche Inc., Nutley, NJ) to give a final concentration of 200 nM. Unlabeled all-*trans*-retinol (Sigma Chemical Co., St. Louis, MO) and retinoic acid (Hoffmann-LaRoche) were used for competitive binding assay, by adding a 200-fold molar excess to the isotope. After incubation, specific binding components with low capacity were assessed by a gel filtration on a column (0.95 × 83 cm) of Sephadex G-75 (Pharmacia Fine Chemicals, Uppsala, Sweden), and each binding activity was calculated from the net displacement of radioactivity in the presence of a molar excess of unlabeled ligand, and expressed as pmol per gram tissue. Specific details for typical illustrative examples are given in the legend to FIGURE 1. Affinity chromatography on a column (0.9 × 6.5 cm) of human PA-coupled Sepharose was performed according to the method of Vahlquist et al.,[24] specific details of which have been described previously.[18]

Other Procedures

Tissue vitamin A content was determined by the trifluoroacetic acid method of Dugan et al.,[25] after extraction with ethyl ether by the method of Ames et al.[26] Ultraviolet absorption studies were carried out with a Shimadzu double-beam spectrophotometer, Model UV-200, using the lipid extract of isolated hepatocytes, which were obtained by digestion of both tumor and surrounding tissue of hepatocellular carcinoma with Dispase I (Godo Shusei Co., Tokyo), as previously reported.[27] α_1-fetoprotein (AFP) in plasma was measured with a use of the kits supplied by Eiken Co., Tokyo.

RESULTS

Occurrence of CRBP(F) in Human Hepatocellular Carcinoma

In noncancerous tissue, [³H]retinol bound to a cytosol component with a similar molecular size to that of purified piscine RBP (MW 16,000) was found to be completely displaced by a 200-fold molar excess of unlabeled retinol, but not by unlabeled retinoic acid, indicating that only CRBP is detectable in the surrounding liver tissue of hepatocellular carcinoma (FIG. 1b). On the other hand, a significant portion of radioactive retinol bound to the cytosol component of the tumor was found to be displaced by unlabeled retinoic acid as well, as shown in FIGURE 1a. When eluates from the gel filtration (Nos. 22 to 30) were combined and applied to a column of human PA-coupled Sepharose, most of radioactive retinol was immediately eluted off without any affinity for PA, excluding the possibility that plasma RBP was responsible for the bindings.

TABLE 1 summarizes the binding activity of each cellular retinoid-binding protein in both tumor and its surrounding tissue of 10 cases with hepatocellular carcinoma. CRBP was detected in both tissues examined, although the level in the tumor was slightly lower (40.4 pmol/g on the average) than that in the surrounding tissue (75.7 pmol/g). In particular, CRBP in Case I.I. (No. 8) was found to be very low, 3.5 pmol/g, in the tumor. In sharp contrast, both CRABP and CRBP(F) were detectable exclusively in the malignant tissues, with the exception of Case I.S. (No. 5) whose surrounding tissue contained a significant level of CRABP (4.1 pmol/g) and CRBP(F) (5.1 pmol/g). CRABP in the tumor was demonstrated in 7 out of 10 specimens examined, its level being 3.2 pmol/g on the average. On the other hand, CRBP(F) was readily detectable in a higher incidence (80%) and higher level (6.9 pmol/g on the average). Moreover, and most importantly, both CRABP and CRBP(F) were detected in 4 out of 5 patients whose plasma AFP level was below 200 ng/ml. Neither CRABP nor CRBP(F) (nor AFP) was elevated in Case K.N. (No. 4).

Depletion of Vitamin A Content in Human Hepatocellular Carcinoma

As shown in TABLE 2, vitamin A contents in surrounding liver tissues of dif-

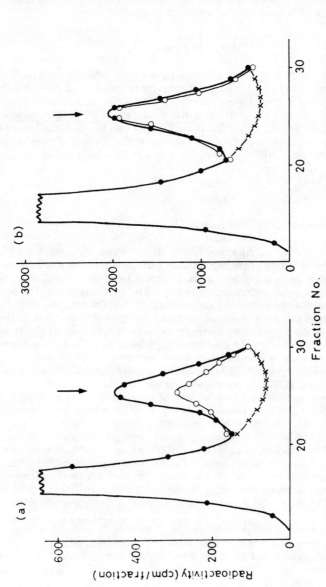

FIGURE 1. Presence of CRBP (F) in the cytosol of tumor (a) of Case K.M. (No. 6), as compared with that of surrounding tissue (b): Elution profiles of gel filtration on Sephadex G-75.

Each 400 μl of the cytosol was incubated at 4 °C for 16 hr with 4 μl of [³H]retinol (1.8 × 10⁵ dpm, 80 pmol) in ethanol to give a final concentration of 200 nM (●———●). Displacement of the radioactivity was done by simultaneously adding a 200-fold molar excess of either unlabeled retinol (×———×) or retinoic acid (○———○). After incubation, each sample was subjected to the gel filtration. Fractions of 1.5 ml each were collected at a flow rate of 13 ml/hr. Arrows (↓) indicate the eluting position of purified piscine RBP (MW, 16,000) on the same column. The large radioactive peak which corresponds to unbound or free [³H]retinol (eluted later than fraction No. 30) has been deleted from the graph. (From Muto, Omori & Sugawara.[14] Used by permission of GANN).

TABLE 1

CELLULAR RETINOID-BINDING PROTEINS: CRBP, CRABP, AND CRBP(F) IN CYTOSOLS OF
TUMOR (T) AND THE SURROUNDING TISSUE (S), OF SURGICALLY REMOVED HEPATOCELLULAR
CARCINOMA AND α_1-FETOPROTEIN (AFP) IN PLASMA OBTAINED FROM THE
PATIENT PRIOR TO SURGERY*

Patient[†]		CRBP		CRABP		CRBP(F)		AFP
No.	Initials	T	S	T	S	T	S	
		(pmol/g)		(pmol/g)		(pmol/g)		(ng/ml)
1	T.S.	25.0	ND[‡]	2.3	–[‡]	9.0	ND	26,000
2	T.M.	67.0	113.9	–	–	10.0	–	5,800
3	T.H.	10.5	ND	6.6	–	4.1	ND	16,000
4	K.N.	48.0	45.0	–	–	–	–	<200
5	I.S.	47.0	52.5	1.6	4.1	4.2	5.1	10,000
6	K.M.	45.2	137.0	5.2	–	9.0	–	<200
7	H.A.	45.6	ND	1.8	ND	5.4	–	<200
8	I.I.	3.5	47.2	3.0	ND	–	–	<200
9	F.T.	60.8	72.0	2.0	ND	10.4	–	21,000
10	M.I.	51.0	62.6	–	–	3.0	–	<200

* From Muto, Omori & Sugawara.[14]
† The patients are all males.
‡ –, Not detectable. ND, not determined because of a limited supply of the sample.

ferent patients with hepatocellular carcinoma were found to be highly variable,
in the range of 20 to 1,000 $\mu g/g$, presumably because of individual differences in
nutritional status. In contrast, almost all of the malignant liver tissues contained
vitamin A in considerably smaller amounts (1/7 to 1/1,000 of that of the noncancerous tissues), with the exception of Case M.I. (No. 10). Histological examina-
tions in this exceptional case, however, revealed that the tumor was truly a malignancy of the hepatocyte, but not of Ito cells or vitamin A (fat)-storing cells.[28,29]

FIGURE 2 shows a large difference in the vitamin A content of lipid extract between the tumor and its surrounding tissue of Case H.A. (No. 7). Prior to lipid ex-

TABLE 2

VITAMIN A CONTENT IN TUMOR (T) AND THE SURROUNDING TISSUE (S) OF A
SURGICALLY REMOVED HEPATOCELLULAR CARCINOMA*

Patient		Vitamin A Content	
No.	Initials	T	S
		(µg/g tissue)	
1	T.S.	1	190
2	T.M.	2	953
3	T.H.	13	131
4	K.N.	5	33
5	I.S.	1	20
6	K.M.	1	100
7	H.A.	1	1,075
8	I.I.	0	270
9	F.T.	20	223
10	M.I.	125	189

* From Muto, Omori & Sugawara.[14]

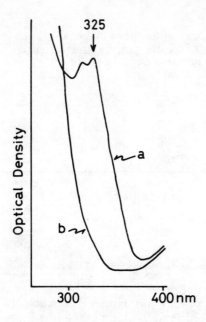

FIGURE 2. UV spectra of lipid extracts from the isolated hepatocytes of tumor (b) and its surrounding tissue (a) of surgically removed hepatocellular carcinoma (Case H.A., No. 7).

traction, isolated hepatocytes were prepared from both tissues to eliminate Ito cells as much as possible. The UV absorption maximum at 325 nm was observed only in the isolated hepatocytes of noncancerous tissue. In contrast, hardly any absorption around 325 nm was detectable in that of the malignant tissue, clearly indicating that the cancer was deficient in vitamin A.

Occurrence of CRBP(F) in Human Fetal Liver

As shown in TABLE 3, vitamin A levels in three human fetal livers obtained at the second trimester were found to be lower than those of the noncancerous tissue of adult liver, most of which showed liver cirrhosis. In addition, three cellular retinoid-binding proteins were constantly detectable; the CRBP(F) level, in particular, was considerably elevated in these fetal livers (37.5 pmol/g on the average).

Occurrence of CRBP(F) in Regenerating Rat Liver

When about 70% of the liver was resected in vitamin A-deficient rats, hepatic regeneration was found to be excellent and almost completed within one week: no difference of hepatic regeneration between the deficient and normal rats was observed.

TABLE 4 shows the time course of changes in cellular retinoid-binding proteins in regenerating livers of vitamin A-deficient rats. CRBP levels were found to be kept almost constant during 14 days after partial hepatectomy: i.e., CRBP was synthesized in direct proportion to the magnitude of hepatic regeneration. In sharp contrast, CRABP and CRBP(F) appeared transiently: i.e., CRABP was

TABLE 3

VITAMIN A AND CELLULAR RETINOID-BINDING PROTEINS LEVELS IN HUMAN FETAL LIVERS*

No.	Weeks of Pregnancy	Vitamin A (µg/g)	CRBP	CRABP (pmol/g)	CRBP(F)
1	20	4	117	0.9	50.8
2	22	34	104	5.7	38.2
3	24	32	55	2.4	23.6

* From Muto, Omori & Sugawara.[14]

detected exclusively one day (24 hr) after the resection, whereas CRBP(F) exhibited a peak at 72 hr (3 days) and rapidly decreased 5 days after partial hepatectomy. AFP was also demonstrated to have a peak coincident with that of CRBP(F) (data not shown).

FIGURE 3 illustrates the time course of changes in vitamin A content and cellular retinoid-binding proteins during hepatic regeneration in normal or vitamin A-supplemented rats. Both CRABP and CRBP(F) also appeared transiently, exhibiting peaks on days 1 and 3, respectively, after hepatectomy, similar to those found in the deficient rats. On the other hand, CRBP levels were found to be remarkably decreased between days 1 and 5 after the resection, probably reflecting reduction in vitamin A contents of the livers.

Occurrence of CRBP(F) in Hyperplastic Nodules During Hepatic Carcinogenesis in Rats

As shown in TABLE 5, a combined cytosol obtained from hyperplastic nodules induced in rat livers was found to contain three cellular retinoid-binding proteins; in particular, the CRBP(F) level was considerably elevated to 43.4 pmol/g, as compared with that of CRABP (3.0 pmol/g). The profile of cellular binding proteins in hyperplastic nodules was virtually similar to that in human fetal livers (TABLE 3).

TABLE 4

TIME COURSE OF CHANGES IN CONTENTS OF CRBP, CRABP AND CRBP(F) IN REGENERATING LIVERS AFTER 70% HEPATECTOMY IN VITAMIN A-DEFICIENT RATS

Days after Resection	CRBP	CRABP (pmol/g)	CRBP(F)
0	170.3	–*	–
1	175.2	4.6	–
2	174.1	–	–
3	183.8	–	18.7
5	184.8	–	2.1
8	181.7	–	–
14	176.3	–	–

* –, Not detectable.

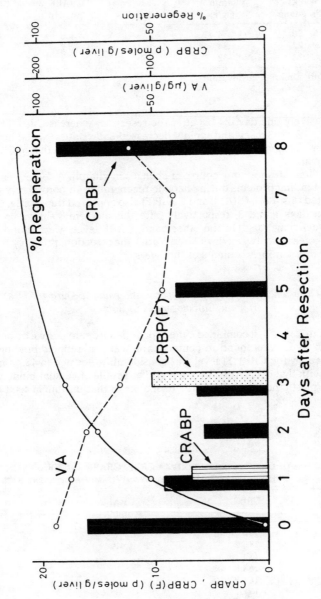

FIGURE 3. Time course of changes in vitamin A and cellular retinoid-binding proteins levels in regenerating livers of normal rats after 70% hepatectomy.

DISCUSSION

The present study has clearly demonstrated that a novel cellular retinoid-binding protein, F-type or CRBP(F), which is virtually lacking in the adult liver, occurs in human hepatocellular carcinoma, human fetal liver, and rat hyperplastic liver nodules (a precancerous state), indicating that CRBP(F) is an onco-fetal protein in nature. In addition, CRBP(F) also appears transiently at a certain phase of hepatic regeneration in rats (3 days after hepatectomy), in parallel with the appearance of α_1-fetoprotein (AFP).

First of all, recent studies have revealed distinct differences in tissue distribution and perinatal development between cellular retinol-binding protein (CRBP) and cellular retinoic acid-binding protein (CRABP). CRBP exists widely in almost all of the tissues except the blood (embryo), and the blood, heart, muscle (adult animals).[30] On the other hand, CRABP is detected in almost all of the tissues except the blood in an embryonic stage, but becomes undetectable during postnatal development, with the exception of a limited number of organs: the testis, ovary, brain, eye, skin and trachea.[16,30] Of interest is the fact that CRABP becomes a phenotypic expression in some experimental[15-17] and human tumors.[12-14] For instance, CRABP is virtually undetectable in normal adult liver, whereas it can be detectable in fetal liver (TABLE 3) and in hepatocellular carcinoma (TABLE 1). In general, however, CRABP is not strictly an onco-fetal protein, since the limited number of tissues mentioned above do contain the protein even in normal adults.

Unfortunately, no detailed information is yet available with regard to the ligand-specificity of either CRBP or CRABP found in the fetal and cancerous tissues, probably because the assay, done by sucrose density gradient sedimentation, is tedious and time-consuming, only three samples each being run at the same time. At least six incubations for each specimen are generally needed for a complete study of these three different binding proteins. To this end, we have generally adopted a technique of gel filtration on Sephadex G-75; consequently, a new molecular species having binding affinity for both retinol and retinoic acid, CRBP(F), was found in human hepatocellular carcinoma (FIG. 1). As already mentioned, this protein is similar to the CRBP that was originally recognized in the fish-eye cytosol,[19] with regard to its molecular size and ligand-specificity. In the fish, CRBP exhibits a binding affinity for both ligands (a bi-functional binder), a lower isoelectric point of 4.0, and a greater mobility on gel electrophoresis (R_m 0.68), as compared with CRABP coexisting in the cytosol. Moreover, CRBP(F), like the fish-type CRBP, is also detected in chick embryo brain, exhibiting a peak at embryonic day 14 (or 7 days prior to hatching), and rapidly disappearing after hatching.[20] Similarly, CRBP(F) was detectable in larger amounts than CRABP in human fetal liver examined at the second trimester (TABLE 3). These findings indicate that CRBP(F) is an ancient protein in both phylogenesis and ontogenesis. In human hepatocellular carcinoma, it is of interest that CRBP(F) was positive in

TABLE 5

CELLULAR RETINOID-BINDING PROTEINS IN HYPERPLASTIC NODULES OF
RAT LIVERS INDUCED BY 2-ACETYLAMINOFLUORENE

	(pmol/g tissue)
CRBP	113.0
CRABP	3.0
CRBP(F)	43.4

80% of cases and detected even in 3 out of 5 patients whose plasma AFP levels were not markedly elevated (TABLE 1). In addition, CRBP(F) appears to be better than CRABP as a practical indicator of cancer, since the former was detected at higher levels in the cancer and was virtually lacking in any normal differentiated tissues, insofar as they were examined. Of interest is the additional finding that the noncancerous, but cirrhotic liver tissue in the exceptional case (No. 5, TABLE 1) contained CRBP(F) in a higher amount than that in the cancer itself, possibly indicating a precancerous state of hepatocellular carcinoma. Although CRBP(F) was not significantly elevated in other human tumors[14] including metastatic liver cancers, stomach and colon cancers, further studies are needed to define the whole profile of CRBP(F) in various kinds of human tumors. Simultaneously, detailed studies on ligand-specificity of the CRBP(F) for a variety of synthetic retinoids currently available will be required, and, moreover, a sensitive assay system for detecting CRBP(F) in the plasma will have to be established.

Of particular importance are the findings with regard to the different time-courses of changes in the three cellular retinoid-binding proteins during hepatic regeneration in rats, suggesting that each binding protein may play a distinct role in cell proliferation and differentiation. First of all, CRBP levels were found to remain almost constant (presumably as a result of de novo synthesis) in parallel to the magnitude of hepatic regeneration in vitamin A-deficient rats (TABLE 4). On the other hand, CRBP levels in normal rats were found to be decreased up to at least 5 days after hepatectomy, in parallel to the reduction in liver vitamin A contents (FIG. 3), suggesting that a net degradation of CRBP is enhanced by decreasing vitamin A levels in the liver through yet unknown mechanism(s). In contrast to CRBP, the other two cellular binding proteins appeared only transiently during hepatic regeneration regardless of vitamin A status: CRABP was detected exclusively at 24 hr (one day) after the resection, when DNA synthesis reaches to the maximum level,[31,32] whereas CRBP(F) exhibited a peak at 72 hr (3 days) after partial hepatectomy, being consistent with that of AFP[33] as well as pyruvate kinase III (fetal type).[34]

Our preliminary studies also revealed that the CRBP(F), partially purified from the regenerating rat liver obtained 3 days after hepatectomy, has a molecular weight of about 15,000, a relative mobility of 0.73 on gel electrophoresis, an isoelectric point of 4.7, and no binding affinity for PA. Thus, CRBP(F) was found to be distinctly different from CRABP with regard to isoelectric point (4.8) and relative electrophoretic mobility (0.69). Although the protein was indistinguishable from CRBP, no evidence has yet been obtained that CRBP(F) might be converted or originated from CRBP itself during the chemical processings (unpublished observations). At present, immunological study† on the cross-reactivity between CRBP(F) and CRBP is currently underway, by use of the monospecific antibody against pure rat liver CRBP.[35] In any event, further studies are obviously required, particularly to isolate and characterize the CRBP(F) and to define the details of binding site(s) for the ligands on the molecule.

Finally, the present study has also demonstrated a large difference in vitamin A content between the cancerous and noncancerous tissues of human hepatocellular carcinoma (TABLE 2). The possible contribution of Ito cells[28,29] to this difference can be excluded, since isolated hepatocytes prepared from the noncancerous, adjacent tissue definitely contained vitamin A, in sharp contrast to those

---

† No inhibition of binding activity of CRBP(F) by adding anti-CRBP was demonstrated in the amounts that clearly depressed the binding activity of CRBP (Omori et al., unpublished observations).

from hepatocellular carcinoma (FIG. 2). Therefore, these results strongly suggest that vitamin A is locally depleted in the cancer, presumably as a result of disturbance in membrane transport of the vitamin from the surrounding tissue and/or its rapid utilization inside the tumor cells. In any event, the present finding will provide additional good reason for the introduction of the retinoids to cancer chemoprevention,[3,4] and metabolism of the retinoids in cancer cells warrants further exploration. Moreover, and most importantly, the CRBP(F) level was remarkably elevated in rat hyperplastic nodules, a precancerous state of hepatocellular carcinoma (43.4 pmol/g, TABLE 5), and showed a level comparable to that in human fetal liver (TABLE 3). In addition, the level of CRBP(F) in the hyperplastic nodules was found to be much higher than that in an established liver cancer (7.2 pmol/g), which was produced in rats fed a normal diet containing 0.06% 3'-methyl-4-dimethyl-amino azobenzene for 6 months (unpublished observations). The protein was also demonstrated in the adjacent, cirrhotic tissue of the exceptional case mentioned above, possibly indicating a precancerous state with biological expression of positive CRBP(F) (as well as CRABP). From these findings, we believe it is worthwhile to explore the possibility that experimental chemoprevention may be achieved by targeting retinoids to the hyperplastic nodules before hepatocellular carcinoma is truly established.

ACKNOWLEDGMENTS

The authors are grateful to Prof. N. Hosoya, University of Tokyo, for his continuous encouragement throughout this study, and to Drs. Y. Shidoji and M. Sato for many useful discussions. We also wish to thank Dr. W.E. Scott, Hoffmann-LaRoche Inc., Nutley, NJ for the generous gifts of the labeled and unlabeled retinoic acid. The kind advice regarding the manuscript given by Prof. DeWitt S. Goodman of Columbia University is greatly appreciated.

REFERENCES

1. WOLBACH, S.B. & P.R. HOWE. 1925. Tissue changes following deprivation of fat-soluble A vitamin. J. Exp. Med. **42**: 753–777.
2. FUJIMAKI, Y. 1926. Formation of gastric carcinoma in albino rats fed on deficient diets. J. Cancer Res. **10**: 469–477.
3. SPORN, M.B., N.M. DUNLOP, D.L. NEWTON & J.M. SMITH. 1976. Prevention of chemical carcinogenesis by vitamin A and its synthetic analogs (retinoids). Fed. Proc. **35**: 1332–1338.
4. SPORN, M.B. & D.L. NEWTON. 1979. Chemoprevention of cancer with retinoids. Fed. Proc. **38**: 2528–2534.
5. BASHOR, M.M. D.O. TOFT & F. CHYTIL. 1973. In vitro binding of retinol to rat-tissue components. Proc. Natl. Acad. Sci. USA **70**: 3483–3487.
6. SANI, B.P. & D.L. HILL. 1974. Retinoic acid: A binding protein in chick embryo metatarsal skin. Biochem. Biophys. Res. Commun. **61**: 1276–1282.
7. ONG, D.E. & F. CHYTIL. 1975. Retinoic acid-binding protein in rat tissue. Partial purification and comparison to rat tissue retinol-binding protein. J. Biol. Chem. **250**: 6113–6117.
8. ONG, D.E. & F. CHYTIL. 1978. Cellular retinol-binding protein from rat liver. Purification and characterization. J. Biol. Chem. **253**: 828–832.
9. ROSS, A.C., Y.I. TAKAHASHI & D.S. GOODMAN. 1978. The binding protein for retinol from rat testis cytosol. Isolation and partial characterization. J. Biol. Chem. **253**: 6591–6598.

10. ONG, D.E. & F. CHYTIL. 1978. Cellular retinoic acid-binding protein from rat testis. Purification and characterization. J. Biol. Chem. **253:** 4551–4554.
11. ROSS, A.C. & D.S. GOODMAN. 1979. Intracellular binding proteins for retinol and retinoic acid: Comparison with each other and with serum retinol-binding protein. Fed. Proc. **38:** 2515–2518.
12. ONG, D.E., D.L. PAGE & F. CHYTIL. 1975. Retinoic acid binding protein: Occurrence in human tumors. Science **190:** 60–61.
13. MUTO, Y., Y. SHIDOJI, M. OMORI, M. SATO, K. SUGAWARA & H. OHNO. 1977. Occurrence of cytosol retinoic acid-binding protein (c-RABP) in primary liver cancer. Kanzo (Acta Hepatol. Jap.) **18:** 370.
14. MUTO, Y., M. OMORI & K. SUGAWARA. 1979. Demonstration of a novel cellular retinol-binding protein, F-type, in hepatocellular carcinoma. GANN **70:** 215–222.
15. ONG, D.E. & F. CHYTIL. 1976. Presence of cellular retinol and retinoic acid binding proteins in experimental tumors. Cancer Lett. **2:** 25–30.
16. SANI, B.P. & T.H. CORBETT. 1977. Retinoic acid-binding protein in normal tissues and experimental tumors. Cancer Res. **37:** 209–213.
17. CHYTIL, F. & D.E. ONG. 1979. Cellular retinol- and retinoic acid-binding proteins in vitamin A action. Fed. Proc. **38:** 2510–2514.
18. SHIDOJI, Y. & Y. MUTO. 1977. Vitamin A transport in plasma of the non-mammalian vertebrates: Isolation and partial characterization of piscine retinol-binding protein. J. Lipid Res. **18:** 679–691.
19. SHIDOJI, Y. & Y. MUTO. 1978. Comparative studies on binding proteins specific for retinol in serum and cytosol of young yellowtail *Seriola Quinqeradiata.* Comp. Biochem. Physiol. **61B.** 315–319.
20. SATO, M., M. OMORI & Y. MUTO. 1979. Demonstration of a novel molecular species in chick embryo brain: Cellular retinol-binding protein, F-type. J. Nutr. Sci. Vitaminol. **25:** 1–7.
21. HIGGINS, G.M. & R.M. ANDERSON. 1931. Experimental pathology of the liver. I. Restoration of the liver of the white rat following partial surgical removal. Arch. Pathol. **12:** 186–202.
22. SATO, M., L.M. DeLUCA & Y. MUTO. 1978. Effects of exogenous retinol and retinoic acid on the biosynthesis of ^{14}C-mannose labelled glycolipids and glycoproteins in rat liver. J. Nutr. Sci. Vitaminol. **24:** 9–23.
23. OKITA, K., M. GRUENSTEIN, M. KLAIBER & E. FARBER. 1974. Localization of α-fetoprotein by immunofluorescence in hyperplastic nodules during hepatocarcinogenesis induced by 2-acetylaminofluorene. Cancer Res. **34:** 2758–2763.
24. VAHLQUIST, A., S.F. NILSSON & P.A. PETERSON. 1971. Isolation of the human retinol-binding protein by affinity chromatography. Eur. J. Biochem. **20:** 160–168.
25. DUGAN, R.E., N.A. FRIGERIO & J.M. SIEBERT. 1964. Colorimetric determination of vitamin A and its derivatives with trifluoroacetic acid. Anal. Chem. **36:** 114–117.
26. AMES, S.R., H.A. RISLEY & P.L. HARRIS. 1954. Simplified procedure for extraction and determination of vitamin A in liver. Anal. Chem. **26:** 1378–1381.
27. TAKAOKA, T., S. YASUMOTO & H. KATSUTA. 1975. A simple method for the cultivation of rat liver cells. Jpn. J. Exp. Med. **45:** 317–326.
28. ITO, T. 1951. Cytological studies on stellate cells of Kupffer and fat storing cells in the capillary wall of the human liver. Acta Anat. Nippon **26:** 2.
29. HIROSAWA, K. & E. YAMADA. 1973. The localization of the vitamin A in the mouse liver as revealed by electron microscope radioautography. J. Electron Microsc. **22:** 337–346.
30. ONG, D.E. & F. CHYTIL. 1976. Changes in levels of cellular retinol- and retinoic acid-binding proteins of liver and lung during perinatal development of rat. Proc. Natl. Acad. Sci. USA **73:** 3976–3978.
31. GRISHAM, J.W. 1962. A morphologic study of deoxyribonucleic acid synthesis and cell proliferation in regenerating rat liver. Autoradiography with thymidine-^{3}H. Cancer Res. **22:** 842–849.
32. MAYFIELD, J.E. & J. BONNER. 1972. A partial sequence of nuclear events in regenerating rat liver. Proc. Natl. Acad. Sci. USA **69:** 7–10.

33. SELL, S., M. NICHOLS, F.F. BECKER & H.L. LEFFERT. 1974. Hepatocyte proliferation and α_1-fetoprotein in pregnant, neonatal, and partially hepatectomized rats. Cancer Res. **34:** 865–871.
34. BONNEY, B.J., H.A. HOPKINS, P.R. WALKER & V.R. POTTER. 1973. Glycolytic isoenzymes and glycogen metabolism in regenerating liver from rats on controlled feeding schedules. Biochem. J. **136:** 115–124.
35. ONG, D.E. & F. CHYTIL. 1979. Immunochemical comparison of vitamin A binding proteins of rat. J. Biol. Chem. **254:** 8733–8735.

RETINOID-BINDING PROTEINS OF BOVINE RETINA: IMMUNOLOGICAL PROPERTIES*

John C. Saari, Gregory G. Garwin, and Sidney Futterman†

Department of Ophthalmology
University of Washington School of Medicine
Seattle, Washington 98195

INTRODUCTION

Neural retina has proved to be a rich source of cellular retinoid-binding proteins. Cellular proteins specific for retinol,[1] 11-*cis*-retinal,[2] and retinoic acid[1] have been purified to apparent homogeneity from extracts of bovine retina and an additional retinol-binding protein has been described[3,14] but not isolated or characterized. The presence of these binding proteins in retina is not altogether unexpected in view of the role of vitamin A in vision. However, retinoic acid has no known function in vision, yet extracts of retina are surprisingly rich in this protein.

The cellular retinoid-binding proteins of bovine retina form a strikingly similar class of proteins. Of course, each interacts with a particular retinoid to form a relatively stable, non-covalent complex and therefore must possess a hydrophobic pocket. In addition, CRalBP,‡ CRBP‡ and CRABP‡ are acidic proteins,[1,2] interacting strongly with basic ion exchange resins. The molecular weights of CRABP and CRBP are indistinguishable at about 16,500,[1] whereas the molecular weight of CRalBP is about double this value at 33,000.[2] SRBP‡ is also acidic and relatively small (MW 21,000),[4] and thus seems to share several properties with the class of cellular retinoid-binding proteins. The similarities noted above suggest that retinoid-binding proteins may share structural features and perhaps may have been derived from a common ancestral gene. We chose to examine the question of the relatedness of the binding proteins using immunological techniques.

EXPERIMENTAL

N-succinimidyl [2, 3-³H]propionate (66 Ci/mmol) was obtained from Amersham Corporation, Arlington Heights, IL; IgGsorb (a preparation of *Staphylococcus aureus* cells) was obtained from The Enzyme Center, Inc., Boston, MA.

CRalBP, CRBP and CRABP were purified according to methods developed in this laboratory.[1,2,5] Human SRBP was a generous gift of the late Dr. Joram Heller. The homogeneity of binding proteins was examined by gel electrophoresis in the presence of SDS with the buffer systems of Weber and Osborn[6] or of Fairbanks *et al.*[7]

* This project was supported in part by Grants EY–02317, EY–00343, and EY–01730 from the National Institutes of Health.

† Deceased May 19, 1979.

‡ The abbreviations used are: CRBP, cellular retinol-binding protein; CRalBP, cellular 11-*cis*-retinal-binding protein; CRABP, cellular retinoic acid-binding protein; SRBP, serum retinol-binding protein; SDS, sodium dodecyl sulfate.

Preparation of Antibodies

CRalBP (80 μg) in 0.15 M NaCl, 10 mM phosphate, pH 7.4 (phosphate buffered saline, PBS) was mixed with an equal volume of Freund's complete adjuvant and injected into female New Zealand white rabbits at 15–20 intradermal sites. Subsequent injections of the same quantity followed at weekly intervals into multiple intradermal sites if the antigen was mixed with Freund's incomplete adjuvant or into intramuscular and subcutaneous sites if the antigen was injected as a solution in PBS. Comparable results were obtained using either approach.

IMMUNOLOGICAL METHODS

Double diffusion immunoprecipitation was performed on agarose-coated microscope slides according to Ouchterlony,[8] immunoelectrophoresis according to Grabar and Williams,[9] and electroimmunodiffusion according to Clarke and Freeman.[10] When the latter technique was used for quantitative analysis, the area under the "rocket" immunoprecipitate was determined by an automatic area analysis computer program and electronic bit-pad.

Preparation of [³H]CRalBP

N-succinimidyl[2, 3-³H]propionate (lmCi) in benzene was taken just to dryness with a stream of N_2 at 30°C and immediately mixed with 0.5 ml of CRalBP (2 mg) that had previously been dialyzed against 0.1 M borate buffer, pH 8.4. After 30 min at 0°, (on ice), 1 nmole of glycine in borate buffer was added.[11] After an additional 30 min at 0°, the reaction mixture was dialyzed against several

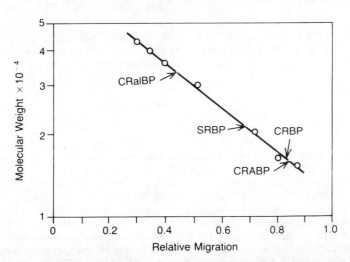

FIGURE 1. The molecular weights of retinoid-binding proteins of bovine blood and retina as determined by polyacrylamide gel electrophoresis in the presence of SDS. The gel system of Fairbanks *et al.*[7] was used with 10% acrylamide gels. The observed molecular weights are: CRalBP, 33,000; SRBP, 21,000; CRBP, 16,600; CRABP, 16,300.

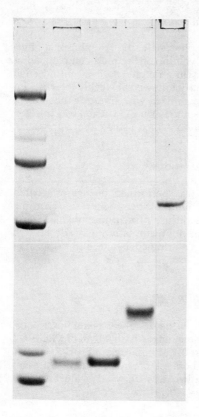

FIGURE 2. Polyacrylamide gel electrophoresis in the presence of SDS. From left to right the lanes contained: proteins of known molecular weight, CRABP, CRBP, SRBP, CRalBP.

changes of 0.05 M Tris, pH 7.5, 0.2 M NaCl, for 3 days. The product ([^{3}H]CRalBP) was analyzed by gel filtration on Sephadex G-25, SDS-polyacrylamide electrophoresis, and double-diffusion immunoprecipitation.

Radioimmunoassay

The procedure of Gupta and Morton[12] was followed. The assay was performed in 1.5 ml plastic conical centrifuge tubes (Bio-Rad). Dilutions of sera and solutions of binding proteins were made in borate-saline-albumin buffer that contained 6 g/L boric acid, 9.5 g/L sodium tetraborate, pH 8.2, 0.15 M NaCl, 10 mM disodium ethylenediaminetetraacetate, 0.5 g/L Triton X-100 and 1% bovine serum albumin. One hundred μL of [^{3}H]CRalBP (approximately 6000 cpm), 100 μL of a one to eight dilution of specific antiserum or preimmune serum and 100 μL of borate-saline-albumin buffer were added to the tubes. After shaking for 1 hr at 37°, the tubes were held at 4° for 4 hr. Two hundred μL of a suspension of *S. aureus* cells (IgGsorb) were added, mixed and incubated at room temperature for 20 min. Following centrifugation in a Beckman Microfuge (8750 × *g*, 5 min), two 50 μL portions of the supernatant were analyzed by liquid scintillation spectrometry.

RESULTS AND DISCUSSION

Properties of Retinoid-binding Proteins of Bovine Retina

Three cellular retinoid-binding proteins have been purified to apparent homogeneity from bovine retina. The specificity of CRBP is directed towards the alcohol form of vitamin A,[13,14] whereas CRABP is specific for the acid form of the vitamin.[13,14] Both of these binding proteins (or proteins with similar properties) are present in many tissues[22,16] in addition to retina and are probably involved in general functions of vitamin A. In contrast, CRalBP appears to be a retina-specific protein,[18] which binds not only 11-*cis*-retinal but also 11-*cis*-retinol.[2] The relatively large amount of CRalBP in neural retina (1 mole per 20 mole of rhodopsin),[2] its specificity directed towards the geometrical isomers of retinaldehyde important in vision,[17] and its apparently unique localization to retina,[18] encourage the belief that this binding protein is important in the visual cycle.

Each of the three retinoid-binding proteins from retina appears to form a one-to-one complex with its respective ligand.[1,2] After isolation of the binding proteins in the absence of exogenous retinoid, the binding site of CRBP appears to be nearly completely occupied with ligand while CRABP purifies with only about 0.2 mole of ligand per mole of binding protein as judged by the fluorescence associated with the native protein compared to that which can be obtained by addition of exogenous ligand. CRalBP isolated in the absence of exogenous ligand contains about one molar equivalent of retinoid, consisting of a mixture of 11-*cis*-retinol and 11-*cis*-retinal.[2]

Binding of retinol to CRBP results in the appearance of fine spectral structure and a red shift in the absorption maximum of the chromophore.[1] A similar spectral shift has been reported for CRPB from testis[19] and liver.[20] Binding of retinoic acid to CRABP induces fluorescence in the ligand[1,21] and a slight perturbation of the absorption spectrum of the ligand.

Binding of 11-*cis*-retinal to CRalBP produces a spectral shift analogous to that seen on binding the chromophore to opsin.[2] The absorption maximum of 11-*cis*-retinal is shifted from 380 nm to 425 nm upon complexing with the binding protein. Irradiation of the protein-ligand complex apparently results in isomerization and dissociation of the chromophore as the absorption of the ligand

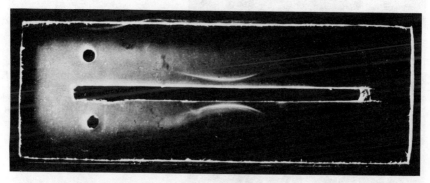

FIGURE 3. Electrophoresis of preparations of CRalBP used as antigens followed by immunodiffusion against antiserum to CRalBP.

shifts from 425 to 380 nm. The remarkable resemblance of this process to that which occurs on binding of 11-*cis*-retinal to opsin and subsequent photoisomerization suggests that CRalBP may be related to opsin. However all the evidence we have obtained to date[2] indicates that the two proteins are unrelated (see below). Following isolation in the absence of exogenous ligand the absorption spectrum of CRalBP reflects the presence of two ligands, 11-*cis*-retinol and 11-*cis*-retinal, producing absorption maxima at 330 and 425 nm, respectively.[2] The complex is fluorescent because of the presence of bound retinol.

The molecular weights of CRBP and CRABP are remarkably similar. Using the technique of SDS-polyacrylamide electrophoresis, we have determined the molecular weights to be $16,800 \pm 500$ and $16,500 \pm 300$, respectively, (FIG. 1). Other laboratories have reported values of about 14,500 for CRBP from testis[19] and liver.[20] The molecular weight of CRABP has been reported to be 17,000 from skin[22] and 14,000 from testis.[21] Since we observed co-electrophoresis of CRBP from liver and retina it seems likely that some of the apparent variation in size of the binding proteins from different tissues is due to differences in laboratory technique. The molecular weight of CRalBP is 33,000, slightly lower than that found for bovine opsin.

IMMUNOLOGICAL PROPERTIES

Purity of Antigens and Preparations of Antisera

All binding proteins were examined by polyacrylamide gel electrophoresis in the presence and absence of SDS and were found to be free of major contaminants (FIG. 2). In particular, the analysis of CRalBP revealed no detectable amounts of CRBP, CRABP or opsin.

CRABP proved to be a very poor antigen in rabbits. Even when it was injected coupled to keyhole limpet hemocyanin,[23] adsorbed to alumina, or as an emulsified polyacrylamide gel band,[24] the protein failed to elicit a precipitating antibody in rabbits. We were able to develop precipitating antibodies to CRBP in rabbits; however the antibody titer was extremely low and many rabbits did not

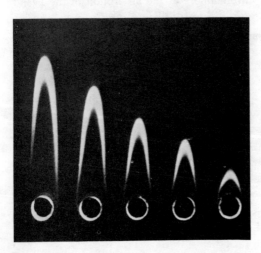

FIGURE 4. Electrophoresis of CRalBP into agarose containing anti-CRalBP (electroimmunodiffusion). The wells contained, from left to right, 13.4, 10.7, 8.0, 5.4 and 2.7 µg of CRalBP in a volume of 10 µL.

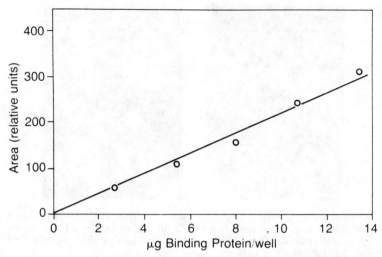

FIGURE 5. Relationship of the area prescribed by the zone of precipitation and the origin (FIG. 4) and the amount of CRalBP/well.

respond. In contrast, CRalBP proved to be a relatively good antigen in that each of six rabbits responded by producing precipitating antibody. The maximum titer produced was low (1:16 as measured by the highest dilution which produced a precipitin band) and we were unable to boost the titer higher. Electrophoresis of CRalBP preparations used to prepare the antibodies, followed by double diffusion of antibody and antigen (immunoelectrophoresis, FIG. 3) produced a single arc of precipitate indicating that the antibody was directed against a single electrophoretic species.

Electroimmunodiffusion

Electrophoresis of solutions of antigen into agarose containing antibody, produced arcs of immunoprecipitate ("rockets", FIG. 4) and, as shown in FIGURE 5, the area prescribed by the arc and the origin was proportional to the amount of antigen applied to the sample well. The sensitivity of the method allows the detection of about 1 µg of CRalBP. None of the other binding proteins produced precipitin bands when applied to the gel in comparable amounts.

Double Diffusion Immunoprecipitation

As mentioned earlier, double diffusion of CRalBP and antibody (double diffusion immunoprecipitation) readily produced a zone of precipitation as shown in FIGURE 6. However, none of the other binding proteins (including SRBP, CRBP, and CRABP) produced a precipitin band when applied at comparable or higher concentrations. In addition, bovine rhodopsin did not form a precipitin band with antiserum directed towards CRalBP. The results suggest that there are no antigenic determinants in CRalBP which are also found on CRBP, CRABP, SRBP or

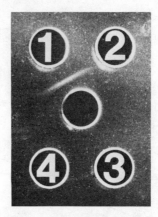

FIGURE 6. Double-diffusion immunoprecipation analysis. The center well depicted in each panel contained 10 μL of antiserum to CRalBP. *Left panel:* Wells 1–4 contained, respectively, 1 μg of SRBP, CRalB, CRBP and CRABP. *Right panel:* Wells 1–4 contained 1.3 μg of CRalBP, 3.8, 1.6 and 0.8 μg of bovine opsin, respectively.

bovine rhodopsin. Since the assay system employed (immunoprecipitation) is not particularly sensitive, we sought to obtain additional information utilizing the more sensitive method of radioimmunoassay.

Development of a Radioimmunoassay for CRalBP

Reaction of CRalBP with [^{3}H]succinimidyl propionate resulted in the formation of a substituted binding protein ([^{3}H]CRalBP) which still formed an im-

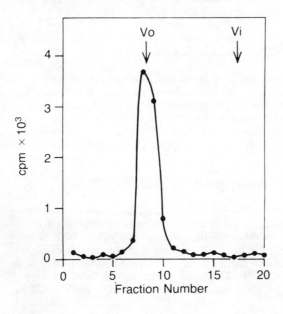

FIGURE 7. Analysis of [^{3}H] CRalBP by gel filtration. The sample of [^{3}H]CRalBP was applied to a column of Sephadex G-25 (0.9 × 30 cm) previously equilibrated with 0.05 m Tris, pH 7.5, 0.2 m NaCl. Fractions of 1 ml were collected.

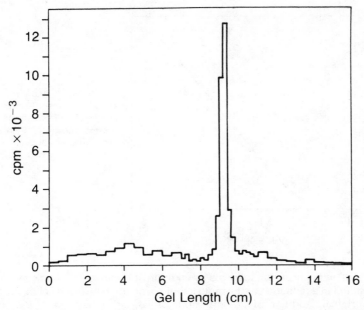

FIGURE 8. Analysis of [³H]CRalBP by polyacrylamide gel electrophoresis in the presence of SDS.[7] The main peak of radioactivity corresponds to the observed R_f of CRalBP. The center of the broad, low peak corresponds to the R_f expected for a dimer of CRalBP.

munoprecipitate with antiserum. Following prolonged dialysis of the labeled protein (3 days, 5°) against buffer, 100% of the radioactivity applied to a column of Sephadex G–25 eluted in the void volume (FIG. 7) showing the absence of low molecular weight, labeled components. Application of [³H]CRalBP to an SDS-polyacrylamide gel showed that 83% of the recovered counts migrated at the R_f of CRalBP and 17% at an R_f expected for a dimer of CRalBP (FIG. 8). The specific activity of [³H]CRalBP was 1.3 Ci/mmole.

Protein A, a surface protein of *S. aureus* cells, shows high affinity for the Fc portion of the IgG molecule.[25] Since the cells and adsorbed IgG are readily spun out of solution by centrifugation, the cells provide a simple and rapid means of separating antigen-antibody complexes from free antigen.[12] Incubation of

TABLE 1

RADIOIMMUNOASSAY FOR CRalBP

Components*	Supernatant Radioactivity† (cpm)
IgGsorb	5644
Preimmune rabbit serum + IgGsorb	5434
Specific antiserum + IgGsorb	1238
Specific antiserum + IgGsorb + 10μg CRalBP	5793

* In addition to the components shown, the assay tube contained [³H]CRalBP. A more complete description of the assay is given in the text.

† The values shown are those from a typical assay and are the averages of duplicate determinations.

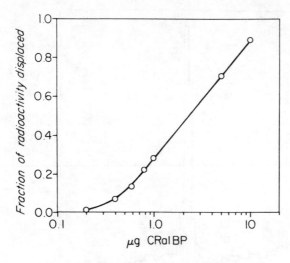

FIGURE 9. Radioimmuno-assay of CRalBP. The fraction of [³H]CRalBP displaced into the supernatant by increasing concentrations of CRalBP was determined as described in the text.

[³H]CRalBP with antiserum followed by addition of *S. aureus* cells and centrifugation resulted in a reduction of the radioactivity in solution to a value of about 15% of the original. Addition of IgGsorb alone or IgGsorb plus preimmune rabbit serum or goat serum failed to diminish the radioactivity of the supernatant (TABLE 1). The addition of unlabeled CRalBP apparently displaces [³H]CRalBP from the antigen–antibody complex, resulting in increased radioactivity in the supernatant. As is shown in FIGURE 9 the radioactivity of the supernatant is proportional to the amount of unlabeled CRalBP added to the assay over a range of 0.1 to about 10 μg. Since the lower limit of sensitivity of the latter technique is determined by the specific activity of the antigen, the method can be improved to allow detection of even smaller amounts of binding protein. Such methodology will be employed in future studies of the development of the visual system.

Radioimmunoassay provides a more sensitive method of determining if the antibody directed against CRalBP will cross-react with any of the other retinoid-binding proteins. Addition of one of the other retinoid-binding proteins will displace radioactivity into the supernatant only if it shares antigenic deter-

TABLE 2

DISPLACEMENT OF [³H]CRalBP FROM AN ANTIBODY-ANTIGEN COMPLEX BY
RETINOID-BINDING PROTEINS

Protein*	Fraction of Radioactivity Displaced
None	0.00
CRalBP	0.88
CRBP	0.00
CRABP	0.00
SRBP	0.03
Rhodopsin	0.01

* Ten μg of protein were added in each case. The details of the assay are described in the text.

minants with the primary antigen, in this case CRalBP. As is shown in TABLE 2, addition of up to 10 μg of SRBP, CRBP, CRABP or opsin did not displace radioactivity from the antigen–antibody complex, in confirmation of the results obtained by immunoprecititation.

Antibodies to SRBP have previously been shown not to form immunoprecipitates with CRBP,[26] and it was recently reported that CRBP showed no cross-reactivity when tested in a radioimmunoassay for SRBP.[19] In accord with this, analysis of amino acid compositional data suggested that SRBP was not a precursor of either CRBP or CRABP.[1] Ong and Chytil have recently reported that antibodies directed against liver CRBP did not cross-react with SRBP or CRABP.[27] In the present analysis we were unable to detect evidence for recognition of SRBP, CRBP, CRABP or opsin by anti-CRalBP. It thus seems unlikely that the class of retinoid-binding proteins will be demonstrated to be structurally related using immunological methods. A more definitive answer to the question will have to await a more sophisticated analysis, perhaps of the amino acid sequences of the proteins.

ACKNOWLEDGMENTS

We would like to thank James Foltz and Brad Clifton for expert photographic assistance and Lynn St. Peter for assistance in the preparation of the manuscript.

REFERENCES

1. SAARI, J.C., S. FUTTERMAN & L. BREDBERG. 1978. Cellular retinol- and retinoic acid-binding proteins of bovine retina. Purification and properties. J. Biol. Chem. **253:** 6432–6436.
2. STUBBS, G.W., J.C. SAARI & S. FUTTERMAN. 1979. 11-*cis*-retinal-binding protein from bovine retina. Purification and partial characterization. J. Biol. Chem. **254:** 8529–8533.
3. HELLER, J. 1976. Intracellular retinol-binding proteins from bovine pigment epithelial and photoreceptor cell fractions. Purification of high molecular weight lipoglycoproteins. J. Biol. Chem. **251:** 2952–2957.
4. KANAI, M., A. RAZ, & DEW. S. GOODMAN. 1968. Retinol-binding protein: the transport protein for vitamin A in human plasma. J. Clin. Invest. **47:** 2025–2043.
5. SAARI, J.C., S. FUTTERMAN, G.W. STUBBS & L. BREDBERG. 1980. Cellular retinol-, retinal- and retinoic acid-binding proteins from bovine retina. Meth. Enzymol. **67:** 296–300.
6. WEBER, K. & M. OSBORN. 1969. The reliability of molecular weight determinations by dodecyl sulfate–polyacrylamide gel electrophoresis. J. Biol. Chem. **244:** 4406–4412.
7. FAIRBANKS, G., T.L. STECK & D.F.H. WALLACH. 1971. Electrophoretic analysis of the major polypeptides of the human erythrocyte membrane. Biochemistry. **10:** 2606–2624.
8. OUCHTERLONY, O. 1968. Handbook of Immunodiffusion and Immunoelectrophoresis. Ann Arbor Science Publishers, Inc., Ann Arbor, MI.
9. GRABAR, P. & C.A. WILLIAMS, JR. 1953. Methode immuno-electrophoretique d'analyse de melanges de substances antigeniques. Biochim. Biophys. Acta **10:** 193–194.
10. CLARKE, H.G. & T.A. FREEMAN. 1966. A quantitative immunophoresis method (Laurell electrophoresis). Protides Biol. Fluids, Proc. Colloq. **14:** 503–509.
11. BOYD, H., S.J. LEACH & B. MILLIGAN. 1972. N-acylsuccinimides as acylating agents for proteins. The selective acylation of lysine residues. Int. J. Peptide Protein Res. **4:** 117–122.
12. GUPTA, R.K. & D.L. MORTON. 1979. Double-antibody method and the protein-A-bearing

cells method compared for separating bound and free antigen in radioimmunoassay. Clin. Chem. **25:** 752–756.

13. SAARI, J.C. & S. FUTTERMAN. 1976. Separable binding proteins for retinoic acid and retinol in bovine retina. Biochim. Biophys. Acta **444:** 789–793.

14. WIGGERT, B., A. MIZUKAWA, T. KUWABARA & G.J. CHADER. 1978. Vitamin A receptors: Multiple species in retina and brain and possible compartmentalization in retinal photoreceptors. J. Neurochem. **30:** 653–659.

15. SANI, B.P. & C.K. BANARJEE. 1978. Purification and properties of retinoic acid-binding protein from chick-embryo skin. Biochem. J. **173:** 643–649.

16. ONG, D.E. & F. CHYTIL. 1975. Retinoic acid-binding protein rat tissue. Partial purification and comparison to rat tissue retinol-binding protein. J. Biol. Chem. **250:** 6113–6117.

17. FUTTERMAN, S., J.C. SAARI & S. BLAIR. 1977. Occurrence of binding protein for 11-*cis*-retinal in retina. J. Biol. Chem. **252:** 3267–3271.

18. FUTTERMAN, S. & J.C. SAARI. 1977. Occurrence of 11-*cis*-retinal-binding protein restricted to the retina. Invest. Ophthalmol. Visual Sci. **16:** 768–771.

19. ROSS, A.C., Y.I. TAKAHASHI & DeW. S. GOODMAN. 1978. The binding protein for retinol from rat testis cytosol. Isolation and partial characterization. J. Biol. Chem. **253:** 6591–6598.

20. ONG, D.E. & F. CHYTIL. 1978. Cellular retinol-binding protein from rat liver. J. Biol. Chem. **253:** 828–832.

21. ONG, D.E. & F. CHYTIL. 1978. Cellular retinoic acid-binding from rat testis. J. Biol. Chem. **253:** 4551–4554.

22. SANI, B.P. & T.H. CORBETT. 1977. Retinoic acid-binding protein in normal tissues and experimental tumors. Cancer Res. **37:** 209–213.

23. VAITUKAITUS, J., J.B. ROBBINS, E. NIESCHLAG & G.T. ROSS. 1971. A method for producing specific antisera with small doses of immunogen. J. Clin. Endocrinol. Metabol. **33:** 988–991.

24. PAPERMASTER, D.S., C.A. CONVERSE & M. ZORN. 1976. Biosynthetic and immunochemical characterization of a large protein in frog and cattle rod outer segment membranes. Exp. Eye Res. **23:** 105–115.

25. KRONVALL, G., U.S. SEAL, J. FINSTAD & R.C. WILLIAMS. 1970. Phylogenetic insight into evolution of mammalian Fc fragment of vG globulin using staphylococcal protein A. J. Immunol. **115:** 140–148.

26. BASHOR, M.M. & F. CHYTIL. 1975. Cellular retinol-binding protein. Biochim. Biophys. Acta **411:** 87–96.

27. ONG, D.E. & F. CHYTIL. 1979. Immunochemical comparison of vitamin A binding proteins of the rat. J. Biol. Chem. **254:** 8733–8735.

RETINOID–BINDING PROTEINS OF RETINA AND RETINOBLASTOMA CELLS IN CULTURE

Gerald J. Chader, Barbara Wiggert, Paul Russell,
and Minoru Tanaka

Laboratory of Vision Research
National Eye Institute
National Institutes of Health
Bethesda, Maryland 20205

Vitamin A plays a special role in the visual process. Evidence from George Wald and his collaborators[1] and many other laboratories over the years have given us a basic understanding of the "visual cycle," a unique sequence of interactions of the retinoid with the protein opsin in the retinal photoreceptor (FIG. 1). In this process, retinoid in the form of 11-*cis*-retinal binds to the protein opsin in a dark reaction to form the visual protein, rhodopsin. Light energy initiates the cleavage of the Schiff base linkage between the retinoid and the protein moiety as well as a neurochemical impulse that is transmitted to the brain as a "visual" stimulus. The retinal released by this process may be rebound to the opsin to again form rhodopsin or be isomerized to the *trans*-form, reduced and transported to the pigment epithelium where is it stored as the retinyl ester until needed again in the photoreceptor visual cycle. Thus, vitamin A and its aldehyde form, retinal, are cycled through a series of complex photosensitive reactions but are conserved in the process much as is a cofactor in an enzymatic reaction. There is little or no net usage or metabolism of the retinoid to nonmetabolically active forms.

The more general role that vitamin A and its natural metabolites play in differentiation and maintenance of epithelial tissues, bone tissues, the reproductive system, etc. is less well understood. It is clear however that the vitamin is necessary for such normal development and function since vitamin A deficiency quickly leads to such clinical problems as xerophthalmia,[2] keratomalacia,[3] reproductive failure,[4] and debilitation of the immune response.[5] Repletion of vitamin A (retinol) and in most cases its natural metabolite, retinoic acid, can reverse many of these effects. Retinoic acid for example when applied topically can reverse the corneal signs of xerophthalmia.[6,7]

As with its general action, the molecular mechanism(s) of vitamin A action are not clear and are probably pleiotropic in nature. Studies on vitamin A-deficient animals indicate that at least one role of retinoid is to act as an intermediate in the cellular biosynthesis of glycoproteins.[8,9] In this process, retinyl phosphate functions as a carrier, transferring sugar moieties (e.g. mannose) across membranes and in the formation of membrane glycoprotein.[9] Protein synthesis in rough endoplasmic reticulum is also affected by vitamin A with a difference in amino acid charging of t-RNA in intestinal preparations from normal and vitamin A-deficient animals.[8] More recently, it has been shown that liver nuclei of vitamin A-deficient rats show decreased RNA synthesis and smaller sized nascent RNA segments when compared to nuclei isolated from retinol-repleted control animals.[10] Retinoic acid has also been implicated in control of transcriptional events in the nucleus, specifically in the control of interferon synthesis in cultured cells.[11] Thus, it appears that retinoids may directly influence gene expression at the nuclear level.

115

0077–8923/81/0359–0115 $01.75/0 © 1981, NYAS

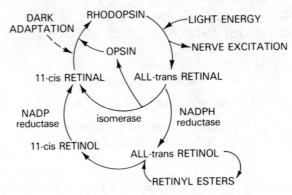

DARK ADAPTATION — RHODOPSIN — LIGHT ENERGY
OPSIN — NERVE EXCITATION
11-cis RETINAL — ALL-trans RETINAL
NADP reductase — isomerase — NADPH reductase
11-cis RETINOL — ALL-trans RETINOL — RETINYL ESTERS

FIGURE 1. General reactions in the visual cycle.

Evidence over the last few years indicates that specific intracellular retinoid-binding proteins (receptors) may act in concert with or modulate the activity of retinoids on cellular events. In 1973, Chytil and collaborators[12] first identified a specific cellular retinol-binding protein (CRBP) in the cytosol fraction of various rat tissues. Since then, such receptor proteins have been described in many known target tissues for retinol including retina,[13,14] pigment epithelium,[13] and cultured retinoblastoma cells.[15] At least two retinol-binding species are observed in the retina, one that seems to be compartmentalized in the photoreceptor outer segments and one that is more generally distributed.[16] As with retinol, specific cellular retinoic acid binding proteins (CRABP) have been described[17] in several tissues. They are also present in the retina[14,18] and in retinoblastoma cells.[15]

MATERIALS AND METHODS

Bovine eyes were obtained from a local abattoir and fertile eggs from Truslow Farms, Chestertown, MD. Homogenization was in Tris buffer (10 mM tris, pH 7.6, containing 1 mM disodium EDTA, 10 mM KC1, and 1 mM dithiothreitol). Supernatant fractions of tissues were obtained after centrifugation at $110,000 \times g$. Nuclei were prepared by discontinous sucrose gradient centrifugation. In some studies, supernatant was incubated for 15 min at 37°C with 1.2 units protease (Type VI, S. Griseus), 100 units phospholipase C, or 50 μg neuraminidase, prior to gradient analysis. Sucrose gradients (4.6 ml) were 5–20% sucrose (w/v) prepared in the Tris buffer. After application of samples, centrifugation was at $243,000 \times g$ for 16 hr.

[1-^{3}H]Retinol (about 2–3 Ci/mmol) was purchased from New England Nuclear Corp, Boston, MA. Other retinoids (e.g. [11, 12-^{3}H]retinoic acid) were generous gifts of the Hoffmann-LaRoche Company, Nutley, NJ. Purity was assessed by thin-layer chromatography on silica gel GF plates (Analtech, Wilmington, DE). Developing systems used were: (1) chloroform/methanol/benzene (1:1:2); (2) ether/2-octanone (19:1). Development was in a N_2 atmosphere at 4°C in dim red light. All retinoid manipulations were in the dark or under dim red light.

Retinoblastoma cells (Y-79) were grown in HEPES-buffered RPMI-1640 medium with 10% fetal calf serum in a 37°C humidified incubator. The medium was changed every 3 days by decanting off half of the spent fluid and then adding an equal volume of fresh medium. To determine retinoid cytotoxicity, cells were first treated with 0.25% trypsin in calcium-magnesium free Dulbecco's buffered saline solution for 10 min. Aliquots were then placed in triplicate or quadruplicate petri dishes for each dosage level. Retinoids were dissolved in 95% ethanol at appropriate concentrations for addition to the medium (1% final concentration). Alcohol was added in all controls and had negligible effects on the cells under these conditions. After 24 hr (retinoic acid, 13-*cis*-retinoic acid, retinol, 9-*cis*-retinol) or 36 hr (retinyl acetate, 13-*cis*-retinyl acetate) of retinoid treatment, cells were harvested, trypsinized, counted and cell viability determined by the trypan blue exclusion method.

Polyacrylamide gel electrophoresis was performed on a Pharmacia electrophoresis apparatus (GE-4) using 15 µl samples. A gradient gel of 4–30% acrylamide was run at 70V for 4 hr at 15°C. The buffer was 90 mM Trisborate, pH 8.4 containing 25 mM disodium EDTA. Thin-layer gel isoelectric focusing of 15 µl samples was on LKB ampholine PAG plates (pH 3.5-9.5) on an LKB Multiphor apparatus. Focusing was for 60 min at 4°C. The anode solution was 1 M H_3PO_4 and the cathode solution was 1M NaOH. Isoelectric points were determined using an Ingold surface pH electrode.

For autoradiography, the retinoblastoma cells were fixed with 2.5% glutaraldehyde followed by 1% osmium tetroxide and embedded with Epon 812. Exposure was for 3 weeks at 4°C.

Results

To initially assess the presence or absence of [³H]retinol receptors in ocular tissues, we used retina and the pigment epithelium-choroid unit from the chick embryo. This system offers the advantage that relatively good yields of retina can be dissected with no contamination from other cell types before about 15 days of embryonic development. Moreover, the retina is an avascular tissue; thus, there could be no confusion between [³H]retinol binding to a true intracellular receptor or merely to contaminating retinol-binding protein (RBP) or albumin from serum. Binding of [³H]retinol was observed in the 2S region (fraction 28) of 5–20% sucrose gradients of retina cytosol[13] as well as in several other chick embryo tissues (FIG. 2). A marked peak of [³H]retinol binding was also apparent at approximately 5S (fraction 19–20) in several tissues other than the retina. This peak can be shown to be due to nonsaturable binding to serum albumin. Antibody to purified serum RBP does not cross-react with chick retina cytosol in immunoprecipitation and immunodiffusion experiments.[19,20] Moreover, it can be shown that the cytosol receptor does not interact with purified serum prealbumin.[19] Purified RBP tagged with [³H]retinol sediments at 2S in sucrose gradients but shifts to about 5S with the addition of a small amount of purified prealbumin. The intracellular [³H]retinol receptor sediments at 2S irrespective of whether prealbumin is present or not indicating that the prealbumin cannot complex to the cytosol receptor as it does to the serum RBP.[19]

Incubation of retina cytosol with various degradative enzymes such as pronase, RNase, DNase, etc. indicated that, as with receptors in other tissues, the binding species are protein in nature. Only a limited number of such receptor proteins are available in the retina since incubation of retina cytosol with nonradiolabeled retinol along with the [³H]retinol leads to a disappearance of the radioactive peak on sucrose gradients due to dilution of the radiolabel.[19] It is thus apparent that there are a limited number of 2S protein receptor sites in retina

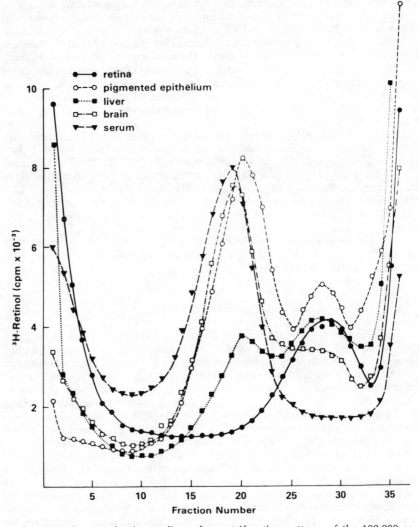

FIGURE 2. Sucrose density gradient ultracentrifugation patterns of the 100,000 × *g* supernatant fraction of several tissues of the chick embryo incubated with 1 μM [³H]retinol for 2 hr at 4° C. Centrifugation was for 16 hr at 243,000 × *g*.

with high affinity and specificity for retinol. In other studies, we have identified another, higher molecular size (7S), receptor type in the retinas of some animal species.[21] This receptor is apparently compartmentalized in the photoreceptor cell outer segment and probably is more involved in the visual process in photoreceptor outer segments rather than in general cell metabolism since its binding to outer segment membranes is light dependent.[21]

A 2S retinoic acid-binding protein is present in retina that is separate and distinct from the retinol receptor even though their molecular sizes are similar.[14,18] FIGURE 3 shows such binding in bovine retina and documents that there are a limited number of such binding sites (i.e. dilution of the [³H]retinoic acid-binding peak by added nonradiolabeled retinoic acid) and that they are specific for retinoic acid (i.e. little if any competition with added nonradiolabeled retinol).

Since a well-defined cell line of human retinoblastoma cells was available,[22] it was of interest to determine if retinoid receptors were present in these cells. Retinoblastoma is a hereditary disease of the retina that is thought to be of viral etiology.[23] The specific retinal cell type (or types) represented in culture is not known, but is probably of epithelial origin since the retina is a neuroepithelial tissue. We felt that this cell line offered a unique opportunity to correlate receptor binding with effects of various retinoids on human cancer cell viability under well-controlled culture conditions.[15]

A specific 2S [³H]retinol receptor is present in the 110,000 × *g* supernatant fraction of the retinoblastoma cells (FIG. 4A). The level of such binding is high, and appears to be at least 10-fold higher than in several rat tissues[24] or normal human retina.[25] Binding is quite specific in these cells since retinoic acid and

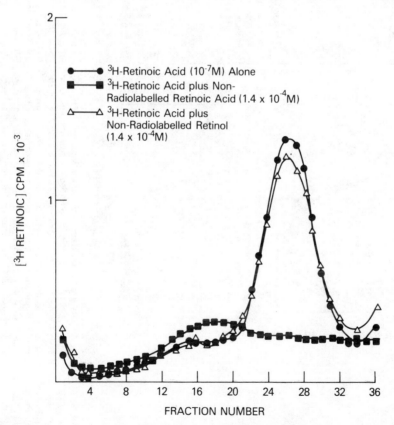

FIGURE 3. Sucrose density gradient pattern of ³H-retinoic acid binding in bovine retina supernatant.

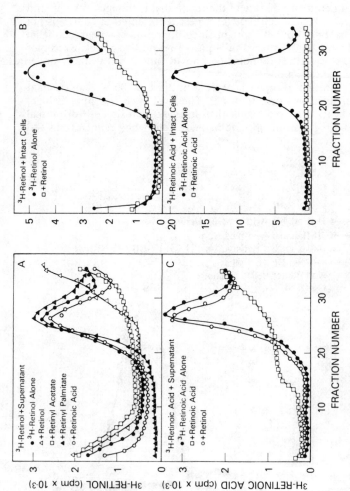

FIGURE 4. Sucrose density gradient ultracentrifugation patterns of [³H]retinoid-binding in cultured retinoblastoma cells. Cells were harvested by centrifugation at 100 × g, washed twice in buffered saline solution and homogenized in 10 mM Tris buffer.¹⁵ (A) Incubation of 100,000 × g cell supernatant with 2.8 × 10⁻⁷M [³H]retinol alone or in the presence of 5.6 × 10⁻⁵M nonlabeled retinol, retinyl acetate, retinyl palmitate or retinoic acid. (B) Incubation of intact cells with 1 μM [³H]retinol alone for 30 min at 37° or in the presence of 2 × 10⁻⁴M nonradiolabeled retinol. Supernatant fraction prepared subsequently. (C) Incubation of supernatant with 2.3 × 10⁻⁸M [³H]retinoic acid alone or in the presence of 4.6 × 10⁻⁶M nonradiolabeled retinoic acid or retinol. (D) Incubation of intact cells with 1 μM [³H]retinoic acid alone or in the presence of 2 × 10⁻⁴M nonradiolabeled retinoic acid for 30 min at 37°C. Supernatant fraction prepared subsequently.

retinyl palmitate do not compete for binding with [³H]retinol; the dilution effect seen with nonradiolabeled retinyl acetate may be due to the fact that (1) the small size of the acetate moiety does not interfere with receptor binding or (2) that enough esterase activity is present in the cells to produce significant concentrations of retinol even at 4°C. Supernatant binding of [³H]retinoic acids (FIG. 4C), is similarly at 2S in sucrose gradients but is separate and distinct from that observed with [³H]retinol.

Prior to cell growth and viability studies with the retinoids, it was of interest to determine if retinoids were actively taken up by intact cells in culture and bound in a manner similar to that seen in supernatant preparations. FIGURES 4 B and D demonstrate that not only is this the case, but that little free [³H]retinoid is taken up and/or retained by the cells under these conditions. Thus, it is probable that most if not all of the intracellular [³H]retinoid is present in receptor-bound form and that the retinoid effects could very well be mediated by the receptor binding. After incubation of intact cells with 1 μM [³H]retinoid, about threefold more [³H]retinol than [³H]retinoic acid is bound to 2S receptor, i.e. 45 vs. 14 pmoles/mg supernatant protein, respectively. Binding data indicate however that [³H]retinol is less firmly bound than [³H]retinoic acid.[15] Computer analysis by the logarithmic plot (Bjerrum's formation) yields dissociation constants (K_D) of 1.4 × 10^{-7} and 3.2 × 10^{-8}, respectively, indicating relatively high but distinctly different (fourfold) affinity values for the two retinoids. These differences may account in some measure for the fact that all-*trans*-retinol has a greater effect on growth and viability of retinoblastoma cells than retinoic acid or several other retinoids tested (FIG. 5). In these studies, the cultured cells were exposed to various concentrations of retinoids for 24 or 36 hr and cell viability was determined. Cell viability is

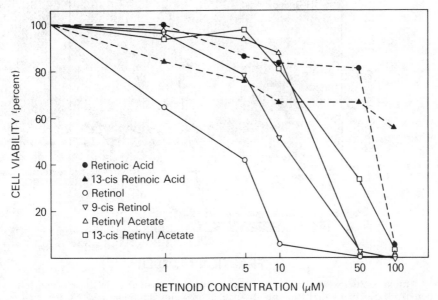

FIGURE 5. Retinoid effects on retinoblastoma cell viability. Values given are averages of triplicate samples which agreed within 10%. Similar results were obtained in two other experiments.

only 65% of the control value with 1μM retinol but over 80% for all other retinoids tested including all-*trans*-retinoic acid and 13-*cis*-retinoic acid. With 10μM retinol, virtually none of the cells remained viable; a 10-fold higher concentration of retinoic acid (i.e. 100μM) is needed to effect comparable cell death. 13-*cis*-Retinoic acid is only minimally effective even at 100 μM. Analogs of retinol (9-*cis*-retinol, 13-*cis*-retinyl acetate, and the *trans*-methoxy retinyl ester) are considerably less effective than the all-*trans*-retinol parent compound. Interestingly, the trans-methoxy analog appeared to exert a positive rather than inhibitory effect on cell growth and viability (data not shown).

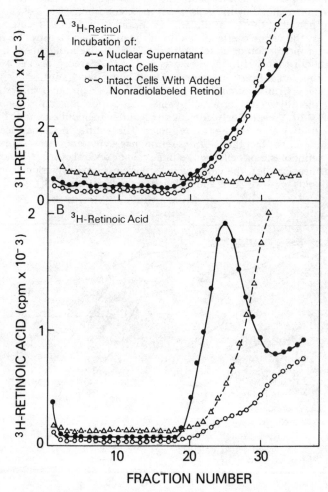

FIGURE 6. Sucrose density gradient ultracentrifugation patterns of nuclear soluble fraction. (A) Incubation with [³H]retinol (B) Incubation with [³H]retinoic acid. Nuclear supernatant prepared prior to incubation with [³H]retinoid (△). Nuclear supernatant prepared after intact cells were incubated with 1 μM [³H]retinoid for 1 hr at 37°C in the absence (●) or presence (O) of 2 × 10⁻⁴M nonradiolabeled retinol.

Significant biochemical differences between retinol and retinoic acid in cellular translocation and compartmentalization are also evident. When nuclei are isolated and the nuclear soluble fraction prepared and then incubated with [³H]retinol or [³H]retinoic acid, no specific binding of either retinoid is observed (FIG. 6 A,B). Similarly, when intact cells are first incubated with 1 μM[³H]retinol and the nuclei subsequently isolated, no specific binding of the retinoid is detectable in the nuclear soluble fraction (FIG. 6A). In contrast (FIG. 6B), a distinct 2S peak of bound [³H]retinoic acid is observed in the soluble fraction of nuclei isolated after preincubation of intact cells with [³H]retinoic acid (6.4 pmoles of [³H]retinoic acid bound/mg of nuclear soluble protein). Binding of [³H]retinoic acid to the nuclear 2S receptor is specific and saturable since a 200-fold excess of nonradiolabeled retinoic acid present during the initial incubation completely dilutes out the [³H]retinoic acid peak.

Results from the techniques of slab gel electrophoresis and isoelectric focusing are in accord with the biochemical evidence indicating uptake of [³H]retinoic acid in retinoblastoma cell nuclei (FIG. 7). The supernatant fraction of retinoblastoma cells incubated with [³H]retinoic acid exhibits only a single gel electrophoretic peak at approximately fraction 22 (FIG. 7A). When nuclei are isolated after such incubation (FIG. 7B), a similar peak was observed with some free [³H]retinoic acid migrating just behind the tracking dye front (fraction 60). With thin-layer gel isoelectric focusing, similar peaks of bound [³H]retinoic acid were observed in whole cell supernatant (FIG. 7C) and supernatant from isolated nuclei (FIG. 7D). Free [³H]retinoic acid migrated at fraction 18 under these conditions.

Incubation of intact retinoblastoma cells with [³H]retinol resulted in some metabolism of the retinoid since new radioactive peaks were detected by thin-layer chromatography within one-half hour of incubation (FIG. 8A–E). At that time, a slight skew of the [³H]retinol peak was observed as well as a small metabolite peak near the solvent front. Subsequently, a definite radiolabeled peak was observed with an R_f similar to that of the [³H]retinoic and standard (fraction 8). These results indicate substantial metabolism of [³H]retinol in the retinoblastoma cells even though the TLC technique is not the most sensitive technique for investigating such metabolic conversions. The nature of the new peak at fraction 8, for example, awaits identification by high pressure liquid chromatography.

Further evidence for nuclear uptake of [³H]retinoic acid is given by the technique of autoradiography. FIGURE 9 shows typical autoradiographs of retinoblastoma cells incubated with [³H]retinol or [³H]retinoic acid.[26] Cells incubated for 1 hour with 1 μM [³H]retinoic acid showed preferential labeling over the convoluted cell nuclei with fewer silver grains present in the cell cytoplasm (FIG. 9A). In contrast, cells incubated with [³H]retinol under similar conditions showed a more general labeling pattern with no preferential nuclear uptake (FIG. 9B). In many cells incubated for this time with [³H]retinol, silver grains were found only in the cytoplasm. Differences in the subcellular distribution of the [³H]retinoids are seen in larger field in FIGURE 10. After incubation with [³H]retinol (FIG. 10A), silver grains are dense over the cytoplasmic areas but the nuclei are clearly less heavily labeled, leading to a halo effect. The [³H]retinoic acid labeling pattern is generally just the opposite (FIG. 10B) with heaviest labeling observed over the nuclei, although some exceptions to this are seen in each field. Thus even though about three times more [³H]retinol than [³H]retinoic acid is taken up and bound by the retinoblastoma cells by 30–60 minutes of incubation (see above), little if any [³H]retinol appears to be taken up into nuclei at this early time. The small amount of radiolabel seen over the nuclear areas after in-

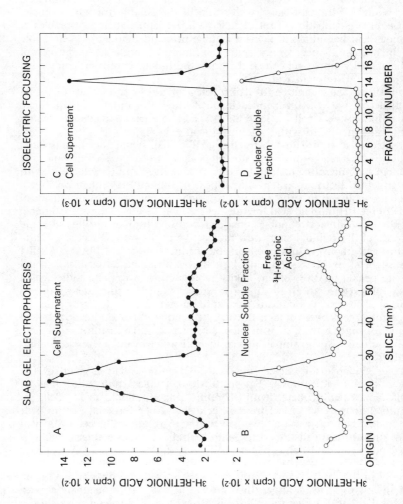

FIGURE 7. Polyacrylamide slab gel electrophoresis (A, B) and isoelectric focusing (C, D) of retinoblastoma cell supernatant (A, C) or nuclear soluble fractions (B, D). Cells were incubated with 2 μM [³H]retinoic acid for 30 min prior to preparation of cell supernatant or for 120 min prior to preparation of nuclear soluble fraction.

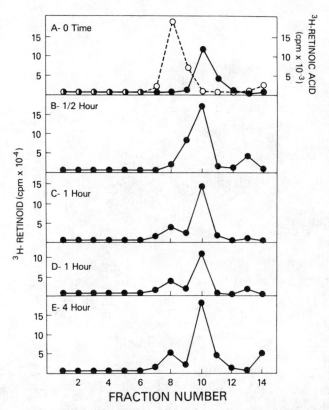

FIGURE 8. Thin-layer chromatography of extract from retinoblastoma cells incubated with 1 μM [³H]retinol for various times. Extraction was with 2:1 chloroform-methanol and chromatography was on Silica Gel G plates with a developing system of 1:1:2 chloroform: methanol:benzene. The position of a [³H]retinoic acid standard (O – – – O) is given for comparison.

cubation with [³H]retinol may be due to conversion to a yet unidentified metabolite. Our findings are thus consistent with the probability that [³H]retinol must be metabolized or otherwise transformed before it is translocated into the nucleus to any great extent. It is interesting to note that the pattern with 13-*cis*-retinoic acid is more like that of [³H]retinol than [³H]retinoic acid after the 1-hr incubation period (FIG. 10c). This may indicate differences in receptor binding or in the nuclear uptake/binding mechanism, although the retinoid does compete with [³H]retinoic acid for 2S binding sites (data not shown).

These studies thus provide evidence that at least one type of retinoid, i.e. retinoic acid, appears (1) to be quickly taken up by or bound to the cell nucleus and (2) to have specific soluble nuclear 2S receptors. It is also clear that such receptors are not present in the nucleus prior to the administration of the retinoid and that such administration appears to cause a redistribution of receptor from cytoplasm to nucleus. Retinoic acid translocation to the nucleus has recently also been reported in embryonal carcinoma cells.[27] With [³H]retinol, our preliminary evidence suggests that conversion to [³H]retinoic acid or a yet unidentified

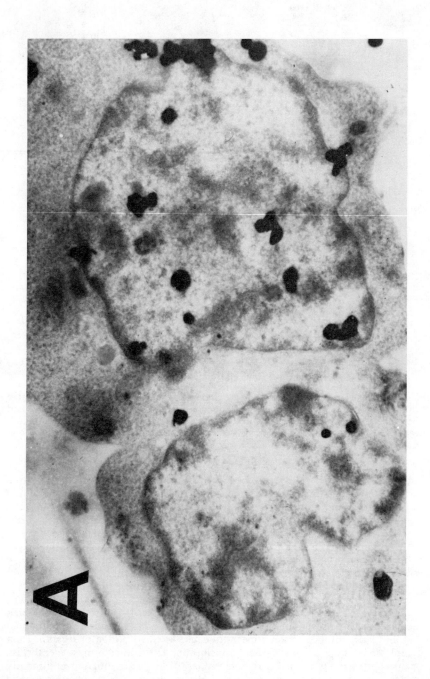

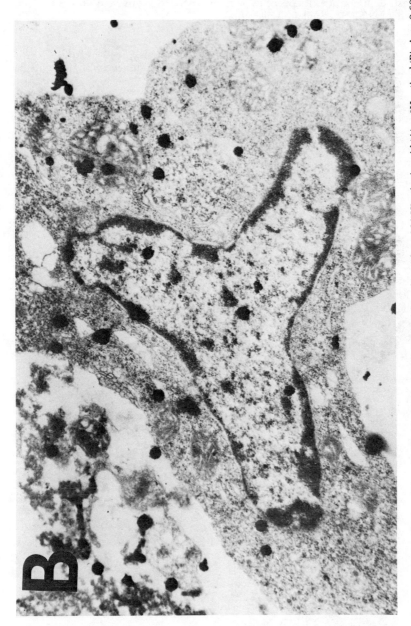

FIGURE 9. Typical autoradiographs of retinoblastoma cells incubated for 1 hr with 1 µM [³H]retinoic acid (A) or ³H-retinol (B). A: × 9,600 B: × 8,260.

metabolite is probably a necessary prerequisite before nuclear uptake. It would appear that the 2S retinol receptor is not present in the nucleus prior to retinol administration nor does it appear to be translocated to the nucleus within the first 1–2 hours of [³H]retinol administration.

DISCUSSION

In many ways, these events are similar to the situation seen with the action of

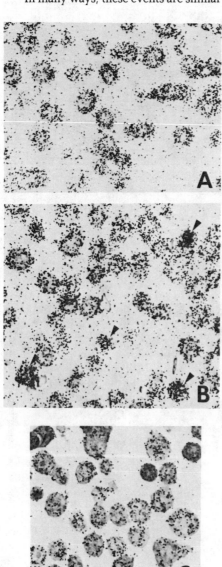

FIGURE 10. Typical autoradiographs of retinoblastoma cells incubated for 1 hr with 1 μM [³H] retinol (A), [³H]retinoic acid (B) or [³H]13-*cis*-retinoic acid (C). × 960.

steroid hormones in target tissues [FIG. 11]. In particular, the two-step mechanism originally proposed by Jensen and coworkers[28] for the mechanism of action of estradiol in the uterus seems to have several analogies to steps in the uptake of retinoid in retinoblastoma cells. There is also good evidence in some steroid hormone target tissues that metabolism precedes specific binding and nuclear translocation of the hormone. With androgens, for example, testosterone may act more as a "prohormone" in that it is converted to 5 α-dihydrotestosterone (DHT) in the prostate before it is selectively bound to a receptor protein and translocated to a specific nuclear "acceptor" site.[29] The form of the hormone active in the nucleus thus appears to be DHT rather than testosterone.

Our present data support the hypothesis of Wolf and De Luca[30] that there is "general agreement that vitamin A is to be regarded as a hormone rather than a vitamin in the classical sense of a coenzyme." The following logical sequence of events may thus take place in retinoblastoma target cells as depicted in FIGURE 10. First, the vitamin A (retinol) arrives at a target tissue bound to the serum retinol-binding protein.[31] There, the vitamin-protein complex interacts with the cell membrane,[32,33] is taken up into the cell and is bound to the retinol receptor (CRBP). A portion of this could then be converted to retinoic acid and bound to its own separate receptor (CRABP) as seen with the metabolism of testosterone and the binding of DHT to its specific cytoplasmic receptor. The possible role of retinoid receptor proteins in such metabolic conversions has yet to be investigated, although it appears that the androgen receptor and the 5 α-reductase enzyme in the prostate are different.[34] The retinoic acid-receptor complex could then be translocated to the nucleus as is the DHT-receptor complex in prostate.[29] Sani has recently also localized retinoic acid-binding protein in nuclei of chick embryo skin and murine tumors.[35] We have not been able to detect any difference between the 2S retinoic acid receptor observed in the entire cell supernatant frac-

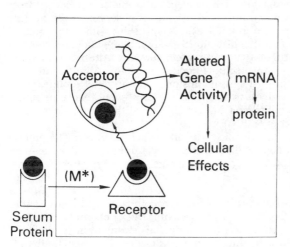

FIGURE 11. Model for the uptake, translocation, and possible action of steroid hormones.

M* -possible metabolism-

prohormone $\xrightarrow[\text{cell}]{\text{target}}$ active hormone

(testosterone)   (dihydrotestosterone)

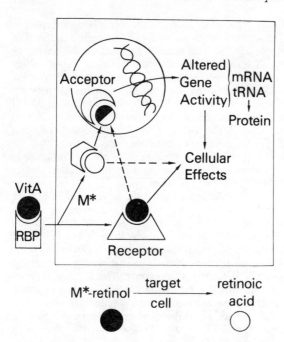

FIGURE 12. Model for the uptake, metabolic conversion, translocation, and possible action of vitamin A.

tion and the 2S "acceptor" observed in the nuclear fraction by the techniques of sucrose gradient ultracentrifugation, slab gel electrophoresis or isoelectric focusing. This, and the fact that no retinoic acid receptor is observed in the nuclear fraction prior to administration of retinoic acid is consistent with the possibility that there is translocation of the cytoplasmic 2S receptor to the nucleus as well as the retinoid itself in the form of a vitamin-protein complex. Alternatively, there may be as yet undetected separate, soluble nuclear "acceptors." Binding to other nuclear elements (chromatin, histones, nonhistone chromosomal proteins, etc.) has yet to be studied in retinoblastoma cells. In any event, receptor-bound retinoic acid (or other metabolite) could effect changes at the genetic level as do the steroid hormones, possibly on RNA metabolism.[10,36,37]

Several important questions remain to be addressed, however. The precise roles of the retinol and retinoic acid receptors are yet unknown. They may be transport vehicles for example or they may have other (e.g. enzymatic) functions. Retinol and retinoic acid-binding proteins are distributed differently in different tissues and appear at different times of development.[24] In the eye, both CRBP and CRABP are present in retina but the retinoic acid receptor appears to be absent in the closely apposed pigment epithelial layer when it is free of choroidal cells.[39] In the cornea, retinol binding is observed in epithelial, stromal and endothelial layers,[40] whereas retinoic acid binding cannot be detected in the epithelium.[18] This is odd since retinoic acid definitely reverses the corneal signs of vitamin A deficiency.

The differences in nuclear binding/uptake phenomena have also yet to be explained. We have found no evidence for nuclear binding or uptake of substantial amounts of [³H]retinol in retinoblastoma cells. In contrast, Chytil and his colleagues have demonstrated the specific binding of the retinol-CRBP complex to liver nuclei. The cellular retinoic-acid receptor is absent in adult liver however and it may be that the retinol-receptor complex mediates all retinoid functions in tissues or cells which do not have retinoic acid binding capacity. Rao *et al.*[41] have also found specific binding proteins for retinol in the nucleosol and chromatin of chicken oviduct. One could simply assume that the various retinoids and their binding proteins performed several different functions in tissues. In photoreceptors, retinal is the only retinoid that supports vision; in reproduction, retinol is the obligate retinoid while in most epithelial cell functions, retinoic acid is as efficacious as retinol. Retinoid effects could thus be somewhat different in liver, oviduct, retina, etc. and the pathways of metabolism, binding and action could be expected to vary. It is interesting that De Luca and his colleagues[42] have recently shown that retinol and retinoic acid have similar effects on properties of transformed fibroblast cells in culture. In their studies, they showed that retinoic acid could be reduced to a "retinol-like" compound and that it may be able to be phsophorylated and participate in glycosylation reactions as does retinol thus suggesting a unified mechanism for some if not all of the retinoid effects. It is yet to be determined however if these effects are independent of the nuclear events described above.

Answers to these questions should tell us much about the prophylactic activity of retinoids in the cancer research field. It is clear that vitamin A and its analogs prevent the development of cancer in several tissues.[43,44] It would seem likely that cellular receptor proteins would mediate the mechanism of action of retinoids in cancer tissue as well as in normal. Whether receptors are involved in such retinoid action or not, understanding the mechanism of action of retinoids in normal tissues should yield basic guidelines for this new and exciting pharmacological approach to cancer prevention.

ACKNOWLEDGMENT

We would like to thank the Hoffmann-LaRoche Company for generously supplying most of the radiolabeled and nonradiolabeled retinoids used in our studies.

REFERENCES

1. WALD, G. 1968. The molecular basis of visual excitation. Nature **219:** 800–807.
2. DOWLING, J. & G. WALD. 1958. Vitamin A deficiency and night blindness. Proc. Natl. Acad. Sci. USA **44:** 648–651.
3. ZAKLAMA, M., M. GABR, S. EL MARAGHI & V. PATWARDHAN. 1973. Serum vitamin A in protein-calorie malnutrition. Am. J. Clin. Nutrition **26:** 1202–1206.
4. MASON, K. 1933. Differences in testes injury and repair after vitamin A deficiency, vitamin E deficiency and inanition. Am. J. Anat. **52:** 153–239.
5. KRISHNAN, S., V. BHUYAN, G. TALWAR & V. RAMALINGA-SWAMI. 1974. Effect of vitamin A and protein–calorie undernutrition. Immunology **27:** 383–391.
6. PIRIE, A., 1977. Effects of locally applied retinoic acid on corneal xerophthalmia in the rat. Exp. Eye Res. **25:** 297–302.
7. SOMMER, A. & N. EMRAN. 1978. Topical retinoic acid in the treatment of corneal xerophthalmia. Am. J. Ophthalmol. **86:** 615–617.
8. WOLF, G. & L. DELUCA. 1969. Recent studies on some metabolic functions of vitamin A. *In* The Fat-soluble Vitamins. H. DeLuca & J. Suttie, Eds.:257–265. University of Wisconsin Press. Madison, WI.

9. DeLuca, L., P. Bhat, W. Sasak & S. Adamo. 1979. Biosynthesis of phosphoryl and glycosyl phosphoryl derivatives of vitamin A in biological membranes. Fed. Proc. **38**: 2535-2539.
10. Tsai, C. & F. Chytil. 1978. Effect of vitamin A deficiency on RNA synthesis in isolated rat liver nuclei. Life Sci. **23**: 1461-1472.
11. Blalock, J. & G. Gifford. 1977. Retinoic acid (vitamin A acid) induced transcriptional control of interferon production. Proc. Natl. Acad. Sci. USA **74**: 5382-5386.
12. Bashor, M., D. Toft & F. Chytil. 1973. In vitro binding of retinol to rat-tissue components. Proc. Natl. Acad. Sci. USA **70**: 4383-3487.
13. Wiggert, B. & G. Chader. 1975. A receptor for retinol in the developing retina and pigment epithelium. Exp. Eye Res. **21**: 143-151.
14. Saari, J. & S. Futterman. 1976. Separable binding proteins for retinoic acid and retinol in bovine retina. Biochim. Biophys. Acta **444**: 789-793.
15. Wiggert, B., P. Russell, M. Lewis & G. Chader. 1977. Differential binding to soluble nuclear receptors and effects on cell viability of retinol and retinoic acid in cultured retinoblastoma cells. Biochem. Biophys. Res. Commun. **79**: 218-225.
16. Wiggert, B., A. Mizukawa, T. Kuwabara & G. Chader. 1978. Vitamin A receptors: Multiple species in retina and brain and possible compartmentalization in retinal photoreceptors. J. Neurochem. **30**: 653-659.
17. Sani, B. & D. Hill. 1974. Retinoic acid: A binding protein in chick embryo metatarsal skin. Biochem. Biophys. Res. Commun. **61**: 1276-1282.
18. Wiggert, B., D. Bergsma, R. Helmsen & G. Chader. 1978. Vitamin A receptors: Retinoic acid binding in ocular tissues. Biochem. J. **169**: 87-94.
19. Abe, T., B. Wiggert, D. Bergsma & G. Chader. 1977. Vitamin A receptors I. Comparison of retinol binding to serum Retinol-Binding Protein and to tissue receptors in chick retina and pigment epithelium. Biochim. Biophys. Acta **498**: 355-365.
20. Wiggert, B., D. Bergsma, M. Lewis, T. Abe & G. Chader. 1977. Vitamin A receptors II Characteristics of retinol binding in chick retina and pigment epithelium. Biochim. Biophys. Acta **498**: 366-374.
21. Wiggert, B., J. Derr, M. Fitzpatrick & G. Chader. 1979. Vitamin A receptors of the retina: Differential binding in light and dark. Biochim. Biophys. Acta **582**: 115-121.
22. Reid, T., D. Albert, A. Rabson, P. Russell, J. Craft, E. Chu, T. Tralka & J. Wilcox. 1974. Characterization of an established cell line of retinoblastoma J. Natl. Cancer Inst. **53**: 347-360.
23. Reid, T. & P. Russell. 1974. Recent observations regarding retinoblastoma II. An enzyme study of retinoblastoma. Trans. Ophthalmol. Soc. UK **94**: 929-957.
24. Ong, D. & F. Chytil. 1975: Retinoic acid-binding protein in rat tissue. Partial purification and comparison to rat tissue retinol-binding protein. J. Biol. Chem. **250**: 6113-6117.
25. Bergsma, D., B. Wiggert, H. Funahashi, T. Kuwabara & G. Chader. 1977. Vitamin A receptors in normal and dystrophic human retina. Nature **265**: 66-67.
26. Russell, P., B. Wiggert, J. Derr, D. Albert, J. Craft & G. Chader. 1980. Nuclear Uptake of Retinoids: Autoradiographic evidence in retinoblastoma cells in vitro. J. Neurochem. In press.
27. Jetten, A. & M. Jetten. 1979. Possible role of retinoic acid binding protein in retinoid stimulation of embryonal carcinoma cell differentiation. Nature **278**: 180-182.
28. Jensen, E., T. Suzuki, T. Kawashima, W. Stumpf, P. Jungblut & E. Desombre. 1968. A two-step mechanism for the interaction of estradiol with rat uterus. Proc. Natl. Acad. Sci. USA **59**: 632-638.
29. Fang, S. & S. Liao. 1971. Androgen receptors. Steroid- and tissue-specific retention of a 17B-OH-5α-androstan-3-one protein complex by the cell nuclei of ventral prostate. J. Biol. Chem. **246**: 16-24.
30. Wolf, G. & L. De Luca. 1969. Recent studies on some metabolic functions of vitamin A. *In* The Fat-Soluble Vitamins. H. DeLuca & J. Suttie, Eds.: 257-265. University of Wisconsin Press. Madison, WI.
31. Muto, Y. & D. Goodman. 1972. Vitamin A transport in rat plasma. Isolation and characterization of retinol-binding protein. J. Biol. Chem. **247**: 2533-2544.
32. Heller, J. 1975. Interaction of plasma retinol-binding protein with its receptor.

Specific binding of bovine retinol–binding protein to pigment epithelium cells from bovine eyes. J. Biol. Chem. **250**: 3613–3619.

33. RASK, L. & P. PETERSON. 1976. In vitro uptake of vitamin A from the retinol–binding plasma protein to mucosal epithelial cells from the monkey's small intestine. J. Biol. Chem. **251**: 6360–6366.

34. MAINWARING, W. 1970. The separation of androgen receptor and 5α-reductase activities in subcellular fractions of rat prostate. Biochem. Biophys. Res. Commun. **40**: 192–198.

35. SANI, B. 1977. Localization of retinoic-acid binding protein in nuclei. Biochem. Biophys. Res. Commun. **75**: 7–12.

36. KAUFMAN, D., M. BAKER, J. SMITH, W. HENDERSON, C. HARRIS, M. SPORN & U. SAFFIOTTI. 1972. RNA metabolism in trachael epithelium: Alteration in hamsters deficient in vitamin A. Science **177**: 1105–1108.

37. SPORN, M., N. DUNLOP & S. YUSPA. 1973. Retinyl acetate: Effect on cellular content of RNA in epidermis in cell culture in chemically defined medium. Science **182**: 722–723.

38. WIGGERT, B., D. BERGSMA & G. CHADER. 1976. Retinol receptors of the retina and pigment epithelium: Further characterization and species variation. Exp. Eye Res. **22**: 411–418.

39. WIGGERT, B., E. MASTERSON, P. ISRAEL & G. CHADER. 1979. Differentiatial retinoid binding in chick pigment epithelium and choroid. Invest. Ophthalmol. Vis. Sci. **18**: 306–310.

40. WIGGERT, B., D. BERGSMA, R. HELMSEN, J. ALLIGOOD, M. LEWIS & G. CHADER. 1977. Retinol receptors in corneal epithelium, stroma and endothelium. Biochim. Biophys. Acta **491**: 104–113.

41. RAO, M., V. PRASAD, G. PADMANABAN & J. GANGULY. 1979. Isolation and characterization of binding proteins for retinol from the cytosol, nucleosol and chromatin of the oviduct magnum of laying hens. Biochem. J. **183**:501–506.

42. DE LUCA, L., S. ADAMO, P. BHAT, W. SASAK, C. SILVERMAN-JONES, I. AKALOVSKY, J. FROT-COUTAZ, R. FLETCHER & G. CHADER. 1979. Recent developments in studies on biological functions of vitamin A in normal and transformed tissues. Pure Applied Chem. **51**: 581–591.

43. SPORN, M., N. DUNLOP, D. NEWTON & J. SMITH. 1976. Prevention of chemical carcinogenesis by vitamin A and its synthetic analogs (retinoids). Fed. Proc. **35**: 1332–1338.

44. MAYER, H., W. BOLLANG & R. RUEGG. 1978. Retinoids, a new class of compounds with prophylactic and therapeutic activities in oncology and dermatology. Experientia **34**: 1105–1119.

THE BIOSYNTHESIS OF A MANNOLIPID CONTAINING A METABOLITE OF RETINOIC ACID BY 3T12 MOUSE FIBROBLASTS

P.V. Bhat and L.M. De Luca*

National Cancer Institute
National Institutes of Health
Bethesda, Maryland 20205

INTRODUCTION

Work from our laboratory[1] has demonstrated that retinoic acid is nearly as effective as vitamin A in restoring normal levels of mannose incorporation into glycoproteins in vitamin A-depleted hamster liver tissue. Inasmuch as this function of retinol may depend on mannosylretinylphosphate, we probed the possibility that a mannolipid of retinoic acid is also formed. This work was conducted in cultured spontaneously transformed 3T12 cells, because these cells showed increased adhesion and mannosylation as a result of retinol and/or retinoic acid treatment.[2,3]

MATERIALS AND METHODS

Transformed mouse fibroblasts (BALB/c 3T12-3) were cultured[2] in Dulbecco's modified Eagle's medium (Grand Island Biological Company, Grand Island, NY) supplemented with 10% calf serum (Flow Laboratories, Rockville, MD), 25 mM HEPES buffer (pH 7.3) and 50 µg/ml of gentamicin. [11-12³H]Retinoic acid (1.28 Ci/mMole) (Hoffmann-La Roche Inc. Nutley, NJ) was mixed with [carboxyl-¹⁴C] retinoic acid (Sp. radioactivity 9.5 mCi/mMole, Amersham-Searle, Arlington Heights, IL). This mixture of labeled retinoic acid was purified by chromatography on DEAE-cellulose acetate in 99% methanol from which purified retinoic acid was eluted with 1 mM ammonium acetate in 99% methanol.

[2-³H]D-Mannose (specific radioactivity 2 Ci/mMole) and [15-³H]retinol (specific radioactivity 1.25 Ci/mMole) were procured from Amersham Searle (Arlington Heights, IL) and New England Nuclear (Boston, MA), respectively. Cells were seeded at 10,000 cells/cm² in 10 cm Falcon tissue culture dishes and grown for 24 hours in normal medium. At this time the medium was changed. Doubly labeled retinoic acid was dissolved in DMSO to a concentration of 2 mg/ml and added to the culture medium to reach a final concentration of 10 µg of retinoic acid per milliliter and 0.5% DMSO. A negative control for the metabolism of retinoic acid was obtained with cells fixed by exposure to formaldehyde vapors.

After incubation with labeled retinoid, the medium was removed and the cells were rinsed with PBS and scraped with a rubber policeman. The combined cell washings and scraped cells were spun at 500 × g for 10 minutes and the washed pellet was lyophilized. The lyophilized cells were extracted with 3 × 10 ml per dish of 99% methanol containing 0.05% butylated hydroxytoluene. The methanolic extract was used for the separation of the metabolites either by thin-layer chromatography (TLC) or by high-pressure liquid chromatography (HPLC).

---

* To whom requests for reprints should be addressed at Building 37, Room 2B26.

0077-8923/81/0359-0135 $01.75/0 © 1981, NYAS

Thin-Layer Chromatography

TLC of the purified metabolites of retinol and retinoic acid was performed in pre-coated silica gel 60F-254 plates (Brinkmann Instrument, Inc). The solvent systems used were (1) chloroform:methanol:water (60:25:4); (2) toluene:chloroform:methanol (4:1:1); and (3) chloroform:methanol:water (60:35:6).

In the doubly labeled experiment with [15-^{3}H]retinol and [15-^{14}C]retinoic acid, the cells were incubated separately with the label for 20 hours and then the medium was changed and incubated with fresh medium for an additional 20 hours. The cells were processed as described above and the lipid extracts were used for the separation of the metabolites by HPLC.

Hydrolysis Studies of the Doubly Labeled Metabolite

The purified metabolite from HPLC was dried under nitrogen and subjected to 0.05N HCl hydrolysis by adding 100 μl of 0.05N HCl prepared in 100% ethanol, and incubating at 25°C for 30 seconds. After 30 seconds the solvents were evaporated and the residue was dissolved in small volume of absolute methanol; and the hydrolysis products were either analyzed by TLC or HPLC. Under these conditions 100% hydrolysis of all-*trans*-retinylphosphate to all-*trans*-anhydroretinol was observed.

High-Pressure Liquid Chromatography

High-pressure liquid chromatography was performed on a Altex Model 322 MP programmable liquid chromatography system. This system was equipped

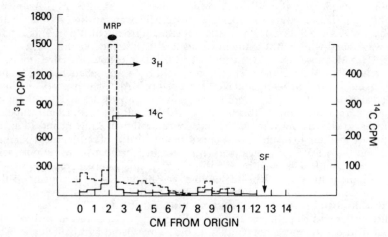

FIGURE 1. Thin-layer chromatography of metabolite I from 3T12 cells incubated with [11, 12 ^{3}H, 15-^{14}C]retinoic acid in solvent system 1. The metabolite was isolated from the total lipid extract by chromatography on DEAE-cellulose acetate. An aliquot from 10 mM fraction from DEAE-cellulose acetate was used for TLC in solvent system 1, along with standard mannosylretinylphosphate.

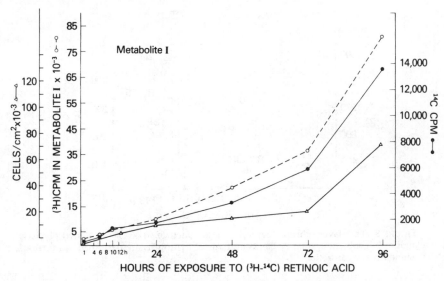

FIGURE 2. The time course of biosynthesis of doubly labeled metabolite I. Studies for the synthesis of metabolite I were conducted at the various time points as described in METHODS. The ^3H:^{14}C ratio in metabolite I was identical to that of the precursor (6:1).

with the recorder, a Linear Model 300 with a maximum AUFS of 0.01. The UV spectrophotometer was a Hitachi Model 100-30 equipped with a variable wavelength between 195 and 850 nm.

Fluorometer Model FS 970 from Schoeffel Instrument Corporation (Westwood, NJ) was also connected with the HPLC system, in series before the spectrophotometer. The HPLC columns were obtained from Whatman Inc., Clifton, NJ. A Partisil-10-ODS Column (4.6 mn I.D. × 25 cm) was used. For the separation of individual retinoids; the column was eluted with acetonitrile:phosphate buffer pH 7.2 (37:63) at an initial flow rate of 2.2 ml/min for 30 min to elute all-*trans*-mannosylretinylphosphate, all-*trans*-retinylphosphate, 13-*cis*- and all-*trans*-retinoic acid. At 30 min the ratio of acetonitrile to phosphate buffer was changed (54:46) and the flow rate was adjusted to 3.5 ml/min to elute 13-*cis*-retinol, all-*trans*-retinol, retinal, retinyl acetate and all-*trans*-anhydroretinol. At 45 min the phosphate buffer was replaced with water and the ratio of acetonitrile to water was changed to (98:2) and flow rate was adjusted to 1.5 ml/min for additional 15 min to elute retinyl palmitate.

RESULTS

Mouse fibroblasts synthesized a product (Metabolite I or MXP) from [11, 12 ^3H; 15-^{14}C]retinoic acid, which behaved identically with standard mannosylretinylphosphate (MRP) upon chromatography on DEAE-cellulose acetate and thin layers of silica gel in solvent system 1 (FIG. 1). The ^3H:^{14}C ratio in this product was identical to that of the precursor (6/1). The time course of the biosynthesis of doubly labeled metabolite I is shown in FIGURE 2, which also shows the rate

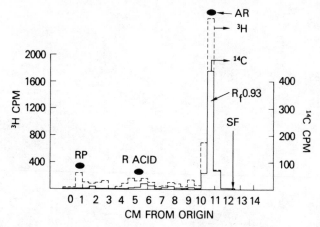

FIGURE 3. Thin-layer chromatography of product of 0.05 N HCl hydrolysis of metabolite I in solvent system 2. The conditions of hydrolysis are described in METHODS. AR: standard anhydroretinol.

of cell growth. Metabolite I constitutes only 4 to 6% of the total radioactivity at this time of culture, the rest of the label being still intact retinoic acid.

Hydrolysis of Metabolite I, under conditions described under METHODS, gave a doubly labeled product (ratio ^{3}H:^{14}C, 6:1) which cochromatographed with standard anhydroretinol, the hydrolysis product of MRP on TLC in solvent system 2 at R$_f$ 0.93, FIGURE 3.

Synthesis of a Doubly Labeled Mannolipid from [2-³H]Mannose and [15-¹⁴C]Retinoic Acid

The lipid extract from doubly labeled 3T12 cells (see METHODS) was first chromatographed on DEAE-cellulose-acetate to remove [2-³H]mannose, and then eluted in 99% methanol, and [15-¹⁴C]retinoic acid or its oxidation products eluted in 1 mM ammonium acetate in 99% methanol. The doubly labeled metabolite I was eluted at 10 mM ammonium acetate, as for standard MRP. FIGURE 4 shows the chromatographic behavior of Metabolite I in solvent 3, identical to that of standard MRP. Hydrolysis, under conditions that release mannosephosphate and anhydroretinol from MRP, yielded [³H]mannosephosphate and a ¹⁴C-labeled product that behaved as anhydroretinol, upon chromatography on thin layers of silica gel in solvent system 2.

Ion Pair Reverse Phase High-Pressure Liquid Chromatography

A new HPLC system was developed, as detailed in METHODS, to separate MRP and RP from all-*trans*-retinoic acid and its oxidized metabolites: 5, 6-epoxyretinoic acid[4]; 4-oxo-retinoic acid[5] and 4-hydroxyretinoic acid.[5,6] FIGURE 5A shows the ion pair HPLC separation of MRP, 4-oxo-retinoic acid, 5, 6-epoxyretinoic acid, retinyl phosphate, 13-*cis*-retinoic acid, all-*trans*-retinoic acid, retinol, retinal, retinylacetate, anhydroretinol and retinyl palmitate.

Biosynthesis of the Mannolipids of [15-³H]Retinol and [15-¹⁴C]Retinoic Acid

3T12-mouse fibroblasts were incubated separately with [15-³H]retinol and [15-¹⁴C]retinoic acid, as indicated in METHODS. The lipid extracts were combined and processed by ion pair reverse phase HPLC. FIGURE 5B shows the elution pattern of the combined radioactive methanolic extract. About 40% of the total ¹⁴C radioactivity was eluted in the area of standard MRP, which is eluted at the void volume. About 10% was eluted in the area of 4-oxo-retinoic acid, 4.8% in the area of 13-*cis*-retinoic acid and about 17% in the area of all-*trans*-retinoic acid. Of the radioactivity derived from [15-³H]retinol, 2.2% was found in the area of MRP, 19% as all-*trans*-retinol and 74% in the area of retinol fatty acid esters. The purity of the radioactive precursors was checked by the same procedure and no radioactive peaks were detected other than the authentic compounds.

The doubly labeled peak eluted as MRP was further purified by a HPLC procedure which employs a stepwise elution with water in acetonitrile. In this proce-

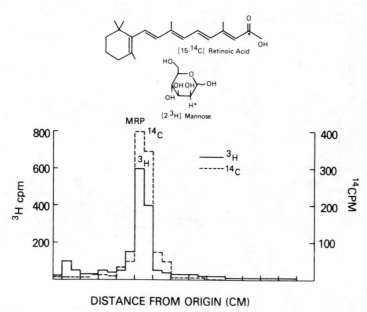

DISTANCE FROM ORIGIN (CM)

FIGURE 4. Thin-layer chromatography of doubly labeled mannolipid from [2–³H]mannose and [15–¹⁴C]retinoic acid in solvent system 3. 3T12 cells were incubated with [2–³H]mannose and [¹⁴C]retinoic acid as described in METHODS. The lipid extract from doubly labeled 3T12 cells was first chromatographed on DEAE-cellulose acetate to remove [2–³H]mannose, eluted in 99% methanol and then eluted with 1 mM ammonium acetate in 99% methanol which elutes free RA and its oxidized products. The doubly labeled metabolite I was eluted by 10 mM ammonium acetate.

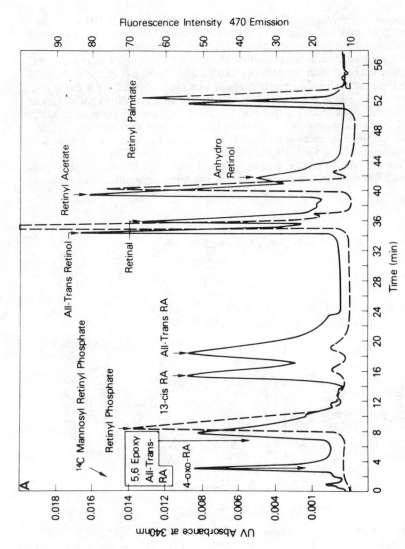

FIGURE 5A. Reversed phase high pressure liquid chromatography of standard retinoids. UV absorption was monitored at 340 nm to detect retinoic acid, anhydroretinol and retinal, in addition to retinol, retinylphosphate and retinylpalmitate. Fluorescence was measured with a 470 emission filter with excitation at 325 nm, which is the UV absorption maximum of retinol, retinyl esters and retinylphosphate. The quantity of each retinoid was 200–250 ng. (————) UV detector and (– – – –) fluorescence detector, connected in series.

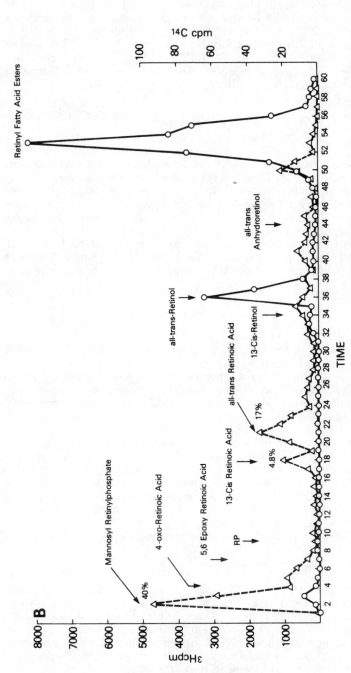

FIGURE 5B. High-pressure liquid chromatographic separation of the metabolites from 3T12 cells incubated separately with [15-³H]retinol and [15-¹⁴C]retinoic acid. The lipid extracts from 3T12-mouse fibroblasts, which were incubated separately with [15-³H]retinol and [15-¹⁴C]retinoic acid were combined and processed by ion-pair reverse phase HPLC as described in FIGURE 5A. 1-min fractions were collected and radioactivity was counted, using hydrofluor (National Diagnostics, NJ) as the counting cocktail.

dure standard [14C]MRP is eluted in 10% water as shown in FIGURE 6A. Moreover 5, 6-epoxy RA, 4-oxo-RA and 4-hydroxy RA or any other known oxidation products of retinol or RA are eluted with 5.5% water in acetonitrile in this procedure (FIG. 6B). The doubly labeled fraction obtained from FIGURE 5B behaved as shown in FIGURE 6B, i.e. as standard MRP. In addition, thin-layer chromatography in solvent 3 of the peak obtained at 10% water from HPLC showed the same R_f as standard MRP.

Hydrolysis Studies

The products coeluting in 10% water in acetonitrile from HPLC (FIG. 6B) were hydrolyzed with mild acid, under conditions that cleave retinyl phosphate to anhydroretinol.[7,8] FIGURE 7A shows the elution pattern of intact retinyl-phosphate in the ion pair HPLC system. FIGURE 7B shows the elution pattern of the hydrolysis product of RP. This product is identical with all-*trans*-anhydroretinol. FIGURE 7C shows the elution pattern of the hydrolysis products of the mannolipids labeled with [15-3H]retinol and [15-14C]retinoic acid. Under these hydrolysis conditions more than 90% of the MRP-like compounds were hydrolyzed. Mannosyl-[15-3H]retinyl phosphate yielded all-*trans*-[3H]anhydroretinol, whereas mannosyl-[15-14C]*retinoid*phosphate (MXP) yielded a product of greater polarity (FIG. 7C).

DISCUSSION

In 1970 De Luca et al.[9] showed that a mannosylphosphoryl derivative of retinol (MRP) was synthesized by rat liver in vivo and in in vitro by microsomal membrane systems. It was proposed that the function of MRP was a specialized one in the biosynthesis of specific glycoproteins and not a general carrier function. In fact, only mannose and galactose[10] were shown to form retinoid phosphate derivatives. In addition to this specificity for the acceptor function of retinyl phosphate, there may also be specificity for its donor function.

Retinoic acid replaces vitamin A in the growth and differentiation function, in most tissues,[11] without supporting vision and reproduction.[12] The lack of activity of this molecule in the visual cycle is due to the fact that RA is not reduced to retinol.[13,14] Mammalian vision requires specifically the molecule of retinol.[3] However, the possibility still existed that a metabolic derivative of retinoic acid containing an alcoholic group might function as retinol in the biosynthesis of specific glycoproteins. Such a derivative would not satisfy the visual function, but it may work as retinol in glycosyl transfer reactions, which may be a less specific system than the visual system.

3T12 Cells were chosen because of the activity of both, retinol and retinoic acid, in increasing adhesion as well as glycosylation in these cells.[2,3] This activity of retinol is not expressed through the action of a cellular binding protein (cRBP) in as much as these cells do not contain such protein. However, they do have a cellular retinoic acid-binding protein (cRABP). 3T12 Cells are unusual in another respect: they dispose of most of the retinol by dehydration to yield the hydrocarbon anhydroretinol, which is inactive in growth and adhesion.[2,15] This retinol dehydratase activity is not found in normal primary mouse dermal fibroblasts, in cultured primary epidermal or intestinal cells, or in vivo.

With regard to mannosylretinylphosphate, 3T12 cells and their microsomes

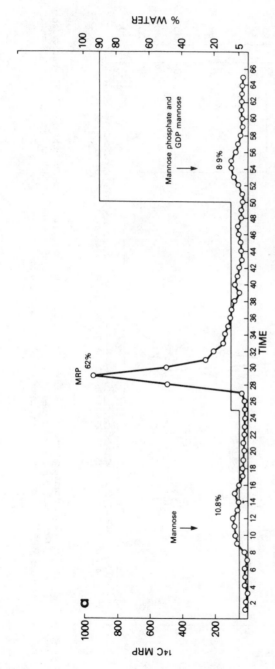

FIGURE 6A. High-pressure liquid chromatography of standard [^{14}C]mannosylretinylphosphate (MRP). [^{14}C]MRP was separated from free mannose, GDP mannose and mannose phosphate by stepwise elution first with 5.5% water in acetonitrile for 25 min, which elutes free mannose and then with 10% water in acetonitrile for additional 25 min to elute MRP and finally with 90% water in acetonitrile for another 15 min to elute GDP mannose and mannosephosphate.

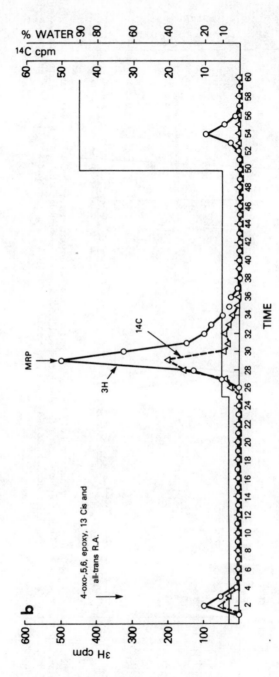

FIGURE 6B. High-pressure liquid chromatography of the doubly labeled fraction (MRP fraction) obtained from FIGURE 5B. The doubly labeled fraction was eluted stepwise from the column as described in FIGURE 6A. More than 90% of the radioactivity was eluted in 10% water in acetonitrile as for standard MRP. The arrow indicates the elution position of standard MRP.

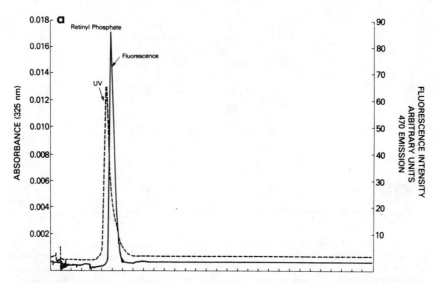

FIGURE 7A. High-pressure liquid chromatography of synthetic retinylphosphate (200 ng) before acid treatment (0.05N ethanolic HCl at 25°C for 30 seconds). The elution conditions and column used were described in FIGURE 5A (- - -) UV detector and (————) fluorescence detector. Absorbance was monitored at 325 nm and fluorescence excitation and emission were at 325 and 470 nm, respectively.

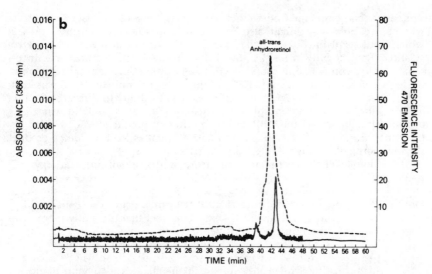

FIGURE 7B. High-pressure liquid chromatography of product of acid hydrolysis of 200 ng of retinylphosphate. The conditions of hydrolysis are as described above, and the conditions of elution and the column used were described in FIGURE 5A. Absorbance was monitored at 366 nm to detect anhydroretinol and the fluorescence excitation and emission were kept at 325 and 470 nm, respectively to detect any unhydrolyzed retinylphosphate. Under these hydrolysis conditions there was 100% hydrolysis of retinylphosphate to anhydroretinol.

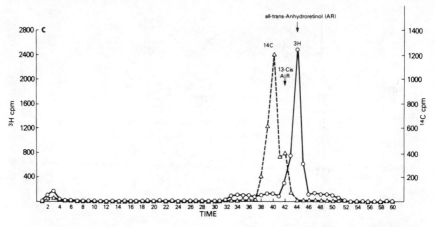

FIGURE 7C. High-pressure liquid chromatography of the products of acid hydrolysis of mannolipids labeled with [15–³H]retinol and [15–¹⁴C]retinoic acid purified as described in FIGURE 6B. The conditions of hydrolysis are as described for synthetic retinylphosphate and elution conditions were as described in FIGURE 5A. More than 90% of the MRP-like compounds were hydrolyzed under these conditions. Mannosyl-[15³H]retinylphosphate yielded all-*trans*-[³H]anhydroretinol, whereas mannosyl-[15¹⁴C]retinoidphosphate yielded a [¹⁴C]product that is more polar than all-*trans*-anhydroretinol and 13-*cis*-anhydroretinol.

synthesize this compound from retinol. Therefore, it was of interest to investigate whether retinoic acid might also form a mannosylretinoidphosphate (MXP), which would explain why the acid can replace the alcohol in adhesion and glyco-sylation. Radioactivity from (11, 12-³H; carboxyl ¹⁴C]retinoic acid was incorporated into a compound indistinguishable from authentic mannosylretinylphosphate by column, thin-layer, and HPLC techniques. The ratio of ³H:¹⁴C was identical to that of the starting RA, thus excluding the possibility that decarboxylation occurs prior to mannosylphosphoryl formation (FIG. 8). This lipid was easily cleaved by mild acid as for MRP, but with different products: MRP yielded all-*trans*-anhydroretinol after mild acid treatment, whereas MXP yielded a product slightly more polar than all-*trans*-anhydroretinol (FIG. 8).

In a double-label experiment using [carbinol-³H]retinol and [carboxyl-¹⁴C] retinoic acid, 3T12 cells synthesized [³H]MRP and [¹⁴C]MXP. MXP represented about 40% of the total radioactivity from [15-¹⁴C]retinoic acid, as shown in FIGURE 5B. The two products were cleaved with mild acid in seconds, yielding all-*trans*-[³H]anhydroretinol and a ¹⁴C-labeled product that is slightly more polar than all-*trans*-anhydroretinol (FIG. 8). We therefore conclude that:

1. 3T12 Cells synthesize mannosylretinylphosphate from retinol.
2. 3T12 Cells synthesize a mannosyl *retinoid* phosphate (MXP) from RA, which constitutes up to 40% of the total metabolites at 40 hours of incubation.
3. Both MRP and MXP are hydrolyzed by mild acid in a few seconds at room temperature. MRP yields mannosephosphate and all-*trans*-anhydroretinol. MXP yields mannose-phosphate and a product that is more polar than all-*trans*- and 13-*cis*-anhydroretinol (FIG. 8).

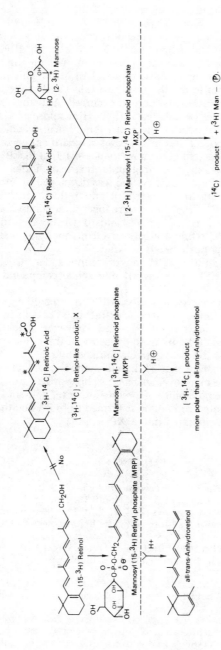

FIGURE 8. Schematic representation of the formation of mannolipids from retinol and retinoic acid in 3T12-3 mouse fibroblasts.

SUMMARY

Retinol and retinoic acid (RA) increase the adhesive properties of spontaneously transformed mouse fibroblasts (BALB/c 3T12-3 cells) and the incorporation of [2-^{3}H]mannose into cellular glycoconjugates. Therefore we searched for a mannolipid of retinoic acid similar to mannosylretinylphosphate (MRP) in these cells.

Radioactively labeled RA was incorporated into a compound of chromatographic characteristics similar to those of standard MRP. This metabolite contained the same ^{3}H:^{14}C ratio as the precursor [11, 12-^{3}H, 15-^{14}C]retinoic acid, demonstrating that no decarboxylation had occurred. A doubly labeled mannolipid was obtained from cells incubated with [2-^{3}H]mannose and [15-^{14}C]retinoic acid. This mannolipid was readily cleaved by mild acid, yielding [^{3}H]mannosephosphate and a compound that migrated as standard anhydroretinol on thin layer of silica gel in toluene:chloroform:methanol (4:1:1) at R_f 0.93. Standard all-trans-MRP yields all-trans-anhydroretinol under these conditions.

An ion pair reverse phase HPLC system was developed to further characterize the mannolipids obtained from retinol and retinoic acid in 3T12 cells. [15-^{3}H]Retinol and [15-^{14}C]retinoic acid were incorporated into mannolipids that cochromatographed upon HPLC with standard MRP. The mixture of the [15-^{3}H]retinol and [15-^{14}C]retinoic acid derived mannolipids was subjected to mild acid hydrolysis, after purification by HPLC. Nearly 100% of the compounds was hydrolyzed, yielding all-trans-[^{3}H]anhydroretinol and a ^{14}C-labeled product, which was eluted from HPLC as a slightly more polar compound than all-trans-anhydroretinol.

The retinoic acid-derived mannolipid (MXP) represented approximately 4% of the total radioactivity in the methanolic extract of 3T12 cells incubated for 20 hours in the presence of labeled retinoic acid. However, if the cells were incubated for an additional 20 hours in the absence of the radioactive precursor, MXP represented 40% of the total extracted radioactivity.

These results demonstrate that 3T12 cells synthesize mannosylretinylphosphate from retinol and a mannosylretinoidphosphate (MXP) from retinoic acid. These results exclude the possibility of a reduction of retinoic acid to retinol, but suggest that a closely related compound is formed from RA and that this retinol-like compound (X) is incorporated into MXP.

REFERENCES

1. DE LUCA, L.M. 1977. The direct involvement of vitamin A in glycosyl transfer reactions of mammalian membranes. Vitam. Horm. **35**: 1-57.
2. ADAMO, S., L.M. DE LUCA, I. AKALOVSKY & P.V. BHAT. 1979. Retinoid-induced adhesion in cultured spontaneously-transformed mouse fibroblasts. J. Natl. Cancer Inst. **62**: 1473-1477.
3. SASAK, W. & L.M. DE LUCA. 1980. Effect of retinoic acid on cell-surface glycopeptides of cultured spontaneously-transformed mouse fibroblasts (BALB/c 3T12-3 cells). Cancer Res. **40**: 1955-1949.
4. MCCORMICK, A.M., J.L. NAPOLI, H.K. SCHNOES & H.F. DE LUCA. 1978. Isolation and identification of 5, 6-epoxyretinoic acid: A biologically active metabolite of retinoic acid. Biochemistry **17**: 4085-4090.
5. FROLIK, C.A., A.B. ROBERTS, T.E. TAVELA, P.P. ROLLER, D.L. NEWTON & M.B. SPORN. 1979. Isolation and identification of 4-hydroxy and 4-oxoretinoic acid. In vitro metabolites of all-trans retinoic acid in hamster trachea and liver. Biochemistry **18**: 2092-2097.

6. FROLIK, C.A., T.E. TAVELA, D.L. NEWTON & M.B. SPORN. 1978. In vitro metabolism and biological activity of all-trans retinoic acid and its metabolites in hamster trachea. J. Biol. Chem. **253:** 7319–7324.
7. DMITROVSKII, A.A. & S.P. POZNYAKOV. 1978. Synthesis, physicochemical properties and biological activity of retinylphosphate. Prikladnaya Biokhimiya i Mikrobiologiya **14:** 558–562.
8. BHAT, P.V. & L.M. DE LUCA. In preparation.
9. DE LUCA, L.M., C.S. SILVERMAN-JONES & R.M. BARR. 1975. Biosynthetic studies on mannolipids and mannoproteins of normal and vitamin A depleted hamster livers. Biochim. Biophys. Acta **409:** 342–352.
10. PETERSON, P.A., L. RASK, T. HELTING, L. OSTBERG & Y. FERNSTEDT. 1976. Formation and properties of retinylphosphate galactose. J. Biol. Chem. **251:** 4986–4995.
11. OLSON, J.A. 1967. The metabolism of vitamin A. Pharmacol. Rev. **19:** 559–
12. THOMPSON, J.N., J.M. HOWELL & G.A.J. PITT. 1964. Vitamin A and reproduction in rats. Proc. Roy. Soc. London, Ser. B. **159:** 510–535.
13. DOWLING, J.E. & G. WALD. 1960. The biological function of vitamin A acid. Proc. Natl. Acad. Sci. USA **46:** 587–608.
14. MOORE, T. 1957. Vitamin A. 279. ELSEVIER. Amsterdam.
15. BHAT, P.V., L.M. DE LUCA, et al. 1979. Retinoid metabolism in spontaneously transformed mouse fibroblasts (BALB/c 3T12-3 cells): Enzymatic conversion of retinol to anhydroretinol. J. Lipid Res. **20:** 357–362.

CHARACTERIZATION OF RETINOIC ACID-INDUCED ALTERATIONS IN THE PROLIFERATION AND DIFFERENTIATION OF A MURINE AND A HUMAN MELANOMA CELL LINE IN CULTURE*

Reuben Lotan,† George Neumann, and Dafna Lotan†

Department of Developmental and Cell Biology
University of California
Irvine, California 92717

† *Department of Biophysics*
The Weizmann Institute of Science
Rehovot, Israel

INTRODUCTION

A few years ago we reported that retinoic acid and retinyl acetate are capable of inhibiting the proliferation of a considerable number of untransformed, transformed, and tumor cell lines in culture.[1] Similar results have been found by others in several additional cell lines.[2-13] Though they have not affected all of the cell lines tested, the ability of retinoids to inhibit the growth of a variety of cell types in different laboratories using a variety of assay procedures suggests that the phenomenon is a fairly general one.

We have been employing a cloned S91 mouse melanoma cell line that is very sensitive to retinoic acid[14] for studies on various biochemical changes induced by it and for evaluation of their relationship to growth inhibition. In this paper we describe recent results on the effects of retinoids on the S91 melanoma cells and, to present a more complete picture, include some of our relevant previous results. Since we have recently reviewed[15] the many important contributions from other laboratories, which inspired some of this work, this presentation will describe mainly our own results.

INHIBITION OF S91 MELANOMA CELL PROLIFERATION BY RETINOIC ACID

When S91 melanoma cells are grown in the presence of 10^{-5}M retinoic acid for several days, their growth is significantly inhibited (FIG. 1). Quantitative analysis of the inhibitory effect indicated that it is time-dependent and dose-dependent (FIG. 2). A reduction in the rate of cellular proliferation becomes apparent after a 2-day exposure to retinoic acid with the extent of reduction in growth rate being concentration-dependent. Thus, cells treated with 10^{-5}M retinoic acid doubled at about one-half of the rate of untreated cells, whereas cells cultured in the presence of 10^{-7}M or 10^{-9}M retinoic acid exhibited a smaller reduction in growth rates (FIG. 2).

Several experiments indicated that the inhibitory effect of retinoic acid, even at 10^{-5}M, is not due to cytotoxicity: (a) the plating efficiency of cells treated for several days is not lower than that of untreated cells; (b) there is no detectable re-

* Supported by grant RO1-CA-22823 from the National Cancer Institute, DHEW.

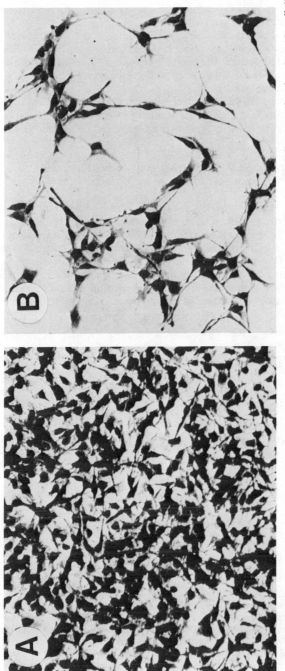

FIGURE 1. Photomicrographs of untreated (A) and retinoic acid-treated (B) S91 melanoma cell cultures. Cells were plated at 3×10^4 cells/35 mm dish in medium containing 0.1% ethanol (A) or 10^{-5}M retinoic acid (B). After 6 days the cells were fixed and stained with Diff-Quick. × 200.

lease of lysosomal enzymes; and (c) the growth-inhibited retinoic acid-treated cells resume the control rate of cell proliferation 2-3 days after the removal of retinoic acid from the growth medium.[14]

Recent studies using the human Hs939 melanoma cell lines have demonstrated that cellular proliferation is inhibited by retinoic acid in a fashion similar to that described above for the mouse melanoma. The human melanoma cells are, however, less sensitive to the growth-inhibitory effect of retinoic acid than the S91 melanoma cells.[10]

It is noteworthy that a reduction in cell proliferation rate by retinoic acid is not limited to malignant cells, since a similar effect was reported on several untransformed fibroblastic cells,[6,8] and on an intestinal epithelial cell line.[9]

Reduction in S91 Melanoma Colony Formation in Semi-Solid Medium by Retinoic Acid

Several retinoids have been shown to possess a remarkable ability to reduce the formation of tumor cell colonies in semi-solid medium.[5,11] It was intriguing to find out whether the S91 melanoma, which is sensitive to retinoic acid in liquid medium, would also be inhibited in semi-solid medium. In initial experiments it was established that the S91 melanoma cells are capable of forming colonies in medium containing 0.5% agarose with an efficiency of 30–40%. This anchorage-independent growth was markedly inhibited by retinoic acid in a concentration-dependent process. Thus, colony formation by cells plated in medium containing

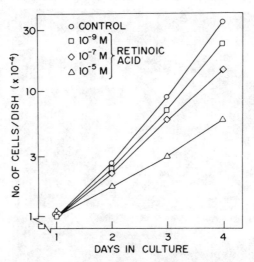

FIGURE 2. Growth curves of S91 melanoma cells in the absence or presence of various retinoic acid concentrations. Cells were seeded in 35 mm dishes in Dulbecco's modified Eagle's minimum essential medium (DMEM) supplemented with 10% fetal bovine serum and containing either 0.1% ethanol only (control) or the indicated retinoic acid concentrations. The cultures were refed on the second day and detached and counted on the indicated days. Each point represents the average of duplicate cultures that did not differ by >10%.

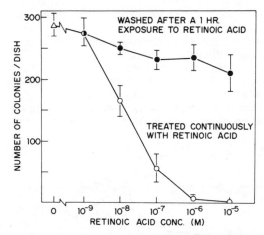

FIGURE 3. Reduction in S91 melanoma colony formation in semi-solid medium by retinoic acid. Cells were suspended at 10^5 cells/ml in 15 ml conical tissue culture tubes in 5 ml medium containing 10% serum and either 0.1% ethanol or the indicated retinoic acid concentrations. After a 1-hr incubation at 37°C, the cells were pelleted by centrifugation and one-half of the samples were resuspended and washed in 5 ml of medium containing serum. The cells were then resuspended at 10^3 cells/ml in medium containing 0.5% agarose and either 0.1% ethanol only (the washed cells) or the indicated retinoic acid concentrations, and 1 ml aliquots were seeded in 35 mm dishes in which 2 ml of 0.5% agarose in medium had been previously allowed to gel. The cultures were refed every 72 hr with 1 ml of fresh medium containing 0.1% (●) or the indicated retinoic acid concentrations (O). After 12 days the number of colonies consisting of at least 32 cells/colony was determined using a microscope at 40× magnification. Each point represents the average (vertical bars, S.E.) of two independent experiments, each performed in duplicates.

0.5% agarose and supplemented with 10^{-9}, 10^{-8}, 10^{-7}, 10^{-6} and 10^{-5}M retinoic acid was reduced by 10, 50, 73, 96 and 100%, respectively.

    Various cytotoxic drugs have been shown to decrease colony formation by different malignant cells after a 1-hr treatment preceding plating in semi-solid medium.[16,17] A recent report indicated that a 1-hr treatment of fresh human melanoma cells with several retinoids, followed by a wash, was sufficient to greatly diminish the ability of some of them to form colonies in agar.[11] This effect could be explained either by cytotoxic effect on the cells or by a rapidly initiated, noncytotoxic effect that does not require the continued presence of the retinoids. The latter possibility seemed at variance with our observations that in liquid medium growth inhibition by retinoic acid is reversible or with another report that the inhibition of colony formation by L929 and by HeLa cells in semi-solid medium is also reversible.[5] To determine whether the S91 melanoma cells behave similarly to the human melanomas, we treated S91 cells for 1 hr with various retinoic acid doses and then washed one-half of the samples to remove residual extracellular retinoic acid. The washed cells were then plated in the absence of retinoic acid, whereas the unwashed cells were plated in the presence of the appropriate retinoic acid concentrations in medium containing 0.5% agarose. The number of colonies in the washed and unwashed cultures was determined after a 12-day incubation, during which the cultures were refed every 3 days with 1 ml of fresh medium with or without retinoic acid. FIGURE 3 shows that whereas cells treated for 1 hr before plating and then continuously exposed to retinoic acid displayed a dose-dependent reduction in colony forming efficiency, cells that were washed after a 1-hr exposure to retinoic acid were only slightly affected at the higher retinoic acid concentrations. Thus, a 1-hr treatment is not sufficient to decrease the colony-forming capacity of S91 melanoma cells: it is the continuous presence of retinoic acid that causes a suppression of their anchorage-independent growth. Preliminary studies with the human Hs939 melanoma cells show that retinoic acid completely inhibits the formation of colonies (>8 cells/colony) in agarose-containing medium in the continued presence of 10^{-7}M retinoic acid.

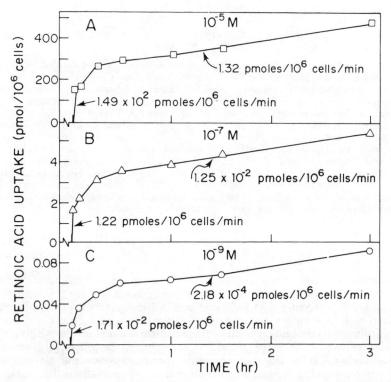

FIGURE 4. Kinetics of retinoic acid uptake by S91 melanoma cells. Cells were seeded in 35 mm dishes at 1.25×10^6 cells/dish in DMEM + 10% fetal bovine serum and incubated for 24 hr at 37°C in 95% air-5% CO_2. Triplicate cultures were then incubated as above with 1 ml of medium + serum containing [11, 12-^{3}H]retinoic acid at either 10^{-5}M, 10^{-7}M or 10^{-9}M (72, 9090, and 9090 cpm/pmol, respectively) for the designated times. At the end of incubation dishes were placed on ice, the medium was removed by aspiration, and the monolayers were washed 3 times, each with 2 ml of DMEM without serum. After detachment with 2 mM EDTA, the cells were pelleted by centrifugation and dissolved in 0.1% Triton x-100. The amount of radioactivity in the cells was measured by liquid scintillation spectrometry. Under these conditions the washing and the EDTA did not remove more than 25% of the cell associated radioactivity. The [^{3}H]retinoic acid was a generous gift of Dr. A. Liebman of Hoffmann-La Roche, Inc., Nutley, NJ.

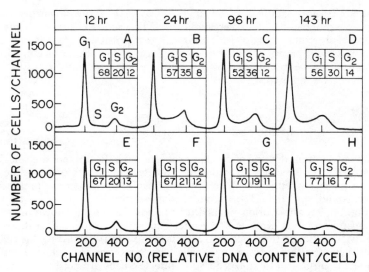

FIGURE 5. DNA distributions obtained by flow microfluorometric analysis of untreated (A-D) and retinoic acid-treated (E-H) S91 melanoma cells. Cells were seeded in 10 cm dishes in the absence or presence of 10^{-5}M retinoic acid at initial densities calculated such that at the designated times the cultures will reach 10^6 cells/dish (subconfluent density). At the indicated times cells were detached by trypsinization as described by Tobey *et al.*,[22] then fixed and stained with mithramycin according to the method of Crissman and Tobey.[23] Fixed and stained cells were stored at 4°C until all samples were harvested. The cells were then examined in a Los Alamos design microfluorometer.[24] The percentages of cells in the different phases of the cell cycle were computed from the DNA distribution curves. It should be noted that the total numbers of cells analyzed in control and treated cultures were different, since the flow of cells was stopped after the G_1 channel registered about 1350 cells.

RETINOIC ACID UPTAKE BY S91 MELANOMA CELLS

In analyzing the causes for the time dependence of retinoic acid-induced growth inhibition and the ineffectiveness of a short treatment in reducing colony formation in semi-solid medium, one must consider the rate of uptake of retinoic acid from the growth medium. We established a procedure to determine the amount of [³H]retinoic acid associated with the cells after incubation and washing and, subsequently, measured the uptake of [³H]retinoic acid at various extracellular concentrations after different incubation periods. The results shown in FIGURE 4 demonstrate that the cells take up retinoic acid rapidly during the first 15 min and much more slowly thereafter. The initial uptake rate is approximately 100 times faster than the subsequent rate resulting in the uptake within the first 15 min of nearly 60% of the amount associated with the cells at 3 hr. Assuming a cell volume of 1,100 μ^3 (see next section) and an even intracellular distribution, one can calculate that during a 3-hr incubation the cells accumulate retinoic acid to concentrations 37, 38 and 60 times higher than the extracellular concentrations 10^{-5}M, 10^{-7}M and 10^{-9}M, respectively. Both the fast and the slow uptake rates are dependent on retinoic acid concentration.

These preliminary experiments suggest that the uptake of retinoic acid is rapid, and therefore cannot itself explain the delay in the expression of growth inhibition by retinoic acid. Further studies will be carried out to elucidate the mechanism of retinoic acid uptake. Specifically, the possibilities that retinoic acid may be passively partitioned into the lipid phase of the cell surface and other membranes,[18] or be internalized by a specific, receptor-mediated transport system,[19-21] will be explored.

ALTERATIONS IN THE CELL CYCLE AND CELL SIZE INDUCED BY RETINOIC ACID IN S91 MELANOMA CELLS

The reduction in the rate of cellular proliferation indicates that the cell cycle is prolonged in retinoic acid-treated cells. To determine which phase of the cell cycle is affected by retinoic acid, cells were grown in the absence or presence of this compound, and their DNA content distributions were analyzed by flow microfluorometry after various incubation periods. The results shown in FIGURE 5 demonstrate that as early as 24 hr after exposure to retinoic acid there is a substantial decrease in the proportion of cells in the S and G_2 phases of the cell cycle with a concomitant increase in G_1 cells. The proportion of G_1 cells in retinoic acid-treated cultures did not exceed 80%; thus the cells are not blocked at this phase but rather the rate of their entry into S phase may be reduced. In CHO cells a block in G_1 phase was demonstrated after treatment with very high retinol con-

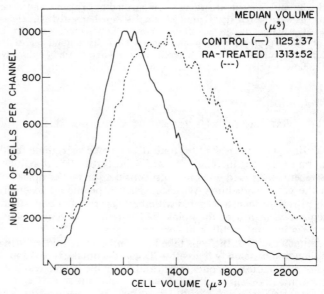

FIGURE 6. Size distribution curves of untreated and RA-treated S91 melanoma cells. Cells were cultured for 5 days in the absence (control) or presence of 10^{-5}M RA. The cells were then detached in 2 mM EDTA in PBS, washed in PBS and suspended in isotonic saline to give a single cell suspension of 2×10^5 cells/ml. The median cell volume was determined using a calibrated Coulter Counter Model Z, and the distribution curves were obtained using a Channelyzer.

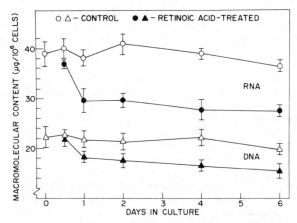

FIGURE 7. Reduction in cellular DNA and RNA content induced by retinoic acid in S91 melanoma cells. The cells were seeded in 10 cm dishes in the absence or presence of 10^{-5}M retinoic acid at initial densities selected so that cell numbers in all cultures will reach 6 × 10^6 cells/dish by the end of the desired periods of incubation. At the indicated times cells were detached in 2 mM EDTA, counted and aliquots containing 5 × 10^6 cells were used for extraction of DNA and RNA by the Schmidt-Tannhauser procedure[26] as modified by Hutchison and Munro.[27] RNA was measured by the orcinol method of Mejbaum[28] and DNA by the diphenylamine reaction as modified by Burton[29] using calf thymus DNA and yeast RNA as standards, respectively.

centrations $(1.2 \times 10^{-4}$M).[25] At such a concentration both retinol and retinoic acid are cytotoxic to the S91 melanoma cells.

The perturbation of the cell cycle in S91 melanoma cells could lead to an uncoupling of the relationship between cell volume increase and cell division due to continued synthesis of cellular constituents in cells that divide at a reduced rate. Measurements of the median cell volume in untreated and retinoic acid-treated cells using a Model Z Coulter counter gave values of 1125±37 μ^3 and 1313±52 μ^3, respectively. Further analysis of the size distribution of untreated and retinoic acid-treated cells revealed a shift of the entire treated population toward larger volumes (FIGURE 6). This increase in cell volume, though significant, is not large enough to be easily discerned by light microscopy.

REDUCTION IN NUCLEIC ACID CONTENT IN RETINOIC ACID-TREATED S91 MELANOMA CELLS

The lower proportion of S phase cells in retinoic acid-treated cultures compared with untreated controls indicated that their DNA content should also be reduced. Indeed, direct analysis of the amounts of cellular DNA by a colorimetric assay demonstrated a significant reduction in the DNA content of cells treated with retinoic acid for longer than 24 hr (FIGURE 7). Concurrent with this effect, a 25% decrease in the RNA content was also measured. In the same cells the amount of protein, determined by the method of Lowry *et al.*,[30] remained essentially unchanged after treatment with retinoic acid. The measured values were 272±21 and 266±17 μg protein/10^6 cells in untreated and in 5-day treated cells, respectively. Similar protein content was found in cells treated with retinoic acid for 2, 3 or 4 days. Thus, expressing the content of nucleic acid (FIGURE 7) or other cellular constituents on a per cell basis or per mg protein is basically the same.

REDUCTION IN THE UPTAKE AND INCORPORATION OF PRECURSORS OF NUCLEIC ACIDS AND PROTEINS BY RETINOIC ACID-TREATED CELLS

The reduced rate of cellular proliferation, the decrease in the proporation of cells in the S phase of the cell cycle, and the lower DNA content in retinoic acid-treated cells indicates that such cells do not enter DNA synthesis as frequently as untreated cells. These phenomena could be caused by retinoic acid-induced changes in the synthesis of various macromolecules.

Measurements of the incorporation of tritium-labeled thymidine, uridine and leucine into nucleic acids and proteins, respectively, demonstrated a progressive reduction of incorporation in treated cells (TABLE 1). Such an effect usually represents a decreased rate of macromolecular synthesis provided that the uptake of the labeled precursor into the cells is not altered by the treatment. This was not, however, the case with S91 melanoma cells; analysis of the acid-soluble material revealed that retinoic acid caused a progressive reduction in the amount of radioactivity found in this fraction (TABLE 1). The extent of reduction in acid-soluble radioactivity followed the same pattern as the reduction in the incorporation of radioactivity into the macromolecules. Since the total cell-associated radioactivity (acid-soluble and acid-insoluble) decreased progressively in retinoic acid-treated cells while remaining constant in the control cells, it follows that the up-

TABLE 1

REDUCED UPTAKE AND INCORPORATION OF TRITIUM-LABELED THYMIDINE, URIDINE AND LEUCINE IN RETINOIC ACID-TREATED S91 MELANOMA CELLS*

Time in Culture (hr)	Radioactivity Incorporated into Macromolecules (treated/control)			Acid Soluble Radioactivity (treated/control) after Labeling with		
	DNA	RNA	Protein	[³H] Thymidine	[³H] Uridine	[³H] Leucine
12	0.64	0.53	0.56	0.69	0.49	0.46
24	0.45	0.25	0.68	0.38	0.31	0.62
48	0.30	0.13	0.47	0.27	0.17	0.55
96	0.17	0.09	0.39	0.15	0.12	0.41

* Cells were plated in 10-cm dishes at initial densities selected so that at the end of the indicated times cells in untreated and in retinoic acid (10^{-5}M)-treated cultures reached 4–5 $\times$ 10^6 cells/dish. One hour before the termination of each incubation, duplicate cultures were labeled with the radioactive precursors at 1 μCi/ml (added directly to the growth medium). The cells were then quickly washed on ice, detached, and counted. Aliquots containing identical cell numbers (usually 4×10^6 cells) were extracted with 0.5 N perchloric acid. After centrifugation (11,000 $\times$ g, 5 min, 4°), the supernatant was removed and used for measurement of acid-soluble radioactivity. The pellet was further extracted to isolate nucleic acids and protein (as described in the caption to FIG. 7), and the radioactivity incorporated into each of these macromolecules was measured. The values are the ratio of the measurements in retinoic acid-treated over untreated controls. The differences between duplicates were <10%.

take of the precursors was inhibited by retinoic acid. Thus, pulse-labeling is not a reliable method for evaluating the rate of macromolecular synthesis in retinoic acid-treated cells. The uptake of [³H]thymidine by other cells was reported to decrease[25] or increase[31,32] after treatment with retinoids. The mechanism by which retinoic acid modifies uptake remains to be elucidated. A likely possibility is that retinoids may change membrane fluidity[33] or the structure of certain cell surface glycoproteins (see below) in a way that may lead to an altered uptake of certain low molecular weight precursors.

STIMULATION OF MELANOGENESIS IN MOUSE S91 AND HUMAN Hs939 MELANOMA CELLS

In many of the above experiments we seeded cells intended for treatment with retinoic acid at higher initial numbers than control cells in order to obtain similar final cell densities in untreated and treated cultures despite the reduced growth rate of the latter. Under conditions that allowed retinoic acid-treated cells to reach high cell densities the production of melanin was considerably higher than in control cultures at the same densities. This effect was not due to the

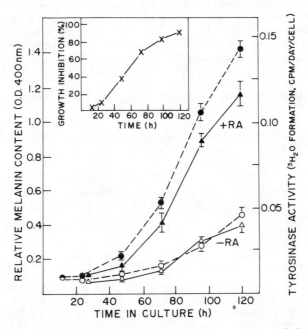

FIGURE 8. Time-course of melanogenesis stimulation by retinoic acid. S91 melanoma cells were cultured in 10 cm dishes in the absence or presence of 10^{-5}M retinoic acid at initial cell densities selected so that all cultures will contain 6–8 × 10^6 cells/dish by the end of the desired incubation periods. Twenty-four hours before the end of each treatment each culture received 0.5 μCi/ml L-[3′, 5′-³H]tyrosine and at the end of this incubation the medium was removed and its ³H₂O content determined by the method of Pomerantz.[36] The cells were detached, counted and 5 × 10^6 aliquots were used for determination of melanin by the method of Whittaker.[37]

higher initial density, since untreated cells produced more melanin when allow-ed to reach a certain density from a lower initial cell number than from a higher cell number. A similar enhancement of melanin production was observed in Hs939 human melanoma cells cultured for longer than 4 days in the presence of 10^{-6}M retinoic acid. Since the human cells are less sensitive to retinoic acid than the S91 cells, there was no need to seed them at a higher initial density than con-trol cells in order to observe stimulation of melanogenesis.

Quantitative analysis of the amounts of melanin produced, and the activity of tyrosinase (the only enzyme involved in melanin biosynthesis[34]) in cells exposed to retinoic acid for various periods, revealed a progressive increase in both (FIGURE 8). A similar, nearly linear relationship between the duration of treat-ment and the synthesis of melanin was found in cultures of human Hs939 cells.[35] In both cell lines stimulation of melanogenesis by retinoic acid was dose-dependent.

Evaluation of the abilities of several retinoids to stimulate melanogenesis and inhibit the proliferation of the S91 and Hs939 melanoma cells indicated that, in addition to retinoic acid, other retinoids are also active (TABLE 2). The retinoids tested differed in their potencies in affecting each of the cell lines; however a positive correlation was found between their ability to inhibit cell proliferation and to stimulate melanogenesis. An exception is retinyl palmitate, which in-hibited growth significantly but failed to enhance melanogenesis.

The stimulation of melanogenesis by retinoic acid was not preceded by an elevation in the intracellular levels of cyclic AMP in either melanoma line. In this respect the effect of retinoic acid differs from that of α-melanocyte-stimulating hormone on S91 melanoma cells.[34]

EFFECTS OF VARIOUS COMPOUNDS ON THE PROLIFERATION OF S91 MELANOMA CELLS

Several studies in various laboratories, using different cell systems or *in vivo*

TABLE 2

EFFECTS OF VARIOUS RETINOIDS ON GROWTH AND MELANOGENESIS IN MOUSE S91 AND HUMAN Hs939 MELANOMA CELLS*

Retinoid[†]	Growth Inhibition (%)		Melanogenesis Stimulation[‡] (T/C)	
	S91	Hs939	S91	Hs939
β-all-*trans*-retinoic acid	90 ± 2	62 ± 5	3.2 ± 0.2	4.5 ± 0.2
13-*cis*-retinoic acid	90 ± 2	61 ± 6	3.3 ± 0.3	4.6 ± 0.3
The TMMP analog of retinoic acid	78 ± 4	34 ± 4	1.8 ± 0.2	1.8 ± 0.2
The phenyl analog of retinoic acid	40 ± 3	<10	2.2 ± 0.2	1.0 ± 0.1
The pyridyl analog of retinoic acid	<10	<10	1.0 ± 0.1	1.0 ± 0.1
Retinyl acetate	70 ± 5	47 ± 3	1.3 ± 0.1	2.9 ± 0.3
Retinyl palmitate	30 ± 2	14 ± 3	1.0 ± 0.1	1.0 ± 0.1

* S91 and Hs939 cells were cultured in 10-cm dishes such that they reached confluence after 6 and 8 days, respectively, in the absence or presence of retinoic acid (10^{-5}M and 10^{-6}M, respectively).

† For structures see FIG. 11.

‡ Values are the ratios of the relative melanin content in treated and control cultures.

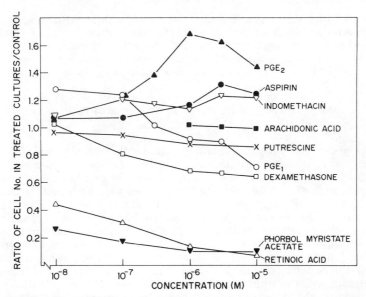

FIGURE 9. Effects of various compounds on the proliferation of S91 melanoma cells. Cells were seeded in 10 cm diameter dishes at 10^5 cells/dish in the absence and in the presence of the indicated compounds at concentrations in the range 10^{-8}M to 10^{-5}M. The cultures were refed on day 3, and the cells were detached and counted on day 6. Cell viabilities at the end of treatment with the highest dose was >85%.

assays, demonstrated an influence of retinoids on prostaglandin biosynthesis,[38-40] ornithine decarboxylase activity, [25,41,42] and tumor promotion.[43] Further, prostaglandins have been shown to inhibit the growth of several tumor cell lines including a mouse melanoma cell line, [44,45] and polyamines may be involved in growth regulation of various cells.[46] Therefore, considering the possibility that changes in their biosynthesis might mediate growth inhibition of S91 melanoma cells by retinoic acid, we tested the effects of prostaglandins themselves, compounds that either stimulate[47] (e.g., arachidonic acid) or inhibit[48] (e.g., aspirin, indomethacine and dexamethasone) prostaglandin synthesis, and polyamines[49] on the proliferation of the S91 melanoma cells. FIGURE 9 shows that none of these compounds alone caused a substantial enough inhibition of cell proliferation to suggest that any of them mediates the inhibitory effect of retinoic acid. Dexamethasone had a significant but small effect compared to retinoic acid, whereas phorbol myristate acetate was somewhat more effective than retinoic acid (FIGURE 9). Additional experiments (not shown) using 10^{-7}M retinoic acid in combination with the various compounds (with the exception of the tumor promoter), at the same or higher concentrations (up to 10^{-5}M), showed neither antagonistic nor synergystic effects of any of the compounds on the ability of retinoic acid to inhibit cell proliferation. The concurrent treatment of the S91 melanoma cells with retinoic and phorbol myristate acetate caused a greater growth inhibition than each of them alone and completely suppressed melanin production.[50]

Although the addition of putrescine together with retinoic acid to the melanoma cells failed to prevent growth inhibition, we tested the effect of retinoic acid on ornithine decarboxylase activity in these cells. Untreated cells,

cells treated for 8 hr and cells treated for 5 days with 10^{-5}M retinoic acid had similar ornithine decarboxylase activities of 1,100, 1,050 and 1,200 pmoles $^{14}CO_2$ released per hr per mg protein from L-[^{14}C]ornithine,[51] respectively.

These experiments failed to implicate any of the above compounds in mediating the effect of retinoic acid on S91 melanoma growth.

CHARACTERIZATION OF THE RETINOIC ACID-BINDING PROTEIN OF S91 MELANOMA CELLS

Specific retinol-binding and retinoic acid-binding proteins found in many normal and malignant tissues and cells have been suggested to mediate various effects of retinoids on growth and differentiation of certain cells.[8, 52-55] It was therefore interesting to find out whether S91 melanoma cells contain such proteins. Recent studies in collaboration with David Ong and Frank Chytil demonstrated the presence of both a retinol-binding protein and a retinoic acid-binding protein in the S91 melanoma cells.[56] The retinoic acid-binding protein of S91 cells was further characterized in our laboratory. Similar to binding proteins described in other normal and malignant cells,[15,52,56] the S91 melanoma binding protein can be detected in the 2S region of sucrose gradients after incubation of cell extracts with [^{3}H] retinoic acid and centrifugation (FIG. 10A). Virtually all of the binding in the 2S region was abolished by pretreatment of cell extracts with pronase, and nearly 50% of the binding was abolished by pretreatment with 1 mM p-chloromercuribenzene sulfonic acid (PCMBS) (FIG. 10A). These results show that retinoic acid is binding to a 2S protein and that the binding depends, at least in part, on thiol groups as shown previously in other cells.[58] About one-half of the radioactivity found in the 2S region was competed off in the presence of a 100-fold excess of unlabeled retinoic acid (FIG. 10A), whereas neither retinol, retinal nor axerophthene were able to compete (FIG. 10B, C). Of several retinoids possessing a free -COOH group at carbon 15, only the phenyl analog of retinoic acid failed to bind to the retinoic acid-binding protein (FIG. 10C).

Some retinoids with a modified ring (e.g., 5,6-epoxy analog of β-retinoic acid) or side chain (e.g., 10-fluoro analog of β-retinoic acid) exhibited a lower potency that β-all-trans-retinoic acid, whereas a retinamide was ineffective (FIG. 10B,C).

The Hs939 human melanoma cells were also found to contain a retinoic acid-binding protein.[15] The amount of this protein per cell was much lower than in the S91 melanoma cells, and no further characterization was therefore attempted.

RELATIONSHIPS AMONG RETINOID STRUCTURE, INHIBITION OF S91 MELANOMA GROWTH, AND BINDING TO THE RETINOIC ACID-BINDING PROTEIN

The ability of 27 different retinoids (FIG. 11) to inhibit the proliferation of S91 melanoma cells was evaluated after exposing the cells for 6 days to various retinoid concentrations in the range 10^{-9} to 10^{-5}M. TABLE 3 presents the doses required for 50% growth inhibition (IC$_{50}$) as well as the extent of inhibition by 10^{-5}M concentrations of the different retinoids. The compounds are grouped according to their structure and rank-ordered according to their potency. The most potent inhibitors possess a free -COOH group at C-15, although their ring structures vary, and a few (e.g., 7,8-dehydro analog of retinoic acid) have a modified side chain. The phenyl and pyridyl analogs exhibited little or no activity in spite of their possession of a free terminal carboxylic group, suggesting that these ring

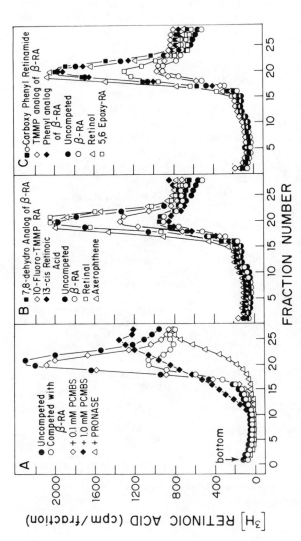

FIGURE 10. Characterization of the retinoic acid-binding protein in S91 melanoma. Cells, grown to confluence on 15 cm tissue culture dishes in DMEM + 10% fetal bovine serum, were washed 4 times with DPBS, suspended in 50 mM Tris-HCl buffer, pH 7.2, at 10^8 cells/ml, and homogenized with 75 strokes of a Dounce homogenizer on ice. Further extraction, including acid treatment, was performed as described by Ong *et al.*[57] Cell extracts containing 0.8 mg protein in 0.2 ml of Tris buffer were incubated for 4 hr on ice with 0.1 μM [11, 12-^{3}H]retinoic acid (10 Ci/mmole) added in 5 μl of isopropanol. The presence of a 2S binding protein was detected in fractions collected after high speed centrifugation of the charcoal-treated incubation mixtures on 5–20% sucrose gradients. (A) Effect of a protease and a thiol-blocking reagent on binding. Aliquots of cell extracts (0.2 ml) were incubated with either 1 mg pronase P/ml (Protease Type VI. Sigma Chemical Co., St. Louis, Mo) for 2 hr at 25° C or with *p*-chloromer-curibenzene sulfonate (PCMBS) at 0.1 mM or 1.0 mM for 1 hr at 4° C. All pretreated samples were then incubated with labeled ligand as described above. Pre-incubation conditions had no effect on 2S binding and are represented by the uncompeted density-gradient profile. A typical profile from an incubation with a 100-fold excess of unlabeled β-all-*trans*-retinoic acid has been superimposed for comparison. (B) an (C) Analog competitions were performed with a 100-fold excess of the appropriate unlabeled competitor added in 5 μl of either isopropanol or DMSO. Each profile represents the mean of 2 or more experiments.

modifications are detrimental to activity. With the exception of the latter two analogs, which also fail to bind to the retinoic acid-binding protein, all the retinoids possessing a free terminal -COOH group both inhibited cell growth and competed with [³H]retinoic acid for binding to the retinoic acid-binding protein (TABLE 3). These results suggest that the retinoic acid-binding protein may play some role in retinoid-induced growth inhibition. Other retinoids with a derivatized carboxyl group, such as amides or with a different terminal group such as

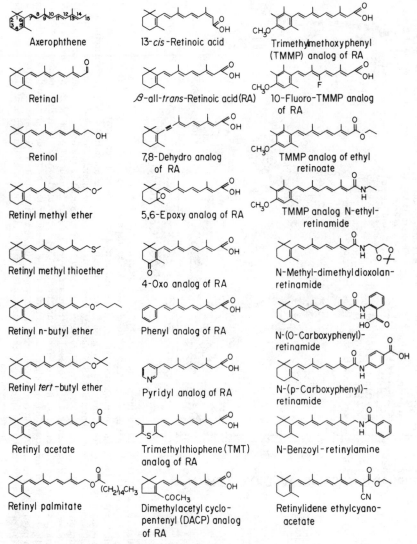

FIGURE 11. Structures and trivial names of retinoids used in this study. The retinoids were the generous gifts of Drs. Beverly Pawson of Hoffmann-La Roche, Inc. (Nutley, NJ) and Fritz Frickel of BASF Aktiengesellschaft (Ludwigshafen, Fed. Rep. of Germany).

TABLE 3

INTERACTIONS OF RETINOIDS WITH S91 MELANOMA CELLS: INHIBITION OF
CELL PROLIFERATION AND BINDING TO CELLULAR RETINOIC ACID-BINDING PROTEIN

Retinoid	IC_{50}* (μM)	% Inhibition of Growth by 10 μM Retinoid[†]	Competition for Binding to CRABP[‡]
β-retinoic acid	0.005	90	+
13-*cis*-retinoic acid	0.005	89	+
7, 8-dehydro analog of retinoic acid	0.016	88	+
4-oxo analog of retinoic acid	0.026	82	+
DACP analog of retinoic acid	0.040	77	+
TMT analog of retinoic acid	0.046	66	+
5, 6-epoxy analog of retinoic acid	0.065	88	+
TMMP analog of retinoic acid	0.31	84	+
10-fluoro-TMMP analog of retinoic acid	2.3	77	+
Phenyl analog of retinoic acid	>10	37	−
Pyridyl analog of retinoic acid	>10	<10	−
N-(O-carboxyphenyl)-retinamide	0.18	98[§]	−
TMMP analog of N-ethyl-retinamide	1.7	82	−
N-(p-carboxyphenyl)-retinamide	2.2	79	NT
N-methyl-dimethyl dioxolan-retinamide	3.5	76	−
TMMP analog of ethyl retinoate	0.75	80	NT
Retinal	0.70	54[§]	−
Retinol	0.75	70	−
Axerophthene	8.0	52	−
Retinyl acetate	0.42	76	NT
Retinyl palmitate	>10	30	NT
Retinyl methyl ether	10.0	48	NT
Retinyl *tert*-butyl ether	>10	39	NT
Retinyl methyl thioether	>10	37	NT
Retinyl *n*-butyl ether	>10	37	NT
N-benzoyl-retinylamine	8.0	58	NT
Retinylidene ethylcyanoacetate	>10	34	NT

* IC_{50}, retinoid concentration that inhibits cell proliferation by approximately 50% after a 6-day treatment. The values were determined graphically from dose-response curves.

† Cells were cultured in the presence of 10 μM of the various retinoids for 6 days and then harvested and counted. Percent of growth inhibition was determined as described earlier.[1] The values are the average of two independent experiments, each performed in duplicate. The differences between the duplicates and between the values obtained in the two independent experiments were less than 10%.

‡ + and − represent the ability and inability, respectively, of a retinoid to inhibit the binding of [³H]retinoic acid to S91 melanoma cell extract.

§ These values were obtained at 10^{-6}M since these retinoids were cytotoxic at 10^{-5}M. NT, not tested.

retinol, retinal and axerophthene, exhibited varying degrees of growth inhibitory activity but failed to bind to the retinoic acid-binding protein (FIG. 10, TABLE 3). Whereas the amides can be enzymatically converted to the acid in the cells and then interact with the retinoic acid-binding protein, the other retinoids may be converted to retinol and bind to the retinol-binding protein also present in the S91 melanoma cells.[56] Alternatively, the alcohol or aldehyde groups can be oxidized to the acid and bind to the retinoic acid-binding protein.

MODULATION OF S91 MELANOMA GLYCOPROTEIN GLYCOSYLATION BY RETINOIC ACID

The ability of retinol and retinoic acid to influence glycosyl transfer reactions by acting as glycosyl donors within cellular membranes has been demonstrated in several systems.[6,13,15,59-61] It was of interest, therefore, to investigate whether a similar effect can be detected in the S91 melanoma cells. Preliminary experiments performed recently suggest that there are specific changes in the incorporation of [3H]glucosamine into certain glycoproteins. FIGURE 12 presents densitometric scans of gels on which [3H]glucosamine-labeled cellular glycoproteins have been separated by electrophoresis. Several changes are easily observed

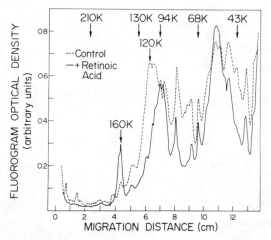

FIGURE 12. Retinoic acid-induced alterations in the incorporation of [3H]glucosamine into specific S91 melanoma glycoproteins. Cells were cultured for 4 days in the absence or presence of 10^{-5}M retinoic acid, then for an additional 2 days in fresh medium (without or with retinoic acid) containing 10 μCi/ml of [6-3H]glucosamine (26 Ci/mmol). The cells were then washed, solubilized in a solution containing 0.25% Nonidet P40 (NP40) and after pelleting the nuclei by centrifugation, the NP40 supernatant was boiled in sodium dodecylsulfate (SDS)-containing electrophoresis sample buffer and subjected to SDS-polyacrylamide slab gel electrophoresis according to Maizel.[62] After electrophoresis, fixation and staining, the gels were destained, impregnated with EN 3HANCE (New England Nuclear), dried onto a filter paper and pressed against an x-ray film. The tritium-labeled cell components were detectd by fluorography.[63] The figure shows the densitometric tracing of the various labeled components detected after development of the film. Migration in the gels was from left (−) to right (+). Numbers on top indicate the migration of the following standard proteins: ovalbumin (43K); bovine serum albumin (68K); phosphorylase B (94K); β-galactosidase (130K), and myosin (210K).

when a comparison is made between control and retinoic acid-treated cell glycoprotein patterns. Prominent among these is the increased incorporation of [^{3}H]glucosamine into a 160K glycoprotein and a marked reduction in the incorporation into a 120K glycoprotein. Other quantitative differences in glycoproteins of lower molecular weight are also apparent. It is noteworthy that labeling cell surface tyrosyl and histidyl by lactoperoxidase-catalyzed ^{125}I-iodination also showed an increased labeling of a 160K component (data not shown). This may indicate that the 160K glycoprotein is a cell surface component.

INHIBITORY EFFECTS OF RETINOIC ACID ON THE DEVELOPMENT AND GROWTH OF S91 MELANOMA CELLS *IN VIVO*

The finding that retinoic acid is capable of inhibiting the proliferation of S91 melanoma cells and of reducing their ability to form colonies in semi-solid medium raised the important question concerning the ability of retinoic acid to inhibit the growth of S91 melanoma tumors in mice. TABLE 4 shows that the S91 clone 2 cells grow in the syngeneic CDF1 mice and that the mean tumor weight after 16 days is proportional to the amount of tumor cells inoculated on day 1. Intraperitoneal administration of retinoic acid to such mice after subcutaneous tumor cell inoculation had no significant inhibitory effect on either the incidence or the growth of tumors from a 10^6 cell initial inoculum. However, a significant inhibition of tumor growth was observed in mice inoculated with 10^5 and 10^4 cells, respectively. In mice inoculated with 10^4 cells there was also a substantial decrease in tumor incidence: only 50% of the mice developed tumors. Whereas there seems to be a difference in the efficacy of retinoic acid doses of 50 and 100 μg/mouse, there is a significantly greater effect by 300 μg/mouse.

In previous experiments the growth of S91 melanoma cells was inhibited by retinyl palmitate in allogeneic (BALB/c)[64] but not in syngeneic (CDF1)[65] mice. In contrast to these results we found inhibition in both BALB/c (not shown) and

TABLE 4

INHIBITORY EFFECTS OF RETINOIC ACID ON THE SUBCUTANEOUS GROWTH OF
S91 MELANOMA CELLS IN CDF1 (BALB/c × DBA/2) MICE*

Retinoic Acid (μg/mouse)	Mean Tumor Weight ± SD 16 Days after Transplantation (No. of mice with tumor/total)		
	10^4 cells	10^5 cells	10^6 cells
None (oil)	153 ± 166 (9/9)	316 ± 174 (9/9)	897 ± 296 (9/9)
50	32 ± 28 (4/10)	168 ± 102 (8/9)	1,024 ± 697 (9/9)
100	33 ± 28 (6/9)	194 ± 145 (9/9)	661 ± 357 (10/10)
300	5 ± 8 (5/9)	84 ± 74 (8/9)	718 ± 365 (9/9)

* Mice (21 ± 1.5 gr, 3 weeks old females, Jackson Laboratories, Bar Harbor, ME) were inoculated subcutaneously in the inguinal region with the indicated numbers of S91 clone C2 cells. Two days later the mice received intraperitoneally 0.1 ml of either corn oil only or 50, 100 or 300 μg of retinoic acid suspended in corn oil. Retinoic acid injections were repeated daily for the first 6 days and every other day thereafter. Sixteen days after tumor transplantation the mice were weighed, sacrificed and the tumors excised, freed from adjacent tissue, and weighed. There was no significant reduction in body weight in any of the treated mice.

CDF1 mice (TABLE 4). Since retinyl palmitate is as potent as retinoic acid in stimulating host-antitumor immune response,[66] the discrepancy between our results and the previous studies with retinyl palmitate[65] may be due to the much higher sensitivity of the S91 melanoma cells to the direct growth inhibitory effect of retinoic acid (IC_{50} = 0.005 μM) as compared with retinyl palmitate (IC_{50}>10 μM).

SUMMARY

We employ the murine S91 and the human Hs939 melanoma cell lines for the characterization of various biochemical changes induced by retinoids. Retinoic acid (RA) causes a time-dependent, and reversible reduction in cell proliferation rate in liquid medium and inhibits growth in agar. The proportion of cells in the G_1 phase of the cell cycle increases in RA-treated cells, and the uptake of TdR, UdR and Leu decreases. The growth inhibitory effect of RA is apparently not mediated via labilization of lysosomes, increase in cAMP or changes in the synthesis of prostaglandins or polyamines. Exposure to RA stimulates tyrosinase activity and increases melanin content severalfold over the levels found in untreated cells. Various retinoids exhibit the activities of RA; however, their potencies vary depending on their structure. Those possessing a free -COOH at C-15 are usually more effective than those with a different group or with a derivatized carboxyl. A positive correlation exists between the ability of retinoids with a free -COOH in C-15 to inhibit growth and to bind to an RA-binding protein found in the S91 melanoma cells. Future studies will explore recently discovered changes in the glycosylation of cell surface components and their relationship to the phenomena described here.

ACKNOWLEDGMENTS

We thank Professor Garth L. Nicolson for support encouragement and laboratory facilities and Adele Brodginski for assistance in manuscript preparation.

REFERENCES

1. LOTAN, R. & G.L. NICOLSON. 1977. J. Natl. Cancer Inst. 59: 1717–1722.
2. KOCHHAR, D.M., J.T. DINGLE & J.A. LUCY. 1968. Exp. Cell Res. 52: 591–601.
3. THOMAS, D.B. & C.A. PASTERNAK. 1969. Biochem. J. 111: 407–412.
4. DION, L.D., J.E. BLALOCK & G.E. GIFFORD. 1977. J. Natl. Cancer Inst. 58: 795–801.
5. DION, L.D., J.E. BLALOCK & G.E. GIFFORD. 1978. Exp. Cell Res. 117: 15–22.
6. PATT, L.M., K. ITAYA & S.I. HAKOMORI. 1978. Nature 273: 379–381.
7. ADAMO, S., L.M. DE LUCA, I. AKALOVSKY & P.V. BHAT. 1979. J. Natl. Cancer Inst. 62: 1473–1478.
8. JETTEN, A.M., M.E.R. JETTEN, S.S. SHAPIRO, & J.P. POON. 1979. Exp. Cell Res. 119: 289–299.
9. SHAPIRO, S.S. & J.P. POON. 1979. Exp. Cell Res. 119: 349–357.
10. LOTAN, R. 1979. Cancer Res. 39: 1014–1019.
11. MEYSKENS, F.L. & S.E. SALMON. 1979. Cancer Res. 39: 4055–4057.
12. LOTAN, R. & G.L. NICOLSON. 1979. Cancer Res. 39: 4767–4771.
13. CLARK, J.N. & A.C. MARCHOK. 1979. J. Cell Biol. 83: CD131 (abstr.).

14. LOTAN, R., G. GIOTTA, E. NORK & G.L. NICOLSON. 1978. J. Natl. Cancer Inst. **60:** 1035-1041.
15. LOTAN, R. 1980. Biochem. Biophys. Acta **605:** 33-91.
16. SALMON, S.E., A.W. HAMBURGER, B. SOEHNLEN, B.G.M. DURIE, D.S. ALBERTO & T.E. MOON. 1978. New Engl. J. Med. **298:** 1321-1327.
17. SALMON, S. 1980. *In* Human Tumor Cloning *In vitro.* S. Salmon, Ed. Alan R. Liss. New York. In press.
18. ROELS, O.A., O.R. ANDERSON, N.S.T. LUI, D.O. SHAH & M.E. TROUT. 1969. Am. J. Clin. Nutr. **22:** 1020-1032.
19. HELLER, J. 1975. J. Biol. Chem. **250:** 3613-3619.
20. RASK, L. & P.A. PETERSON. 1976. J. Biol. Chem. **251:** 6360-6366.
21. MARAINI, G., S. OTTONELLO, F. GOZZOLI & A. MERLI. 1977. Nature **265:** 68-69.
22. TOBEY, R.A., H.A. CRISSMAN & P.M. KRAEMER. 1972. J. Cell Biol. **54:** 638-645.
23. CRISSMAN, H.A. & R.A. TOBEY. 1974. Science **184:** 1247-1298.
24. VAN DILLA, M.A. T.T. TRUJILLO, P.F. MULLANEY & J.R. COULTER. 1969. Science **163:** 1213-1214.
25. HADDOX, M.K., K.F.F. SCOTT & D.H. RUSSELL. 1979. Cancer Res. **39:** 4930-4938.
26. SCHMIDT, G. & S.J. THANNHAUSER. 1945. J. Biol. Chem. **161:** 83-89.
27. HUTCHISON, W.C. & H.N. MUNRO. 1961. Analyst **86:** 768-813.
28. MEJBAUM, W. 1939. Hoppe-Seyler's Ztschr. fur Physiol. Chem. **258:** 117-120.
29. BURTON, K. 1956. Biochem. J. 62: 315-323.
30. LOWRY, O.H., N.U. ROSEBROUGH, A.L. FARR & R. J. RANDALL. 1951. J. Biol. Chem. **193:** 265-275.
31. YUSPA, S.H., K. ELGJO, M.A. MORSE & F.J. WIEBEL. 1977. Chem. Biol. Interactions **16:** 251-264.
32. FOSTER, R.C., M.K. FELDMAN & D.L. WONG. 1977. In Vitro **13:** 204-205 (abstr.).
33. MEEKS, R.G. & R.F. CHEN. 1979. Fed. Proc. **38:** 540 (abstr.)
34. PAWELEK, J.M. 1976. J. Invest. Dermatol. **66:** 201-209.
35. LOTAN, R. & D. LOTAN. 1980. Cancer Res. **40:** 3345-3350.
36. POMERANTZ, S. H. 1968. J. Biol. Chem. **241:** 161-168.
37. WHITTAKER, J.R. 1963. Develop. Biol. **8:** 99-127.
38. ZIBOH, V.A., B. PRICE & J. FULTON. 1975. J. Invest. Dermatol. **65:** 370-374.
39. HARRISON, S.D., E.J. HIXON, J.A. BURDESHAW & E.P. DENINE. 1977. Nature **269:** 511-512.
40. LEVINE, L. & K. OHUCHI. 1978. Nature **276:** 274-275.
41. VERMA, A.K. & R.K. BOUTWELL. 1977. Center Res. **37:** 2196-2201.
42. KENSLER, T.W. & G.C. MUELLER. 1978. Cancer Res. **38:** 771-775.
43. VERMA, A.K., B.G. SHAPAS, H.M. RICE & R.K. BOUTWELL. 1979. Cancer Res. **39:** 419-425.
44. THOMAS, D.R., G.W. PHILPOTT & B.M. JAFFE. 1974. Exp. Cell Res. **84:** 40-46.
45. SANTORO, M.G., G.W. PHILPOTT & B.M. JAFFE 1977. Cancer Res. **37:** 3774-3779.
46. JANNE, J., H. POSO & A. RAINA. 1978. Biochim. Biophys. Acta **473:** 241-293.
47. HONG, S.C.L., R.P. CYNKIN & L. LEVINE. 1976. J. Biol. Chem. **251:** 776-780.
48. FLOWER, R.J. 1974. Pharmacol. Rev. **26:** 33-67.
49. RUPNIAK, H.T. & D. PAUL. 1978. J. Cell Physiol. **94:** 161-170.
50. LOTAN, R. 1978. J. Cell Biol. **79:** CD144 (abstr.).
51. CLARK. J.L. & J.L. FULLER. 1975. Biochemistry **14:** 4403-4409.
52. CHYTIL, F. & D.E. ONG. 1978. Vitam. Horm. **36:** 1-32.
53. WIGGERT, B., P. RUSSELL, M. LEWIS & G. CHADER. 1977. Biochem. Biophys. Res. Commun. **79:** 218-225.
54. JETTEN, A.M. & M.E.R. JETTEN. 1979. Nature **278:** 180-182.
55. LOTAN, R., G. NEUMANN & D. LOTAN. 1980. Cancer Res. **40:** 1097-1102.
56. LOTAN, R., D.E. ONG & F. CHYTIL. 1980. J. Natl. Cancer Inst. **64:** 1259-1262.
57. ONG, D.E., C. MARKERT & J.F. CHUI. 1978. Cancer Res. **38:** 4422-4426.
58. SANI, B.P. & C.K. BANERJEE. 1978. Biochem. J. **173:** 643-649.
59. DE LUCA, L.M. 1978. *In* Handbook of Lipid Research. H.F. DeLuca, Ed. Vol. **2:** 1-67. Plenum Publishing Corp. New York.

60. DE LUCA, L.M. 1977. Vitam. Horm. **35:** 1-57.
61. WOLF, G. 1977. Nutr. Rev. **35:** 97-99.
62. MAIZEL, J. 1975. *In* Methods in Virology. K. Marmorosh & A. Koprowski, Eds. Vol. **5:** 179-245. Academic Press. New York.
63. BONNER, W.M. & R.A. LASKEY. 1974. Eur. J. Biochem. **46:** 83-88.
64. FELIX, E.L., B. LOYD & M.H. COHEN. 1975. Science **189:** 886-887.
65. FELIX, E.L., M.H. COHEN & B.C. LOYD. 1976. J. Surg. Res. **21:** 307-312.
66. LOTAN, R. & G. DENNERT. 1979. Cancer Res. **39:** 55-58.

RETINOL–BINDING PROTEIN METABOLISM IN LIVER CELLS *IN VIVO* AND *IN VITRO**

John Edgar Smith, Carmia Borek, and DeWitt S. Goodman

Departments of Medicine, Radiology, and Pathology
Columbia University College of Physicians and Surgeons
New York, New York 10032

The plasma transport of vitamin A, from the liver stores of vitamin A to peripheral vitamin A-requiring tissues, is a highly regulated process. Vitamin A is transported in plasma mainly as retinol bound to a specific transport protein, retinol-binding protein (RBP) (see references 1 and 2 for recent reviews). RBP has been purified from the plasma of several species; however, most structural and chemical studies have been done with human RBP,[3] whereas many of the metabolic studies have been done with rat RBP.[4] In all mammalian species studied to date RBP has been found to be a relatively small protein with a molecular weight of about 20,000 and with a single binding site for one molecule of retinol. In plasma, RBP circulates as a protein-protein complex with prealbumin in a 1:1 molar ratio. The RBP-prealbumin complex plays an important role in sparing RBP from glomerular filtration and renal catabolism.[1,2,5]

RBP is synthesized in the liver and is secreted into the plasma mainly as holo-RBP, that is, with bound retinol.[6,7] This is the form in which retinol is normally delivered from the liver to the extrahepatic sites of action of the vitamin. Information currently available suggests that the delivery process involves cell surface receptors for RBP.[8–11] Studies with monkey small intestinal mucosal cells[8] and with bovine pigment epithelial cells[8,10] have suggested that retinol is taken up at specific RBP receptor sites, without the concomitant uptake of RBP. After delivering the retinol, the resulting apo-RBP has a lower affinity for prealbumin[12] and is rapidly cleared from the circulation by glomerular filtration.

The delivery of retinol to peripheral tissues appears to be regulated mainly by factors that regulate the rates of RBP synthesis and secretion by the liver. In particular, the nutritional vitamin A status of the animal specifically regulates the secretion of RBP from the liver. In the vitamin A-deficient state, the secretion of RBP from the liver is blocked, resulting in the accumulation of an enlarged pool of RBP in the liver and a concomitant decline in the serum RBP concentration.[6,13] After the repletion of a vitamin A-deficient animal with retinol, RBP is rapidly secreted from the expanded liver pool of RBP into the serum as holo-RBP.[1,6,13,14]

While these studies have clearly shown that the secretion of RBP from the liver is a highly regulated process, they have not defined the molecular or cellular mechanisms involved in the regulation of RBP secretion. Our research on the regulation of RBP synthesis and secretion has addressed three main objectives: (1) to determine which subcellular structures and anatomical pathways are involved in RBP secretion; (2) to characterize the molecular changes in RBP that occur during secretion; and (3) to explore in detail the factors that regulate RBP metabolism in the liver cell, with studies employing isolated liver cells in culture *in vitro*.

* This research was supported by Grants HL21006, AM 05968, CA 12536, and CA 13696 from the National Institutes of Health.

These studies have all employed the rat as an animal model, and a sensitive and specific radioimmunoassay for rat RBP.[6]

SUBCELLULAR LOCALIZATION OF RBP; ROLE OF THE GOLGI IN RBP SECRETION

The roles of various subcellular organelles and structures in the metabolism and secretion of RBP have been studies with both normal and vitamin A-deficient rats. These studies have employed assays for a variety of marker enzymes and other constituents, along with the immunoassay for RBP. When liver homogenates were separated by differential centrifugation, approximately 80% of the RBP was found associated with the liver microsomes.[15] Additional subfractionation of the microsomal fraction showed that RBP was enriched in both the rough and smooth microsomal fractions (J.E. Smith & J.A. Resnick, unpublished observations). RBP was particularly enriched in the rough microsomal fraction (3.8 ± 0.5-fold over the homogenate), which contained 49 ± 4% of the liver microsomal RBP.

Evidence has been obtained that suggests that the Golgi apparatus is importantly involved in the secretion of RBP from the liver. In one study,[16] the levels of RBP, prealbumin, and several marker enzymes were determined in homogenates, crude subcellular fractions, and isolated Golgi apparatus prepared from the livers of vitamin A-deficient and control rats. Vitamin A deficiency led to a marked increase (3.5-fold) in hepatic RBP concentration and to slight increases in hepatic prealbumin levels, without affecting the levels of a number of marker enzymes localized in various subcellular compartments. The distributions of total protein and marker enzymes among various subcellular fractions were nearly identical in control and vitamin A-deficient preparations. In particular, vitamin A deficiency had no effect on the yield or enzymatic composition of isolated Golgi-rich fractions. In vitamin A-deficient rats, where the normal secretion of RBP was blocked, a maximum of less than 10% of the total liver RBP was accounted for in the Golgi. In contrast, in control rats, where secretion of RBP was proceeding at a normal rate, the relative amount of RBP in Golgi increased to about 23% of the total liver pool. The data suggest that the Golgi apparatus is involved in the pathway of RBP secretion from the liver.

In related recent studies, the effects of colchicine were explored on the secretion and metabolism of RBP by the liver.[14] Colchicine treatment of retinol-deficient rats markedly inhibited the retinol-stimulated secretion of RBP from the liver into the serum. The effect of colchicine was most profound during the early period after retinol injection, particularly during the first 30 to 60 minutes. The serum RBP level of colchicine-treated rats was only 36% as great as that of control rats 90 minutes after retinol injection. In parallel experiments, a quantitatively similar inhibition of very low density lipoprotein (VLDL) secretion by colchicine was observed. In contrast, colchicine did not affect the overall rate of hepatic protein synthesis, as estimated from the incorporation of [³H]leucine into total liver and serum protein; the secretion of newly synthesized protein was, however, inhibited. When retinol-deficient rats were first treated with colchicine and then injected with retinol, to stimulate RBP secretion, the RBP content of a Golgi-rich fraction from the liver homogenate increased markedly, to a maximum of 34% of the total liver RBP. This increase in the Golgi RBP content was particularly evident when compared to the level of prealbumin in the Golgi, which was not influenced by retinol. The inhibition of RBP secretion by colchicine suggests that the microtubules play a role in RBP secretion. By analogy to studies on VLDL and albumin[17], these data provide presumptive evidence that the Golgi apparatus and secretory vesicles are involved in RBP secretion.

Taken together, these recent studies are consistent with the suggestion that the Golgi apparatus is involved in the normal pathway of RBP secretion in the liver cell, and that the block in RBP secretion found in retinol deficiency occurs at a site before the RBP molecule reaches the Golgi. With the information available, however, it is not yet possible to define precisely the site of blockage of RBP secretion observed in vitamin A deficiency, nor to define the anatomic locus where retinol normally complexes with RBP in the liver cell.

ISOLATION AND PARTIAL CHARACTERIZATION OF LIVER MICROSOMAL RBP

We have recently isolated and partially characterized immunoreactive RBP from the liver microsomes of normal rats. These studies were undertaken to explore the question of whether microsomal RBP in part represents an intrahepatic precursor that is converted to plasma RBP during the process of secretion. If liver microsomal RBP were significantly composed of a "pro-RBP" precursor, then the identification and characterization of the precursor would provide useful information on the molecular events that occur during the process of RBP secretion. These events could then be studied directly, as potential regulatory steps in the overall process of RBP secretion.

Solubilization and Isolation of Microsomal RBP

Procedures were developed for the solubilization and isolation of immunoreactive RBP from liver microsomes. The final sequence of procedures employed involved four major steps: (1) solubilization of RBP with buffer containing 2% Triton X-100; (2) gel filtration on Sephadex G-100 in buffer containing 0.05% Triton X-100; (3) chromatography on DEAE Sepharose; and (4) affinity chromatography on prealbumin linked to Sepharose.

Whole rat liver was minced and was then homogenized with 3 volumes (v/w) of 0.03 M disodium ethylenediaminetetraacetic acid, 0.25 M sucrose, 0.025 M KCl, adjusted to pH 8.0, containing 40 mg of soybean trypsin inhibitor per liter. The homogenate was centrifuged at 3000 × *g* for 10 minutes to remove the cellular debris. The pellet was washed with a volume of the same homogenizing solution equal to the original liver weight and recentrifuged. The combined supernatant suspensions were centrifuged at 37,000 × *g* for 2 hours, to provide a crude microsomal pellet. By extracting the microsomal pellet twice with this same homogenizing solution containing 2% Triton X-100, 98% of the RBP was solubilized from the pellet.

The resulting extract (containing the solubilized RBP) was diluted with an equal volume of 0.1 M Tris-HCl buffer, pH 8.6. The diluted extract was then applied to a column of Sephadex G-100 previously equilibrated with 0.1 M Tris-HCl, pH 8.6, containing 0.05% Triton X-100, and elution was carried out with this same buffer. The RBP eluted from the column as a single peak, following and well separated from rat prealbumin. The concentration of the two proteins was below the critical concentration for formation of the RBP-prealbumin complex, so that the separate elution of rat RBP and prealbumin does not imply that the complex cannot form in the liver.

The RBP-containing fractions were pooled and applied directly to a DEAE

Sepharose CL-6B column. After a sample was applied, the column was washed with 12 liters of 0.1 M Tris-HCl, pH 8.6 to remove most of the Triton X-100. The RBP was then eluted from the column in a single step with 0.1 M Tris-HCl, pH 8.6 containing 0.1 N NaCl. The partially purified liver microsomal RBP was concentrated in a stirred ultrafiltration cell and diluted with 0.05 M Tris-HCl, pH 7.4, containing 0.5 M NaCl before the final concentration.

In the final purification step, the concentrated liver RBP solution was applied directly to a Sepharose-4B-human prealbumin column, and the column was eluted as described by Vahlquist et al.[18] The results of this procedure are shown in FIGURE 1. As shown in the lower panel of FIGURE 1, affinity chromatography separated the liver microsomal RBP into three different peaks. The major peak, which eluted prior to the buffer change, gave a single band of protein on poly-

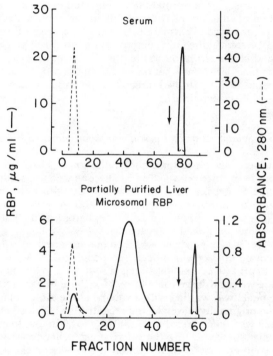

FIGURE 1. Chromatography of serum and liver RBP on a Sepharose-4B-prealbumin affinity column.

The prealbumin affinity column was prepared by coupling 200 mg of human prealbumin to cyanogen bromide-activated Sepharose-4B. Elution was first carried out with 0.05 M Tris-HCl, pH 7.4, containing 0.5 M NaCl. At the points indicated by the vertical arrows, the buffer was removed, and elution was continued instead with deionized water adjusted to pH 8.0 with NH_4OH. *Upper Panel:* 20 ml of whole rat serum was applied directly to the affinity column. *Lower Panel:* 30 ml of partially purified rat liver microsomal RBP (obtained from 245 g of rat liver) was applied to the column. As shown in this experiment, 3 peaks of immunoreactive liver RBP were separately eluted by the procedures employed. These peaks were designated liver RBP-I (first, small peak, in fractions 0–10), liver RBP-II (second major peak, in fractions 20–40) and liver RBP-III (third peak, eluted after buffer change).

acrylamide disc gel electrophoresis in sodium dodecyl sulfate. The overall yield of liver microsomal RBP by this sequence of procedures was 44%.

Characterization of Liver Microsomal RBP

The final step in the purification procedure provides information about the relative affinity of the liver microsomal RBP fractions for prealbumin. A typical pattern for the elution of serum RBP from the prealbumin affinity column is shown in the top panel of FIGURE 1. Serum RBP formed a tight complex with the prealbumin linked to the column support, and was eluted only after the reduction of the ionic strength of the eluant. The lower panel shows the elution pattern of liver RBP on the same column. In contrast to serum RBP, the affinity chromatography procedure separated liver RBP into three distinct fractions.

About 20% of the liver microsomal RBP bound very tightly to the prealbumin-Sepharose and was eluted from the column only after the ionic strength of the eluant was reduced, similar to the results seen with serum RBP. This fraction of liver RBP (designated liver RBP-III) was highly fluorescent and had fluorescence excitation and emission spectra identical to those obtained with holo-RBP from serum. This liver RBP-III represented holo-RBP (i.e., RBP containing bound retinol).

The second and major peak (designated liver RBP-II) represented 70% or more of the total immunoreactive liver microsomal RBP. In contrast to liver RBP-III, liver RBP-II was not fluorescent at 334 nm excitation, and represents a form of apo-RBP. While liver RBP-II definitely had an affinity for prealbumin (shown in FIG. 1, lower panel, by the retarded elution) the affinity was distinctly less than that shown by holo-RBP from serum (FIG. 1, top panel). Interestingly, apo-RBP isolated from serum appears to show two species, one of which binds tightly to the prealbumin column, like holo-RBP, while the other elutes from the prealbumin column earlier than liver RBP-II. Thus, liver RBP-II appears to be a form of apo-RBP that displays an affinity for prealbumin that is distinctly different from apo-RBP from serum.

An experiment was conducted to determine if liver RBP-II could bind retinol. A sample of liver RBP-II was concentrated and mixed with a 500-fold molar excess of retinol. The material was then chromatographed on the Sepharose-4B-human prealbumin affinity column in the manner described above. As shown in FIGURE 2, all of the liver RBP-II showed an increased affinity for prealbumin after the addition of retinol. Most of the liver RBP now eluted from the prealbumin affinity column only after the ionic strength of the eluant was reduced. The RBP so eluted was highly fluorescent and exhibited fluoresence spectra identical to those of holo-RBP from serum. Thus liver RBP-II can bind retinol, and the binding of retinol greatly increased its affinity for prealbumin.

The fraction of liver RBP that did not bind to the prealbumin affinity column (designated liver RBP-I, see FIG. 1) may represent a damaged RBP product that forms during the isolation. When purified liver RBP-II is rechromatographed on the prealbumin affinity column (either with or without addition of retinol) a small amount of RBP usually elutes as liver RBP-I (see FIG. 2). In contrast, liver RBP-I elutes only as liver RBP-I whether retinol is added or not. On sodium dodecyl sulfate disc gel electrophoresis, a partially purified preparation of liver RBP-I contained a band of protein with a molecular weight similar to that of serum RBP.

Since Triton X-100 could possibly extract retinol from the liver microsomal RBP, an experiment was conducted to determine whether liver RBP-II may have been produced during the isolation procedure, as a result of exposure to Triton X-100. A sample of liver microsomes, prepared as described above, was homo-

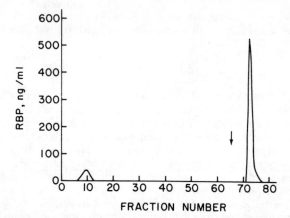

FIGURE 2. Effect of the addition of retinol on the elution of liver microsomal RBP from the Sepharose-4B-prealbumin affinity column.

Fifteen ml of a solution containing 10.5 μg of purified liver RBP-II (see legend to Fig. 1) was mixed with 1.5 ml of ethanol containing 75 μg of retinol (500-fold molar excess) and incubated at room temperature for 1 hour. The entire sample was applied to the column. Elution was then carried out as described in the legend to FIGURE 1.

genized by 20 strokes in a Potter-Elvehjem homogenizer (pestle at 1000 rpm). The sample was then frozen and immediately thawed. The entire procedure was repeated five times. Approximately 38% of the liver immunoreactive RBP was "released" (solubilized) from the microsomes by this mechanical procedure. The RBP so obtained was partially purified by a batch procedure with DEAE Sepharose CL-6B, and was then applied to the prealbumin affinity column. This material, which had never been exposed to Triton X-100, showed an elution pattern that was very similar to the pattern shown in the lower panel of FIGURE 1. Thus, in this experiment, the major portion of the liver microsomal RBP also eluted as liver RBP-II and showed no fluorescence when excited at 334 nm. These results

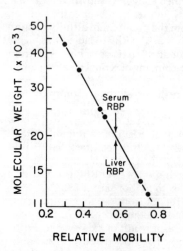

FIGURE 3. Estimation of molecular weight by sodium dodecyl sulfate-disc gel electrophoresis.

The arrows show the observed relative mobilities for purified rat serum RBP and rat liver RBP-II. The standard proteins (solid circles) were: ovalbumin, pepsin, chymotrypsinogen A, trypsin, ribonuclease, and cytochrome C.

indicate that most of the immunoreactive RBP in normal rat liver is apparently present in microsomes as apo-RBP, rather than as holo-RPB. These observations do not agree with an earlier report of Glover *et al.*[19] that suggested that nearly all of the liver RPB is present as holo-RBP. This report[19] was based on studies using fluorescence scanning of polyacrylamide gels. We also have observed a highly fluorescent material that migrates slightly slower than RBP on polyacrylamide gel electrophoresis; however the fluorescence spectrum of this material was markedly different from the fluorescence spectrum of holo-RBP from serum. Thus, we believe that this fluorescent material does not represent holo-RBP.

As shown in FIGURE 3, the molecular weight of liver RBP-II, as estimated by sodium dodecyl sulfate disc gel electrophoresis,[20] appears to be very close to, if not identical to that of serum RBP.

The three fractions of liver microsomal RBP all showed ^{125}I-RBP displacement curves, in the rat RBP radioimmunoassay, which were indistinguishable from those obtained with purified serum RBP (FIG. 4). This was not surprising, since we previously found that whole liver homogenates and pure serum RBP give identical displacement curves.[6] The lack of an immunological difference further confirms the similarity of these proteins.

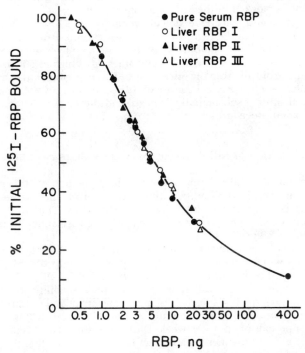

FIGURE 4. The displacement of antibody-bound ^{125}I-RBP by serum RBP and by liver RBP fractions.

The mean concentration of each of the liver RBP samples was determined by radioimmunoassay. Diluted samples containing known amounts of RBP were then added to the assay tubes. The three liver RBP fractions (liver RBP-I, -II, and -III) were obtained by differential elution from the prealbumin affinity column (see FIG. 1).

These results demonstrate that liver microsomal RBP from normal rats exists in part as holo-RBP (liver RBP-III), but mainly as a form of apo-RBP with a low but definite affinity for prealbumin (liver RBP-II). This apo-RBP has a molecular weight that is very close to, if not identical with, that of serum RBP, and is immunologically indistinguishable from serum RBP in the rat RBP radioimmunoassay. This apo-RBP from liver microsomes can bind retinol, to form holo-RBP, and the holo-RBP so formed appears to have fluoresence spectral characteristics and affinity for prealbumin that are characteristic of holo-RBP from serum.

Taken together, these observations do not support the suggestion that microsomal liver RBP may in part represent an intrahepatic precursor ("pro-RBP") molecule. Of the various properties examined, liver microsomal apo-RBP differed from serum RBP only with regard to its affinity for prealbumin. The quantitative (but not qualitative) differences observed in the affinity of apo-RBP solubilized from liver microsomes (as compared to apo-RBP from serum) for prealbumin may reflect conformational differences in the two proteins.

Studies are also in progress in our laboratory to isolate and characterize liver microsomal RBP from vitamin A-deficient rats. Most of the liver RBP from such rats appears to be present as liver RBP-II. Although these studies are not complete, the available data do not provide evidence for the existence of a chemically different (e.g., larger-sized) precursor of plasma RBP in liver microsomes when RBP secretion is blocked in the retinol-deficient state.

These data suggest that conversion of liver apo-RBP (RBP-II) to holo-RBP may itself be the key step in the regulation of the secretion of RBP. Accordingly, we have attempted to release (solubilize) RBP from isolated liver microsomes by the addition of retinol. However, retinol added at levels as high as 500 μg/ml did not cause the release of RBP from the microsomes. This experiment may have little to do with the actual physiological control of RBP secretion, however, since the endoplasmic reticulum is substantially damaged and altered during homogenization and fractionation procedures.

REGULATION OF RBP METABOLISM IN LIVER CELLS IN CULTURE

While much useful information about the regulation of RBP metabolism has been obtained with whole animal studies, the interpretation of these results is frequently clouded due to the interplay between organs. Thus, we have developed an *in vitro* liver cell culture system to study the regulation of the synthesis and secretion of RBP.[21]

In preliminary screening experiments we found two differentiated rat hepatoma cell lines which synthesized easily assayable amounts of RBP, the MH_1C_1 cell line developed by Richardson *et al.*[22] and the H_4II EC_3 (called "H4") cell line of Pitot *et al.*[23] Both of these cell lines demonstrate the ability to synthesize a number of plasma proteins, such as albumin, transferrin, and prothrombin. Both cell lines were found to survive in culture *in vitro*, without growth, in a serumless medium[24] for periods of up to one week. During this time the cells produced RBP in essentially a linear manner with respect to time of incubation.[21]

The serumless medium of Neuman and Tytell[24] does not contain vitamin A, so that the hepatoma cells incubated in this medium represent vitamin A-deficient cells. In incubations of 48 hours or less, we found the cells to retain 14 to 56% of the RBP within the cells. These cells, therefore, resemble a liver cell in a vitamin A-deficient rat. The addition of retinol to the serumless medium (at levels of 0.1 or 1 μg/ml) stimulated the secretion of RBP from the cells into the medium. In longer experiments (2 to 3 days) the addition of retinol to the medium also stimulated the total production of RBP. Addition of retinyl palmitate at comparable levels had a similar effect. Assays were also made for rat serum albumin. In contrast to its effects on RBP, retinol did not influence either the cell-to-medium distribution or the net synthesis of albumin. These data suggest that these cell lines respond to vitamin A depletion and repletion in a similar manner as does the intact rat liver cell *in vivo.*

Reports in the literature have suggested that the adrenal cortical hormones accelerate the rate at which vitamin A is mobilized from the liver.[25] All of these studies were conducted prior to the isolation of RBP.[2] We have accordingly, studied the effects of the glucocorticoid hormones on RBP metabolism in the liver cell culture system.

Cortisol, corticosterone, and the synthetic glucocorticoid analog dexamethasone all markedly stimulated the net synthesis of RBP by the rat hepatoma cells. When retinol and dexamethasone were added together to the incubation medium, the stimulatory effects were roughly additive. An optimal effect was obtained with approximately $5–10 \times 10^{-9}$ M dexamethasone. In contrast, neither retinol nor dexamethasone had an effect on the net synthesis or cell-to-medium distribution of rat serum albumin or prealbumin. The presence of dexamethasone did not appear to alter the stimulatory effect of retinol on the secretion of RBP from the cells into the medium. Thus, dexamethasone and retinol appear to have distinctly separate effects on RBP metabolism by the liver cell.

Progesterone blocked the stimulatory effect of dexamethasone in the concentration range (for progesterone) of 10^{-7} to 10^{-5} M. Progesterone alone in this concentration range had no effect on RBP metabolism. By analogy with other studies (e.g., ref.[26]) these observations with progesterone suggest that steroid hormone receptors are involved in the dexamethasone effect.

Recently, we have also adapted a system for the culture of primary rat hepatocytes[27] to the study of RBP metabolism (D. R. Soprano & J. E. Smith, unpublished observations). The primary hepatocytes were found to produce RBP for up to 7 days in culture. The primary hepatocytes may prove useful in studies on regulatory factors that cannot be studied in the hepatoma cells.

Thus, these various liver cell culture systems should provide good models for the further detailed study of the mechanisms involved in the regulation of RBP synthesis and secretion by the liver cell.

ACKNOWLEDGMENTS

The authors express their appreciation to R. A. Kaufmann, H. Mason, E. W. Johnson, Jr., and J. L. Muzicka for their expert technical assistance.

REFERENCES

1. SMITH, J.E. & DEW.S. GOODMAN. 1979. Retinol-binding protein and the regulation of vitamin A transport. Fed. Proc. **38:** 2504–2509.
2. GOODMAN, DEW.S. 1981. Retinoid-binding Proteins in Plasma and in Cells. Ann. N. Y. Acad. Sci. **359:**.
3. KANAI, M., A. RAZ & DEW.S. GOODMAN. 1968. Retinol-binding protein: the transport protein for vitamin A in human plasma. J. Clin. Invest. **47:** 2025–2044.
4. MUTO, Y. & DEW.S. GOODMAN. 1972. Vitamin A transport in rat plasma. Isolation and characterization of retinol-binding protein. J. Biol. Chem. **247:** 2533–2541.
5. VAHLQUIST, A., P.A. PETERSON & L. WIBELL. 1973. Metabolism of vitamin A trans-

porting protein complex. I. Turnover studies in normal persons and in patients with chronic renal failure. Eur. J. Clin. Invest. **3**: 352-362.

6. MUTO, Y., J.E. SMITH, P.O. MILCH & DEW.S. GOODMAN. 1972. Regulation of retinol-binding protein metabolism by vitamin A status in the rat. J. Biol. Chem. **247**: 2542-2550.

7. SMITH, J.E., Y. MUTO, P.O. MILCH & DEW.S. GOODMAN. 1973. The effects of chylomicron vitamin A on the metabolism of retinol-binding protein in the rat. J. Biol. Chem. **248**: 1544-1549.

8. RASK, L. & P.A. PETERSON. 1976. In vitro uptake of vitamin A from the retinol-binding plasma protein to mucosal epithelial cells from monkey's small intestine. J. Biol. Chem. **251**: 6360-6366.

9. HELLER, J. 1975. Interactions of plasma retinol-binding protein with its receptor. Specific binding of bovine and human retinol-binding protein to pigment epithelium cells from bovine eyes. J. Biol. Chem. **250**: 3613-3619.

10. CHEN, C.-C. & J. HELLER. 1977. Uptake of retinol and retinoic acid from serum retinol-binding protein by retinal pigment epithelial cells. J. Biol. Chem. **252**: 5216-5221.

11. BHAT, M.K. & H.R. CAMA. 1979. Gonadal cell surface receptor for plasma retinol-binding protein. A method for its radioassay and studies on its level during spermatogenesis. Biochim. Biophys. Acta **587**: 273-281.

12. FEX, G., P.-Å. ALBERTSSON & B. HANSSON. 1979. Interaction between prealbumin and retinol-binding protein studied by affinity chromatography, gel filtration and two-phase partition. Eur. J. Biochem. **99**: 353-360.

13. NAVAB, M., J.E. SMITH & DEW.S. GOODMAN. 1977. Rat plasma prealbumin. Metabolic studies on effects of vitamin A status and on tissue distribution. J. Biol. Chem. **252**: 5107-5114.

14. SMITH, J.E., D.D. DEEN, JR., D. SKLAN & DEW.S. GOODMAN. 1980. Colchicine inhibition of retinol-binding protein secretion by rat liver. J. Lipid Res. **21**: 229-237.

15. HARRISON, E.H., J.E. SMITH & DEW.S. GOODMAN. 1979. Unusual properties of retinyl palmitate hydrolase activity in rat liver. J. Lipid Res. **20**: 760-771.

16. HARRISON, E.H., J.E. SMITH & DEW.S. GOODMAN. 1980. Effects of vitamin A deficiency on the levels and distribution of retinol-binding protein and marker enzymes in homogenates and Golgi-rich fractions of rat liver. Biochim. Biophys. Acta **628**: 489-497.

17. REDMAN, C.M., D. BANERJEE, K. HOWELL & G.E. PALADE. 1975. Colchicine inhibition of plasma protein release from rat hepatocytes. J. Cell Biol. **66**: 42-59.

18. VAHLQUIST, A., S.F. NILSSON & P.A. PETERSON. 1971. Isolation of the human retinol binding protein by affinity chromatography. Eur. J. Biochem. **20**: 160-168.

19. GLOVER, J., C. JAY & G.H. WHITE. 1974. Distribution of retinol-binding protein in tissues. Vitam. Horm. **32**: 215-235.

20. WEBER, K. & M. OSBORN. 1969. The reliability of molecular weight determinations by dodecyl sulfate-polyacrylamide gel electrophoresis. J. Biol. Chem. **244**: 4406-4412.

21. SMITH, J.E., C. BOREK & DEW.S. GOODMAN. 1978. Regulation of retinol-binding protein metabolism in cultured rat liver cell lines. Cell **15**: 865-873.

22. RICHARDSON, U.I., A.H. TASHJIAN, JR. & L. LEVINE. 1969. Establishment of a clonal strain of hepatoma cells which secrete albumin. J. Cell Biol. **40**: 236-247.

23. PITOT, H.C., C. PERAINO, P.A. MORSE, JR. & V.R. POTTER. 1964. Hepatomas in tissue culture compared with adapting liver *in vivo*. Natl. Cancer Inst. Monograph **13**: 229-245.

24. NEUMAN, R.E. & A.A. TYTELL. 1960. Serumless medium for cultivation of cells of normal and malignant origin. Proc. Soc. Exp. Biol. Med. **104**: 252-256.

25. STOEWSAND, G.S. & M.L. SCOTT. 1964. Effect of stress from high protein diets on vitamin A metabolism in chicks. J. Nutr. **82**:188-196.

26. ROUSSEAU, G.G., J.D. BAXTER & G.M. TOMKINS. 1972. Glucocorticoid receptors: Relations between steroid binding and biological effects. J. Mol. Biol. **67**: 99-115.

27. DAVIS, R.A., S.C. ENGELHORN, S.H. PANGBURN, D.B. WEINSTEIN & D. STEINBERG. 1979. Very low density lipoprotein synthesis and secretion by cultured rat hepatocytes. J. Biol. Chem. **254**: 2010-2016.

THE EFFECT OF VITAMIN A STATUS ON THE DIFFERENTIATION AND FUNCTION OF GOBLET CELLS IN THE RAT INTESTINE*

James Allen Olson

Biochemistry and Biophysics Department
Iowa State University
Ames, Iowa 50011

Wanee Rojanapo

National Cancer Institute
Bangkok, Thailand

Adrian J. Lamb

Faculty of Science
Mahidol University
Bangkok, Thailand

INTRODUCTION

Vitamin A deficiency produces profound changes in the epithelia of diverse species. The two most commonly observed changes are an increased keratinization produced by squamous cell proliferation and a loss of mucus-secreting cells. The molecular role of vitamin A in inducing these cellular changes is still unclear.

Of various mucus-producing cells, the goblet cells of the rat small intestine have received particular attention. Manville[1] first noted that the number of goblet cells along the intestinal villus of a vitamin A-deficient rat was reduced in vitamin A deficiency. Subsequently, L. DeLuca and colleagues[2] showed that the prevalence of goblet cells fell to about 50% and that protein synthesis was equally depressed in intestinal tissues of vitamin A-deficient rats. More recently Zile *et al.*[3] found that the cell cycle time of rat jejunal crypt cells was lengthened by 14% in vitamin A deficiency. In the last several years L. DeLuca and Wolf have presented a great deal of evidence to support their hypothesis that vitamin A serves as a carrier molecule for the incorporation of carbohydrates into specific glycoproteins.[4-6]

We have reinvestigated the formation and activity of goblet cells as a function of vitamin A status for several reasons. First of all, we have developed a standardized and rapid method of inducing vitamin A deficiency[7] which minimizes secondary and nonspecific effects of the deficiency state. Secondly, we were interested in determining the relative sequence in which signs of vitamin A deficiency appeared, and how the reduction of goblet cell prevalence related to these other signs. Thirdly, we wished to determine the extent to which the dynamics of intestinal cell division and cellular migration might be affected by the deficiency;

* This research was supported by grants from the National Institutes of Health (AM-11367), the Rockefeller Foundation (No. 65701), and the Faculty of Graduate Studies, Mahidol University. The work was taken from the Ph.D. thesis of Wanee Rojanapo, which was submitted to the Faculty of Graduate Studies, Mahidol University, in partial fulfillment of degree requirements.

0077–8923/81/0359–0181 $01.75/0 © 1981, NYAS

and finally, we wanted to evaluate the function of vitamin A-deficient goblet cells relative to their secretory and synthetic abilities and the types of products produced.

METHODS AND RESULTS

The Induction of Rapid Synchronous Vitamin A-Deficiency

On the basis of an observation by Moore and Holmes[8] that vitamin A-deficient rats and mice could be temporarily cured by timely, repeated treatment with retinoic acid, a concerted effort was made to define an optimal system for cycling rats on diets first containing and then free of retinoic acid. Since retinoic acid, unlike vitamin A, is not stored in the liver, and since in small doses it is very rapidly metabolized and excreted, a synchronous state of vitamin A deficiency might be rapidly produced. Weanling rats were fed a vitamin A-deficient diet until until their growth rate plateaued, and then were given the same diet supplemented with, and then lacking in, 2 μg retinoic acid per gram diet in repeating 18 day:10 day supplementation and deprivation phases. Animals have been cycled in this way for over a year without difficulty. Generally three to four cycles are required to produce an optimal response to the withdrawal of retinoic acid, i.e. to deplete the last traces of retinol within tissues. Thus, in the experiments presented here, all animals have been cycled three or four times before being studied.

In order to synchronize the deficient state in these animals, 10 μg of retinoic acid in oil were given to all animals by stomach tube at T_0, i.e. the time of retinoate withdrawal from the diet, and concomitantly 400 μg of retinyl palmitate in oil were given to the control animals. Thereafter, both control and vitamin A-deficient animals were force-fed twice daily with 5 grams of food in a slurry. By this procedure control and vitamin A-deficient animals were very closely matched in general nutritional status. It is our feeling that the pair-feeding technique, which induces a state of semi-starvation both in control and in deficient animals, is not as useful as the method described here. Incidently, if the vitamin A-deficient animals are fed somewhat more food than the controls, their rate of growth and body composition are essentially the same as control animals (A.J. Lamb, unpublished observations).

Goblet cells usually account for about 20% of the total cells in the duodenal crypt and a somewhat smaller portion of total cells on the duodenal villus. When vitamin A deficiency is imposed, this prevalence starts to fall around day 2 of deficiency and reaches approximately 60% of the normal level by day 4 (FIG. 1). Thereafter, the number remains constant throughout the deficiency period. When a dose of retinoic acid (100 μg) is given to deficient animals on day 8, an increased prevalence is noted within 12 hr, and complete recovery occurs within 1 to 2 days (FIG. 1).[9] Although the reduction in goblet cell prevalence is a relatively early manifestation of vitamin A deficiency, decreased food intake and a consequent reduction in growth rate are the earliest observable signs.[10] As shown in FIGURE 2, a plateau phase of growth is induced within 1 day after withdrawal of retinoic acid, and at approximately 5 days a rapid decrease in weight is observed.[10] Upon treatment with retinoic acid, the growth rate resumes at an accelerated pace, and then after 5 days returns to the initial rate.

As shown in TABLE 1, a large number of signs, namely increased taurine excretion, decreased sensitivity to pilocarpine, tracheal metaplasia and the like, all

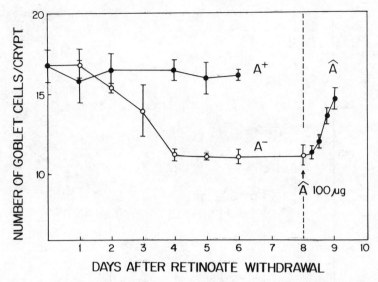

FIGURE 1. The effect of the withdrawal and administration of retinoate on the number of goblet cells in duodenal crypt glands of rats cycled 4 × on retinoic acid. (From Rojanapo *et al.*[9] Used by permission of the publishers of *J. Nutr.*)

appear at about the 6th day of deficiency, concomitant with the rapid weight loss.[10,11] A third group of signs, which consist of marked histological changes in tissues and of neurological and bone disorders, occur late in the deficiency state. Apart from this latter group of signs, it is clear that animals at day 8 of deficiency clearly show many of the classical signs of vitamin A deficiency.

DYNAMICS OF CELLULAR DIFFERENTIATION AND THE MIGRATION OF MUCOSAL CELLS AS A FUNCTION OF VITAMIN A STATUS

The intestine is a highly dynamic tissue. After cells are formed in the crypt, it takes less than 48 hr for cells to move up the villus and to be shed from the villus tip. Thus, all the cells in the crypt and on the villus at day 8 of deficiency, except for a few germ cells at the base of the crypt, have been formed during the deficiency state.

We first wished to determine whether the steady state storage of mucin in goblet cells was in any way affected by vitamin A deficiency. Since goblet cells are identified by staining with the periodic acid-Schiff reagent (PAS), a goblet cell which has secreted all of its mucin would obviously not be identified as such. In order to determine the steady state level of goblet cell "charging" with mucin, we used two drugs, atropine, which inhibits mucus secretion, and pilocarpine, which stimulates it. With atropine no change in the prevalence of goblet cells was noted, i.e. essentially all goblet cells are in the "charged" state under normal conditions. On the other hand, pilocarpine induced a rapid discharge of mucin, as noted by a fall in the apparent number of mucin-containing cells, followed by a rapid increase in mucin synthesis (FIG. 3).[9] On the other hand, the secretion of

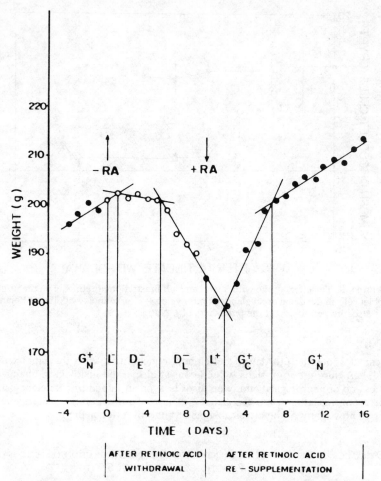

FIGURE 2. Empirical lines of best fit for the weight of a typical retinoate cycled rat following withdrawal and resupplementation with retinoic acid (2 μg/g diet). G_N^+, normal growth phase; L^-, lag phase after retinoate withdrawal; D_E^-, early phase of weight decline; D_L^-, late phase of rapid weight decline; L^+, lag phase after retinoate resupplementation; G_C^+, compensatory phase of catch-up growth. (From Anzano et al.[10] Used by permission of the publishers of J. Nutr.)

mucin from goblet cells and the rate of re-appearance of goblet cells, which is a direct measure of mucin synthesis and storage, were unaffected by vitamin A status. We must point out that these results were obtained by PAS staining of crypt sections, and consequently reflect the overall increase in mucin accumulation independent of the nature of the substance formed.

In order to obtain some information about the migration rate of cells, A^+ and A^- animals were injected with tritiated thymidine on day 8 of deficiency, and the position of the highest labeled cell on the villus as a function of time was

TABLE 1

APPEARANCE OF SIGNS OF VITAMIN A DEFICIENCY IN CYCLED RATS
AFTER RETINOATE WITHDRAWAL

Sign	Usual Day of Onset	Total Percent Incidence
Decreased food intake	1–2	100
Weight plateau	2–3	100
Decreased intestinal goblet cells	2–3	80
Rapid weight loss	6–8	100
Increased taurine excretion	6–8	80
Decreased pilocarpine-induced salivation	6–8	80
Matted hair	6–8	80
Tracheal metaplasia	6–8	80
Periocular porphyrin deposits	6–8	60
Salivary gland changes	9–10	80
Decreased stomach emptying	12	70
Twisting	12	5
Leg crippling	12	5

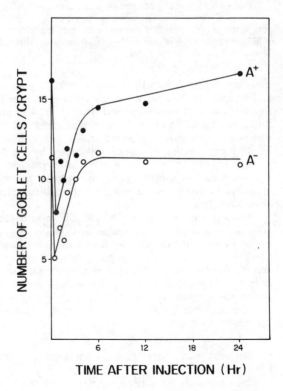

FIGURE 3. The effect of pilocarpine administration on the number of PAS-positive goblet cells in the duodenal crypt glands of force-fed control and deficient (day 8) rats. (From Rojanapo *et al.*[9] Used by permission of the publishers of *J. Nutr.*)

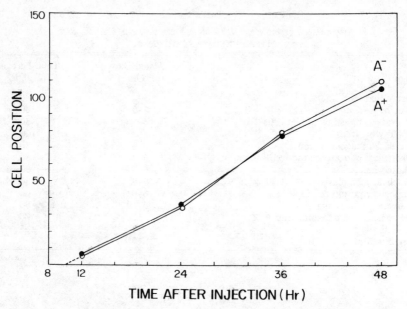

FIGURE 4. The effect of vitamin A status on the rate of migration of columnar epithelial cells from the crypt villus junction to the villus tip in force-fed control and deficient (day 8) rats. Each point represents the mean migration position of the highest labeled cell on 30 villi taken from each of 2 animals in each category. (From Rojanapo et al.[9] Used by permission of the publishers of *J. Nutr.*)

determined.[9] AS shown in FIGURE 4, no difference was observed between the A+ and A− animals. Neither were any differences noted in the percentage of mitotic figures labeled at various periods from 1 to 24 hr after injection. Thus, although differing slightly from earlier observations[3] both cell cycle time and migration rate were apparently unaffected under these conditions of vitamin A deficiency. In other regards the villus was unaffected by the deficient state: its length, the number of cells on the villus and in the crypts, and its general histological structure remained the same.[3,9] Thus, the decrease in goblet cell prevalence cannot be explained on the basis of changes in the cellular dynamics in the intestinal crypt or on the villus.

Since oligomucus cells are probable intermediate forms between the germ cells and goblet cells, we thought that the prevalence of oligomucus cells might be increased, but this was not found to be the case. Thus, we can present two possible explanations for this puzzling partial effect of vitamin A deficiency on goblet cell prevalence: (1) that the intestine possesses two different types of goblet cells, the differentiation of one of which is blocked in vitamin A deficiency; and (2) that the formation of goblet cells and oligomucus cells, which must be limited to a specific period among germ cells in the crypt, is in some way delayed in the deficiency state.

PHYSICAL AND CHEMICAL CHARACTERISTICS OF INTESTINAL GLYCOPROTEINS

Two methods have been employed for the location of intact proteins and glycoproteins from mucosal cells: a mild extraction of cells with an aqueous solution of ethylenediamine tetra-acetate (EDTA), which mainly extracts water soluble glycoproteins and proteins,[12] and a more rigorous extraction with 1% sodium dodecyl sulfate, which extracts both water-soluble and membrane-bound proteins and glycoproteins.[13] In the past a number of other extraction methods have been used which involve the presence of dithiothreitol (DTT), limited proteolysis, and the like. We will focus here on the mildest of all of these procedures, namely the dilute EDTA extraction method.

When the clarified mucosal extract is chromatographed on a column of Sepharose 4B, three major fractions are obtained (FIG. 5).[14] The three fractions differ markedly in their characteristics. Peak I consists of a very large aggregate, or group of aggregates, which can be cleaved to five smaller sub-units by treatment with DTT. Peak I is rich in hexose, fucose, and sialic acid, and contains an acidic, threonine rich protein. Major chemical and physical characteristics of Peak I are given in TABLE 2. Peaks II and III are more heterogeneous, contain much smaller quantities of carbohydrate, and are somewhat less affected by treatment with DTT. Antibodies to peaks I, II and III predominantly react with goblet cells and secreted mucin when studied by immunofluorescence. Antibodies to peaks II and III, however, do not react with peak I. We will now focus on peak I, mainly because it is the most homogeneous, the most carbohydrate rich, and as we shall see, the component whose synthesis is most affected by vitamin A status.

When peak I isolated from extracts of vitamin A deficient rats at day 8 of deficiency is compared with the same peak obtained from control animals, essential-

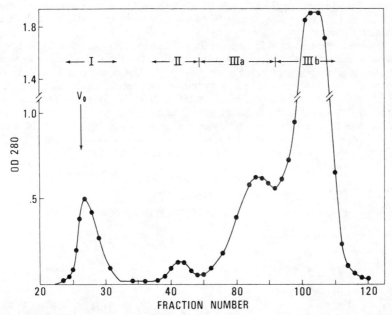

FIGURE 5. Elution pattern of water soluble intestinal proteins and glycoproteins extracted with aqueous EDTA[12] from a Sepharose 4B column pre-equilibrated with 10 mM K-PO$_4$ buffer, pH 7.0.

TABLE 2

CHARACTERISTICS OF WATER-SOLUBLE PEAK I FROM THE DUODENUM OF A$^+$ RATS

Molecular weight	>10^6 Daltons
Sedimentation coefficient	11.7 S
Relative amount	4.73 mg %
Protein	20.0%
Hexose	18.6%
Fucose	8.6%
Sialic acid	7.8%
Major amino acids	
Threonine	21.5 Mole %
Valine*	13.0
Proline	10.7
Serine	7.9
Glutamate	7.8
Aspartate	6.3
Half-cystine	2.0

* Non-symmetric peak.

ly no differences in physical properties or chemical composition were noted (TABLE 3). These data are expressed as the ratio of values found in deficient animals to those found in controls. It should be noted that peak I must be derived as well as from cells other than goblet cells, otherwise the ratios would necessarily all be less than unity. This observation came as a surprise to us, namely that the amount and composition of high molecular weight glycoproteins, all of which were formed in cells whose whole life span was spent in a deficient state, were essentially normal.

We also studied the incorporation of radioactively labeled sulfate, glucosamine, fucose, and threonine into glycoprotein fractions of A$^+$ and A$^-$ animals. In full conformation of previous studies by L. DeLuca, Wolf and their collaborators,[4-6] the incorporation of a carbohydrate precursor into high molecular weight glycoprotein fractions, but not into other glycoprotein fractions, was markedly depressed in the deficient state (TABLE 4). Similarly, we confirmed that the incorporation of threonine into intestinal proteins was reduced by about one-half.[2] Unlike carbohydrate uptake, however, the depression in the incorporation of the threonine was about the same in all protein fractions.

TABLE 3

EFFECT OF VITAMIN A DEFICIENCY (DAY 8) ON CHARACTERISTICS OF
WATER-SOLUBLE PEAK I

	A$^-$/A$^+$
Molecular weight	same
Sedimentation coefficient	1.03
Relative amount	1.00
Protein	1.10
Hexose	0.97
Fucose	0.97
Sialic acid	1.03

TABLE 4

RELATIVE INCORPORATION OF L-[1-14C] FUCOSE AND L-[3H]THREONINE (G) INTO
WATER-SOLUBLE DUODENAL PROTEINS AND GLYCOPROTEINS IN A+ AND A- (DAY 8) RATS

Precursor	Fraction	Ratio (A-/A+) of SA (cpm/mg protein)
Fucose	Total	0.54
	I	0.25
	II	0.86
	IIIB	0.71
Threonine	Total	0.60
	I	0.52
	IIIA	0.67

DISCUSSION

We now have a set of clear but not fully cohesive observations. On the one hand, the morphology of the duodenum and jejunum is not affected by vitamin A deficiency, not indeed are the cellular dynamics of division and migration changed. Nonetheless, the prevalence of goblet cells decreases from about 20% to about 12% of total cells in the crypt. Secondly, the amount, carbohydrate content, protein content, and molecular size of glycoproteins in peak I are not apparently affected at day 8 of deficiency. Thirdly, the relative uptake of fucose into glycoproteins is only 25% of normal in peak I, although it is 70–90% of normal in other peaks. Fourthly, the relative uptake of threonine into protein is about 60% of normal in all protein fractions. Finally, all mucosal cells of the intestine present at day 8 were generated during the period of vitamin A deficiency.

Four possible interpretations might be given of these results. First of all, in keeping with the L. DeLuca-Wolf hypothesis,[4-6] the synthetic rate in vitamin A-deficient rats may be markedly reduced for specific glycoproteins because of the absence or lowered concentration of retinyl phosphate or a similar retinoic acid-derived carrier.† Thus, since the rate of synthesis is reduced, the time needed to reach a steady state level must be increased. We must note, however, that vitamin A deficiency was well established in these animals, that the concentration of retinoic acid and of its metabolites must have been extremely low, and that all sugars analyzed were equally affected by the deficiency.

Another explanation might be that *both* the rates of synthesis *and* of catabolism of specific glycoproteins are markedly depressed in vitamin A deficiency. This seems unlikely for several reasons; namely that goblet cells eliminate glycoproteins by secretion rather than by steady-state turnover, and that goblet cell filling in vitamin A deficient cells after pilocarpine treatment appears to be normal.

Two other possibilities might be voiced, although the mechanism by which vitamin A might act is not clear, namely that the feedback control of glycoprotein synthesis by steady-state levels of glycoproteins is enhanced in vitamin A defici-

---

†L. DeLuca and G. Wolf have pointed out that intestinal mucin does not contain mannose, the major, if not sole, hexose for which retinol might serve a general carrier function. Thus the markedly reduced incorporation of fucose into mucin in the goblet cells of vitamin A-deficient rats must necessarily be due to some other metabolic disturbance.

ency, or that the accessibility of outer carbohydrate chains of large glycoproteins to fucose addition is reduced. No specific evidence is presently at hand to support any of the latter suggestions. Nonetheless, other explanations besides those suggested earlier might exist for the well-established observation that the incorporation of carbohydrates into high molecular weight glycoproteins of goblet cells is reduced in vitamin A deficiency.

SUMMARY

The prevalence of goblet cells in duodenal crypts decreased to 60% of normal at day 4 of deficiency.

Villus and crypt length, total mucosal cell number, cell cycle time, and migration rate were unaffected at day 8 of deficiency.

The carbohydrate content, protein content, and molecular size of high molecular weight glycoproteins (peak I) were unaffected at day 8 of deficiency.

The incorporation of L-[^{3}H]threonine (G) into proteins of all peaks were reduced to 60% of normal at day 8 of deficiency.

The incorporation of L-[1-^{14}C]fucose into glycoprotein fell to 25% of normal in peak I, and to 70 to 90% of normal in other peaks at day 8 of deficiency.

In vitamin A deficiency, a defect seems to exist either in the rate of differentiation of intestinal goblet cells at a critical period, or in the differentiation of a subclass of vitamin A-sensitive goblet cells.

Some possible explanations for the decreased synthetic rate of some glycoproteins in the presence of normal steady-state concentrations in A$^-$ rats are discussed.

REFERENCES

1. MANVILLE, I.A. 1937. The inter-relationship of vitamin A and glucuronic acid in mucine metabolism. Science **85**: 44–45.
2. DeLUCA, L., E.P. LITTLE & G. WOLF. 1969. Vitamin A and protein synthesis by rat intestinal mucosa. J. Biol. Chem. **244**: 701–708.
3. ZILE, M., E.C. BUNGE & H.F. DeLUCA. 1977. Effect of vitamin A deficiency on intestinal cell proliferation in the rat. J. Nutr. **107**: 522–560.
4. DeLUCA, L.M. 1977. The direct involvement of vitamin A in glycosyl transfer reactions of mammalian membranes. Vitam. Horm. **34**: 1–57.
5. DeLUCA, L.M., P.V. BHAT, W. SASAK & S. ADAMS. 1979. Vitamin A and glycoprotein and membrane metabolism. Federation Proc. **38**: 2535–2539.
6. WOLF, G., S. MASUSHIGE, J.B. SCHREIBER, M.J. SMITH, T.C. KIORPES, & R.S. ANDERSON. 1979. Recent evidence for the participation of vitamin A in glycoprotein synthesis. Federation Proc. **38**: 2540–2543.
7. LAMB, A.J., P. APIWATANAPORN & J.A. OLSON. 1974. Induction of rapid, synchronous vitamin A deficiency in the rat. J. Nutr. **104**: 1140–1148.
8. MOORE, T. & P.D. HOLMES. 1971. The production of experimental vitamin A deficiency in rats and mice. Laboratory Animals **5**: 239–250.
9. ROJANAPO, W., A.J. LAMB & J.A. OLSON. 1980. Prevalence, metabolism and migration of goblet cells in rat intestine following the induction of rapid synchronous vitamin A deficiency. J. Nutr. **110**: 178–188.
10. ANZANO, M.A., A.J. LAMB & J.A. OLSON. 1979. Growth, appetite, sequence of pathological signs and survival following the induction of rapid, synchronous vitamin A deficiency in the rat. J. Nutr. **109**: 1419–1431.

11. LAMB, A.J., J. NAEWBANIJ & M.A. ANZANO. 1979. Altered taurine metabolism in vitamin A deficiency. Federation Proc. **38:** 762.
12. FORSTNER, J., N. TAICHMAN, V. KALNINS & G. FORSTNER. 1973. Intestinal goblet cell mucus. Isolation and identification by immunofluorescence of a goblet cell glycoprotein. J. Cell. Sci. **12:** 585–602.
13. ADACHI, N. J. AZUMA, M. JANADO & K. ONODERA. 1973. Solubilization and characterization of ovomucin without modification. Agric. Biol. Chem. **37:** 2175–2180.
14. ROJANAPO, W., J.A. OLSON & A.J. LAMB. 1980. Biochemical and immunological characterization and the synthesis of rat intestinal glycoproteins following the induction of rapid synchronous vitamin A deficiency. Biochim. Biophys. Acta. In press.

STUDIES ON THE MECHANISM OF INDUCTION OF EMBRYONAL CARCINOMA CELL DIFFERENTIATION BY RETINOIC ACID

Michael I. Sherman, Klaus I. Matthaei, and Joel Schindler

Roche Institute of Molecular Biology
Nutley, New Jersey 07110

CHARACTERIZATION OF EMBRYONAL CARCINOMA CELL LINES

Teratocarcinomas are tumors that can contain a variety of different cell types.[1-4] These derive from the differentiation of embryonal carcinoma (EC) cells, the stem cells of the tumor. In general, EC cells are also responsible for the malignancy of teratocarcinomas; the differentiated cell types, after being isolated from EC cells and reinjected into suitable hosts, tend not to be tumorigenic.[1-4] Knowledge of the way in which EC cells are triggered to differentiate could, therefore, be of some practical value in the treatment of teratocarcinomas in humans. An understanding of the mechanisms by which differentiation of EC cells is controlled might also be of general significance because EC cells resemble early embryonic cells in several respects,[3,5] the most impressive of which is their ability, when injected into early mouse embryos, to contribute to the formation of normal tissues of the resulting individuals.[6-8]

Studies on the regulation of differentiation of EC cells are facilitated by the availability of a large number of murine EC cell lines. Cells from these lines share a common morphology (see, e.g., FIG. 1A); however, perhaps through differences in isolation and initial culture procedures, they differ in certain respects, most notably in their ability to differentiate under various conditions. All of the EC lines we have studied will form tumors when injected into appropriate hosts but, as demonstrated in TABLE 1, the extent of differentiation of EC cells in these tumors varies. Characteristically, cells from "pluripotent" EC lines such as OC15 S1 or C86 S1 give rise to teratocarcinomas that contain a diverse array of cell types[9]; on the other hand, tumors from Nulli-SCC1 cells, for example, contain relatively few differentiated derivatives (P. McCue, unpublished observations).

During exponential growth in culture, EC cells show little tendency to differentiate. When the cultures reach high density, cells from some, but not all, of the lines gives rise to differentiated derivatives based upon morphological and biochemical criteria (TABLE 1). A more effective procedure for promoting differentiation of EC cells is to culture them under conditions wherein they fail to adhere to the substratum and thus form three-dimensional aggregates,[10-12] but even this approach will not stimulate cells from all EC lines to differentiate (TABLE 1).

Alterations of the culture medium can affect the differentiation of EC cells. For example, Avner *et al.*[13] have reported that varying the carbon source can influence the direction of differentiation of cells from a pluripotent EC line. Differentiation of EC cells can be promoted with hexamethylenebisacetamide,[14] a chemical used originally to stimulate differentiation of Friend erythroleukemia cells.[15] It seems that the most potent agent yet tested for promotion of differentiation of EC cells is retinoic acid (RA).[16,17] As indicated in TABLE 1, cells from all EC lines but one give rise to differentiated progeny in response to RA. In tests with a limited number of EC lines it has been observed that several other retinoids are

192

TABLE 1

RESPONSE OF CELLS OF SEVERAL MURINE EMBRYONAL CARCINOMA LINES TO
STIMULI FOR DIFFERENTIATION*

| | Ability to Differentiate as a Result of: | | | |
| | Tumor Formation | High Density Growth | Aggregation | Retinoic Acid Treatment |
Cell Line				
OC15 Sl	+ + +[9]	+ + +[9]	+ + +[17]	+ + +[17]
C86 Sl	+ + +[9]	+ + +[9]	+ + +[17]	+ + +[17]
PCC4.azal	+ + +[21]	− [10,21,‡]	+ +[10]	toxic[16,17]
PCC4.azalR	+ [†]	− [17]	+ +[17]	+ + +[17]
F9	+ [20]	+ [20]	+ [20]	+ + +[16,17]
Nulli-SCCl	+ [†]	− [11]	− [11,17]	+ + +[17]

* The ability of cells from several EC lines to differentiate under the indicated conditions was tested in various studies as indicated. Tumors were generally induced by the subcutaneous injection of EC cells. Aggregates were generated by culturing the cells in bacteriological petri dishes. RA was effective in stimulating differentiation when added to cultures at concentrations between 10^{-8}M and 10^{-5}M. Scoring was as follows: + + +, extensive differentiation; + +, moderate levels of differentiation; +, low levels of differentiation; −, differentiated cell types not detected.

† Tumors contained structures resembling primitive neuroectodermal tubules (P. McCue & M. Sherman, unpublished observations).

‡ Lo & Gilula[23] have recently reported that PCC4.azal cells differentiate when they reach high densities. We have never observed this to occur with PCC4.azal cells cultured in our laboratory.

also capable of stimulating differentiation though retinol and retinal are ineffective.[16,18,19]

EC cells that can be stimulated to differentiate by culture at high density or by aggregation give rise initially to non-EC cell types, which we shall refer to as the "primary differentiated derivative." The primary differentiated derivative is not the same for all EC lines; however, a particular primary differentiated derivative is reproducibly observed whenever EC cells from a given line are placed under conditions that promote differentiation.[10-12] When cells are treated with RA, they appear to give rise to the same primary differentiated derivative as they do when they are stimulated to differentiate by other means.[16,17] It seems, therefore, that RA does not influence the direction of differentiation but merely facilitates the transition to the primary differentiated derivative.

Subsequent to the appearance of primary differentiated derivatives in EC cultures from a number of lines, some of the remaining stem cells appear to shift their program and give rise to other differentiated cell types (reviewed by Graham[3]). It is not clear how such a change is effected. Preliminary evidence suggests that RA promotes this shift in some cases and suppresses it in others. For example, F9 cells, when they are stimulated to differentiate by aggregation, produce only cells resembling primitive endoderm.[20] However, in the presence of RA, F9 aggregates will generate fibroblastic cells in addition to endoderm-like cells.[17] Conversely, the differentiative ability of PCC4·azalR cells subjected to RA treatment, even after extended periods of time, appears to be largely, if not totally, restricted to cells bearing a morphological resemblance to the primary differentiated derivative (ref. 17 and unpublished observations). Although there are alternative explanations for the latter result, it is possible that RA stimulates differentiation of PCC4·azalR cells to the primary derivative so effectively that the population of undifferentiated stem cells becomes exhausted before the formation of other cell types can occur. This raises the question of how thoroughly a culture of EC cells can be induced to differentiate by RA. Since differentiated progeny are generally not malignant, we attempted to approach this question by testing the tumorigenicity of EC cells after increasing exposure times to RA.

TUMORIGENICITY OF RETINOIC ACID-TREATED EMBRYONAL CARCINOMA CELLS

The cells used in this study were PCC4·azalR. These cells were derived[17] from PCC4·azal EC cells, which die in the presence of RA.[16,17] PCC4·azalR cells differ from the parental cells in that they are tolerant to RA at concentrations as high as 10^{-5} M. However, PCC4·azalR cells resemble PCC4·azal cells in all other ways studied: both have the characteristic EC morphology, both fail to differentiate in monolayer culture but can be stimulated to differentiate if grown as aggregates for several days, and they have a similar or identical primary differentiated derivative.[10,17] PCC4·azalR cells respond to RA at concentrations between 10^{-9} and 10^{-5} M by undergoing differentiation to a fibroblast-like cell type.[17] We have seeded these cells at moderate densities (10^6 cells/75 cm^2 culture flask) in the presence of RA at 10^{-5} M or in the presence of 0.1% ethanol, the vehicle in which the RA was added. Within 5 days of exposure to RA, the cells formed clusters from which emerged cells with a fibroblastic morphology. RA-treated and control (ethanol-treated) cells were passaged at a density of 10^6 per flask each week for 4 weeks. The proportion of fibroblastic, non-EC cells in the RA-treated cultures (FIG. 1B) increased with time such that at the end of 2 weeks the vast majority of the cells had the morphology of the primary differentiated derivative. The control cultures contained only cells with an EC morphology, i.e., resembling those illustrated in FIGURE 1A.

After two weeks of culture, we injected subcutaneously four mice with a large inoculum (10^6 cells) of control cells. Four mice were also injected with the same number of RA-treated cells. After 4 weeks of culture, eight more mice were similarly inoculated. In all eight mice receiving control PCC4·azalR cells, tumors were palpable within 10 to 12 days. By 15 to 20 days, the swellings reached 2 cm and the tumors were collected for histological analyses. By contrast, despite the fact that the inoculum used was excessively large, there was no external sign of tumor growth in six of eight mice injected with RA-treated PCC4·azalR cells, even after 100-120 days. Autopsies of the mice after this period confirmed the absence of tumors (W. Wooding, personal communication). Tumors were observed in two mice injected with RA-treated cells. A tumor was palpable 25 days after one mouse received cells that had been exposed to RA for 2 weeks. In the second case, the mouse had been injected with cells that had been exposed to RA for 4 weeks. In this instance, the tumor was palpable within 12 days of inoculation. Histological analyses revealed that all the tumors, whether from control or RA-treated PCC4·azalR cells, contained predominantly EC cells with a minor population of elongated cells resembling primitive neuroectoderm.

These results indicate that RA treatment of the EC cultures had greatly reduced the malignancy of the cells, presumably through stimulating EC cells to produce nontumorigenic differentiated derivatives. The fact that the tumors arising in animals injected with RA-treated cells were teratocarcinomas is consistant with the view that at least some EC cells persisted in the cultures. Accordingly, we submitted to closer inspection cultures of PCC4·azalR cells treated con-

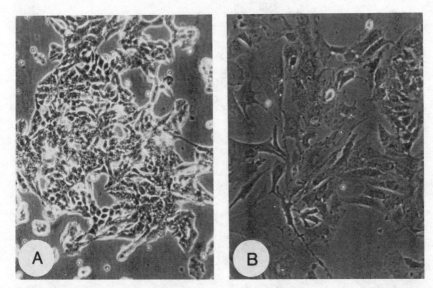

FIGURE 1. Morphology of embryonal carcinoma cells before and after treatment with retinioic acid. (A) PCC4.azalR cells in the absence of retinoic acid. (B) Differentiated cells observed after 4 weeks of continuous treatment of PCC4.azalR cultures with 10^{-5} M RA.

tinuously with RA. Although, as mentioned above, the cultures did not contain cells with overt EC phenotype after 14 days of treatment, a small number of foci of nonfibroblastic cells were observed after 21 days (FIG. 2A). The cells in these foci became progressively more rounded with time (FIG. 2B) until after 28 days they assumed morphologies associated with EC cells: rounded, loosely adherent cells with birefringent boundaries (FIG. 2C) or flattened, tightly packed cells with large nuclei and prominent nucleoli (FIG. 2D).

On the basis of these studies, we cannot eliminate the possibility that some primary differentiated derivative cells, once formed in RA-treated cultures, "dedifferentiated" to produce tumorigenic EC cells once again. However, we believe a much more plausible explanation of our results is that the cultures contained a minor population of EC cells which does not differentiate in response to RA and which can proliferate rapidly to form tumors once injected into appropriate hosts. We are presently attempting to isolate RA-resistant EC cells from such cultures for further analysis. At the same time, as described in the following section, we have succeeded by other means in obtaining cultures of EC cells that are unresponsive to RA.

ISOLATION AND CHARACTERIZATION OF *dif*⁻ EMBRYONAL CARCINOMA CELL LINES

In an effort to obtain EC cells which fail to differentiate in response to RA, we treated PCC4·azalR cells with the mutagen *N*-methyl-*N*-nitro-*N*-nitroso-guanidine and then seeded them at clonal density in the presence of RA. We obtained two clonal lines which, after subcloning, were capable of proliferating rapidly in the continuous presence of 10^{-5} M retinoic acid without showing any

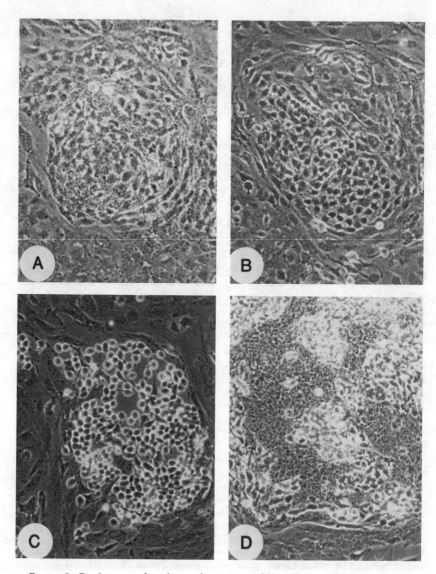

FIGURE 2. Persistence of embryonal carcinoma-like cells in cultures treated with retinoic acid. Foci of atypical cells were observed in PCC4.azalR cell cultures after (A) 21 and (B) 25 days of continuous culture. After 28 days of culture (C and D) the morphology of the cells in such foci closely resembled that of EC cells in the absence of RA.

signs of differentiation (Schindler, Matthaei & Sherman, Proc. Natl. Acad. Sci. USA, in press). We have named the lines *dif 1* and *dif 3*. Unlike parental PCC4·azalR cells, the *dif⁻* lines seem to differentiate poorly, if at all, in response to aggregation (Schindler, Matthaei & Sherman, in press). *Dif⁻* cells are highly tumorigenic; histological analyses of these tumors are currently in progress.

Work carried out in this laboratory has revealed that PCC4·azalR cells possess a retinoic acid-binding protein (RABP) which resembles those found in other RA-responsive cell types.[18] Furthermore, there is a good correlation between the ability of RA analogs and metabolites to stimulate differentiation of PCC4·azalR cells and to compete for sites on the binding protein.[18,19] On the basis of these studies, Jetten and Jetten[18] proposed that RABP was involved in the stimulation of differentiation of EC cells. Accordingly, we have assayed the *dif⁻* cell lines for levels of RABP. As indicated in TABLE 2, cells from the parental line, PCC4·azalR, possess ample amounts of RABP activity in the 17,000 dalton (2S) region of a sucrose gradient. On the other hand, cytoplasmic extracts of cells from both *dif⁻1* and *dif⁻3* lines bind negligible amounts of [³H]RA.

SUMMARY AND CONCLUSIONS

On the basis of our studies, we conclude that RA is a potent promoter of differentiation of EC cells. We have demonstrated that the tumorigenicity of PCC4·azalR EC cultures can be effectively reduced following exposure of the cells to RA. This is presumably a result of differentiation of the EC cells to non-tumorigenic derivatives. However, even after several weeks of exposure to RA, there remains in the culture a subpopulation of unresponsive EC cells. The reason why these cells do not differentiate in the presence of RA is currently under investigation.

We have also derived by mutagen treatment and clonal selection EC cells that fail to respond to RA. Preliminary indications are that these cells have lost the capacity to differentiate when subjected to other manipulations which stimulate differentiation of the parental EC cells. This is an important observation since the mutants were selected only by their lack of response to RA. Unlike the parental cells, which have relatively large amounts of RABP, *dif⁻* cells appear either to lack RABP or to possess an altered binding protein which has a greatly reduced affinity for RA. These observations are consistent with the view that some function of the RA-RABP complex is critical in the sequence of events leading to differentia-

TABLE 2

BINDING OF RETINOIC ACID TO CYTOPLASMIC EXTRACTS OF
PCC4·azalR AND *dif⁻* EMBRYONAL CARCINOMA CELLS

Cell Line	RABP Levels*
PCC4.azalR	1.7
dif⁻1	<0.03
dif⁻3	<0.03

* EC cells were grown in monolayer culture as described,[17] washed, collected with a rubber policeman, and pelleted. Cells were disrupted and cytoplasmic extracts were obtained by high speed centrifugation.[18] The extracts were incubated with $5 \times 10^{-8} M$ [³H]RA (~30 Ci/mmole) with or without $10^{-5}M$ unlabeled RA for 4 hr at 4°. After removal of unbound RA with charcoal-coated dextran,[22] extracts were layered on a 5–20% sucrose gradient and centrifuged in a Beckman SW50.1 rotor at $220,000 \times g$ for 18 hr. The specific binding of [³H]RA to RABP was determined from the radioactivity in the 2S region of the gradient[18] after correction for nonspecific binding [(cpm in sample incubated only with [³H]RA) − (cpm in sample incubated with [³H]RA plus unlabeled RA)]. Values are expressed in terms of pmoles [³H]RA bound specifically to RABP/mg total protein in the cytoplasmic extract.

tion of EC cells. However, further studies are required before we can establish the generality of this proposal. We are presently investigating whether the level and/or function of RA-RABP complexes in cells from the EC lines listed in TABLE 1 can explain their varying tendencies to differentiate.

ACKNOWLEDGMENTS

We wish to thank Drs. William Wooding and Peter McCue for carrying out tumor analyses and Dr. Dennis Stacey for comments on the manuscript.

REFERENCES

1. DAMJANOV, I. & D. SOLTER. 1974. Experimental teratoma. Current Topics Pathol. **59:** 69–130.
2. SHERMAN, M.I. & D. SOLTER, Eds. 1975. Teratomas and Differentiation. Academic Press. New York.
3. GRAHAM, C.F. 1977. Teratocarcinoma cells and normal mouse embryogenesis. *In* Current Concepts in Mammalian Embryogenesis. M. I. Sherman, Ed.: 315–394. MIT Press. Cambridge, MA.
4. SOLTER, D. & I. DAMJANOV. 1979. Teratocarcinoma and the expression of oncodevelopmental genes. Methods Cancer Res. **18:** 277–332.
5. MARTIN, G. 1978. Advantages and limitations of teratocarcinoma stem cells as models of development. *In* Development in Mammals. M. H. Johnson, Ed.: 225–265. North-Holland. Amsterdam.
6. BRINSTER, R.L. 1974. The effect of cells transferred into the mouse blastocyst on subsequent development. J. Exp. Med. **140:** 1049–1056.
7. MINTZ, B. & K. ILLMENSEE. 1975. Normal genetically mosaic mice produced from malignant teratocarcinoma cells. Proc. Natl. Acad. Sci. USA **72:** 3585–3589.
8. PAPAIOANNOU, W.E., M.W. McBURNEY, R.L. GARDNER & M.J. EVANS. 1975. Fate of teratocarcinoma cells injected into early mouse embryos. Nature **258:** 70–73.
9. McBURNEY, M. W. 1976. Clonal lines of teratocarcinoma cells in *in vitro:* Differentiation and cytogenetic characteristics. J. Cell Physiol. **89:** 441–455.
10. SHERMAN, M.I. 1975. Differentiation of teratoma cells line PCC4·azal *in vitro. In* Teratomas and Differentiation. M.I. Sherman & D. Solter, Eds.: 189–205. Academic Press. New York.
11. MARTIN, G.R. & M.J. EVANS. 1975. The formation of embryoid bodies *in vitro* by homogeneous embryonal carcinoma cell cultures derived from isolated single cells. *In* Teratomas and Differentiation. M.I. Sherman & D. Solter, Eds.: 169–187. Academic Press. New York.
12. NICOLAS, J.F., P. DUBOIS, H. JAKOB, J. GAILLARD & F. JACOB. 1975. Tératocarcinome de la souris: Différenciation en culture d'une lignée de cellules primitives à potentialités multiples. Ann. Microbiol. (Inst. Pasteur) **126A:** 3–22.
13. AVNER, P., P. DUBOIS, J.F. NICOLAS, H. JAKOB, J. GAILLARD & F. JACOB. 1977. Mouse teratocarcinoma. Carbon source patterns for growth and *in vitro* differentiation. Exp. Cell Res. **105:** 39–50.
14. JAKOB, H., P. DUBOIS, H. EISEN & F. JACOB. 1978. Effects de l'hexaméthylène-bisacétamide sur la différenciation de cellules de carcinome embryonnaire. C.R. Acad. Sci. Ser. D **286:** 109–111.
15. REUBEN, R.L., R.L. WIFE, R. BRESLOW, R.A. RIFKIND & P. MARKS. 1976. A new group of potent inducers of differentiation in murine erythroleukemia cells. Proc. Natl. Acad. Sci. USA **73:** 862–866.
16. STRICKLAND, S. & V. MAHDAVI. 1978. The induction of differentiation in teratocarcinoma stem cells by retinoic acid. Cell **15:** 393–403.
17. JETTEN, A.M., M.E.R. JETTEN & M.I. SHERMAN. 1979. Stimulation of differentiation of

several murine embryonal carcinoma cell lines by retinoic acid. Exp. Cell Res. **124:** 381-391.

18. JETTEN, A.M. & M.E.R. JETTEN. 1979. Possible role of retinoic acid binding protein in retinoid stimulation of embryonal carcinoma cell differentiation. Nature **278:** 180-182.
19. TROWN, P.W., A.V. PALLERONI, O. BOHOSLAWEC, B.N. RICHELO, J.M. HALPERN, N. GIZZI, R. GEIGER, C. LEWINSKI, L.J. MACHLIN, A. JETTEN & M.E.R. JETTEN. 1980. Relationship between binding affinities to cellular retinoic acid binding protein *in vitro* and *in vivo* properties for 18 retinoids. Cancer Res. **40:** 212-220.
20. SHERMAN, M.I. & R.A. MILLER. 1978. F9 embryonal carcinoma cells can differentiate into endoderm-like cells. Develop. Biol. **63:** 27-34.
21. JAKOB, A., T. BOON, J. GAILLARD, J. F. NICOLAS & F. JACOB. 1973. Tératocarcinome de la souris: Isolement, culture et propriétés de cellules à potentialités multiples. Ann. Microbiol. (Inst. Pasteur) **124B:** 269-282.
22. MARCAL, J.M., N.J. CHEW, D.S. SALOMON & M.I. SHERMAN. 1975. Δ^5, 3β-Hydroxysteroid dehydrogenase activities in rat trophoblast and ovary during pregnancy. Endocrinology **96:** 1270-1279.
23. LO, C. & N.B. GILULA. 1980. PCC4·azal teratocarcinoma stem cell differentiation in culture. I. Biochemical studies. Develop. Biol. **75:** 78-92.

ACTION OF RETINOIDS AND PHORBOL ESTERS ON CELL GROWTH AND THE BINDING OF EPIDERMAL GROWTH FACTOR

Anton M. Jetten

Laboratory of Experimental Pathology
National Cancer Institute
National Institutes of Heatlh
Bethesda, Maryland 20205

Retinoids play, outside the visual process, a diverse and essential role in growth and development of vertebrates.[1,2] Many of the biological effects have been identified by the study of nutritional deprivation *in vivo* as well as *in vitro*. These studies include the requirement of vitamin A for the male reproductive system; during vitamin A deficiency the germinal epithelium in the testis fails to produce sperm and the epididymal epithelium undergoes metaplasia to a keratinized state.[3] The latter seems to be a more general response of epithelial cells to vitamin A deficiency, since uterine, vaginal, and respiratory epithelium[4,5] and epidermis cells[6] also undergo squamous metaplasia and eventually keratinization.

Another activity of retinoids, which may be related, at least partially, to the maintenance of mucous secretion of epithelial cells, is their capability of delaying or preventing the development of certain epithelial carcinomas *in vivo* and in organ cultures.[7-10] The anticarcinogenic activity of some retinoids has also been established by *in vitro* studies, which show an inhibition of chemical transformation by various retinoids.[11-13] However, caution is warranted for considering retinoids solely as anticarcinogenic agents, since some reports have suggested a tumor-promoting effect *in vivo*.[14] Furthermore, retinoids can induce biochemical properties in cells that often accompany the transformed state.[15,16]

EFFECTS OF RETINOIDS ON CELL GROWTH

Growth control may appear to fulfill a key role both in the maintenance and differentiation of epithelial tissues as well as in the suppression of tumor formation.[17] There are, however, contrary reports on the effects of retinoids on cell growth. A number of studies have shown growth-stimulating activity by retinoids; *in vivo* and in explant cultures vitamin A can stimulate the proliferation of skin, corneal, and tracheal epithelial cells.[18,19] Similar effects have been observed with cultured cells *in vitro*[20]; Lasnitzki[21] reported that vitamin A enhanced the proliferation of chick heart fibroblasts. In contrast to these findings are the studies that reported a growth-inhibitory effect by retinoids in many untransformed and chemically, virally, and spontaneously transformed cell lines.[22-26] This inhibitory action can be divided into two categories: reduction in saturation density and inhibition of exponential growth rate. TABLE 1 summarizes the influence of retinoic acid on growth in a number of cell lines. In some cell lines, like mouse fibroblasts 3T6, 3T3A31-1-BP-2, melanoma Cloudman S91-M3, and mammary carcinoma mcf-7 both growth parameters were affected, however to a different extent. In other cell lines, like BHK-21, V79, A431, and 407, retinoic

200

acid did not inhibit growth significantly in either way. The effects of retinoids on growth of 3T6 cells were reversible; 4 or 5 days after omission of the retinoic acid, growth rate and saturation density returned to those of untreated cells. Another way to determine the action of retinoids on growth is to study the serum requirement for retinoic acid-treated and untreated cells. FIGURE 1 shows the effect of various serum concentrations on growth of retinoic acid-treated and untreated 3T6 cells. At all serum concentrations tested, the growth rate of retinoic acid-treated cells was drastically reduced, but the reduction was more dramatic at low serum concentrations; at 0.5% calf serum the increase in the number of 3T6 cells grown in the presence of retinoic acid was 25% whereas the number of untreated cells increased by 400%. These results indicate that retinoic acid-treated cells have a stronger serum requirement than untreated cells.

STIMULATION OF THE BINDING OF EPIDERMAL GROWTH FACTOR TO FIBROBLAST 3T6 CELLS BY RETINOIC ACID

The findings above show that retinoids affect the growth of many cell lines.

TABLE 1

EFFECT OF RETINOIC ACID ON GROWTH OF VARIOUS
UNTRANSFORMED AND TRANSFORMED CELL LINES*

Cell Type	Designation	Reduction in Saturation Density (%)	Inhibition of Exponential Growth Rate (%)
Mouse fibroblast	3T6	64	30
	3T12	37	5
	3T12 CLA	42	6
	BALB/c 3T3	33	21
	BALB/c 3T3SV	<5	<5
	BALB/c 3T3 A31-1-1	37	29
	BALB/c 3T3 A31-1-BP-2	61	33
	BALB/c 3T3 A31-1-DMBA-1	25	N.D.
	C3H/10T½-CL8	33	31
	C3H/10T½-MCA	42	26
Mouse epidermal	JB-6	41	N.D.
Mouse melanoma	Cloudman S91-M3	49	79
Human epidermal carcinoma	A431	<5	<5
Syrian hamster kidney	BHK-21	5	<5
Human intestine	407	<5	<5
Mink lung	MV1-Lu	<5	65
Human mammary carcinoma	mcf-7	36	81
Chinese hamster lung	V79	<5	<5

* Cells were grown in Dulbecco's modified Eagle's (DME) medium containing 10% calf serum, except for C3H/10T½-MCA and mcf-7 which were grown in DME containing 10% fetal calf serum and C3H/10T ½-CL8 an Cloudman S91-M3 which were cultured in DME/ Ham's F12 (1:1) medium containing 10% fetal calf serum. Reduction in saturation density and growth rate by 10^{-5}M retionic acid were determined as described previously.[24] For C3H/10T ½-CL8 and MCA and mcf-7 10^{-6}M was used.

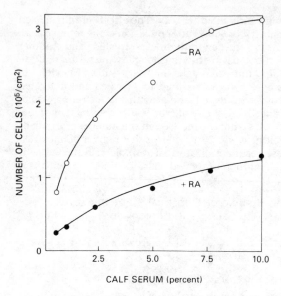

FIGURE 1. Serum requirement of retinoic acid-treated and untreated 3T6 cells. Cells were pregrown in DME-medium containing 10% calf serum in the presence of retinoic acid dissolved in ethanol or in the presence of ethanol alone (0.15% v/v final concentration). After trypsinization cells were subcultured in 35 mm cluster dishes (2 × 10^5 cells per well) in DME/F12 (1:1) medium containing various concentrations of calf serum and in the presence (●) or absence (O) of 10^{-5}M retinoic acid. After 3 days of incubation, cell count was determined in a Coulter counter and plotted against the serum concentration.

Propagation of eukaryotic cells has been demonstrated to be dependent on the presence of macromolecular growth factors.[27] One of these growth factors, is the epidermal growth factor (EGF), a polypeptide with a molecular weight of 6045 that binds to specific receptors at the cell surface of responding cells.[28-30] EGF can stimulate proliferation of various epidermal and epithelial tissues both *in vivo* and in culture.[28] It is also a potent mitogen for many fibroblast cells.[31,32] Since retinoids affect the growth of many cell lines, we undertook the present study to determine the binding of EGF and the mitogenic activity of this growth factor in retinoic acid-treated and untreated cells.

FIGURE 2 shows a time course study of the effect of retinoic acid on the binding of EGF to 3T6 cells. During a 3-day period of retinoic acid treatment, binding of EGF increased dramatically and reached a maximum at 4 days that was five to sevenfold the level of EGF binding to untreated cells. This stimulation of EGF binding was reversible, as shown in FIGURE 3. When 3T6 cells, that were cultured in the presence of retinoic acid for 4 days, were subcultured in the absence of this retinoid, EGF binding decreased gradually and after 5 days binding levels returned to that of control cells. At that time the morphology was indistinguishable from that of untreated cells.

FIGURE 4 shows the extent of EGF binding to retinoic acid-treated and untreated 3T6 cells as a function of the time of addition. No major differences were observed in the shape of the binding curves between retinoic acid-treated and control cells. Maximum binding was reached after 45 to 60 min. Further incubation with ^{125}I-labeled EGF led to a decrease in cell-associated radioactivity. This reduction in binding has been reported for other cell lines and reflects the degradation of ^{125}I-EGF in the lysosomes and subsequent secretion of ^{125}I-tyrosine.[33,34]

The increase in EGF binding was dependent on the concentration of retinoic acid, as described previously.[35] Even at 10^{-8}M retinoic acid binding of EGF was enhanced twofold; binding reached a maximum at 3.10^{-6}M, fivefold above control levels. FIGURE 5 shows a comparison between the action of various concen-

FIGURE 2. Binding of ^{125}I-labeled mouse EGF to retinoic acid-treated and control 3T6 cells.

Cells were grown in DME medium containing 10% calf serum in the presence (●) and absence (O) of 10^{-5}M retinoic acid. At different time intervals after the addition of retinoic acid binding of ^{125}I-EGF was determined and plotted against time. Measurement of the binding of EGF was performed as described previously.[34,35] In the binding assays 0.825 ng EGF per ml (Collaborative Research, Waltham, MA) was added to each well.

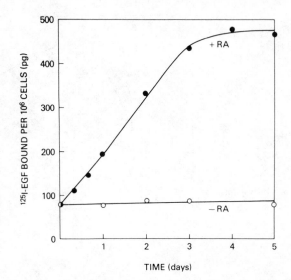

trations of retinoic acid on EGF binding and the effects on cell-to-substratum adhesiveness and the production of glycosaminoglycans. The increase in glycosaminoglycans followed the change in adhesiveness much more closely than did the increase in EGF binding. This may indicate a direct relationship between the increased adhesiveness and enhancement of glycosaminoglycans, as suggested earlier.[24] At low concentrations retinoic acid had a stronger effect on EGF binding (increased at 10^{-8}M by approximately 25% of maximum change)

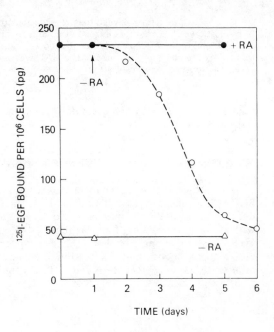

FIGURE 3. Reversibility of the effect of retinoic acid on EGF binding.

3T6 cells were grown for 4 days in the presence of retinoic acid (10^{-5}M). Then binding of EGF was determined at various time intervals after the removal of retinoic acid (O) and during the continued presence of retinoic acid (●). △, EGF binding to untreated cells.

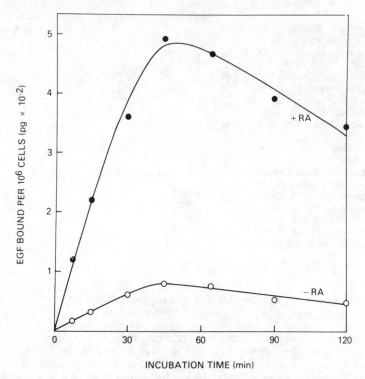

FIGURE 4. Time course of the binding to EGF to retinoic acid-treated and untreated 3T6 cells.

Cells were grown for 3 days in the presence and absence of retinoic acid (10^{-5}M). After trypsinization cells were subcultured in the same medium in 35 mm cluster dishes (1-2 × 10^5 cells per well). After a 48-hr incubation the time course of the binding of EGF to retinoic acid-treated (●) and untreated cells (O) was determined. The EGF binding was assayed as described previously.[35]

than adhesiveness and glycosaminoglycans (increased at 10^{-8}M by 3 and 6%, respectively).

RETINOIC ACID AFFECTS THE NUMBER OF EGF RECEPTORS, NOT AFFINITY

As has been shown above in various ways, retinoic acid enhanced binding of EGF to 3T6 cells. This stimulation can be brought about by either an increase in unoccupied receptors or increased affinity to the EGF receptor, a glycoprotein with a molecular weight of approximately 185,000.[36] We have shown recently[35] via Scatchard plot analyses that retinoic acid has no marked effect on the affinity of ^{125}I-labeled mouse EGF for the binding site of its receptor but increases the number of EGF receptors at the cell surface from 2.07 × 10^4 receptors per cell for control cells to 1.51 × 10^5 receptors per cell after retinoic acid treatment.

SPECIFICITIES OF THE ACTION OF RETINOIDS

TABLE 2 summarizes the effects on the binding of EGF and several other biological properties by various analogs. The specificity of the retinoids to stimulate EGF binding to 3T6 cells paralleled the specificity with which they inhibited growth, increased cell-to-substratum adhesiveness of these cells, and induced differentiation of embryonal carcinoma cells.[24,37,38] The action of the various analogs also correlated well with their ability to compete with retinoic acid for the binding site of retinoic acid-binding protein. However, retinol and retinyl acetate formed an exception; these compounds did not compete for the binding site of the retinoic acid-binding protein but were still active. The activity of retinol and retinyl acetate in some cell lines may be explained by the presence of retinol-binding protein, but their activity in 3T6 cells cannot be explained in this way, since no retinol-binding protein could be detected in these cells (unpublished data).

The enhancement of EGF binding is not restricted to 3T6 cells. As shown in FIGURE 3, a large number of untransformed, spontaneously and chemically transformed mouse fibroblast cell lines exhibited increased levels of EGF binding after treatment with retinoic acid. The EGF binding was also enhanced in 3T3 cells, but not in its virus-transformed derivative 3T3SV, which correlates well with our previous findings that several other biological properties were affected

FIGURE 5. Comparison between changes in EGF binding, cell-substratum adhesiveness and production of glycosaminoglycans induced by various concentrations of retinoic acid. 3T6 fibroblasts were treated with various concentrations of retinoic acid for 5 days, then binding of ^{125}I-EGF (O), adhesiveness ($\bullet$) and production of glycosaminoglycans ($\triangle$) were determined as described previously.[24] The results were normalized using the following equation $P = \dfrac{\Delta x}{\Delta max} \times 100$; where P is defined as the percent of the maximum difference, Δmax as the difference between the values of the parameter at 0M and 10^{-5}M RA and Δx as the difference between 0M and xM RA.

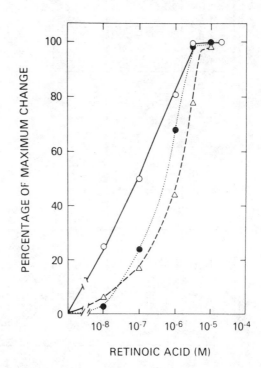

TABLE 2

COMPARISON OF THE ACTION OF RETINOIDS ON SEVERAL CELL PROPERTIES*

Basic Chemical Structure	R	Relative EGF Binding	Inhibition of Growth (%)	Increase in Adhesiveness	Competition for RABP Binding Site	Stimulation of Differentiation
(structure)	CH_2OH CH_2OCOCH_3 $COOH$ CH_2OCH_3	2.71 3.03 5.68 1.14	36 39 65 14	+ + ++ –	– – + –	T 100 100 0
(structure)	$COOH$ CH_2OCH_3	3.81 1.07	61 14	++ –	+ –	100 0
(structure)	$COOH$	5.63	64	++	+	100
(structure)	$COOH$	0.98	9	–	–	0
(structure)	$COOH$	4.18	56	++	+	100
(structure)	$COOH$	0.84	8	–	–	0

* 3T6 cells were grown in the presence of 10^{-5}M of the indicated analog and after five days of incubation EGF binding was determined as described previously.[34,37] From the obtained data the relative EGF binding, defined as binding of ^{125}I-EGF to retinoid-treated cells/binding to control cells, was calculated. This was compared to inhibition of growth, increase in adhesiveness of 3T6 cells, competition with retinoic acid for the binding site of retinoic acid-binding protein, and ability to stimulate differentiation of embryonal carcinoma cells.[24,37] T means retinoid was toxic.

by retinoids in 3T3 but not in 3T3SV cells.[24] This difference in responsiveness may be attributed to the presence and absence of the retinoic acid-binding protein in 3T3 and 3T3SV, respectively.[24] Retinoic acid also stimulated severalfold the binding of EGF to three mouse epidermal cell lines, namely JB-6 and its tumorigenic derivatives T62 and T3. Furthermore, treatment of mink lung MV1-Lu and rat kidney 536-3 cells with retinoic acid enhanced EGF binding by approximately 60 and 300 percent, respectively. These results indicate that this action of retinoids is not limited to a specific cell type or to a particular species. However, this effect is not a general phenomenon since binding of EGF was not affected significantly by retinoic acid in BHK-21, mammary carcinoma mcf-7, chinese hamster lung V79, human intestine 407, and human epidermal carcinoma A431 cells.

The action of retinoic acid on cell surface glycoproteins appeared to be of a specific nature. As shown in TABLE 4, retinoic acid enhanced the binding of EGF to 3T6 and 3T12 CLA cells by more than sevenfold while Con A binding was increased by only 32 and 24 percent, respectively. No effect was observed on the binding of insulin.[35]

EFFECT OF TUNICAMYCIN ON RETINOIC ACID-TREATED AND UNTREATED CELLS

Many aspects of the behavior of cells such as adhesiveness, contact inhibition, movement, and tumorigenicity are influenced by composition, arrangement, and interaction of cell surface macromolecules. It has been suggested[39,40] that the phosphorylated metabolites of retinoids may be involved in the process-

TABLE 3

EFFECT OF RETINOIC ACID ON THE BINDING OF EGF TO VARIOUS CELL LINES*

| Cell Type | Designation | ^{125}I-EGF Binding (10^3 dpm/per 10^6 cells) | | |
		Control	RA-treated	Relative Binding
Mouse fibroblast	3T6	3.82	25.98	6.0
	3T12 CLA	2.18	16.54	7.6
	BALB/c 3T3	4.59	15.14	3.3
	BALB/c 3T3 SV	4.92	5.93	1.2
	BALB/c 3T3 A31-1-DMBA-1	1.74	6.20	3.56
	BALB/c 3T3 A31-1-BP-2	0.14	0.16	1.14
	BALB/c 3T3 A31-1-1	2.68	11.42	4.26
	C3H/10T1/2-CL8	2.55	10.36	4.06
	C3H/10 T1/2-MCA	1.67	7.77	4.65
Mouse epidermal	JB-6	3.70	9.36	2.53
	T62	3.17	10.58	3.34
	T3	2.73	9.57	3.51
Mink lung	MV1-Lu	14.64	23.27	1.59
Rat kidney fibroblast	NRK-536-3	3.00	9.55	3.18

* Cells were grown as mentioned in FIGURE 1. Binding of EGF was determined as described previously.[34-37]

TABLE 4

EFFECT OF TUNICAMYCIN ON THE BINDING OF EGF AND CON A TO RETINOIC
ACID-TREATED AND UNTREATED CELLS*

Cell Line	Treatment	125I-EGF Binding (10³ dpm/ 10⁶ cells)	Inhibition (%)	125I-Con A Binding (10³ dpm/ 10⁶ cells)	Inhibition (%)
3T6	Control	3.61		34.93	
	+Tunicamycin	0.61	83	27.92	20
	+RA	26.11		46.17	
	+RA, +Tunica- mycin	1.31	95	29.04	37
3T12	Control	2.31		29.12	
	+Tunicamycin	0.18	92	18.64	36
	+RA	16.40		35.82	
	+RA, Tunicamycin	0.66	96	19.34	46

* 3T6 and 3T12 ClA cells were grown in DME medium containing 10% calf serum in the presence (+RA) and absence of 10^{-5}M retinoic acid for 3 days. Cells were subcultured in the same medium in 35 mm cluster dishes. After 32 hr of incubation tunicamycin (0.5 µg/ml final concentration) or methanol was added and incubation was continued for an additional 20 hr. At that time, the binding of 125I-EGF (1 ng/ml) or 125I-Con A (25 ng/ml) was measured as described previously. From these data the percent inhibition of binding by tunicamycin was calculated.

ing of specific glycoconjugates and in this way alter a number of cell surface-modulated phenomena, such as those just mentioned. Therefore, we examined the influence of tunicamycin on retinoic acid-treated and untreated cells. This was of interest because tunicamycin is an antibiotic that inhibits protein glycosylation[41-43] by blocking the transfer of N-acetylglucosamine-phosphate from UDP-N-acetylglucosamine to dolichyl phosphate. Control 3T6 cells treated with tunicamycin were more spindle-like and rounded up and less adhesive than untreated cells (FIG. 6A–B). Meanwhile, retinoic acid-grown 3T6 cells treated with tunicamycin maintained the very flat morphology characteristic for retinoic acid-treated 3T6 cells (FIG. 6 D,E); the cells became less adhesive but remained much more adhesive than cells not treated with retinoic acid. These results show that morphology and adhesiveness of retinoic acid-grown cells were largely maintained after treatment with tunicamycin and are thus consistent with the idea that retinoic acid increases the retention of cell surface macromolecules that play a role in these phenomena.[44]

TABLE 4 shows the effect of tunicamycin on the binding of EGF and Con A to their cell surface receptors in retinoic acid-treated and untreated 3T6 and 3T12 cells. In all instances tunicamycin dramatically reduced the binding of EGF, while Con A binding was affected to a much smaller extent. Furthermore, the binding of Con A to retinoic acid-grown cells was consistently more inhibited by tunicamycin than the binding to control cells.

ACTION OF RETINOIC ACID AND TPA ON CELL GROWTH AND EGF BINDING.

Many studies have used retinoids in combination with tumor promoters such as phorbol esters. Some reports have shown antagonism between these compounds[45,46] while others have demonstrated a synergistic interaction.[15,16] In contrast to the action of retinoic acid, TPA has been shown to stimulate mitogenic activity and to reduce binding of EGF in various cell lines.[33,47,48] Therefore, we compared the action of TPA and retinoic acid on cell growth and EGF binding in 3T6 cells.

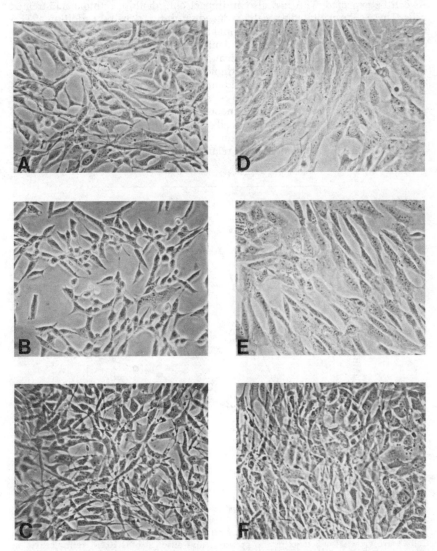

FIGURE 6. Effect of tunicamycin and TPA on the morphology of retinoic acid-treated and untreated 3T6 cells.
Cells were grown for 4 days in the presence and absence of 10^{-5}M retinoic acid and treated with tunicamycin (0.5 μg/ml) or TPA (100 ng/ml) for 20 hr. A–C, Control cells; D–F, Retinoic acid-treated cells; B, E, Tunicamycin-treated cells; C, F, TPA-treated cells.

As mentioned above, 3T6 cells grown in the presence of retinoic acid showed a strong contact inhibition; cells appeared much flatter than control cells and had no tendency to overlap (FIG. 6A,D). When these cells were treated with TPA, cell morphology was reversed to that of control cells (FIG. 6F). TPA did not have a marked effect on the morphology of untreated 3T6 cells (FIG. 6C) and since these cells did not show contact inhibition, this seemed not to be changed any further. As can be expected, TPA had also an impact on growth of retinoic acid-treated cells. These cells exhibited a greatly reduced saturation density[24]; addition of TPA restored growth and cells reached a final saturation density almost equal to that of control cells (FIG. 7). TPA did not significantly alter the saturation density of untreated 3T6 cells. These results indicate that TPA largely abolished the contact inhibition of 3T6 cells induced by retinoic acid.

The effect of TPA and retinoic acid on the binding of EGF is shown in TABLE 5. When TPA alone was added to 3T6 cells, EGF binding was drastically reduced within 5 hours of treatment. Simultaneous treatment with retinoic acid did not have any effect on this reduction. Cells grown for 3 days in the presence of retinoic acid also exhibited a strong reduction in EGF binding after the addition of TPA, although the reduction was relatively smaller than in control cells.

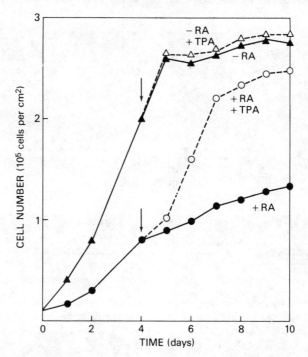

FIGURE 7. Action of TPA on growth of retinoic acid-treated and untreated 3T6 cells. Cells were grown for 3 days in the presence and absence of 2.10^{-6}M retinoic acid in DME/F12 medium containing 10% calf serum. Cells were subcultured in the same medium containing 2.5% calf serum and in the continued presence (●) and absence (▲) of retinoic acid at an initial density of 2×10^4 cells/cm². After 4 days of incubation TPA (50 ng/ml; *open symbols*) was added (*arrow*). Medium was renewed every day. Cell numbers were determined at different time intervals.

TABLE 5

COMPARISON OF THE ACTION OF RETINOIC ACID AND TPA ON THE BINDING OF
EGF TO 3T6 CELLS†

Cell Line	Treatment	^{125}I-EGF Binding (pg/10^6 cells)	Relative Binding
3T6 (grown in the presence of 0.15% ethanol)	Control	84.1	1.0
	+TPA, 5 hr	5.1	0.06
	+TPA, 2 days	7.7	0.09
	+PDA, 5 hr	80.6	0.96
	+RA, 5 hr	97.7	1.16
	+TPA, +RA, 5 hr	3.0	0.04
	+RA*	89.5	1.06
3T6 (grown in the presence of 10^{-5}M RA for 3 days)	Control	451.2	5.37
	+TPA, 5 hr	65.3	0.78
	+TPA, 2 days	71.5	0.85
	+PDA, 5 hr	440.8	5.24

† Cells were treated with 50 ng/ml 12-O-tetradecanoyl phorbol-13-acetate (TPA), 50 ng/ml phorbol-13,20-diacetate (PDA) and 10^{-5}M retinoic acid (RA) for the times indicated. Controls received identical amounts of DMSO or ethanol. RA* indicates 10^{-5}M retinoic acid was present during EGF-binding assay. EGF concentration was 1.25 ng/ml.

Therefore, the actions of retinoic acid and TPA on EGF binding do not appear to be of an antagonistic nature.

Retinoic acid-treated cells grown initially in 1% serum and then for 2 days in serum-free medium became quiescent at a lower density than did control cells (FIG. 8). In both the retinoic acid-treated and untreated cells mitogenic activity could be stimulated by the addition of EGF and/or insulin, although in the presence of these growth factors the densities reached by retinoic acid-treated cells were always lower than those of control cells. Addition of TPA alone did not enhance mitogenic activity in control cells whereas proliferation was stimulated in retinoic acid-treated cells. Simultaneous treatment with TPA and EGF or insulin increased proliferation of retinoic acid-treated cells as well as control cells. Under these conditions, however, TPA did not seem to enhance the proliferation of control cells any further while it appeared to have an additional stimulation on retinoic acid-treated cells. Retinoic acid-grown cells treated with TPA and growth factors reached densities almost equal to that of cells not treated with retinoic acid. These results indicate that EGF and insulin do not stimulate mitogenic activity in retinoic acid-treated cells as effectively as in control cells. This inhibition caused by retinoic acid treatment appears to be abolished by TPA.

INFLUENCE OF LECTINS ON EGF BINDING

Carpenter and Cohen have shown that pretreatment of cells with various lectins inhibit binding of EGF to its receptor.[53] In order to determine whether retinoic acid or TPA alter carbohydrate moieties at the cell surface and therefore affect EGF binding, we studied the inhibitory action of concanavalin A (Con A), wheat germ agglutinin (WGA) and peanut agglutinin (PA) on the binding of EGF to retinoic acid, TPA and untreated 3T6 cells. As shown in FIGURE 9, Con A and

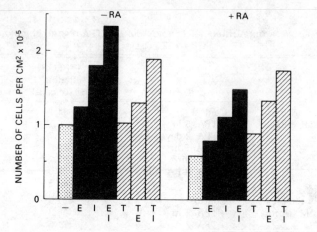

FIGURE 8. Effect of EGF, insulin and TPA on growth of quiescent retinoic acid-treated and untreated 3T6 cells.

Cells were grown in the presence and absence of $10^{-6}M$ retinoic acid for 3 days and then subcultured in DME/F12 (1:1) medium containing 1% calf serum plus and minus $10^{-6}M$ retinoic acid at an initial density of 4.10^5 cells per 35 mm dish. After one day incubation medium was changed to DME/F12 (1:1) containing 1 μg transferrin/ml and 1 mg bovine serum albumin/ml. After another 2-day incubation period, EGF (E; 10 ng/ml), insulin (I; 0.5 μg/ml) and TPA (T; 50 ng/ml) were added separately or together as indicated. Cell count was determined after 4 days.

WGA inhibited EGF binding dramatically whereas PA caused only a minor reduction. The inhibitory action of Con A and WGA were for a large part readily reversed by the addition of α-methyl mannoside (α MM) and N-acetylglucosamine or neuraminic acid. Furthermore, these lectins decreased EGF binding to retinoic acid-treated, retinoic acid plus TPA-treated and untreated 3T6 cells to almost the same extent at all concentrations tested. It can be concluded that these results do not reveal changes in the terminal carbohydrates of the EGF receptor or a glyco-

TABLE 6

COMPARISON OF THE BINDING OF EGF TO VARIOUS EMBRYONAL CARCINOMA CELL LINES AND THEIR DIFFERENTIATED DERIVATIVES*

Cell Line		^{125}I-EGF Binding (pg per 10^6 cells)
Embryonal carcinoma	PCC4 aza 1R	1.2
	OC15S1	1.9
	F9	0.9
Differentiated derivatives	PCC4 D1	67.1
	15 D1	59.8
	15 D2	2.2
	F9 D1	1.9

* Cells were grown in DME/Ham's F12 (1:1) containing 10% fetal calf serum. The differentiated derivatives were obtained after induction with 10^{-7} or $10^{-8}M$ retinoic acid. EGF binding was determined as described previously[34,35]; EGF concentration was 1.25 ng/ml.

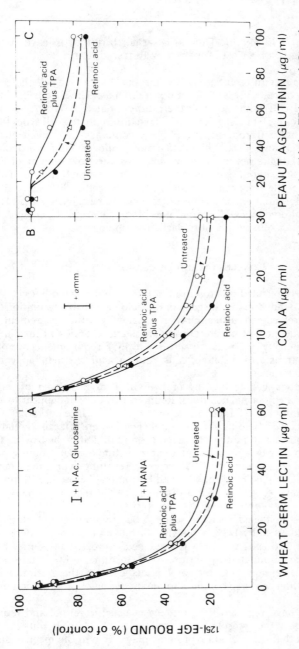

FIGURE 9. Inhibition of ^{125}I-EGF binding by Con A, WGA and PA to retinoic acid-treated (●), retinoic acid plus TPA-treated (○) and untreated (△) 3T6 cells. Cells were treated with $2 \cdot 10^{-6}$ M retinoic acid for 5 days and with 30 ng/ml TPA for 3 hr. Before EGF binding was determined cells were pretreated with various concentrations of Con A, WGA, and PA in binding buffer. To test reversibility of the inhibitory action of the lectins, cells were incubated with 50 mM of each of α-methylmannoside (α MM), N-acetyl-glucosamine or neuraminic acid (NANA) for an additional 5 min.

protein/glycolipid closely associated with the receptor after treatment of 3T6 cells with retinoic acid or TPA.

INCREASE IN EGF BINDING DURING DIFFERENTIATION OF EMBRYONAL CARCINOMA CELLS INDUCED BY RETINOIC ACID.

Retinoids can induce differentiation of embryonal carcinoma cells,[37,38,49] the undifferentiated stem cells present in teratocarcinomas. These cells exhibited very low binding of EGF while some of their differentiated derivatives showed much higher levels of EGF binding (TABLE 6). Two differentiated cell types PCC4 D1 and 15D1 that had a fibroblastic morphology contained high levels of EGF binding whereas F9D1 and 15D2, which had a more endoderm-like morphology, showed, like the original embryonal carcinoma cells very low binding of EGF. The EGF binding could therefore be used as a marker to monitor differentiation, as shown recently for the embryonal carcinoma OC15S1 cells.[50] FIGURE 10 shows the induction of differentiation of the embryonal carcinoma cells PCC4 aza 1R by retinoic acid as monitored by EGF binding. This binding increased concomitantly with the appearance of cells with a fibroblastic morphology.

CONCLUSION AND DISCUSSION

The action of retinoic acid on growth of 3T6 cells and many other cell lines can be separated into reduction of the growth rate and decrease in saturation density. Retinoic acid-treated cells also exhibit an enhanced serum requirement and appear to be more dependent on growth factors, such as EGF and insulin. Increased saturation density and reduced serum and EGF requirements are often associated with the transformed state of cells; retinoic acid treatment appears to reverse these characteristics.

Retinoids can enhance the binding of EGF in a large number of mouse fibroblast and several epidermal cell lines. Retinoic acid does not appear to alter significantly the affinity of EGF for its receptor at the cell surface but rather to increase the number of EGF binding sites. It is not clear if there is a causal relationship between the increase in number of receptors and inhibition of growth. One possible explanation may be a reduction in the production of endogenous growth factors, which are able to bind to the EGF receptor, resulting in an enhancement in the number of unoccupied receptor sites and inhibition of growth. Alternatively, Brown et al.[33] have suggested that an increased requirement for EGF may result in a stimulation of synthesis of EGF receptors.

The action of retinoic acid does not seem to be limited to the inhibition of mitogenic activity induced by EGF, since growth rate and saturation density of retinoic acid-grown 3T6 cells were always reduced compared to control cells, whether growth was stimulated by serum, EGF, insulin, or EGF and insulin together. Therefore, retinoic acid may not affect each of these stimuli in a unique way, but influence a step common to the induction of proliferation by all these factors.

Several studies have reported the presence of specific retinol and retinoic acid-binding proteins in the cytosol of many cell types.[51,52] Thus far, only supportive evidence exists that these binding proteins play a role in the mechanism of action of retinoids. We have shown that the biological activities of several retinoid analogs correlate well with their ability to bind to the retinoic acid-

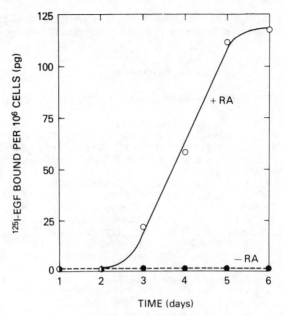

FIGURE 10. Increase in EGF binding during differentiation of PCC4 aza 1R cells induced by retinoic acid. Cells were grown at low density in DME/F12 (1:1) medium containing 10% fetal calf serum in the presence (O) and absence (●) of $10^{-7}M$ retinoic acid. At various time intervals after the addition of retinoic acid, binding of EGF was determined and plotted against time.

binding protein.[24,37] Retinol and retinyl acetate form an exception; these analogs do not bind to the retinoic acid-binding protein, but are still biologically active in spite of the fact that 3T6 and 3T12 cells do not contain retinol-binding protein and that no conversion of retinol to retinoic acid could be observed in 3T12 cells (unpublished data). This latter fact may argue against a role of the binding proteins in the action of at least some retinoids. Even more uncertainty exists about what the role of these binding proteins may be. Chytil[51] has suggested that retinoids may act via a mechanism similar to that of steroid hormones; complexes of retinoic acid and binding protein are transported into the nucleus, whence they modify gene transcription. However, no hard evidence exists to support this hypothesis. Alternatively, it has been shown[39,40] that retinoids can be metabolized to phosphorylated and glycosylated intermediates, which may play a role in the glycosylation of specific glycoconjugates. The binding proteins may be involved either in the biosynthesis of these metabolites or in the glycosylation reactions. The specific nature of the action of retinoic acid on cell surface glycoproteins, described here, may provide a useful tool to distinguish between these two hypotheses.

ACKNOWLEDGMENTS

I am grateful to Dr. Luigi M. De Luca, in whose Section this work was conducted, for his support and comments on the manuscript. I thank Dr. Beverly A. Pawson of Hoffmann-La Roche for providing the retinoid analogs.

REFERENCES

1. MOORE, T. 1967. *In* The Vitamins. W. Sebrell & R. Harris, Eds. Vol. 1: 245–266. Academic Press, New York.
2. DE LUCA, L.M. 1977. Vitamin. Horm. 35: 1–57.
3. HOWELL, J.M., J.N. THOMPSON & G. PITT. 1963. J. Reprod. Fertil. 5: 159–163.
4. HOWELL, J.M., J. THOMPSON & G. PITT. 1964. J. Reprod. Fertil. 7:251–260.
5. HARRIS, C., M. SPORN, D. KAUFMAN, J. SMITH, F. JACKSON, & U. SAFFIOTTI. 1972. J. Natl. Cancer Inst. 48: 743–749.
6. FELL, H.B. 1957. Proc. R. Soc. London, Ser. B. 146: 242–256.
7. BOLLAG, W. 1975. Chemotherapy 21: 236–247.
8. MOON, R., C. GRUBBS & M. SPORN. 1976. Cancer Res. 36: 2626–2630.
9. CHOPRA, D. & L. WILKOFF. 1976. J. Natl. Cancer Inst. 56: 583–589.
10. SPORN, M.B., N. DUNLOP, D. NEWTON & W. HENDERSON. 1976. Nature 263: 110–113.
11. SPORN, M.B., N. DUNLOP, D. NEWTON & J. SMITH. 1976. Fed. Proc. 35: 1332–1338.
12. UMEZAWA, K., H. FUKAMACHI, T. HIRAKAWA, S. TAKAYAMA, T. MATSUSHIMA & T. SUGIMURA. 1979. Toxicol. Lett. 4: 87–92.
13. BERTRAM, J.S. 1980. Cancer Res. 40: 3141–3146.
14. POLLIACK, A. & I. LEVY. 1969. Cancer Res. 29: 327–332.
15. WILSON, E. & E. REICH. 1978. Cell 15: 385–392.
16. LEVINE, L. & K. OHUCHI. 1978. Nature 276:274–275.
17. TODARO, G.J., J. DE LARCO & M. SPORN. 1978. Nature 276: 272–274.
18. SHERMAN, B.S. 1961. J. Invest. Dermatol. 37: 469–480.
19. LAWRENCE, D. & H. BERN. 1963. Ann. N.Y. Acad. Sci. 106: 646–653.
20. DICKER, P. & E. ROZENGURT. 1979. Biochem. Biophys. Res. Commun. 91: 1203–1210.
21. LASNITZKI, I. 1955. Exp. Cell Res. 8: 121–125.
22. LOTAN, R. 1980. Biochim. Biophys. Acta 605: 33–91.
23. LOTAN, R. 1979. Cancer Res. 39: 1014–1019.
24. JETTEN, A.M., M.E.R. JETTEN. S. SHAPIRO & J. POON. 1979. Exp. Cell Res. 119: 289–299.
25. DION, L.D., J. BLALOCK & G. GIFFORD. 1977. J. Natl. Cancer Inst. 58: 795–801.
26. ADAMO, S., L.M. DE LUCA, I. AKALOVSKY, P. BHAT. 1979. J. Natl. Cancer Inst. 62: 1473–1477.
27. GOSPODAROWICZ, D., J. MORAN & A. MESCHER. 1978. *In* Molecular Control of Proliferation and Differentiation. J. Papaconstaniou & W. Rutter, Eds. :32–63. Academic Press. New York.
28. CARPENTER, G. & S. COHEN. 1979. Ann. Rev. Biochem. 48: 193–216.
29. TODARO, G. J., J. DE LARCO & S. COHEN. 1976. Nature 264: 26–31.
30. DAS, M. & C.F. FOX. 1978. Proc. Natl. Acad. Sci. USA 75: 2644–2648.
31. DE LARCO, J. & G. TODARO. 1978. J. Cell Physiol. 94: 335–342.
32. CARPENTER, G. & S. COHEN. 1976. J. Cell Physiol. 88: 227–238.
33. BROWN, K.D., Y. YEH & R. HOLLEY. 1979. J. Cell Physiol. 100: 227–238.
34. SHOYAB, M., J. DE LARCO & G. TODARO. 1979. Nature 279: 387–391.
35. JETTEN, A.M. 1980. Nature 284: 626–628.
36. DAS, M., MIYAKAWA, C.F. FOX, F. PRUSS, A. AHARONOV & H. HERSCHMAN. 1977. Proc. Natl. Acad. Sci. USA 74: 2790–2794.
37. JETTEN, A.M. & M.E.R. JETTEN. 1979. Nature 278: 180–182.
38. JETTEN, A.M., M.E.R. JETTEN & M.I. SHERMAN. 1979. Exp. Cell Res. 124: 381–391.
39. DE LUCA, L.M., J. FROT-COUTAZ, C. SILVERMAN-JONES & P. ROLLER. 1977. J. Biol. Chem. 252:2575–2579.
40. DE LUCA, L.M., S. ADAMO, P. BHAT. W. SASAK, C. SILVERMAN-JONES, I. AKALOVSKY, J. FROT-COUTAZ. T. FLETCHER & G. CHADER. 1979. Pure Appl. Chem. 51: 581–591.
41. STRUCK, D. & W. LENNARZ. 1977. J. Biol. Chem. 252: 1007–1013.

42. DUKSIN, D. & P. BORNSTEIN. 1977. Proc. Natl. Acad. Sci. USA **74:** 3433–3437.
43. OLDEN, K., PRATT & K. YAMADA. 1978. Cell **13:** 461–473.
44. HASSELL, J. J. PENNYPACKER, K. KLEINMAN & K. YAMADA. 1979. Cell **17:** 821–826.
45. COLBURN, N., B. FORMER, K. NELSON & S. YUSPA. Nature.
46. BOUTWELL, R. & A. VERMA. 1979. Pure and Appl. Chem. **51:** 857–866.
47. LEE, L. & I. WEINSTEIN. 1978. Science **202:** 313–315.
48. LEE, L. I.B. WEINSTEIN. 1979. Proc. Natl. Acad. Sci. USA **76:** 5160–5172.
49. STRICKLAND, S. & V. MAHDAVI. 1978. Cell. **15:** 393–404.
50. REES, A., E. ADAMSON & C. GRAHAM. 1979. Nature **281:** 309–311.
51. CHYTIL, F. & D.E. ONG. 1979. *In* Receptors and Hormone Action II. B.W. O'Malley & L.B. Birnbaumer, Eds. :573–591. Academic Press, New York.
52. SANI, B.P. & T. CORBETT. 1977. Cancer Res. **37:** 209–213.
53. CARPENTER, J.L. & S. COHEN. 1977. Biochem. Biophys. Res. Commun. **79:** 545–552.

EFFECTS OF RETINOIDS ON NEOPLASTIC TRANSFORMATION, CELL ADHESION, AND MEMBRANE TOPOGRAPHY OF CULTURED 10T1/2 CELLS*

John S. Bertram,† Lawrence J. Mordan,† Steven J. Blair,‡ and Sekwen Hui‡

*Departments of Experimental Therapeutics† and Biophysics‡
Roswell Park Memorial Institute
Buffalo, New York 14263*

INTRODUCTION

As discussed in detail at this conference, natural and synthetic analogs of vitamin A (retinoids) have been demonstrated to be capable of inhibiting the development of chemically induced carcinomas in a variety of laboratory animals and at a variety of anatomical sites.[1-4] Furthermore, dietary deficiency in experimental animals has been shown to enhance susceptibility to chemical carcinogenesis[5], and there is recent suggestive evidence from epidemiological studies in human populations that groups ingesting low levels of vitamin A are at increased risk of lung[6] and bladder[7] cancer. Because of the importance of these observations, we have studied the effects of retinoids in the C3H/10T1/2 CL8 cell line of mouse embryo fibroblasts,[8] which is readily transformable by many chemical[9] and physical agents[10] and in which transformation can be readily quantitated[9]. In this line transformation is expressed as a lack of post-confluence inhibition of growth and transformed foci appear as piled up regions of overlapping cells amid a highly regular monolayer of growth-inhibited nontransformed cells. That about 90% of these morphologically transformed foci are malignant can be demonstrated by injection into immunosuppressed syngeneic C3H mice.[9] In many studies the behavior of these cells to carcinogens has been shown to reflect *in vivo* events

This paper will discuss our recent studies on the cell biology of retinoid action, structure/activity requirements for activity of retinoids in the 10T1/2 cells, and the effects of retinoids on the cell membrane.

METHODS

Cells and Culture Conditions

A transformable line of mouse embryo fibroblasts designated C3H/10T1/2 CL8 (10T1/2)[8] and neoplastically transformed lines derived from the parent cell line by treatment with chemical carcinogens were used throughout this study.[11] Cultures were passaged weekly in basal medium Eagle's (BME) supplemented with 10% heat-inactivated fetal calf serum (HIFCS) without antibiotics, and were

* Supported by United States Public Health Service Grant CA-25439 to J.S.B. and ACS Grant BC248 and Career Development Award KO4 CA-00084 to S.H.

free of mycoplasmal contamination. For experimental use cells were obtained from stock cultures by trypsinization and were plated out into plastic Petri dishes at the stated cell concentrations in serum supplemented BME containing 25 μg/ml gentamicin. Trypsinization procedures and electronic cell counting were performed as before.[11,12]

Chemicals and Drug Treatments

Retinyl acetate, retinol, retinaldehyde all-*trans*-retinoic acid and 3-methylcholanthrene were obtained from Sigma Chemical Co., St. Louis, MO. Other retinoids were obtained from Dr. M. Sporn, National Cancer Institute, Bethesda, MD. Retinoids were stored in liquid nitrogen, were dissolved in acetone immediately before use, and 25 μl aliquots were added to 5 ml of culture medium to yield the required concentration. MCA was also dissolved in acetone prior to treatment. Control cultures received 25 μl of acetone, which was non-toxic. All manipulations were carried out under "gold" fluorescent lights and cells were incubated in the dark.

Transformation Assay

We seeded 10T1/2 cells at a density of 1000 cells or 200 cells/60mm Petri dish to measure transformation and toxicity, respectively. One day after seeding

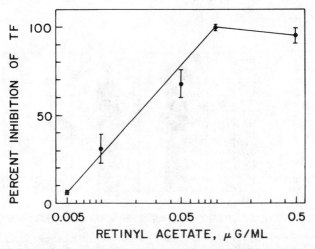

FIGURE 1. Concentration-response relationship for the inhibition by RA of MCA-induced neoplastic transformation. Starting 7 days after MCA exposure, cultures were treated weekly with the appropriate concentration of RA for 4 weeks and then scored for transformed foci. The percentage of inhibition of TF was calculated in relation to cultures that received MCA plus acetone. Values represent the mean of measurements from 2 experiments. The data plotted in FIGURES 1 to 5 were calculated as follows. The total number of transformed foci (types II and III) in each of 2 experiments, each utilizing 12 dishes/data point, were determined, and the TF was calculated from the formula given in TABLE 1. (Reproduced by permission of *Cancer Research*.[11])

dishes were treated for 24 hr with 2.5 µg/ml 3-methylcholanthrene (MCA) in acetone or with acetone alone. Cultures used to determine cytotoxicity were fixed and stained after 7–10 days in culture, while dishes used to determine transformation were maintained for a maximum period of 35 days in BME + 5% HIFCS with weekly medium changing. Of the transformed foci induced by MCA, both type II and type III foci have been used in the calculation of transformation frequencies (TF). This is defined as the:

$$\frac{\text{mean number of transformed foci/dish}}{\text{mean number of surviving cells/dish}} \times 100$$

Full details of the transformation assay have been described previously.[9,11,12]

Adhesion Assay

We grew 10T1/2 cells to confluence in BME + 5% HIFCS and treated them with appropriate concentrations of retinoid, *i.e.* a concentration previously shown to inhibit transformation by about 50%, or to exert minimal toxicity, and 10-fold higher concentration in a separate group of cultures. After 4 days, the period shown to be required for retinyl acetate to exert its maximum effect, cultures were washed with saline and covered with 2 ml of 0.5% trypsin/2 × 10^{-4}M EDTA in phosphate-buffered saline. Cultures were placed at 37°C on an orbital shaker in a 37° room and the release of cells from the substrate measured by serial sampling and electronic particle counting of the supernatant.[13]

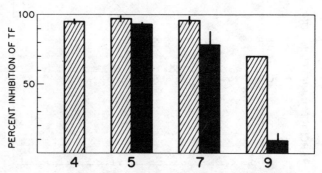

FIGURE 2. Reversibility of the inhibition by RA of MCA-induced neoplastic transformation. Seven days after MCA exposure, cultures were treated with RA (0.5 µg/ml). Cultures were either continuously treated with the weekly application of RA (hatched bars), or treated weekly for 4 weeks with RA and then grown in drug-free medium (solid bars). Cultures were fixed and scored for transformed foci at the indicated times after the start of RA treatment. The percentage of inhibition in TF was calculated in relation to the corresponding MCA-plus-acetone-treated cultures, which of necessity were fixed 5 weeks after plating. Values represent the mean of measurements from 2 experiments. Bars show S.E. For further details on the calculations used, see the legend to FIGURE 1. (Reproduced by permission of *Cancer Research*.[11])

COMPOUND (SOURCE)   STRUCTURE

1. All-trans-retinylacetate
   (Sigma Chemical Co.)

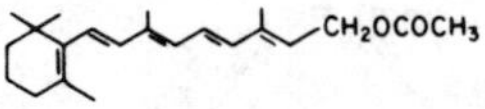

2. All-trans-retinoic acid
   (Sigma Chemical Co.)

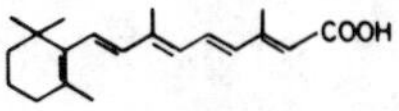

3. 13-cis-retinoic acid
   (Hoffmann- LaRoche
   Nutley, New Jersey)

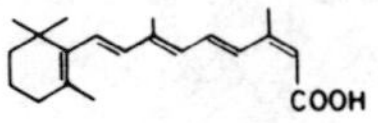

4. N-4-Hydroxyphenylretinamide
   (Johnson and Johnson)

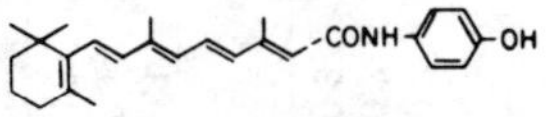

5. N-Ethylretinamide
   (Hoffmann - LaRoche
   Nutley, New Jersey)

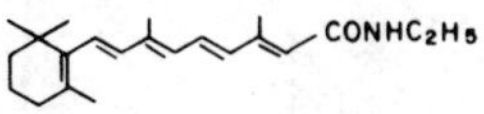

6. N-Benzoylretinamine
   (BASF)

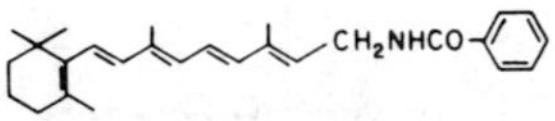

7. Retinylidene Dimedone
   (N. Acton and A. Brossi NIH)

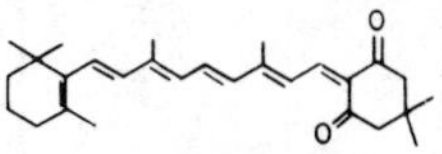

8. Aryl triene analog of
   retinoic acid
   (M. Dawson and P. Hobbs
   SRI International
   Menlo Park, CA.)

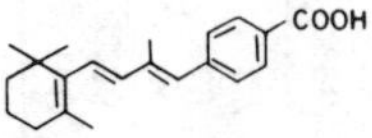

9. C17-Carboxylic analog of
   retinoic acid
   (C. Heathcock
   Univ. of California
   Berkeley)

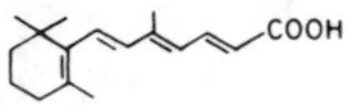

10. Thiophene analog of
    retinoic acid
    (BASF)

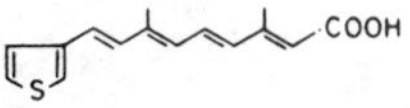

FIGURE 3. Chemical structures and sources of the retinoids used in this study. Additional addresses: BASF Aktiengesellschaft, 6700 Ludwigshafen am Rhein, Germany; Johnson & Johnson, New Brunswick, NJ. (Reproduced by permission of *Cancer Research*.[13])

TABLE 1

EFFECTS OF VARIOUS RETINOIDS ON THE PLATING EFFICIENCY AND ON MCA-INDUCED TRANSFORMATION FREQUENCY IN THE 10T½ CELL LINE*

Treatment†	Retinoid Concentration (μg/ml)	PE (% of control)	No Dishes‡	T/dish§	TF¶	TF (% of control)
Acetone Control 0.5%	0	100 (25)	35	0	<0.01	0
MCA Control 2.5 μg/ml	0	100	36	2.24 ± 0.1	0.90	100
Retinyl acetate	0.3	96	11	0.09	0.04	4.2
	0.1	107	11	0.45 ± 0.2	0.17	18.7
	0.03	91	9	1.11 ± 0.2	0.49	54.6
	0.01	95	11	1.73 ± 0.3	0.73	81.0
N-4-hydroxyphenyl retinamide	3.0	2.7	ND	–	–	–
	1.0	67	ND	–	–	–
	0.3	79	10	0.2 ± 0.1	0.1	11.2
	0.1	96	12	0.33 ± 0.1	0.13	15.3
	0.03	99	12	0.75 ± 0.3	0.3	33.9
Retinylidene dimedone	3.0	1.5	ND	–	–	–
	1.0	52	12	0	0	0
	0.3	84	12	0	0	0
	0.1	97	12	0.58 ± 0.3	0.24	26.8
	0.03	96	12	2.58 ± 0.4	1.1	120.0
	0.01	99	12	2.0 ± 0.3	0.81	90.6
N-ethyl retinamide	3.0	28	12	0	0	0
	1.0	43	12	0.42 ± 0.1	0.38	43.1
	0.3	82	12	1.08 ± 0.2	0.52	59.1
	0.1	76	12	1.92 ± 0.2	1.01	113.1
N-benzoyl retinylamine	3.0	68	ND	–	–	–
	1.0	80	12	0.92 ± 0.3	0.46	51.3
	0.3	71	12	1.92 ± 0.2	1.07	120.0
	0.1	70	12	1.33 ± 0.4	0.75	84.3

Compound	Concentration	Surviving colonies/dish (% of control)	No. of dishes[‡]	Transformants/dish[§]	Transformation frequency[¶]	% of control
All-*trans*-retinoic acid‖	0.3	30	10	0	0	0
	0.1	40	12	1.33 ± 0.4	1.32	147.7
	0.03	52	12	1.67 ± 0.3	1.29	144.2
	0.01	74	12	1.75 ± 0.3	0.94	105.1
	0.003	93	ND	–	–	–
13-*cis*-retinoic acid‖	0.3	32	ND	–	–	–
	0.1	38	11	1.45 ± 0.2	1.54	171.6
	0.03	67	8	2.0 ± 0.3	1.19	133.1
	0.01	102	11	2.0 ± 0.2	0.78	87.5
	0.003	97	10	2.2 ± 0.2	0.9	100.4
Thiophene analog	3.0	91	12	1.42 ± 0.3	0.62	69.4
	1.0	101	12	1.33 ± 0.4	0.53	58.9
	0.3	116	11	2.05 ± 0.2	0.82	91.5
MCA control** 2.5 µg/ml	0	100 (25)	12	1.08 ± 0.3	0.43	100
Aryltriene analog	1.0	94	12	0.17 ± 0.1	0.07	16.2
	0.3	96	11	0.91 ± 0.4	0.38	88.1
	0.1	101	11	0.64 ± 0.3	0.25	58.7
	0.03	98	12	1.0 ± 0.2	0.41	95.1
C$_{17}$ Carboxylic acid analog	3.0	101	12	1.33 ± 0.4	0.53	123.1
	1.0	107	12	1.42 ± 0.3	0.56	131.5
	0.3	97	ND	–	–	–
	0.1	108	12	1.58 ± 0.3	0.63	146.3

* To determine plating efficiency (PE) cells were continuously exposed to the retinoid, which was added 24 hr after plating. To determine effects on transformation, retinoids were added to cultures previously initiated with MCA as described in the text.

† For structures see FIGURE 3.

‡ Number of dishes evaluated in the transformation assay.

§ Type III morphological transformants.

¶ Transformation frequency calculated as

$$\frac{\text{Number of transformants/dish}}{\text{Number of surviving colonies/dish}} \times 100.$$

To obtain number of surviving colonies/dish multiply PE control by 2.5 for a control PE of 25%.

‖ Representative results from 3 separate experiments.

** Carcinogen only control for the aryltriene and C17 carboxylic acid analogs.

Data from *Cancer Research.*[13]

Reconstruction Experiments

Confluent monolayers of 10T1/2 cells in BME + 5% HIFCS were overlaid with 100 neoplastically transformed cells. After 24 hr, when the transformed cells had attached, cultures were treated with retinyl acetate or retinol and were fixed after 7 days in culture without further medium change. The number and size of the colonies of transformed cells growing on the confluent monolayers of 10T1/2 cells were then determined.

Scanning Electron Microscopy (SEM)

The 10T1/2 cells or the transformed cell line MCA T10T1/2 derived from the parent line by MCA treatment, were grown on glass cover-slips or on plastic Petri dishes and after the appropriate treatment were fixed with 2.5% glutaralydehyde in PBS for 2 hr at 4°C. Samples were critical-point-dried and gold-coated prior to examination in a ETEC Autoscan SEM at 20 KV. Cell morphology was classified as either flat, semi-flat, raised polygonal, spindle, or rounded according to previously published criteria.[14] Cell surface topography was quantitated using an electronic digitizer (Ladd Industries Burlington, VT).

RESULTS

Effects of Retinoids on 3-MCA-Induced Transformation

Dose Response

Retinoids were added 7 days after removal of the carcinogen in order not to interfere with the processes of metabolic activation and fixation of the carcinogenic lesion, which appear to be complete at this time.[15] MCA was used as a test carcinogen throughout these studies because it induces reproducible transformation at nontoxic concentrations, and because the transformation induced is dose-dependent.[9,12]

When nontoxic concentrations of retinyl acetate (0.5 μg/ml or less) were added to MCA-treated cells beginning 7 days after removal of MCA and repeated at each weekly medium change, it was found that the expression of neoplastic transformation was reduced in a dose-dependent manner. In cultures exposed to MCA and to weekly acetone (solvent control) treatments, approximately two transformed foci/dish developed by day 35 when cultures were fixed and stained. However as shown in FIGURE 1, transformation was progressively inhibited by retinyl acetate, and a 50% decrease in transformation was obtained with 0.02 μg/ml. Retinol and retinaldehyde were approximately equipotent in this respect.

Reversibility

To examine whether the inhibition of transformation induced by retinyl acetate was reversible on withdrawing treatment, large numbers of replicate cultures were plated and treated with the standard transforming concentration of 2.5 μg/ml MCA and with weekly applications of retinyl acetate 0.5 μg/ml, exactly as in the experiment reported in FIGURE 1. After 35 days, one group of cultures was fixed and stained, the others were randomized into two groups. One group was maintained on weekly retinyl acetate treatments, the second was maintained in drug-free medium. Representative samples from both groups were fixed and stained at intervals 1, 3, and 5 weeks after randomization. As shown in FIGURE 2, cultures maintained on weekly retinyl acetate exhibited few transformed foci until the final week of the experiment. Even then inhibition of transformation was still 70% complete. In contrast, a progressively increasing number of foci developed in the cultures maintained on drug-free medium such that at the time of termination of the experiment the number of transformed foci was the same as in cultures never exposed to retinyl acetate. Thus inhibition of transformation by retinyl acetate is reversible in nature and cannot involve selective cytotoxicity of initiated cells.

Structure Activity Determinations

A large number of synthetic retinoids have been tested for their activities in reversing squamous metaplasia in the hamster trachea[16] and many have also been tested as inhibitors of carcinogenesis *in vivo*. To determine if the 10T1/2 cell line responds to structurally diverse retinoids we tested a range of compounds (shown in FIG. 3) for their ability to inhibit MCA-induced transformation. As before, retinoids were added weekly beginning 7 days after removal of 2.5 μg/ml of MCA. The results presented in TABLE 1 indicate a good correlation between the activity of diverse retinoids to inhibit MCA-induced transformation and their activities in other systems, with the notable exception of all-*trans*- and 13–*cis*–retinoic acids. These compounds were by far the most toxic in the assay system, but even at nontoxic levels did not inhibit the expression of transformation except in the case of all-*trans*-retinoic acid tested at a toxic level of 0.3 μg/ml. At lower, but still toxic concentrations, both compounds apparently enhanced TF, but the actual yield of transformants uncorrected for toxicity, was reduced in comparison with acetone-treated controls. It is difficult to interpret these results, which were obtained under conditions of repeated toxicity.

TABLE 2

EFFECT OF RETINOIDS ON THE PLATING EFFICIENCY AND GROWTH OF TRANSFORMED CELLS PLATED ON CONFLUENT MONOLAYERS OF 10T1/2 CELLS*

Retinoid Concentration μg/ml	Colony Number and Size (mm²) (% control)					
	Transformed Line A		Transformed Line B		Transformed Line C	
	Number	Size	Number	Size	Number	Size
RA 0.1	137 ± 12	103 ± 1	116 ± 15	123 ± 10	134 ± 5	126 ± 13
RA 1.0	115 ± 3	114 ± 2	109 ± 8	131 ± 1	115 ± 13	120 ± 5
ROL 0.1	149 ± 47	121 ± 3	104 ± 7	120 ± 9	123 ± 21	133 ± 32
ROL 1.0	119 ± 13	127 ± 13	139 ± 26	129 ± 7	111 ± 10	136 ± 23

* Reconstruction experiments were performed using confluent monolayers of 10T1/2 cells grown in BME plus 5% serum. About 100 transformed cells were seeded onto the 10T1/2 monolayer, and after 24 hr replicate cultures received the appropriate concentration of retinoid. Dishes were fixed and stained after 7 days of treatment without further medium change. Cultures were scored for the number and size of the transformed foci. (Data from *Cancer Research*.[11])

The most potent compound tested was N-4-hydroxyphenylretinamide, which was highly active in reducing the TF to 34% of controls at a concentration of 0.03 μg/ml. Retinyl acetate reduced the TF to 55% of controls at that concentration. Two compounds were included that had previously been shown to be inactive in the hamster trachea assay. Both the thiophene analog and the C17 carboxylic acid analogs of all-*trans*-retinoic acid were essentially without toxicity or activity in the transformation assay.

Reconstruction Experiments

The transformation experiments described above cannot distinguish between an effect of retinoids on the ability of transformed cells to express the transformed phenotype, versus an action on initiated cells to prevent the aquisition of the transformed phenotype. These are subtle differences that are highly important

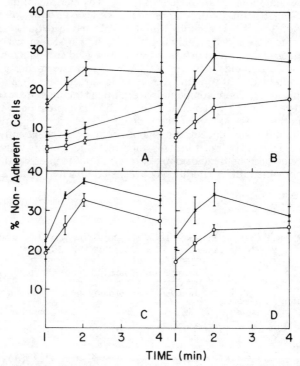

FIGURE 4. Effects of retinoids active in the transformation assay on the rate of release of trypsin/EDTA treated cells from a plastic substrate. 10T1/2 cells were grown to confluence and 4 days prior to assay treated with the appropriate retinoid or acetone as control. The rate of release of cells induced by a trypsin/EDTA solution was determined in 4 replicate cultures as described in the METHODS section. ×———×, low dose O———O, high dose of the respective retinoid. *Panel A*, Retinyl acetate 0.3 μg/ml and 0.3 μg/ml; △———△, acetone control 0.5%; *Panel B*, Retinylidene dimedone 0.3 μg/ml and 0.1 μg/ml; *Panel C*, N-4-hydroxyphenyl retinamide, 0.3 μg/ml and 0.1 μg/ml; *Panel D*, N-ethylretinamide, 3.0 μg/ml and 1.0 μg/ml. (Reproduced by permission of *Cancer Research*.[13])

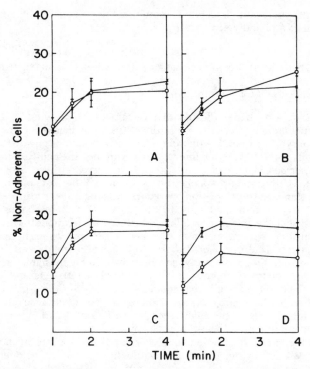

FIGURE 5. Effects of retinoids inactive or weakly active in the transformation assay on the rate of release of trypsin/EDTA-treated cells from a plastic substrate. Experimental protocol as FIGURE 4. *Panel A*, Retinoic acid 0.3 μg/ml and 0.1 μg/ml; *Panel B*, 13-*cis*-retinoic acid 0.3 μg/ml and 0.1 μg/ml; *Panel C*, C17-carboxylic acid analog 3.0 μg/ml and 1.0 μg/ml; *Panel D*, Thiophene analog 3.0 μg/ml and 0.3 μg/ml. (Reproduced by permission of *Cancer Research*.[13])

both mechanistically and clinically in the development of retinoids as chemopreventive agents. If retinoids are capable of inhibiting the expression of the transformed phenotype, then retinoids should be active against established malignant cells. To test this possibility, we set up reconstruction experiments in which confluent monolayers of 10T1/2 cells were overlaid with a few established transformed cells previously isolated from carcinogen-treated cultures. One day after seeding with the transformed cells, test cultures were treated with 0.1 or 1.0 μg/ml of retinyl acetate or retinol while controls received acetone. Cultures were then incubated for 7 days to allow the development of foci of transformed cells on the confluent monolayer of 10T1/2 cells. As seen in TABLE 2, both the number and size of transformed foci growing in the presence of retinoids were greater than in acetone-treated controls, indicating that concentrations of retinoid 50-fold greater than required to inhibit transformation by 50%, were not able to decrease the growth of established cells. Also supporting this conclusion, is our finding that when retinoids were added to carcinogen-treated cultures after the phenotypic expression of transformation (about day 28 postplating), no effect on the subsequent growth of the transformed foci was seen.[11] These observations can be interpreted to mean that retinyl acetate is inhibiting the progression of a carcinogen-initiated cell to a phenotypically transformed cell.

EFFECTS OF RETINOIDS ON MEMBRANES AND MEMBRANE INTERACTIONS

Effects of Retinoids on Cell/Substrate Adhesion

Previous reports had indicated that certain retinoids would increase the degree of attachment of cells to a plastic substrate as evidenced by increased resistance to trypsinization.[17,18] In order to extend our studies on structure/activity correlations in the 10T1/2 cell line we have examined the ability of many of the retinoids described in FIGURE 3 and TABLE 1, to decrease the rate of release of trypsin-treated cells from a plastic Petri dish. Because of the slow rate of release of cells by our standard trypsinization procedure utilizing 0.1% trypsin, we exposed cells to 0.5% trypsin and, in addition, to 2×10^{-4}M EDTA. In preliminary studies, it was found that the increase in adhesion caused by treatment with 0.3 μg/ml retinyl acetate only became maximal after 3–4 days of continuous treatment (data not shown), thus all cultures were exposed to 4 days of retinoid treatment prior to assay. As shown in FIGURE 4, retinyl acetate induced a highly significant ($p<0.01$) dose-dependent decrease in the initial rate of release of cells and an overall decrease in the number of cells that could be released over the 4-min incubation period. More extended incubation could not be carried out because of the irreversible clumping of cells, occasionally seen in the FIGURE 4 and 5 as an apparent decrease in cell number at the 4-min time point.

The synthetic retinoids tested gave very variable responses in the adhesion assay. Thus N-4-hydroxyphenylretinamide, the most potent retinoid tested in the transformation (TABLE 1) assay, caused a significant ($p<0.01$) *decrease* in adhesion of 10T1/2 cells and furthermore the lowest concentration tested (0.1 μg/ml) caused the greatest effect. Similarly N-ethylretinamide, the other retinamide tested, decreased adhesion at the lowest concentration tested (1.0 μg/ml) but had no significant effect when tested at 3.0 μg/ml. The dimedone analog when tested at concentrations of 0.1 and 0.3 μg/ml, which inhibited transformation to 20% and 0% of control, respectively (TABLE 1), only caused an increase in adhesion at the highest concentration tested. In agreement with the lack of activity of the retinoic acids in reducing transformation in the 10T 1/2 system, neither of these compounds had any pronounced effects on adhesion in this system (FIG. 5). Compounds shown to be essentially inactive in all test systems (i.e. the thiophene analog and the C17 carboxylic acid analog) were also without major effects on adhesion. However it should be noted that the thiophene analog, which exhibited weak activity in the transformation assay, caused a significant ($p<0.05$) increase in adhesion at the highest concentration tested.

Effects on Cell Spreading

Logarithmic phase cultures of nontransformed and of transformed cells were exposed to retinyl acetate and the extent of cell-spreading assessed by SEM. Logarithmic phase cultures were used because in confluent cultures of non-transformed cells the cells were highly homogeneous while in cultures of transformed cells extensive overlapping made analysis difficult. Classification of cell morphology was achieved on the basis of the extent of spreading of the entire cell on the plastic substate, and cells were divided into the 6 categories listed in TABLE 3.

TABLE 3

EFFECT OF RETINYL ACETATE ON THE MORPHOLOGICAL TYPES OF 10T1/2 AND MCA T10T1/2 CELLS

		Percent Incidence					
		Logarithmic 10T1/2			Logarithmic MCA T10T1/2		
			Retinyl Acetate			Retinyl Acetate	
Morphological Type*	Confluent 10T1/2	Acetone Control	0.05	0.50	Acetone Control	0.50	5.0
Flat	92.0	56.9	59.4	87.3**	8.9	28.4**	25.6**
Semi-Flat	4.0	24.8	27.5	7.7***	21.7	28.9***	32.0***
Raised polygonal	2.0	13.4	10.1	3.0**	45.6	31.2**	31.2***
Rounded	0	1.3	0	1.0	14.7	5.2**	8.0**
Spindle	2.0	2.9	2.9	1.0***	8.9	5.7	3.2
Number of cells analyzed	50	306	207	300	292	211	125
Cell density†	302	69.2 ± 1.8	70.0 ± 6.3	67.3 ± 7.4	95 ± 17	115 ± 8	130 ± 15

* For description of the morphological types see the text and Mordan et al.[14]
† Number of cells/mm^2 ± standard deviation (S.D.).
** Significantly different (p < 0.05) from controls.

Flat cells were those with extensive spreading of membrane away from the nucleus and in close contact with the substrate, the other morphological types listed in TABLE 3 were progressively less well spread on the substrate (see FIGS. 9, 10, 11, 12).

It will be seen in TABLE 3 that control 10T1/2 cultures are more extensively flattened than MCA T10T1/2 cultures, and that treatment with 0.5 µg/ml retinyl acetate induces a major shift towards more extensive flattening in both cell types. In 10T1/2 cells the morphological profile became indistinguishable from that seen in confluent cultures; however this was achieved without a decrease in the doubling time of about 16 hr in these logarithmic phase cultures (data not shown). In contrast confluent cultures have a stable cell number and a labeling index of less than 2% versus 55% in logarithmic cultures.[19] While treatment of transformed cells increased the number of more flattened cells in the population, the treated population was not as extensively flattened as the control 10T1/2 cells and no further flattening was achieved by a 10-fold increase in drug concentration.

Effects on Surface Topography

Retinyl acetate caused a 3-fold increase in upper cell surface area of flat cells but had no similar effect on other morphological types or on transformed cells (FIG. 6). On all types of 10T1/2 cells examined there was a large increase in the number of blebs (80-fold in flat cells) (FIG. 7) and these blebs were larger than in control cultures (FIG. 8). However statistical analysis of this latter parameter was difficult because of the scarcity of blebs on control cells. Blebs were seen much more frequently in control transformed cells, but their numbers were not consistantly increased by retinyl acetate treatment, although an increase was seen in their mean diameter (FIGS. 7 and 8). In flat transformed cells microvilli were increased in number over controls though it is not clear whether this increase was a result of a redistribution of microvilli-rich, less flattened cells towards the flat cell morphology (data not shown). Scanning electron micrographs of control and

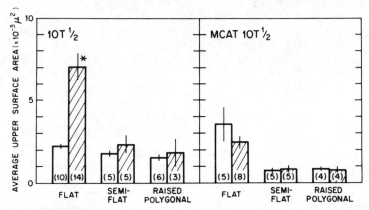

FIGURE 6. Upper surface areas of major morphological types of 10T1/2 and MCA-T10T1/2 cells. Open bars are control, acetone-treated cells. Striped bars are retinyl acetate (0.5 µg/ml) treated cells. Values are mean ± standard deviation. (*) Indicates significant difference (p < 0.05) from control value. In parentheses are the numbers of cells measured in each category.

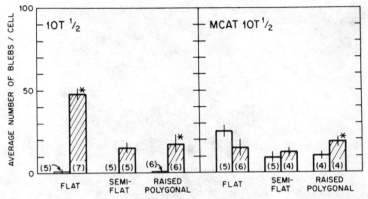

FIGURE 7. Average number of blebs per cell on 10T1/2 and MCA T10T1/2 cells. Values in parentheses represent the number of blebs counted. For key to other symbols see legend to FIGURE 6.

treated nontransformed and transformed cells are presented in FIGURES 9, 10, 11, and 12, respectively.

DISCUSSION

The 10T1/2 mouse embryo fibroblast cell line has been shown to be sensitive to the inhibitory effects of retinoids on carcinogen-induced neoplastic transformation. Because retinoids are active up to 3 weeks after exposure to the carcinogen, because for retinyl acetate at least, drug removal leads to complete reversibility of these inhibitory effects (FIG. 2), and because retinoids did not cause inhibition when added to cultures after phenotypic transformation had oc-

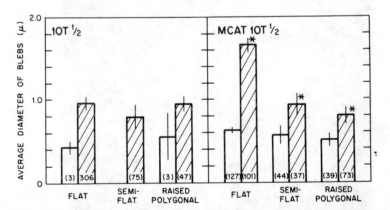

FIGURE 8. Average diameter of blebs on 10T1/2 and MCA T10T1/2 cells. Values in parentheses indicate the number of blebs measured. For key to symbols see legend to FIGURE 6.

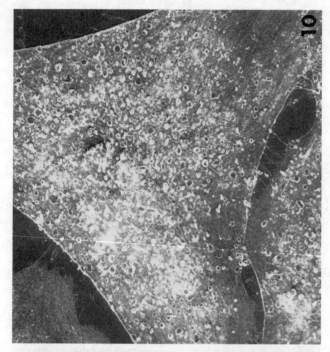

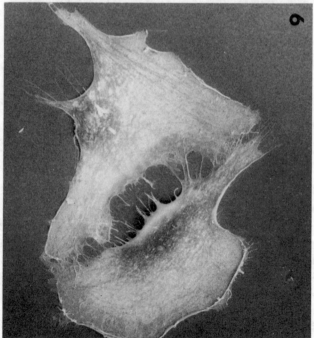

FIGURE 9. SEM of a control 10T1/2 cell of flat morphology.

FIGURE 10. SEM of a flat 10T1/2 cell treated 4 days previously with 0.5 µg/ml retinyl acetate.

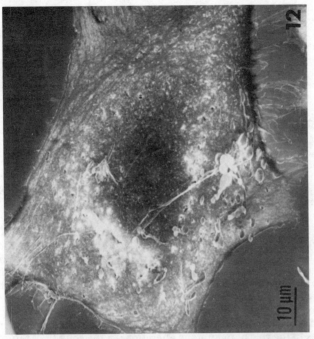

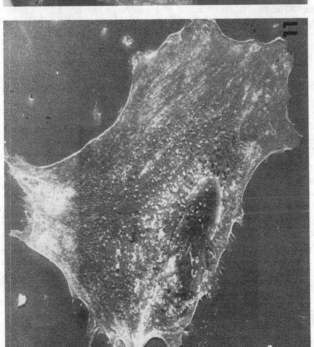

FIGURE 11. SEM of a control MCA T10T1/2 cell of flat morphology.

FIGURE 12. SEM of a flat MCA T10T1/2 cell treated 6 days previously with 0.5 μg/ml retinyl acetate. For magnification of Figures 9–12 see bar on FIGURE 12.

curred (see text and TABLE 2), we have concluded that retinyl acetate is acting to block the progression of an initiated cell to a phenotypically transformed cell. This conclusion is strengthened by *in vivo* data from other laboratories which have shown that retinoids extend the latent period between exposure to a carcinogen and the development of malignancy,[1] that the effects of retinoids are reversible,[20] and that retinoids block both the biological (tumor formation) and a biochemical response to the tumor promoter tetradecanoyl phorbol acetate (TPA),[21] which is believed to accelerate the progression phase of carcinogenesis. The activity of retinoids in a cell line believed to be of fibroblastic origin and which on transformation yields cells producing sarcomas when injected into syngeneic mice,[9] suggests that the activity of retinoids in inhibiting carcinogenesis is not necessarily restricted to epithelial tissues. This concept has not been adequately tested *in vivo*.

Of great surprise and interest was the finding that all-*trans* and 13-*cis*-isomers of retinoic acid failed to inhibit transformation but yet were highly toxic to 10T1/2 cells. This is in contrast to the good correlation between structure and activity in the 10T1/2 line and in the hamster trachea organ culture assay for several synthetic retinoids of diverse chemical structure (TABLE 1). Since metabolic activation of retinoic acid does not appear to be required,[21,22] the intriguing possibility arises that 10T1/2 cells are not capable of utilizing retinoic acids to form the mannosylated intermediates described at this conference by Bhat[24] and shown to be involved in glycosylation reactions distinct from those utilizing derivatives of retinol.[25]

Because of recent reports of the activity of many retinoids in causing increased adhesion of cultured fibroblasts and because of the clues such a correlation might give as to the role of membrane alterations in the activity of retinoids, we examined a series of retinoids for their ability to decrease the rate and/or the extent of release of cells from a plastic substrate when exposed to trypsin/EDTA. While retinyl acetate caused a major dose-dependent increase in cell adhesion, 4-hydroxyphenylretinamide, the most active retinoid tested in the transformation assay (TABLE 1), caused a decrease in adhesion at a concentration of 0.1 µg/ml which was nontoxic and highly active in the transformation assay. Unfortunately, too little is known of the biochemistry of cell/substrate adhesion for these results to imply more than that some change in the cell membrane is produced by retinoids, and that this change does not appear to be consistent between structurally diverse active retinoids.

This presumed alteration in plasma membrane is again evident in our studies of cell surface topography as revealed by SEM. Retinyl acetate treatment (0.5 µg/ml) caused an increase in cell spreading as evidenced by a threefold increase in upper cell surface area and a pronounced increase in the percent of flattened cells, but since no increase in either of these parameters was observed at a concentration of 0.05 µg/ml, a level at which retinyl acetate causes a decrease in carcinogen-induced transformation and an increase in cell adhesion, it is apparent that cell spreading and flattening are not sensitive indicators of biological activity, if indeed a linkage exists. Similar reservations must be made about the significance of the major increase in plasma membrane blebing that was observed in all morphological classes of 10T1/2 cells. Since these effects were produced by retinyl acetate concentrations that cause no decrease in colony-forming ability or in the growth rate of logarithmically growing cells it is clear that blebing is not a result of overt cell toxicity; however there is as yet no evidence to link these morphological changes to the biological effects of retinoids on carcinogenesis. However the recent observations presented at this conference on the biochemical effects produced by retinoids on membrane components,[26,27] and our findings on retinoid-induced modifications of membrane biosynthesis in 10T1/2 cells,[28] coupled with the known role of membrane glycoproteins as cell surface receptors and the deficiencies of membrane glycoproteins in the transformed state[24] all lead to the conclusion that retinoids, by altering membrane biosynthesis, could influence the development of the transformed state.

REFERENCES

1. GRUBBS, C.J., R.C. MOON, M.B. SPORN & D.L. NEWTON. 1977. Inhibition of mammary cancer by retinyl methyl ether. Cancer Res. **37:** 599-602.
2. SAFFIOTTI, U., R. MONTESANO, A.R. SELLAKUMAR & S.A. BORG. 1967. Experimental cancer of the lung. Inhibition by vitamin A of the induction of tracheobronchial squamous metaplasia and squamous cell tumors. Cancer **20:** 857-864.
3. BOLLAG, W. 1972. Prophylaxis of chemically induced benign and malignant epitehlial tumors by vitamin A acid (retinoic acid). Eur. J. Cancer **8:** 689-693.
4. GRUBBS, C.J., R.C. MOON, R.A. SQUIRE, G.M. FARROW, S.F. STINSON, D.G. GOODMAN, C.C. BROWN & M.B. SPORN. 1977. 13-Cis-Retinoic acid: Inhibition of bladder carcinogenesis induced in rats by N-butyl-N-(4-hydroxybutyl)nitrosamine. Science **198:** 743-744.
5. COHEN, S.M., J.F. WITTENBERG & G.T. BROYAN. 1976. Effect of avitaminosis A and hypervitaminosis A on urinary bladder carcinogenicity of N-[4-(5-nitro-2-furyl)-2-thiazolyl] formamide. Cancer Res. **36:** 2334-2339.
6. METTLIN, C., S. GRAHAM & M. SWANSON. 1979. Vitamin A and lung cancer. J. Natl. Cancer Inst. **62:** 1435-1438.
7. METTLIN, C. & S. GRAHAM. 1979. Dietary risk factors in human bladder cancer. Am. J. Epidemiol. **110:** 255-263.
8. REZNIKOFF, C.A., D.W. BRANKOW & C. HEIDELBERGER. 1973. Establishment and characterization of a cloned line of C3H mouse embryo cells sensitive to postconfluence inhibition of cell division. Cancer Res. **33:** 3231-3238.
9. REZNIKOFF, C.A., J.S. BERTRAM, D.W. BRANKOW, & C. HEIDELBERGER. 1973. Quantitative and qualitative studies on chemical transformation of cloned C3H mouse embryo cells sensitive to postconfluence inhibition of cell division. Cancer Res. **33:**3239-3249.
10. TERZAGHI, M. & J.B. LITTLE. 1976. X-irradiation-induced transformation in a C3H mouse embryo-derived cell line. Cancer Res. **36:** 1367-1374.
11. MERRIMAN, R.L., & J.S. BERTRAM. 1979. Inhibition *in vitro* of 3-methylcholanthrene (MCA) induced malignant transformation of C3H/10T1/2 CL8 (10T1/2) mouse fibroblasts by retinoids. Cancer Res. **39:** 1661-1666.
12. BERTRAM, J.S. 1977. Effects of serum concentration on the expression of carcinogen-induced transformation in the C3H/10T1/2 CL8 cell line. Cancer Res. **37:** 514-523.
13. BERTRAM, J.S. 1980. Structure activity relationships among various retinoids and their ability to inhibit neoplastic transformation and to increase cell adhesion in the C3H/10T1/2 CL8 cell line. Cancer Res. **40:** 3141-3146.
14. MORDAN, L.J., S.J. BLAIR, S. HUI & J.S. BERTRAM. Effects of retinyl acetate on morphology and membrane topography of C3H/10T1/2 CL8 cells and their transformed counterparts measured by scanning electron microscopy. Cancer Res. Submitted.
15. BERTRAM, J.S., P.R. LIBBY & R.L. MERRIMAN. 1980. Modulation of carcinogen-induced transformation by actinomycin D in the C3H/10T1/2 cell line. J. Natl. Cancer Inst. **64:** 1393-1399.
16. SPORN, M.B., N.M. DUNLOP, D.L. NEWTON & W.R. HENDERSON. 1976. Relationships between structure and activity of retinoids. Nature **263:** 110-113.
17. ADAMO, S., L.M. DELUCA, I. AKALOVSKY & P.V. BHAT. 1979. Retinoid-induced adhesion in cultured transformed mouse fibroblasts. J. Natl. Cancer Inst. **62:** 1473-1477.

18. JETTEN, A.M., M.E.R. JETTEN, S.S. SHAPIRO & J.P. POON. 1979. Characterization of the effects of retinoids on mouse fibroblast cell lines. Exp. Cell Res. **119:** 289–299.
19. BERTRAM, J.S., P.R. LIBBY & W.M. LeSTOURGEON. 1977. Changes in nuclear actin levels with change in growth state of C3H/10T1/2 cells and the lack of response in malignantly transformed cells. Cancer Res. **37:** 4104–4111.
20. THOMPSON, H.J. C.J. GRUBBS, R.C. MOON & M.B. SPORN. 1978. Continual requirement of retinoid for maintenance of mammary cancer inhibition. Proc. Am. Assoc. Cancer Res. **19:** 74.
21. BOUTWELL, R.K. & A.K. VERMA. 1981. The influence of retinoids on polyamine and DNA synthesis in mouse epidermis. Ann. N.Y. Acad. Sci. **359:**.
22. DeLUCA, H.F., M. ZILE & W.K. SIETSEMA. 1981. The metabolism of retinoic acid to 5,6-epoxyretinoic acid; retinoyl-β-glucuronide, and other polar metabolites. Ann. N.Y. Acad. Sci. **359:**.
23. FROLIK, C.A. 1981. The *in vitro* and *in vivo* metabolism of all-*trans* and 13-*cis*-retinoic acid in the vitamin A deficient hamster. Ann. N.Y. Acad. Sci. **359:**.
24. BHAT, P.V. & L.M. DeLUCA. 1981. The biosynthesis of a mannolipid containing a metabolite of retinoic acid by 3T12 mouse fibroblasts. Ann. N.Y. Acad. Sci. **359:**.
25. FROT-COUTAZ, J., R. LETOUBLON & R. GOT. 1981. *In vitro* vitamin A-mediated glycosylation: Recent developments in the enzymatic studies. Ann. N.Y. Acad. Sci. **359:**.
26. QUILL, H. & G. WOLF. 1981. Formation of α-1,2- and α-1,3- linked mannose disaccharides from mannosyl retinyl phosphate by rat liver membrane enzymes. Ann. N.Y. Acad. Sci. **359:**.
27. SHIDOJI, Y., W. SASAK, C.S. SILVERMAN-JONES & L.M. DeLUCA. 1981. Recent studies on the involvement of retinyl phosphate as a carrier of mannose in biological membranes. Ann. N.Y. Acad. Sci. **359:**.
28. DOMANSKA-JANIK, K., W. KLOHS, J.S. BERTRAM. & R.J. BERNACKI. 1980. Effect of retinyl acetate on sugar incorporation and membrane enzyme activity in 10T1/2 murine fibroblasts. Proc. Am. Assoc. Cancer. Res. **21:** 83.
29. EMMELOT, P. 1973. Biochemical properties of normal and neoplastic cell surfaces: A review. Eur. J. Cancer **9:** 314–333.

THE MODULATING EFFECT OF RETINOIDS AND A TUMOR PROMOTER ON MALIGNANT TRANSFORMATION, SISTER CHROMATID EXCHANGES, AND Na/K ATPase*†

Carmia Borek, Richard C. Miller, Charles R. Geard, Duane Guernsey, Robert S. Osmak, Melanie Rutledge-Freeman, Augustinus Ong, and Herbert Mason

Radiological Research Laboratory, Department of Radiology
Cancer Center/Institute of Cancer Research and
Department of Pathology
College of Physicians and Surgeons
Columbia University
New York, New York 10032

INTRODUCTION

Within the last decade a variety of vitamin A analogs (retinoids) have been shown to inhibit the expression of malignancy both in experimental systems and in the clinic (for recent review see ref. 17) At the same time there has been a revived interest and increased awareness of the effectiveness of substances, mostly of plant origin and called tumor promoters, in promoting carcinogenesis.[2] One of these compounds TPA‡ (12-0 tetradecanoyl-phorbol 13-acetate)[10] has been used extensively in studies utilizing all culture systems.[36]

While an antagonism between TPA and retinoids has been recognized in some carcinogenesis systems, in growth-related enzymatic systems *in vivo* and *in vitro* and in differentiation *in vitro* (for review see ref. 16) no studies have been carried out where the effects of retinoids and TPA, alone and in combination were evaluated on oncogenic transformation *in vitro*.

In earlier reports we have shown that a vitamin A analog inhibits radiation-induced transformation *in vitro*[9] and that retinoids and TPA exert antagonistic effects on vitamin A-binding protein production.[6] Since the tumor promoter TPA has been reported to enhance radiation-induced transformation,[12,23] it seemed a logical step to follow up these various studies and to investigate whether:

* This investigation was supported by Contract DE-AC02-78EVO4733 from the Department of Energy and by Grant Numbers CA 12536 and CA 23952 to the Radiological Research Laboratory/Department of Radiology, and by Grant Number CA 13696 to the Cancer Center/Institute of Cancer Research, awarded by the National Cancer Institute, Department of Health, Education and Welfare.

† By acceptance of this article, the publisher and/or recipient acknowledges the U.S. Government's right to retain a nonexclusive royalty-free license in and to any copyright covering this paper.

‡ *The abbreviations used are: TMMP-ERA, trimethylmethoxyphenyl analog of N-ethyl retinamide; TMMP-RA, trimethylmethoxyphenyl analog of β-retinoic acid; 13-RA, 13-cis-retinoic acid; β-RA, β-all-trans-retinoic acid; TPA 12-O-tetradecanoyl-phorbol-13-acetate; DMSO, dimethyl sulfoxide; BrdU, bromodeoxyuridine; BP, benzo-a-pyrene; SCE, sister chromatid exchange. Gy min⁻¹, gray per minute.*

0077-8923/81/0359-0237 $01.75/0 © 1981, NYAS

(1) The antagonism between vitamin A and TPA on cell differentiation *in vitro*[6] prevails in their effects on radiation-induced transformation *in vitro*.

(2) If it does, is the antagonism mediated via DNA damage as reflected by sister chromatid exchanges or via other cellular and molecular events?

MATERIALS AND METHODS

Cell Cultures

We used two cell systems for the transformation studies the C3H/10T½ mouse heteroploid cell line[30] and freshly cultured diploid hamster embryo cells.[5]

(1) Mouse C3H/10T½ C1. 8 cells. Cells were cultured and maintained as previously described.[30]

Cell growth was assayed by plating 4×10^4 cells per dish 18 hr prior to irradiation and/or exposure to retinoids and/or TPA. Cells were in contact with the retinoids and TPA throughout the testing period, which included medium change every 6 days.

Transformation experiments involved the use of stock cells between passages 9 and 14. Cells were plated 18 hr before treatment at densities that would result in survival of about 40 clones per dish for the determination of plating efficiency and cell survival. Cells were fixed in 10% formalin and stained with Giemsa 12 days after plating.

Concurrently, cells were plated for transformation studies into 50 cm² Petri dishes in a way that approximately 400 reproductively viable cells survived the treatments. In those cultures requiring retinoids, cells were exposed to the compound for 4 days. TPA, where appropriate, was in contact with the cells throughout the cell incubation period. Cells in medium alone or medium plus TPA were subsequently refed weekly until termination of the experiment 5 weeks after plating when cells were fixed and stained with Giemsa. At that time transformed non-contact-inhibited cells had overgrown the confluent monolayer of normal cells. The frequencies of darkly staining transformed foci indicating a loss of cell contact inhibition were recorded and assessed according to the criteria established by Reznikoff *et al.*[29] Only Types 2 and 3 transformed clones were scored as transformation.

Cells were seeded in 25 mm flasks (Falcon) at a concentration per flask of 10^3 cells seeded on 3×10^4 syngeneic feeder cells[3,4] in the presence of 7.1 μM β-RA. The cultures were irradiated 24 hr after seeding with 3 Gy of x-rays. TPA was added immediately after irradiation. β-RA remained in the medium for 3 days following irradiation; after this time medium free of retinoid, but containing TPA was used for cell feeding. Because Syrian hamster cells metabolize TPA[26] it was considered prudent to change the medium every 2 days. The first medium change contained both retinoid and TPA, but the subsequent changes contained TPA alone. Control plates consisted of untreated cells, unirradiated, retinoid-treated cells, and unirradiated, TPA-treated cells.

The duration of the experiment was 10 days, after which cultures were fixed, stained, and scored for transformation using morphological criteria as described previously.[5] Transformed colonies were scored from among the surviving colonies thus allowing the evaluation of plating efficiency, cell killing, and cell transforming within the same experiment.

Chemicals

The vitmain A analogs TMMP-ERA, TMMP-RA, and 12-RA were obtained from Hoffmann-La Roche of Nutley, NJ. β-RA was kindly donated by Dr. M. Sporn. Care was taken to avoid exposing the retinoids and cells containing BrdU to anything other than subdued natural or gold light.

Retinoids were diluted in ethyl alcohol with the final concentration of retinoid and alcohol in the medium at 7.1 μM and less than 0.05%, respectively.

TPA (Consolidated Midland Corp., Brewster, NY) was prepared in DMSO prior to each experiment. The final concentrations of TPA and DMSO in the growth medium were 0.16 μM (0.1 μg/ml) and 0.01%, respectively.

In addition to the retinoids and TPA, colcemid (5 μM) (Grand Island Biological Co., Grand Island, NY), BrdU (3 μM) (Calbiochem-Behring, La Jolla, CA) were used in the SCE studies.

Method of Irradiation

Attached cells were irradiated, at room temperature using a Siemens Stabilipan x-ray machine operating at 300 kVp and 12 mA, with 0.2 mm Cu external filtration. The dose rate from measurements with a Victorren R-meter at the location of the cells was calculated at 0.32 Gy min^{-1} (1 Gy = 1 gray = 100 rad).

Sister Chromatid Exchanges (SCE)

Asynchronous log-phase cells (3 × 10^5 cells per 100 mm dish) were treated with BrdU (3 μM) for 24 to 26 hr before irradiation (3 Gy), TPA and/or retinoid. Cells were fixed at various times 10 to 20 hr after irradiation with mitoses being accumulated with colcemid for the final 6 hr. In each of five duplicate experiments, cells were exposed to BP for the whole period thereby serving as a positive indicator of sister chromatid exchange induction. Prior to fixation, all cells were trypsinized from the dishes, made hypotonic with 0.075 M KCι for 12 min, then fixed in cold, fresh methanol, acetic acid (3:1). After two fixative changes, cell suspensions were dropped onto wetted slides and air dried.

Cells were stained in 2% Giemsa (Gurrs R66) in 0.3 M Na$_2$ HPO$_4$ at pH 10.4 (adjusted with 1 N NaOH) for 10 to 30 min.[1] This staining procedure differentiates chromatids that have incorporated BrdU over two replication cycles (darkly stained) from chromatids that incorporated BrdU in one cycle (lightly stained). Cells that have been in BrdU for one, two or three replication cycles are rapidly assessed and the frequencies of each were recorded in mitotic cell samples of 200 from each treatment. The percentage of cells in mitosis (mitotic index) was also determined from samples of 1,000 cells from each treatment.

Sister chromatid exchanges were recorded on a per chromosome basis in samples of 1,000 to 2,000 chromosomes from each treatment from cells in their second metaphase after BrdU incorporation; that is, a comparison was made between cells which were maintained as controls or in the presence of TPA and/or retinoid for two replication cycles as well as cells that were irradiated in their second cycle. Radiation-induced SCEs are thus induced in one cycle only, whereas the chemicals *can* induce SCEs in both cell cycles.

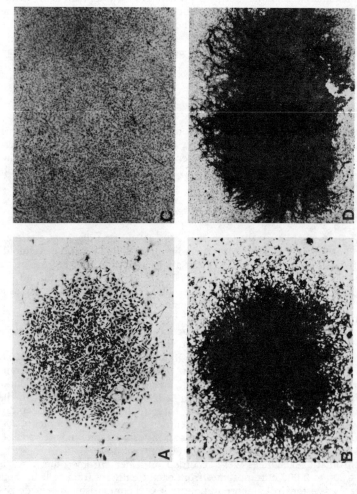

FIGURE 1. (A) A 12-day-old normal colony of hamster embryo cells (Giemsa, ×17.5). (B) A 12-day-old colony of hamster cells transformed by 3 Gy of x-irradiation. Note the dense multilayering within the colony compared to the normal and the criss-cross irregular pattern at the periphery of the colony (Giemsa, ×17.5). (C) A monolayer of untransformed 10T½ mouse cells 6 weeks in culture. Note the flat sheet of cells (Giemsa, ×17.5). (D) A type III focus of 10T½ cells transformed by 3 Gy of x-irradiation and 6 weeks in culture. Note the dense multilayering within the focus (Giemsa, × 17.5). (From Borek *et al.* 1979. *Proc. Natl. Acad. Sci. USA* **76:** 1800. Reproduced with permission.)

RESULTS

When evaluating the effect of the retinoids on the cell, the use of TMMP-RA and 13-RA[22] was discontinued because of their high toxicity.

Cell Growth

The distinct morphological differences between the normal and radiation-transformed cells in both the hamster embryo cells and the C3H 10T½ cells can be seen in FIGURE 1. In contrast to the flat contact-inhibited appearance of the normal cells, the transformed cells pile up in dense multilayers. Loss of contact inhibition is apparent and is well observed at the periphery of the transformed clone or focus.

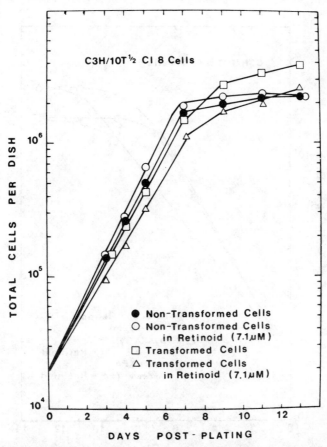

FIGURE 2. Growth characteristics of normal and radiation-transformed C3H/10T½ cells in the presence and absence of the retinoid TMMP-ERA. Cells were in contact with the retinoid throughout and were counted in a Coulter counter after trypsinization from 100 mm cell dishes.

Cell doubling time for controls and radiation-transformed cells was evaluated in both retinoid-free media and in media containing TMMP-ERA (see FIG. 2). While untransformed and transformed cells showed a similar doubling time in the absence of the retinoid, the transformed cells were clearly inhibited in their growth by the retinoid (FIG. 2). In FIGURE 3 the effects of the various treatments on normal cell growth are evaluated. Cell doubling times were similar for controls, TPA-treated cells, TMMP-ERA-treated or both combined but the presence of TPA-treated cells, TMMP-ERA-treated or both combined, in all cases resulted in a marked increase in saturation density as compared to untreated controls or cells treated with the retinoid alone. Exposure of the cells to x-rays alone or in combination with retinoids and/or TPA resulted in reduced growth rate compared to the untreated controls. Again, however, the presence of TPA determined the final saturation density of the cells.

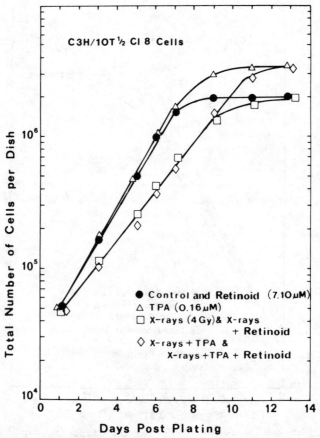

FIGURE 3. Growth characteristics of C3H/10T½ cells exposed to the combination of 4 Gy x-rays, TMMP-ERA and TPA. Cells were in contact with the counter after trypsinization from 100 mm cell dishes.

TABLE 1

THE MODULATION OF RADIATION-INDUCED CELL TRANSFORMATION BY TPA AND
RETINOID TMMP-ERA IN THE C3H/10T½ CELL LINE

Treatment	SF (PE)*	Number of Surviving Cells (10⁴)	Number of Transformed Foci[†]	Rate of[‡] Transformation (10⁻⁴)	Mean rate of Transformation (10⁻⁴) ± 1 SE
Control[§]	(0.18)	2.10	0	0	0
TPA (0.16 μM)[6]	0.93	3.74	0	0	0
Retinoid (7.1 μM)[§]	0.75	1.58	0	0	0
Retinoid, TPA[§]	0.67	2.72	0	0	0
4 Gy[¶]	0.34	1.22	8	6.56	8.78 ± 1.29
	0.30	2.88	25	8.68	
	0.30	1.17	13	11.10	
4 Gy, TPA	0.31	1.53	16	10.45	16.15 ± 1.59
	0.58	3.23	60	18.58	
	0.68	1.39	27	19.42	
4 Gy, retinoid	0.26	1.14	6	5.27	4.37 ± 0.93
	0.32	2.46	10	4.07	
	0.33	1.58	6	3.79	
4 Gy, retinoid, TPA	0.36	2.89	16	5.54	2.46 ± 0.54
	0.39	2.70	5	1.85	
	0.32	1.14	0	0	

* Plating efficiency (PE) = $\dfrac{\text{number of surviving colonies in control}}{\text{total cells plated}}$

Survival fraction (SF) = $\dfrac{\text{number of surviving colonies}}{\text{total cells plated} \times \text{(PE)}}$

[†] Sum of types 2 and 3 transformations.

[‡] Frequency of transformation = $\dfrac{\text{transformed foci}}{\text{surviving cells}}$; Standard errors (SE) were determined assuming a Poisson distribution.

[§] Values represent the average of three experiments.

[¶] 1 Gy = 100 rad.

Cell Survival in the 10T½ Hamster Embryo Cells After Treatment with X-rays, TPA or Retinoid

The data presented in TABLES 1 and 2 indicate that both hamster embryo and the mouse cells behaved qualitatively in a similar manner; i.e., radiation decreased cells survival, the retinoid TMMP-ERA (mouse cells) and β-RA (hamster cells) induced some cytotoxicity. TPA treatment resulted in little cell death and the combination of radiation and TPA resulted in enhanced cell survival compared to irradiation alone.

Modulation of Radiation-induced Transformation by TPA and Retinoids

As seen in TABLES 1 and 2, no transformation was observed when cells were

TABLE 2

THE MODULATION OF RADIATION-INDUCED CELL TRANSFORMATION BY TPA AND
AND ALL-*TRANS*-RETINOIC ACID IN HAMSTER EMBRYO CELLS

Treatment	SF (PE)*	Number of Colonies Counted	Total of Colonies Transformed	Mean Rate of Transformation[†] $(10^{-3}) \pm 1$ SE
Control	1.00	3800	0	0
TPA (0.16 µM)	0.70	2612	0	0
Retinoid (7.1 µM)[‡]	0.62	2424	0	0
Retinoid, TPA	0.89	2030	0	0
3 Gy	0.40	1064	8	6.99 ± 1.65
	0.44	1544	10	
3 Gy, TPA	0.48	1789	20	12.52 ± 1.81
	0.58	2019	28	
3 Gy, retinoid	0.31	1901	5	2.94 ± 0.79
	0.44	2768	9	
3 Gy, retinoid TPA	0.41	1710	5	2.41 ± 0.85
	0.37	1590	3	

* Survival fraction (SF) = $\dfrac{\text{number surviving colonies}}{\text{total cells plated} \times \text{PE}}$

Plating efficiency (PE) = $\dfrac{\text{number of surviving colonies in control}}{\text{total cells plated}}$

† Standard errors (SE) were determined assuming a Poisson distribution.
‡ All-*trans*-retinoic acid (β-RA).

exposed to TPA alone, retinoid alone, or the combination of both; TPA added immediately after irradiation resulted in a marked enhancement in the yield of transformation in both the hamster and the mouse cells. In contrast, the 4-day presence of retinoids in the cultures exposed to radiation markedly reduced the transformation rate. The combination of x-rays, continuous exposure of cells to TPA, and 4-day exposure of the cells to retinoids resulted in a transformation frequency similar to that of the cells exposed to x-rays and retinoid. Thus, retinoids present for only 4 days were clearly able to completely eliminate in an irreversible manner the promoting effects of the continuous exposure to TPA and also much of the inducing action of x-rays.

Sister Chromatid Exchanges

Sister chromatid exchange analyses carried out on the mouse 10T½ cells (FIG. 4) are presented in TABLE 3. Five experiments were carried out with the retinoid TMMP-ERA. As seen in TABLE 3, there is a variability between experiments. In general, it is clear that while both TPA and retinoid induce a small increase in SCE over the control they have little effect on SCE frequencies. Radiation, given here at a dose of 3 Gy doubled the yield of SCE, and the presence of TPA and retinoid alone or combined enhanced this level slightly.

These results were obtained in parallel with a positive control of BP. BP within the same experiment increased SCE fivefold, while in two experiments the presence of BP slowed the movement of the 10T½ cells through the cycle such that only first division cells were seen. TPA and retinoid had little effect (both first and second division cells were found). The x-ray dose of 3 Gy did induce a mitotic delay, but this was not further influenced by TPA or the retinoid, which is in agreement with cell growth results (FIG. 3).

The striking contrast between the effects of TPA and retinoid on transformation and their comparatively negligible effects on sister chromatid exchanges are illustrated as histograms in FIGURE 5. Although retinoid and TPA treatments did not induce transformation, they slightly increased SCEs; Radiation treatment induced both transformation and an increase in SCEs; Radiation-induced transfor-

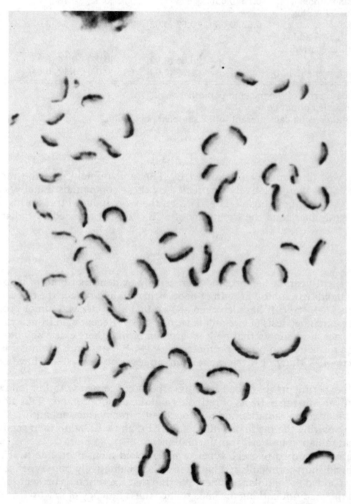

FIGURE 4. Sister chromatid exchanges in a normal culture of C3H10T½ cells.

TABLE 3

MEAN YIELD OF SISTER CHROMATID EXCHANGES PER CHROMOSOME FROM
MOUSE C3H/10½ CELLS

	Experiments with Retinoid TMMP-ERA				
Treatment	1	2	3	4	5
Control	0.31 (0.01)*	0.25 (0.02)	0.23 (0.02)	0.29 (0.02)	0.47 (0.02)
TPA (0.16 μM)	0.36 (0.02)	0.24 (0.02)	0.36 (0.02)	0.26 (0.02)	0.48 (0.03)
Retinoid (7.1 μM)	0.35 (0.02)	0.28 (0.01)	0.34 (0.02)	0.45 (0.02)	0.44 (0.02)
TPA plus retinoid	0.27 (0.01)	0.29 (0.01)	0.25 (0.02)	0.33 (0.01)	0.47 (0.02)
3 Gy	0.58 (0.03)	0.52 (0.04)	0.47 (0.02)	0.61 (0.03)	0.66 (0.03)
3 Gy plus TPA	0.54 (0.03)	0.62 (0.03)	0.53 (0.02)	0.53 (0.02)	0.83 (0.03)
3 Gy plus retinoid	0.56 (0.03)	$-$[†]	0.52 (0.02)	0.76 (0.02)	$+$[†]
3 Gy plus TPA plus retinoid	0.67 (0.03)	0.57 (0.02)	0.64 (0.03)	0.64 (0.03)	0.83 (0.03)
3 Gy with TPA added after time of irradiation	$+$[‡]	0.65 (0.03)	0.53 (0.02)	0.64 (0.03)	$+$[†]
Benzo (a) pyrene (2 μM)	$+$[‡]	1.23 (0.04)	1.16 (0.03)	1.17 (0.04)	$+$[‡]

* Standard error of the mean in parentheses.
[†] Mishandled or not done.
[‡] No 2nd division cells present in the sampled population.

mation was dramatically modulated by TPA and retinoid, but the radiation-induced SCEs were relatively unaffected by these compounds. Finally, retinoid eliminated the promoting effect of TPA on the x-ray induced transformation but only slightly increased the frequency of SCE over that induced by radiation.

DISCUSSION

In recent years it has become increasingly evident that both *in vitro* and *in vivo*, retinoids can inhibit growth of neoplastic cells and reduce the effects of carcinogens.[2,7,9,17,19,21,24] It has also been shown that plant-derived tumor promoters enhance carcinogenesis *in vivo* and *in vitro*.[2,14,16,28,36] Recent data from a variety of laboratories have shown that both *in vivo* and *in vitro* there exists an antagonism between retinoids and tumor promoters[6,13,14,18,34,35,37] or tumor promoter like sarcoma factor.[33] Many of these interactions in a variety of systems have been reviewed.[17]

The experiments described here have been concerned with the following:

(1) Evaluating the effects of retinoids and the tumor promoter TPA alone and in combination on radiation-induced oncogenic transformation; and

(2) Exploring the mode of action of the TPA and retinoid in their modulating effect on radiation-induced transformation.

We have studied two cell types, a heteroploid mouse cell line (C3H/10T½) and diploid short-term cultured hamster cells. Qualitatively both types of rodent cells responded in a similar manner. We find that the retinoids present for only 4 days in the medium bathing the cells reduce the frequency of *in vitro* transformation induced by ionizing radiation in an irreversible manner. This contrasts with

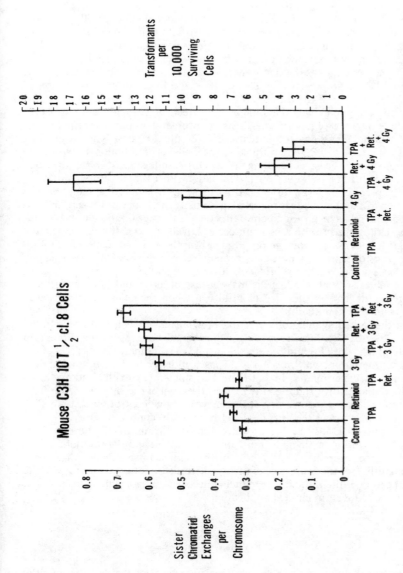

FIGURE 5. Comparison of the effects of x-rays, retinoid TMMP-ERA and TPA on transformation induction (*right side*) and sister chromatid exchanges (*left side*) in C3H/10T½ cells. Standard errors of the mean are indicated. For the SCE studies cells were scored up to 20 hr after irradiation, while transformation incidence was assessed at 5 weeks after irradiation with TPA in continuous cell contact and retinoid present for 4 days only.

the report where methylcholantrene was used as a carcinogen and the inhibition of transformation by the retinoid was reversible.[21]

In addition, our findings show that the retinoid is effective not only in reducing radiation-induced transformation but also in eliminating the promoting effect of TPA on the transformation.

The ability of the retinoid to inhibit the promotional effect of TPA occurred even though the cells were in chronic exposure to TPA while being exposed to the retinoids for only 4 days. The antagonistic effects between the retinoid and TPA are not reflected in their effect on growth. Single cells exposed to both retinoid and TPA grew into clones that were more compact than those developing in the absence of TPA. The presence of TPA dictated the final cell saturation density even in the presence of the retinoid (FIG.3).

Our attempt to elucidate the antagonistic effects of TPA and retinoids led us to a study at the level of DNA damage. Sister chromatid exchanges are indicators of such damage. Thus, the frequencies of SCEs provide a basis for evaluating whether the effects of TPA and retinoid are at the level of initiation or expression in the multistage process of carcinogenesis. Our results suggest that these compounds have little or no effect on the initiation process. This implies that the phase of expression is more influenced by these agents. An enhancing effect of retinoids on SCE induction was reported in human lymphocytes (11) and TPA has been claimed to have an enhancing effect on exchange induction.[15,16,25] Our negative finding agrees with recent studies of Loveday and Latt[20] and of Thompson et al.[32] It does not support the proposal of Kinsella and Radman[15] that TPA influences transformation by increasing somatic recombination. Our results showing that SECs do not reflect the effect of either agent on the frequency of transformation imply also that, while SCE may be useful as an indicator of primary carcinogen-mutagen,[27,28] they are of little use when secondary agents modify cellular responses to initiators.

In further pursuing the problem of the antagonism between TPA and retinoid we are currently finding in ongoing experiments (Guernsey and Borek, in preparation) that the TPA and retinoid alone and in combination markedly affect the cellular membrane enzymes Na/K ATpase, under conditions mimicking the transformation experiments. In both the hamster embryo cells and the C3H 10T½ the retinoid, β-RA significantly *reduced* the level of the enzyme, while TPA significantly *enhanced* the activity of the enzyme above control when both TPA and retinoid are present the enzyme level returned to control level.

The retinoids TMMP-ERA and β-RA dramatically inhibited the effects of radiation in including malignant transformation *in vitro* and the promotional effect of the tumor promoter TPA. While the exact mechanisms by which they interact and influence the frequency of malignant transformation are unknown, the powerful action of the retinoids in reducing induced transformation suggest that they could serve well in clinical applications.

REFERENCES

1. ALVES, P. & J. JOHNASSON. 1978. New staining method for the detection of sister chromatid exchanges in BUdR labelled chromosomes. J. Cell Sci. 32: 185–195.
2. BERENBLUM, I. 1975. Sequential aspects of chemical carcinogenesis: Skin. In Cancer: A Comprehensive Treatise. F.F. Becker, Ed.: 429–454. Plenum Press. New York.
3. BOLLAG, W. 1971. Therapy of chemically induced skin tumors of mice with vitamin A palmitate and vitamin A acid. Experientia 27: 90–92.

4. BOREK, C. 1979. Malignant transformation *in vitro:* Criteria, biological markers, and application in environmental screening of carcinogens. Radiat. Res. **79:** 209–232.
5. BOREK, C., E.J. HALL & H.H. ROSSI. 1978. Malignant transformation in cultured hamster embryo cells produced by x-rays, 430 keV monoenergetic neutrons, and heavy ions. Cancer Res. **38:** 2997–3005.
6. BOREK, C. & L. SACHS. 1966. *In vitro* transformation by x-irradiation. Nature **210:** 276–278.
7. BOREK, C. & J.E. SMITH. 1978. Tumor promoter inhibits production of liver retinol binding protein. J. Cell Biol. **79:** CU 341 (abstracts).
8. CHYTIL, F. & D.E. ONG. 1976. Mediation of retinoic acid-induced growth and anti-tumor-activity. Nature **260:** 49–51. 1976.
9. HARISIADIS, L., R.C. MILLER, E.J. HALL & C. BOREK. 1978. A vitamin A analogue inhibits radiation-induced oncogenic transformation. Nature **274:** 486–487.
10. HECKER, E. 1975. Carcinogens and Carcinogenesis. *In* Handbuch der Allgemeinen Pathologie, Geschwulste Tumors II, IV 16, pp. 651–676. E. Grundmann, Ed. Springer-Verlag. Berlin-Heidelberg.
11. JUHL, H.J., C.C. SCHURER, C.R. BARTRAM, F.V. KOHL, H. MELDERIS, P.V. WICHERT & H.W. RUDIGER. 1978. Retinoids induce sister-chromatid exchanges in human diploid fibroblasts. Mutation Res. **58:** 317–320.
12. KENNEDY, A.R., S. MONDAL, C. HEIDELBERGER & J.B. LITTLE. 1978. Enhancement of x-ray transformation by 12-*o*-tetradecanoyl-phorbol-13-acetate in a cloned line of C3H mouse embryo cells. Cancer Res. **38:** 439–443.
13. KENSLER, T.W. & G.C. MUELLER. 1978. Retinoic acid inhibition of the comitogenic action of mezerin and phorbol ester in bovine lymphocytes. Cancer Res. **38:** 771–775.
14. KENSLER, T.W., A.K. VERMA, R.K. BOUTWELL & G.C. MUELLER. 1978. Effects of retinoic acid and juvenile hormone on the induction of ornithine decarboxylase activity by 12-*o*-tetradecanoyl-phorbol-13-acetate. Cancer Res. **38:** 2896–2899.
15. KINSELLA, A.R. & M. RADMAN. 1978. Tumor promoter induces sister chromatid exchanges: Relevance to mechanisms of carcinogenesis. Proc. Natl. Acad. Sci USA **75:** 6149–6153.
16. LITTLE, J.B., H. NAGASAWA & A.R. KENNEDY. 1979. DNA repair and malignant transformation: Effect of x irradiation, 12-*o*-tetradecanoyl-phorbol-13-acetate, and protease inhibitors on transformation and sister-chromatid exchanges in mouse 10T½ cells. Radiat. Res. **79:** 241–255.
17. LOTAN, R. 1980. Effects of vitamin A and its analogs (retinoids) on normal and neoplastic cells. Biochem. Biophys. Acta. Reviews on Cancer. **3605:** 33–91.
18. LOTAN, R. 1978. Retinoic acid stimulates and phorbol myristate acetate inhibits melanogenesis in cultures of murine S91 melanoma cells. J. Cell Biol. **79:** CD 144 (Abstracts).
19. LOTAN, R. & G.L. NICOLSON. 1977. Inhibitory effects of retinoic acid or retinyl acetate on the growth of untransformed, transformed, and tumor cells *in vitro.* J. Natl. Cancer Inst. **59:** 1717–1721.
20. LOVEDAY, K.S. & S.A. LATT. 1979. The effect of a tumor promoter, 12-*o*-tetradecanoyl-phorbol-13-acetate (TPA) on sister-chromatid exchange formation in cultured Chinese hamster cells. Mutation Res. **67:** 343–348.
21. MERRIMAN, R.L. & G.S. BERTRAM. 1979. Reversible inhibition by retinoids of 3-methylcholanthrene-induced neoplastic transformation in C3H/10T½/clone 8 cells. Cancer Res. **39:** 1661–1666.
22. MILLER, R.C., C.R. GEARD, R.S. OSMAK, M. RUTLEDGE-FREEMAN, A. ONG, H. MASON, A. NAPHOLZ, N. PEREZ, L. HARISIADIS & C. BOREK. 1980. Retinoids and a tumor promoter modify radiation induced transformation but not sister chromatid exchanges in rodent cells. Cancer Res. In press.
23. MONDAL, S. & C. HEIDELBERGER. 1976. Transformation of C3H/10T½ CL 8 mouse embryo fibroblasts irradiation and a phorbol ester. Nature (London) **260:** 710–711.
24. MOON, R.C., C.J. GRUBBS & M.B. SPORN. 1975. Inhibition of 7, 12-dimethylbenz(a) anthracene-induced mammary carcinogenesis by retinyl acetate. Cancer Res. **36:** 2626–2630.
25. NAGASAWA, H. & J.B. LITTLE. 1979. Effect of tumor promoters, protease inhibitors,

and repair processes on x-ray induced sister chromatid exchanges in mouse cells. Proc. Natl. Acad. Sci. USA **76:** 1943–1947.

26. O'BRIEN, T.G. & L. DIAMOND. 1978. Metabolism of tritium labeled tetradecanoyl phorbol-13 acetate by cells in culture. Cancer Res. **38:** 2562–2566.

27. PERRY, P. & H.J. EVANS. 1975. Cytological detection of mutagen-carcinogen exposure by sister chromatid exchange. Nature (London) **258:** 121–125.

28. PETERSON, A.R., S. MONDAL, D.W. BRANKOW, W. THON. & C. HEIDELBERGER. 1977. Effects of promoters on DNA synthesis in C3H/10T½ mouse fibroblasts. Cancer Res. **37:** 3223–3227.

29. REZNIKOFF, C.A., J.S. BERTRAM, D.W. BRANKOW & C. HEIDELBERGER. 1973. Quantitative and qualitative studies of chemical transformation of cloned C3H mouse embryo cells sensitive to postconfluence inhibition of cell division. Cancer Res. **33:** 3239–3249.

30. REZNIKOFF, C.A., D.W. BRANKOW & C. HEIDELBERGER. 1973. Establishment and characterization of a cloned line of C3H mouse embryo cells sensitive to postconfluence inhibition of division. Cancer Res. **33:** 3231–3238.

31. SPORN, M.B., & D.L. NEWTON. 1979. Chemoprevention of cancer with retinoids. Fed. Proc. **38:** 2528–2534.

32. THOMPSON, L.H., R.M. BAKER, A.V. CARRANO & K.W. BROOKMAN. 1980. Failure of the phorbol ester TPA to enhance sister chromatid exchange, mitotic segregation or expression of mutations in Chinese hamster cells. Cancer Res. In press.

33. TODARO, G.J., J.E. DE LARCO & M.B. SPORN. 1978. Retinoids block phenotypic cell transformation produced by sarcoma growth factor. Nature (London) **276:** 272–274.

34. VERMA, A.K. & R.K. BOUTWELL. 1977. Vitamin A acid (retinoic acid), a potent inhibitor of 12-o-tetradecanoyl-phorbol-13-acetate-induced ornithine decarboxylase activity in mouse epidermis. Cancer. Res. **37:** 2196–2201.

35. WEEKS, C.E., T.J. SLAGA, H. HENNINGS, G.L. GLEASON & W.M. BRACKEN. 1979. Inhibition of phorbol ester-induced tumor promotion in mice by vitamin A analog and anti-inflammatory steroid. J. Natl. Cancer Inst. **63:** 401–406.

36. WEINSTEIN, I.B., H. YAMASAKI, M. WIGLER, L.S. LEE, P.B. FISHER, A. JEFFREY & D. GRUNBERGER. 1979. Molecular and cellular events associated with the action of initiating carcinogens and tumor promoters. *In* Carcinogens: Identification and Mechanisms of Action. A. Clark Griffin & Charles R. Shaw, Eds.: 399–418. Raven Press. New York.

37. WERTZ, P.W. T.W. KENSLER, G.C. MUELLER, A.K. VERMA & R.K. BOUTWELL. 1979. 5, 6-epoxyretinoic acid opposes the effects of 12-o-tetradecanoyl phorbol-13-acetate in bovine lymphocytes. Nature (London) **277:** 227–229.

38. WOLFF, S. 1977. Sister chromatid exchange. Ann. Rev. Genet **11:** 183–201.

RETINOIDS INHIBIT PROMOTER-DEPENDENT PRENEOPLASTIC PROGRESSION IN MOUSE EPIDERMAL CELL LINES

Nancy H. Colburn,*† Stephen Ozanne,* Ulrike Lichti,* Theresa Ben,*
Stuart H. Yuspa,* Edmund Wendel,† Edward Jardini,†
and Gina Abruzzo†

*Laboratory of Experimental Pathology and
†Laboratory of Viral Carcinogenesis
National Cancer Institute
Bethesda, Maryland 20205

INTRODUCTION

We have recently described a cell culture system for studying promoter-dependent preneoplastic progression.[1,2] The JB6 cell line has been derived from primary mouse epidermal cultures and found to respond to tumor-promoting but not to nonpromoting phorbol esters with an irreversible induction of tumor-cell phenotype, as measured by colony formation in 0.33% agar at 14 days. The mechanism appears to involve induction of a new phenotype rather than selection of preexisting anchorage-independent cells.[3] The JB6 precursor cells are nontumorigenic while the phorbol ester-induced anchorage-independent transformants are tumorigenic (Colburn, submitted). Thus in view of its rapidity and irreversibility this anchorage-independence response to phorbol esters by JB6 cells appears to be analogous to late-stage skin tumor promotion *in vivo*. Inhibition of preneoplastic progression by retinoids has been shown for a number of epithelial systems.[4,5] Boutwell and coworkers have reported that retinoids applied to mouse skin one hour before TPA during the promotion phase inhibited tumor yield substantially.[6,7] The experiments described in this report were undertaken (1) to determine whether retinoids are active in inhibiting late-stage promotion in cell culture; (2) to use retinoid inhibition as an approach to identifying molecular and cellular events that are required in the process of tumor promotion, and (3) to investigate the mode of action of retinoids in tumor prophylaxis.

RETINOIDS INHIBIT INDUCTION OF ANCHORAGE INDEPENDENCE BY TPA

As shown in TABLE 1, 12-O-tetradecanoyl-phorbol-13-acetate (TPA) was added to JB6 cells at the time of suspension in 0.33% agar. The 614 per 10^4 cell yield of colonies induced by TPA was at least 50 times that found in the solvent control. Colony induction was reduced by about 51 to 88% by simultaneous exposure in agar to 10^{-8} to 10^{-5} M retinoic acid.

In order to determine whether the inhibitory activity could be attributed to cytotoxicity rather than a specific retinoid activity, retinoids were assayed for effects on attachment efficiency on plastic and cloning efficiency in soft agar. Attachment efficiency of JB6 cells and its clonal derivatives was inhibited by 10^{-6} to 10^{-5} M retinoic acid by zero to 20%, indicating little or no significant effect. A perhaps more relevant cytotoxicity assay is cloning efficiency in soft agar by

0077-8923/81/0359-0251 $01.75/0 © 1981, NYAS

TABLE 1

INHIBITION BY RETINOIC ACID (ROIC) OF TPA-INDUCED COLONY FORMATION IN
SEMISOLID AGAR*

Treatment	Colonies per 10^4 Cells	Colony Yield as % of TPA Control
1.6×10^{-8} M TPA	614	100
TPA + 10^{-8} M Roic	264	48.9
TPA + 10^{-7} Roic	240	39.5
TPA + 10^{-6} M Roic	160	26.6
TPA + 10^{-5} M Roic	78	12.3

* JB6 cells,[2,18] were suspended in 0.33% agar medium containing 10% serum and TPA without or with added retinoic acid, then layered over 0.5% agar and scored for colonies at 14 days as previously described.[1] Colony yields have been corrected for background level found in 0.1% DMSO solvent controls (generally $\leqslant$ 12 per 10^4 cells). Handling of retinoids was carried out using gold light. Variation in colony yield was $\pm$ 1 to 14% for the mean of 2 to 3 experiments.

tumorigenic cells, since the same end point is measured as that for the preneoplastic progression assay. Retinoic acid, if cytotoxic for mouse epidermal cell lines at the concentrations used would be expected to inhibit colony formation by tumorigenic cell lines. Such inhibition would not prove cytotoxicity since it could involve noncytotoxic inhibition of expression of tumor cell phenotype. However, lack of inhibition would argue for lack of cytotoxicity. As shown in FIGURE 1, retinoic acid addition at 10^{-8} to 10^{-6} M to either of three independently derived tumorigenic cell lines produced no significant inhibition of colony formation in agar. Colony yields ranged from about 1000 to 5000 colonies per 10,000 cells. Only 10^{-5} M retinoic acid on the D11a cell line showed significant inhibition. The less active C22 acid showed no significant inhibition of agar colony formation.

FIGURE 2 shows the effects of a series of retinoids on TPA induction of anchorage independence in JB6 cells. The dimethyl methoxyethylcyclopentenyl derivative and retinoic acid were the most active inhibitors, with the former being slightly more active. Both compounds also showed high activity for inhibition of skin tumor promotion.[7] In contrast to that found for some promotion or progression systems,[8,9] the dimedone derivative and retinyl acetate showed low inhibitory activity.

Todaro, De Larco and Sporn[9] have reported that inhibition of sarcoma growth factor induction of agar colony formation requires retinoic acid pretreatment in addition to simultaneous treatment. As shown in TABLE 2, the effect of retinoic acid pretreatment on TPA induction of anchorage independence in JB6 clone 21 cells was assayed. Exposure to 10^{-6} M retinoic acid for 24 or 48 hours in monolayer culture prior to suspending cells in agar with TPA produced no inhibition of subsequent colony induction. Nor did pretreatment increase the inhibitory effect observed after simultaneous exposure to TPA and retinoic acid: the 58 and 55% of TPA control values found were close to the 52% found for simultaneous but not prior treatment.

EFFECT OF RETINOIC ACID ON THE
ACTIVITY OF OTHER PROMOTERS OF ANCHORAGE INDEPENDENCE

Mezerein, a nonphorbol diterpene found to have low tumor-promoting activi-

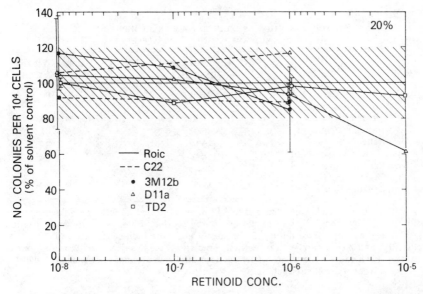

FIGURE 1. Lack of inhibition by retinoic acid of colony formation in agar by tumorigenic cells. Mouse epidermal cell lines 3 M12b, D11a, and TD2 were derived after exposure to *N*-methyl-*N*-nitro-*N*-nitroso-guanidine (3M12b) or 7,12-Dimethylbenz[a]anthrancine by methods described earlier.[2,18] Retinoic acid (Roic) or the all-*trans* C22 acid (C22) were added to the cells at the time of suspending in agar containing 20% fetal bovine serum. The shaded area indicates average standard error for the untreated control and the vertical bars for the treated samples.

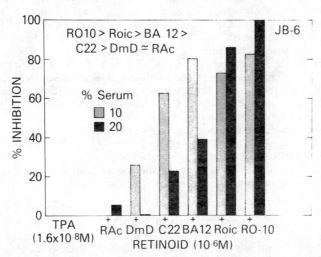

FIGURE 2. Inhibition of TPA-induced colony formation in agar by a series of retinoids. RO-10, dimethyl methoxyethylcyclopentenyl derivative; BA 12, 13-desmethyl retinoic acid; C22, all-*trans* C22 acid; DmD, dimedone derivative; RAc, retinyl acetate. Retinoids were added simultaneously with 1.6×10^{-8} M TPA as indicated in the note to TABLE 1. Clone 21 refers to JB6 Clone 21, which shows a greater anchorage-independence induction response to TPA than does the parent JB6 line.[11]

TABLE 2

RETINOID INHIBITION OF INDUCED ANCHORAGE INDEPENDENCE
REQUIRES SIMULTANEOUS, NOT PRIOR TREATMENT*

Treatment	Colonies per 10^4 Cells	Colony Yield as % of TPA Control
1.6×10^{-8} M TPA	2790	100
+ 24-hr Retinoic acid (Roic) pretreatment	3780	136
+ 48-hr-Roic pretreatment	2820	101
+ Simultaneous Roic	1452	52
+ 24-hr Roic pretreatment ⎱ + Simultaneous Roic ⎰	1614	58
+ 48-hr Roic Pretreatment ⎱ + Simultaneous Roic ⎰	1536	55

* JB6 clone 21 cells were exposed to 10^{-6} M retinoic acid (Roic) in monolayer culture during late logarithmic growth for 24 or 48 hours prior to harvesting by trypsinization (0.06% at room temperature for 4–5 minutes). Cells were then suspended in 0.33% agar plus TPA and 20% serum with or without Roic and scored as described in the legend to TABLE 1. Each value is the mean colony yield for duplicate samples after background (0.1% DMSO solvent control) subtraction.

ty when assayed as a complete promoter[10] but high and retinoid-sensitive activity as a second stage promoter,[10] was also found to induce anchorage independence in JB6 cells.[11] Initial experiments indicate that mezerein induction of anchorage independence is also inhibited by retinoic acic (Colburn *et al.,* in progress).

Epidermal growth factor (EGF), a cocarcinogen for mouse skin[12] and inducer of anchorage independence in JB6 cells[11,3] was also assayed for susceptibility to retinoid inhibition as shown in FIGURE 3. In contrast to the effect on TPA induction of anchorage independence, EGF induction was enhanced by simultaneous retinoic acid exposure at 10^{-7} and 10^{-6} M. Retinoic acid enhancements were more marked in 10% than in 20% serum with enhancements as high as 20-fold, a finding similar to that of Rizzino and Crowley,[13] who found the differentiation-inducing activity of retinoic acid to be 100-fold greater in serum-free than in 10% serum-containing medium. In the same experiments in which it enhanced EGF activity 10^{-6} M retinoic acid inhibited TPA induction of anchorage independence by about 60% (not shown). As reported elsewhere in this volume,[14] Jetten has found that retinoic acid increases the level of available EGF receptors in several cell lines including JB6 cells. This suggests the possibility that the level of receptors may be rate limiting for induction of anchorage independence by EGF. Also indicated is that retinoids may antagonize diterpenes but not at least one polypeptide growth factor in induction of tumor cell phenotype.

MECHANISM OF INHIBITION

Since virtually all tumor promoters stimulate cell proliferation[5] it has been postulated that mitogenic activity is necessary or even sufficient for effecting promotion. Recent advances in studying promotion as a stagewise process[5,10] should make possible the investigation of the role of mitogenesis in various stages of promotion. We have recently obtained several lines of evidence which suggest that

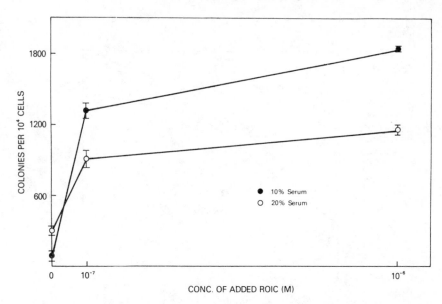

FIGURE 3. EGF induction of anchorage independence is enhanced by retinoic acid. JB6 clone 21 cells were suspended in soft agar to which EGF (10 ng/ml) was added with or without retinoic acid and colonies were scored at 14 days. The variability for duplicate dishes is shown by the vertical bars.

mitogenic stimulation by phorbol esters is not required in late-stage promotion. Exposure of cells to TPA under conditions in which mitogenic stimulation by TPA is prevented does not reduce the induction of anchorage independence (colony yield in agar) (Colburn & Ozanne, submitted). Selection of cells that are resistant to mitogenic stimulation by TPA produces no decreases in anchorage-independence response to TPA (Colburn & Wendel, in preparation). Experiments with retinoid inhibitors have also yielded results compatible with the above suggested lack of requirement for promoter-induced mitogenesis.

As shown in FIGURE 4, 1.6×10^{-8}M TPA induced a doubling of quiescent cells in monolayer culture. Simultaneous exposure to 10^{-6}M retinoic acid reduced the mitogenic effect of TPA by about 10%. Thus the target(s) of retinoids in antagonizing late-stage promotion by TPA must not be involved in mitogenic response. Further evidence for this is presented in TABLE 3 which presents the results of monitoring the labeling index as an indicator of mitogenic response. At 6 days post-plating, or one day before the cell number underwent an increase in response to TPA, TPA exposure produced an increased labeling index. Although $10^{-9}-10^{-8}$ M retinoic acid produced a partial inhibition of the TPA effect, the concentrations most active in antagonizing the TPA promotion of anchorage independence, namely $10^{-7}-10^{-6}$ M, produced no inhibition of TPA-stimulated labeling index. At 8 days post-plating, when the TPA-treated cell number approached a plateau, retinoic acid produced little or no decrease in labeling index.

Since the studies of O'Brien *et al.*[15] have demonstrated a consistent correlation between tumor-promoting activity and ornithine decarboxylase (ODC)-inducing activity, ODC induction has been proposed to be a mediator of tumor

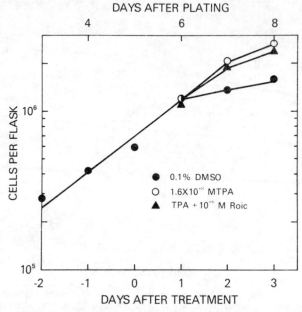

FIGURE 4. Effect of retinoic acid on TPA-induced mitogenesis. TPA was added to late logarithmic JB6 clone 21 cells in monolayer culture in the presence of 5% serum with or without simultaneously added 10^{-6} M retinoic acid (Roic). Medium containing TPA ± Roic or DMSO was replaced daily. The solvent control (0.1% DMSO) is shown for comparison.

TABLE 3

LACK OF INHIBITION OF TPA-INDUCED MITOGENESIS BY 10^{-6} – 10^{-7} M RETINOIC ACID (ROIC)*

| Treatment | Percent Labeled Nuclei after Untreated Cells Approached Quiescence | |
	6-Days Post-plating	8-Days Post-plating
None	2.0	5.0
1.6×10^{-8} M TPA	9.5	15.5
TPA + 10^{-9} M Roic	5.5	12.0
TPA + 10^{-8} M Roic	4.5	16.5
TPA + 10^{-7} M Roic	10.0	27.5
TPA + 10^{-6} M Roic	15.0	17.5

* JB6 clone 21 cells were plated at 5×10^4 cells per 60 mm dish and were exposed continuously to TPA with or without retinoic acid in MEM medium containing 5% fetal bovine serum in monolayer culture. Beginning at 6 days medium containing TPA ± Roic was changed daily. A terminal 1-hour tritiated thymidine incorporation (1 μc/ml) was carried out. Cells were processed for radioautography on the plastic petri dish bottoms which were coated with 2:1 Kodak NB-2 nuclear track emulsion and glycerol and developed for 2 weeks at 4°C.

promotion. One approach to testing this possibility for late-stage promotion was to determine whether retinoids would antagonize TPA induction of ODC at the same concentrations at which they antagonize TPA induction of anchorage independence. As shown in FIGURE 5, the process of replating cells in fresh medium led to a substantial ODC induction in JB6 cells as it has in other cell lines. [16] No ODC induction due to TPA was observed. Simultaneous exposure to 10^{-7} to 10^{-5}M retinoic acid produced 50 to greater than 90% decreases in ODC-specific activity. Thus, although TPA-dependent ODC induction does not occur, ODC may nevertheless be one of the required events in TPA induction of anchorage independence.

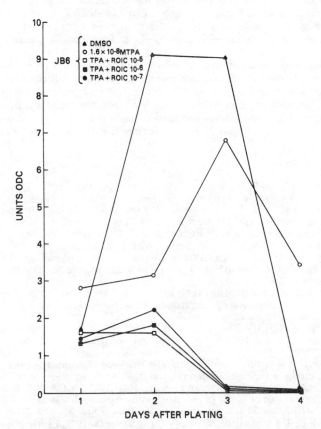

FIGURE 5. Retinoic acid inhibits medium-induced ornithine decarboxylase induction. Ornithine decarboxylase (ODC) was determined as described previously[19] by measuring the activity of cell lysates in stimulating the production of $^{14}CO_2$ from [^{14}C]Ornithine during a 1-hr incubation at $37\,^{\circ}$C. ODC activity is expressed as nmoles CO_2 produced per mg protein per hour. DMSO (0.1%) or TPA with or without retinoic acid (10^{-5} – 10^{-7} M) was added at the time of plating JB6 cells in monolayer culture. The cells remained in logarithmic growth throughout the 4-day period without medium change.

DISCUSSION

Induction of anchorage independence in JB6 mouse epidermal cell lines, a cell culture response to tumor promoters which appears to be analogous to late-stage tumor promotion in mouse skin, is sensitive to inhibition by retinoids. The mechanism of retinoid inhibition appears not to involve antagonism of the mitogenic activity of TPA but may involve prevention of medium-induced ODC. ODC synthesis has been implicated by Haddox et al.[17] as a target of retinoids when they block cell cycle traverse in CHO cells.

The observation that retinoic acid pretreatment fails to show inhibitory activity or to enhance the inhibitory activity observed with simultaneous treatment suggests the possibility of a direct interaction between TPA and retinoic acid. However, this appears unlikely since, if it occurred, mitogenesis by TPA should also be inhibited. The data suggest that TPA and retinoic acid produce short-lived antagonistic changes in a common target. Current studies in our laboratory are concerned with investigating cell surface glycoproteins (Dion & Colburn) gangliosides and glycosaminoglycans (Leela & Colburn) as possible common targets.

The retinoid enhancement of EGF induction of anchorage independence contrasts with the inhibition of sarcoma growth factor (SGF) induction of anchorage independence reported by Todaro et al.[9] for normal rat fibroblast cells. The observation that retinoids enhance EGF receptor levels [14] in the same cells in which they enhance anchorage-independence induction raises the interesting possibility that promoter receptor levels may be rate-limiting in the process of tumor promotion.

REFERENCES

1. COLBURN, N.H., B.F. FORMER, K.J. NELSON & S.H. YUSPA. 1979. Tumor promoter induces anchorage independence irreversibly. Nature 281: 589–591.
2. COLBURN, N.H., W.F. VORDERBRUEGGE, J. BATES & S.H. YUSPA. 1978 Epidermal cell transformation in vitro. In Mechanisms of Tumor Promotion and Carcinogenesis. T.J. Slaga, A.Sivak & R.K. Boutwell, Eds: 257–271. Raven Press. New York.
3. COLBURN, N.H. 1979. The use of tumor promoter responsive epidermal cell lines to study preneoplastic progression. In Neoplastic Transformation in Differentiated Epithelial Cell Systems in Vitro. L.M. Franks & C.B. Wigley, Eds: 113–134. Academic Press. New York.
4. SPORN, M.B., N.M. DUNLOP, D.L. NEWTON & J.M. SMITH. 1976. Prevention of chemical carcinogenesis by vitamin A and its synthetic analogs (retinoids). Fed. Proc. 35: 1332–1338.
5. COLBURN, N.H. 1979 Tumor promotion and preneoplastic progression. In Carcinogenesis, Vol. 5, Modifiers of Carcinogenesis. T.J. Slaga, Ed: 33–56. Raven Press. New York.
6. BOUTWELL, R.K. & A.K. VERMA. 1981. The influence of retinoids on polyamine and DNA synthesis in mouse epidermis. Ann. N.Y. Acad. Sci. 359:.
7. VERMA, A.K., B.G. SHAPAS, H.M. RICE & R.K. BOUTWELL. 1979. Correlation of the inhibition by retinoids of tumor promoter-induced mouse epidermal ornithine decarboxylase activity and of skin tumor promotion. Cancer Res. 39: 419–425.
8. MOON, R.C., C.J. GRUBBS, M.B. SPORN & D.G. GOODMAN. 1977. Retinyl acetate inhibits mammary carcinogenesis induced by N-methyl-N-nitrosourea. Nature 267: 620–621.
9. TODARO, G.J., J.E. DE LARCO & M.B. SPORN. 1978 Retinoids block the phenotypic cell transformation produced by sarcoma growth factor (SGF). Nature 276: 272–274.
10. SLAGA, T.J., A.J.B. KLEIN-SZANTO, S.M. FISCHER, C.E. WEEKS, K. NELSON & S. MAJOR. 1980. Studies on the mechanism of action of anti-tumor promoting agents: their specificity in two-stage promotion. Proc. Natl Acad. Sci. USA 77: 2251–2254.

11. COLBURN, N.H., B. KOEHLER & K.J. NELSON. 1980. A cell culture assay for tumor pro-
    moter dependent progression toward neoplastic phenotype: Detection of tumor pro-
    moters and promotion inhibitors. Teratogenesis, Carcinogenesis, and Mutagenesis 1:
    87-96.
12. ROSE, S.P., R. STAHN, D.S. PASSOVOY & HERSCHMAN. 1976. Epidermal growth factor en-
    hancement of skin tumor induction in mice. Experientia 32: 913-915.
13. RIZZINO, A. & C. CROWLEY. 1980. The growth and differentiation of the embryonal car-
    cinoma cell line, F9 in defined medium. Proc. Natl Acad. Sci. USA 77: 457-461.
14. JETTEN, A. Action of retinoids and phorbol esters on cell growth and the binding of epi-
    dermal growth factor. Ann. N.Y. Acad Sci. 359:.
15. O'BRIEN, T.G., R.C. SIMSIMAN & R.K. BOUTWELL. 1975. Induction of the polyaminebio-
    synthetic enzymes in mouse epidermis and their specificity for tumor promotion.
    Cancer Res. 35: 2426-2433.
16. O'BRIEN, T.G., M.A LEWIS & L. DIAMOND. 1979. Ornithine decarboxylase activity and
    DNA synthesis after treatment of cells in culture with 12-0-teradecanoylphor-
    bol-13-acetate. Cancer Res. 39: 4477-4480.
17. HADDOX, M.K., K.F. SCOTT & D.H. RUSSELL. 1979. Retinol inhibition of ornithine decar-
    boxylase induction and G_1 progression in Chinese hamster ovary cells. Cancer Res.
    39: 4930-4938.
18. COLBURN, N.H., W.F. VORDERBRUEGGE, J.R. BATES, R.H. GRAY, J.D. ROSSEN, W.H. KEL-
    SEY & T. SHIMADA. 1978. Correlation of anchorage-independent growth with
    tumorigenicity of chemically transformed mouse epidermal cells. Cancer Res. 38:
    624-634.
19. YUSPA, S.H., U. LICHTI, T. BEN, E. PATTERSON, H. HENNINGS, T.J. SLAGA, N. COLBURN
    & W. KELSEY. 1976. Phorbol-ester tumor promoters stimulate DNA synthesis and or-
    nithine decarboxylase activity in mouse epidermal cell cultures. Nature 262:
    402-404.

MODULATION OF TERMINAL DIFFERENTIATION AND RESPONSES TO TUMOR PROMOTERS BY RETINOIDS IN MOUSE EPIDERMAL CELL CULTURES

Stuart H. Yuspa, Ulrike Lichti, Theresa Ben, and Henry Hennings

In Vitro Pathogenesis Section
Laboratory of Experimental Pathology
National Cancer Institute
Bethesda, Maryland 20205

For more than 25 years, retinoids have been known to alter the state of differentiation of epidermis or similar stratifying squamous epithelia.[1-4] The nature of this alteration often varied in experimental systems depending on species studied, dose or analog used, or method of applications.[5] More recently retinoids have been shown to modify epidermal carcinogenesis by preventing the occurrence of tumors during the promotion phase,[6] or by causing existing tumors to regress.[7,8]

This laboratory has utilized cultured mouse keratinocytes for a variety of studies related to differentiation and chemical carcinogenesis. Previous data have substantiated the validity of this cell culture model for defining normal epidermal function as well as alterations associated with tumor initiation and promotion.[9-12] This model has also been useful for defining the molecular events associated with retinoid-induced alterations in differentiation and carcinogenesis. The results of some of these studies are summarized in TABLE 1. Retinoid concentrations of 10^{-5} – 10^{-6}M have resulted in epidermal metaplasia with morphological characteristics of a secretory epithelium.[9,18,19] Under these conditions retinoids have generally been growth inhibitory.[9,15] While semiconservative DNA synthesis is decreased, DNA repair synthesis is quantitatively unaffected by retinoid exposure.[15] Glycoprotein synthesis and the nature of epidermal glycoproteins are rapidly altered after retinoid exposure.[13,14] Both metabolism and macromolecular binding of polycyclic aromatic hydrocarbon carcinogens are changed in epidermal cells exposed to retinoids. At considerably lower levels of exposure to retinoids (10^{-7} – 10^{-9}M), the effects of phorbol ester tumor promoters in skin are modified.[6,16,17] Tumor promotion itself is inhibited *in vivo* at these exposure levels.[6]

Recently Hennings *et al.* have reported that ionic calcium is a critical regulator of epidermal growth and differentiation in cell culture.[20] By adjusting Ca⁺⁺ to a low level (0.02 – 0.09 mM) in culture medium, epidermal cells proliferate rapidly and do not stratify. The addition of Ca⁺⁺ to a level of 1.0 – 2.0 mM induces a rapid sequence of changes resulting in terminal differentiation of most or all of the epidermal cells in culture. The capability of controlling growth and differentiation in the epidermal population by manipulating Ca⁺⁺ prompted us to reexamine the role of retinoids in this process. A portion of this report will present results of this study.

In attempting to better understand the mechanism of tumor promotion in epidermis, we have been studying the induction of the enzyme ornithine decarboxylase (ODC) which results from exposure to the potent tumor promoter 12-0-tetradecanoyl phorbol-13-acetate.[21,22] Some of these studies have utilized inhibitors of tumor promotion. Such studies are useful because they provide insight

0077-8923/81/0359-0260 $01.75/0 © 1981, NYAS

TABLE 1

RETINOID EFFECTS ON MOUSE KERATINOCYTES

High Concentrations (10^{-5} M)	Reference
1. Phenotypically alter epidermal morphology from the keratinizing to a secretory epithelium.	9
2. Rapidly and specifically change epidermal glycopeptides (possibly mediated by the synthesis of retinyl phosphate and its glycosylated derivatives).	13, 14
3. Inhibit epidermal proliferation after a delay of one cell cycle.	9, 15
4. Inhibit induced aryl hydrocarbon hydroxylase activity	15
5. Alter carcinogen binding to cellular macromolecules.	15
Low Concentrations ($10^{-9} - 10^{-7}$M)	
6. Inhibit ornithine decarboxylase induction by phorbol esters.	16
7. Inhibit promoter dependent preneoplastic progression.	17

into both the mechanisms of inhibition and pathways that may be critical for promotion itself. The discovery that ultraviolet light induces ODC in epidermis *in vivo*[23] and *in vitro*[24] has provided an inducer which is likely to work through at least a partially distinct pathway.[12,24] Since retinoids are known to be potent inhibitors of TPA-induced ODC,[6,12,25] comparative studies with UV as inducer would likely yield information on the mechanism of retinoid inhibition. The second portion of this report will deal with these studies.

MATERIALS AND METHODS

Source of Chemicals

The tumor promoter 12-o-tetradecanoyl phorbol-13-acetate (TPA) was obtained from Chemical Carcinogenesis (Eden Prairie, MN). Retinoic acid and the dimethylmethoxy-ethyl cyclopentenyl analog of retinoic acid were from Hoffmann-La Roche through the courtesy of Dr. Luigi De Luca and Dr. Michael Sporn, respectively.

Labeled compounds were purchased from New England Nuclear as follows: 1-[^{14}C]DL-ornithine monohydrochloride (42–54 mCi/mmole), [2,3-^{3}H[N]]–putrescine (25–40 Ci/mmole), [^{3}H–methyl]thymidine (5 Ci/mmole). Unlabeled putrescine dihydrochloride and Trizma Base were from Sigma (St. Louis, MO), casein (Hammerstem) from Schwartz/Mann (Orangeburg, NY), ethylene diamine-tetracetic acid (EDTA) and $CaCl_2$ from Fisher (Fairlawn, NJ), DMSO, silylation grade, was from Pierce Chemical Company, Rockford, IL. Ethylenebis (oxyethylenenitrilo)-tetraacetic acid (EGTA) was from J.T. Baker, Phillipsburg, NJ.

Cell Isolation and Culture

The techniques for the isolation and cultivation of newborn mouse epidermal cells have been previously reported.[9] Standard medium consists of medium 199 (NIH Media Unit), 10% fetal bovine serum (FBS, Reheis Chemical Company,

Kankakee, IL) and 1% antibiotic-antimycotic solution (Gibco). The techniques for preparation of medium with reduced ionic calcium have been previously described.[20,26] Stock solutions of TPA and retinoids were dissolved in DMSO and added to media to give a final solvent concentration of 0.1%. Ultraviolet irradiation was performed on washed cell monolayers by exposure to ultraviolet light (UVC, 254 nm) from a germicidal lamp (General Electric G30T8, 30 watt) at a distance of 48 cm and with a flux of 2–3 $J/m^2/sec$ (Blak-Ray UV light meter, Model J 255, Ultraviolet Products Inc., San Gabriel, CA).

Biochemical Assays

Assays for ODC activity were performed on lysates of frozen cultured cells as previously described.[22] DNA synthesis was determined after a 1-hr pulse with [³H]TdR as previously reported.[21] Protein was determined by the method of Lowry as detailed by Layne.[27] Epidermal transglutaminase was assayed by an adaptation of the method of Ogawa and Goldsmith[28] which measures the enzyme catalyzed formation of ι amino-γ-glutamyl bonds between [³H]putrescine and casein. Approximately 6×10^6 epidermal cells were lysed by freeze thawing in 300 μl of buffer mixture composed of 50 mM Tris (pH 7.5), 2.5 mM dithiothreitol, 0.13 M NaCl, 0.83 mM EDTA and 8.3 mM $CaCl_2$. The reaction mixture consisted of a total of 200 μl as follows: 100 μl cell lysate, 20 μl casein (20μg/ml), and 30 μl [³H]putrescine (5 mM final concentration) and the additional 50 μl as buffer or EGTA (100 mM). After 10 minutes at 37°, 50 μl of reaction mixture was spotted on Whatman 3MM filter paper strips and immediately immersed in ice-cold 10% TCA containing, 1.0% putrescine. Filter papers were gently agitated through 3 TCA washes of 20 min each, immersed in ice-cold absolute ethanol and dried. Radioactivity bound to casein that precipitated on filter paper was counted in Instagel (Packard, Downers Grove, IL) in a Beckman LS 300 scintillation counter. Background radioactivity from parallel assays lacking cell lysate was substracted from all samples. Protein concentration for each lysate was determined as for ODC assay. The Ca^{++} dependence of enzymatic activity was determined by the addition of a final concentration of 25 mM EGTA to the assay mixture. Preliminary experiments indicated linear enzyme kinetics during the 10 min of assay. All assays described above were performed in duplicate on replicate samples from each experiment and all experiments were performed at least twice.

RESULTS AND DISCUSSION

Effect of Retinoids on Induced Differentiation

Recently we have shown that ionic calcium is a critical regulator of proliferation and differentiation in mouse epidermal cell cultures.[20,26] At low ionic calcium (0.02 – 0.1 mM) epidermal cells proliferate rapidly, maintain a monolayer without stratification, survive *in vitro* for many months and can be subcultured and cloned. At levels of ionic calcium above 0.1 mM, epidermal cells stratify, have a limited growth potential and terminally differentiate after 10 days in culture.[9,20,26] At both Ca^{++} levels, keratin biosynthesis continues. When cultures maintained under low Ca^{++} conditions are switched to Ca^{++} levels above 0.1 mM, proliferation stops and a rapid sequence of events leads to terminal differentiation of most cells with sloughing of cornified cells into the culture medium.

To study the effect of retinoids on this induced terminal differentiation we designed experiments according to the time sequence in FIGURE 1. Cells were plated and grown for 4 days in growth medium (0.09 mM Ca^{++}) and then exposed to 10^{-6}M retinoic acid or solvent (0.1% DMSO) for 3 days in this same medium. Groups were then subdivided and either continued in the low Ca^{++} medium or switched to medium containing 1.2 mM Ca^{++} to induce differentiation. Retinoic acid or solvent was continued throughout the experiment. FIGURE 2A illustrates the appearance of epidermal cells cultured for 10 days in 0.09 mM Ca^{++} medium. Such cells grow as a monolayer and rapidly become confluent but do not stratify. Individual cells are of polygonal shape with distinct intercellular spaces. A number of round cells are seen floating in the medium. Exposure to retinoic acid does not significantly alter this morphology except that individual cells appear flatter. With the elevation of calcium to 1.2 mM, epidermal cell morphology changes rapidly (FIGS. 2B,D,F.H). Distinct spaces between cells disappear within several hours and the cells become larger, more angular and develop phase-dense cell outlines similar to those reported for differentiating human keratinocytes.[29] Numerous granules, some of which are keratohyalin granules (unpublished data), accumulate in these differentiating cells as vertical stratification and squame formation become more distinct by 48 hr (FIG. 2D). After 3–4 days nuclei are lost and sheets of differentiated cells detach from the plastic substrate leaving a sparce population of cells that detach more slowly. Retinoic acid alters these morphological changes (FIGS. 2C,E,G,I). Retinoid-treated cultures retain distinct intracellular spaces, and cells maintain a more circular shape and "glassy" appearance. For the first 48 hr after Ca^{++} addition, stratification and granule formation are suppressed and dense cell outlines do not appear. By 72 hr after induction however, some granulation and superficial cell formation can be observed (FIG. 2G). Single cells then begin to detach but sheets of squames are never seen. Ultimately, even retinoid-treated cultures lose cells in substantial numbers and the remaining population does not continue to grow. The retinoid affects are much less pronounced if exposure does not begin prior to Ca^{++} induction of differentiation.

The preceding observations indicated that retinoids could delay and alter the nature of Ca^{++}-induced terminal differentiation, but could not prevent cell death

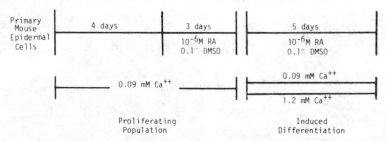

FIGURE 1. Time scale for studying the effect of retinoic acid on epidermal differentiation. Primary epidermal cells were plated in Medium 199 containing 2% fetal calf serum and adjusted to a Ca^{++} concentration of 0.09 mM. After 4 days experimental cells were exposed to 10^{-6}M retinoic acid while controls received only solvent (0.1% DMSO). After an additional 3 days groups were subdivided further, and a portion of the cultures in each group was induced to terminal differentiation by adjusting Ca^{++} concentrations to 1.2 mM. Studies were performed during the subsequent 5 days with daily medium changes.

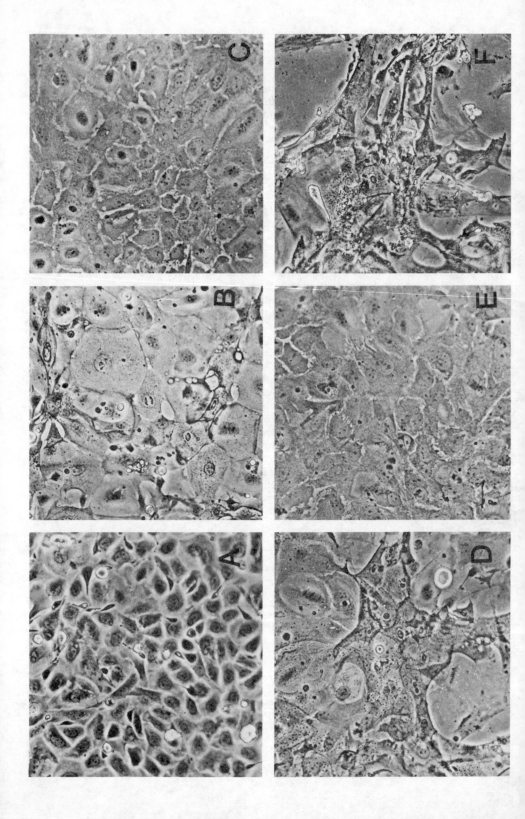

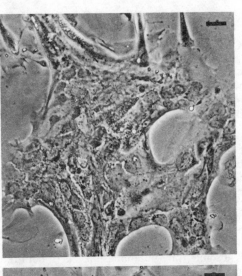

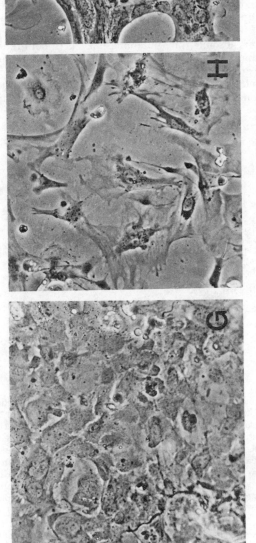

FIGURE 2. Morphological alterations associated with induced terminal differentiation in the presence or absence of 10^{-6}M retinoic acid. Cells were treated in accordance with the time scale in FIGURE 1. (A): Cells maintained in 0.09 mM Ca^{++} (0.1% DMSO) for 10 days. Parallel cultures receiving RA were similar in appearance, although individual cells appeared flatter. (B), (D), (F), (H): Control cells 24, 48 and 72 hr and 5 days, respectively, following the increase in Ca^{++} to 1.2 mM. (C), (E), (G), (I): RA-treated cells after 24, 48 and 72 hr and 5 days, respectively in 1.2 mM Ca^{++}.

which resulted from this process. Several features of the morphological alterations suggested specific pathways where retinoids might interfere. Changes in
cell shape, cell-cell contact and phase-dense cell outline which were prevented by
retinoic acid indicated that the production of a cornified envelope, catalyzed by
epidermal transglutaminase, might be affected. The transglutaminase enzyme
catalyzes the formation of ε (γ-glutamyl)–lysine crosslinks in specific membrane-
associated proteins; these crosslinks result in a rigid and highly insoluble epidermal membrane that is associated with the differentiated state.[30]

During Ca++–induced terminal differentiation, the activity of epidermal transglutaminase increases relative to uninduced controls (FIG. 3). This parallels an increase in ε(γ-glutamyl)-lysine dipeptide bond formation (Hennings et al., unpublished). In retinoic acid-treated cells, this relative rise in transglutaminase activity associated with Ca++ elevation is not observed, at least for the times studied
(a second experiment showed a similar pattern at 72 hr). These results suggested
that interference by retinoids with the Ca++-induced rise in transglutaminase activity could account for the suppression of membrane changes during epidermal
differentiation. However, absolute transglutaminase levels in both retinoic acid
groups (0.09 mM Ca++ and 1.2 mM Ca++) were 2–5 fold higher than in the solvent
group. Thus, retinoids appear to suppress only the relative changes in activity
associated with Ca++ elevation. These findings indicate that elevated transglutaminase activity alone is not sufficient to induce the changes of terminal dif-

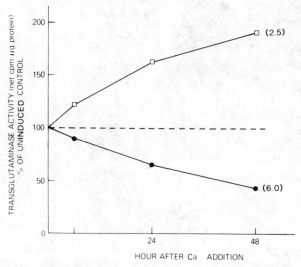

FIGURE 3. Effect of retinoic acid on transglutaminase activity in epidermal cells induced
to differentiate. Cells were treated in accordance with the time scale in FIGURE 1. After elevation of Ca++ to 1.2 mM, cultures were assayed for transglutaminase activity as described
in METHODS. At 48 hr both attached and sloughed cells were combined for assay in all
groups. Activity is expressed as the relative change in specific activity at each timepoint in
cells switched to 1.2 mM Ca++ versus their respective control group maintained in 0.09 mM
Ca++. Absolute transglutaminase specific activity (CPM – background/μg protein) for the
0.1% DMSO or 10^{-6}M RA groups in 1.2 mM Ca++ at 48 hr are shown in parentheses. All
points represent the average of duplicate determinations on duplicate samples which
varied by less than $\pm$ 15%. □———□ 0.1% DMSO; ●———● 10^{-6}M RA.

ferentiation. It is conceivable that retinoids alter the intracellular distribution of this enzyme making it less available to its endogenous substrate. Alternatively, retinoids could alter the substrate (endogenous acceptor) so that effective production of a cornified envelope is blocked.

While precise mechanisms by which retinoids interfere with terminal differentiation in epidermal cells have not been elucidated, the foregoing studies utilize a model that should facilitate new approaches to this question. Preliminary data have indicated differentiation-associated pathways where changes can be observed. However, there are no data to determine whether such changes are primary or secondary. Indirect control must be considered. For example, recent studies indicate that binding of the attachment protein fibronectin is significantly increased by retinoids in chondrocyte cultures.[31] If an epithelial attachment protein accumulated on retinoid-treated epidermal cells (such cells are noted to be flatter) it might increase the affinity of the cells for the plastic substrate. This change could prevent close cell-cell contact and vertical stratification, both of which were inhibited by retinoids. In turn specific biochemical changes would be inhibited or delayed. Future studies will be directed to defining the possible specific molecular and biological changes associated with retinoid exposure.

Molecular Interactions of Retinoids and Tumor Promoters

The induction of the enzyme ornithine decarboxylase (ODC) has been a reproducible and sensitive cellular change which occurs in epidermis after exposure to phorbol ester tumor promoters.[22,23] While a requisite role for ODC induction in tumor promotion has not been defined, several observations suggest it may be a relevant response. These include the close correlation of promoter potency and ability to induce ODC in mouse epidermis for phorbol esters[22,32,33] and the concomitant inhibition of phorbol ester-stimulated tumor promotion and ODC induction by retinoids.[6,17,25] Furthermore, ODC induction is the only consistent marker *in vivo* and *in vitro* of a response to skin tumor promoters other than those of the phorbol ester series.[33,34] In contrast to these positive associations of ODC and tumor promotion are reports of a dissociation of these events. Anti-inflammatory steroids are potent inhibitors of phorbol ester promotion of mouse skin tumors,[35] but do not inhibit and in fact enhance the induction of ODC.[21] Mezerine, a diterpene ester structurally similar to phorbol esters, is a potent inducer of ODC but an extremely weak tumor promoter for mouse skin.[36] Taken together these results suggest that ODC induction may be necessary for tumor promotion but is not sufficient to complete the process.

The observation that retinoids markedly inhibit the induction of ODC by TPA in mouse skin was of particular interest both for the general question of how retinoids alter cells and for specifically studying cellular interaction sites with TPA. To better define this effect, an alternative ODC inducer was sought which was likely to have a different mechanism of action. Germicidal ultraviolet light (UVC 10 J/m^2) provides such a stimulus *in vitro*[16] while UVB light (290–320 nm) has been shown to do the same *in vivo*.[23] *In vitro* ODC induction by UVC shares some properties previously identified for TPA[16] (TABLE 2) while other properties are quite different. A specific difference involves the kinetics of induction by UVC which are both more rapid and biphasic. Combined exposure to optimal doses of UV and TPA are additive suggesting different pathways of stimulation. Both inducers require transcription and translation. These properties have led us to conclude that each inducer works by a common pathway from gene activation

TABLE 2

COMPARISON OF ODC INDUCTION BY TPA AND UV *IN VITRO*

Dose optimum	10^{-8} M	10 J/M^2
Peak activity	6–9 hr	4 hr, 15 hr (biphasic)
Degree of induction	20–40×	2–3 ×, 10–20×
Requires transcription	+	+
Requires translation	+	+
Occurs *in vivo*	+	+
	Induction from combined exposure is additive	

to enzyme synthesis termed the "efferent pathway" and a specific and differing mode of stimulation for each inducer which leads to gene activation, termed the "afferent pathway." Using such a working model, one can ask questions about specific events in each pathway and in particular localize the site of action of agents which alter ODC induction such as retinoids.[12]

TABLE 3 shows the effects of retinoids on UVC- and TPA-induced ODC. Retinoic acid markedly inhibits induction by TPA, even at low doses and with a steep dose-response curve. Maximum inhibition of 86% is achieved at 10^{-5}M but substantial inhibition occurs at 10^{-9}M. In contrast the induction by UV is much less sensitive to retinoic acid with a maximum inhibition of only 36% at 10^{-6}M. Similar results were seen when RO 10–1770 (the dimethylmethoxyethyl-cyclo-pentenyl analog of retinoic acid) was used as inhibitor. The insensitivity of UVC induction to retinoids is not a function of photodegradation of the inhibitor itself or an intermediate induced by the inhibitor. This is clearly shown in TABLE 3

TABLE 3

INHIBITION OF ORNITHINE DECARBOXYLASE INDUCTION BY RETINOIDS

		% Inhibition (Relative to Controls not Exposed to Retinoids)		
	Concentration	TPA (9 hr)*	UV (15 hr)*	TPA + UV (9 hr)*
Retinoic acid†	10^{-11}	5	7	0
	10^{-10}	14	3	6
	10^{-9}	59	7	43
	10^{-8}	65	22	46
	10^{-7}	65	29	48
	10^{-6}	73	36	
	10^{-5}	86	36	
RO 10.1770‡	10^{-11}	15	1	
	10^{-10}	23	14	
	10^{-9}	55	21	
	10^{-8}	71	36	
	10^{-7}	81	38	
	10^{-6}	86	46	

* Number in parenthesis indicates the peak time of ODC activity for each inducer.
† Average of 3 experiments.
‡ Single experiment.

where retinoic acid was used to inhibit ODC induced by combined exposure to TPA and UVC. In this case the dose-response characteristics and degree of inhibition by retinoids at the maximum time for TPA induction (9 hr) was similar for combined exposure and for TPA alone. This would not be expected if photodegradation of the inhibitor were taking place in which case an inhibitory curve similar to that of UV alone (with no inhibition at 10^{-9}M and a low maximum inhibition) would be seen. The slight decrease in inhibitory potency of retinoic acid in the combined exposure (48% inhibition at 10^{-7}M) versus the inhibition of TPA alone (65% at 10^{-7}M) can at least be partially accounted for by the contribution of the UV-induced enzyme during combined exposure since this component is less inhibited by retinoid.

Another indication of the specificity of retinoid action on TPA-induced ODC comes from studies of the relative effectiveness of retinoic acid inhibition with respect to time of exposure. FIGURE 4 indicates that retinoic acid exposure prior to TPA, even if discontinued after TPA exposure, yields most effective inhibition. A pretreatment of only 4 hr is as effective as longer exposures. However, effectiveness drops off rapidly when retinoid is given after TPA even if the duration of treatment is as long as the duration of effective pretreatments. The situation is quite different for UV induction. In this instance, retinoid pretreatment is less effective than exposure after UV irradiation, even when the duration of exposures was similar.

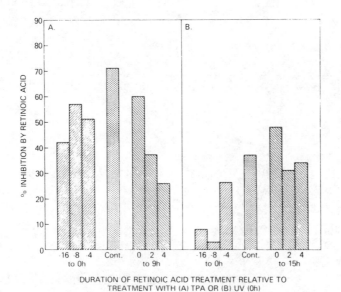

DURATION OF RETINOIC ACID TREATMENT RELATIVE TO
TREATMENT WITH (A) TPA OR (B) UV (0h)

FIGURE 4. Effectiveness of retinoic acid inhibition of TPA- and UV-induced epidermal ODC activity relative to time of exposure to retinoid. Primary mouse epidermal cells were plated under standard culture conditions and exposed to 10^{-7}M retinoic acid at various times after plating. Exposure to TPA (1.6×10^{-8}M) or UVC (10 J/m^2) occurred at 24 hr after plating. The extent of retinoid inhibition is expressed relative to controls receiving inducer (TPA or UVC) but not exposed to retinoid. In cells exposed to retinoid continuously (▨), fresh retinoic acid was added at the time of exposure to inducer. ODC activity was assayed at 9 hr after TPA exposure and at 15 hr after UVC exposure.

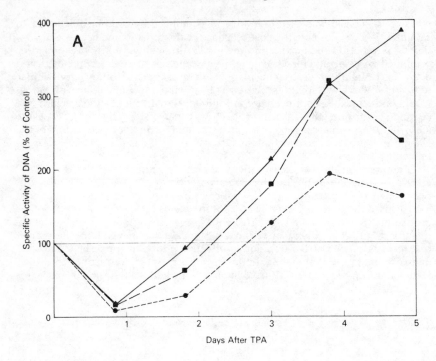

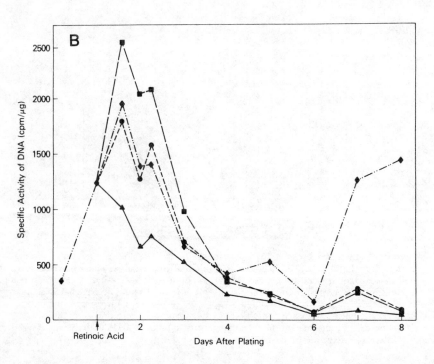

Retinoic acid appears to act differentially and specifically on TPA-induced ODC. To rule out the possibility that this effect was related to an overall inhibition of cellular functions by combined TPA and retinoic acid treatment, studies were undertaken to define these effects on DNA, RNA, and protein synthesis. FIGURE 5 indicates that retinoic acid at a dose of 10^{-6}M does not significantly alter the stimulatory effect of TPA on DNA synthesis. At 10^{-5}M inhibition is seen. Similarly DNA synthesis in cells not treated with TPA (FIG. 5B) is not significantly changed until 10^{-5}M concentrations of retinoids are used. The slight stimulatory effect at 10^{-6}M, without change in the kinetics of [^{3}H]TdR incorporation, could be related to the increase in precursor uptake in retinoid-treated cells.[15] These data indicate that at retinoid doses effective for ODC inhibition, significant alterations in TPA-stimulated or constitutive DNA synthesis does not occur. Furthermore, it appears that retinoids do not alter ODC induction by causing a shift in the cell cycle. In other studies retinoic acid at doses of 10^{-8} – 10^{-6}M had essentially no effect on overall protein synthesis as measured by [^{3}H]leucine incorporation either with or without TPA. Likewise retinoids did not alter [^{3}H]uridine incorporation after TPA but stimulated [^{3}H]uridine incorporation slightly at 10^{-6}M in the absence of TPA.

The present data indicate that retinoids act to inhibit TPA-induced ODC activity largely at a unique portion of the induction pathway, probably in the afferent limb. This effect occurs rapidly since a short pretreatment with retinoic acid achieves near-maximum inhibition. We have previously shown that monosaccharide incorporation into glycopeptides is rapidly altered after treatment with retinoids.[14] While subcellular distribution of these glycoprotein changes was not studied, it is likely that cell surface membrane components are involved. Retinoids have been shown to cause a number of membrane changes in other systems.[37,38] Enhanced binding of large cell surface proteins after retinoid treatment has already been discussed.[31] Many of the effects of TPA are similar to those of growth factors and hormones and it has been suggested that these effects are mediated via a transmembrane signal responding to ligand binding at a specific receptor site.[39] Recent evidence indicates the existence of a specific membrane receptor for phorbol esters; these do not appear to be the site of direct competition by retinoic acid.[40] It seems reasonable to suggest that the unique inhibitory action of retinoic acid on the ODC induction by TPA and on tumor promotion results from membrane changes which alter or mask the effects of the promoter at the cell surface.

FIGURE 5. Effect of retinoic acid on [^{3}H]thymidine incoporation into epidermal DNA. (A): Epidermal cells were plated under standard culture conditions and exposed to retinoic acid at 20 hr after plating. Four hours later cultures were exposed to TPA (1.6 × 10^{-7}M) or solvent (0.1% DMSO) for 1 hr. This medium was then replaced with fresh RA- or solvent-containing medium, which was renewed daily during the course of the experiment. At the indicated times, cultures were pulse-labeled for 1 hr with 1 μCi/ml [^{3}H]thymidine, washed and frozen. Specific activity was determined as described previously.[21] Data are expressed as a percentage of the appropriate control which did not receive TPA. ▲——▲ TPA only; ■——■ TPA + 3.3 × 10^{-6}M RA; ●——● TPA + 1.7 × 10^{-5}M RA. (B) Primary epidermal cells were plated in standard medium and 24 hr later exposed to RA at various concentrations. Medium was changed daily. At indicated times cultures were pulsed for 1 hour with 1 μCi/ml [^{3}H]thymidine and assayed for incorporation into DNA. ◆——◆ Control; ■——■ 3.3 × 10^{-7}M RA; ●——● 3.3 × 10^{-6}M RA; ▲——▲ 3.3 × 10^{-5}M RA. In both A and B, all points represent an average of duplicate samples which varied by less than ± 10%.

Acknowledgment

We thank Dr. Luigi De Luca for supplying retinoic acid and Dr. Michael Sporn for supplying the dimethylmethoxycyclopentenyl analog of retinoic acid. The photographic assistance of Mr. Douglas Jones and the secretarial help of Mrs. Margaret Green were also appreciated.

References

1. Sabella, J.D., H.A. Bern & R.H. Kahn. 1951. Proc. Soc. Exp. Biol. Med. **76:** 499-503.
2. Kahn, R.H. 1954. Am. J. Anat. **95:** 309-335.
3. Lawrence, D.J. & H.A. Bern. 1958. J. Invest. Dermatol. **31:** 313-325.
4. Hardy, M.H. 1968. J. Embryol. Exp. Morphol. **19:** 157-180.
5. Logan, W.S. 1972. Arch. Dermatol. **105:** 748-753.
6. Verma, A.K. & R.K. Boutwell. 1977. Cancer Res. **37:** 2196-2201.
7. Bollag, W. 1970. Int. J. Vit. Res. **40:** 299-314.
8. Prutkin, L. 1968. Cancer Res. **28:** 1021-1030.
9. Yuspa, S.H. & C.C. Harris. 1974. Exp. Cell Res. **86:**95-105.
10. Yuspa, S.H. 1978. In In Vitro Carcinogenesis: Guide to the Literature, Recent Advances and Laboratory Procedures. U. Saffiotti & H. Autrup, Eds.: 47-56. U.S. Government Printing Office, Washington, D.C. DHEW Publication No. (NIH). 78-844.
11. Steinert, P. & S.H. Yuspa. 1978. Science **200:** 1491-1493.
12. Yuspa, S.H., U. Lichti, D. Morgan & H. Hennings. 1980. In The Biochemistry of Normal and Abnormal Epidermal Differentiation. I.A. Bernstein & S. Seiji, Eds.: 173-190. University of Tokyo Press, Tokyo.
13. De Luca, L. & S.H. Yuspa. 1974. Exp. Cell Res. **86:** 106-110.
14. Adamo, S., L.M. De Luca, C.S. Silverman-Jones & S.H. Yuspa. 1979. J. Biol. Chem. **254:** 3279-3287.
15. Yuspa, S.H., K. Elgjo, M. Morse & F.J. Wiebel. 1977. Chem. Biol. Interactions **16:** 251-264.
16. Lichti, U., E. Patterson & S.H. Yuspa. 1979. Proc. Am. Assoc. Cancer Res. **20:** 105.
17. Colburn, N.H. 1980. In Neoplastic Transformation in Differentiated Epithelial Cell Systems in Vitro. L.M. Franks & C.B. Wigley, Eds.: 113-134. Academic Press. London. In press.
18. Barnett, M.L. & G. Szabo. 1973. Exp. Cell Res. **76:** 118-126.
19. Hardy, M.H., P.R. Sweeney & C.G. Bellous. 1978. J. Ultrastruct. Res. **64:** 246-260.
20. Hennings, H., D. Michael, C. Cheng, P. Steinert, K. Holbrook & S.H. Yuspa. 1980. Cell **19:** 245-254.
21. Lichti, U., T.J. Slaga, T. Ben, E. Patterson, H. Hennings & S.H. Yuspa. 1977. Proc. Natl. Acad. Sci. USA **74:** 3908-3912.
22. Yuspa, S.H., U. Lichti, T. Ben, E. Patterson, H. Hennings, T.J. Slaga, N. Colburn & W. Kelsey. 1976. Nature **262:** 402-404.
23. Verma, A.K., N.J. Lowe & R.K. Boutwell. 1979. Cancer Res. **39:** 1035-1040.
24. Lichti, U., G.T. Bowden, E. Patterson, T. Ben & S.H. Yuspa. 1980. Photochem. Photobiol. **32:** 177-181.
25. Verma, A.K., H.M. Rice, B.G. Shapas & R.K. Boutwell. 1978. Cancer Res. **38:** 793-801.
26. Hennings, H., K. Holbrook, P. Steinert & S.H. Yuspa. In Biochemistry of Normal and Abnormal Epidermal Differentiation. I.A. Bernstein & M. Seiji, Eds.: 3-22. University of Tokyo Press, Tokyo.
27. Layne, E. 1957. In Methods in Enzymology. S.P. Colowick & N.O. Kaplan, Eds. Vol. **2:** 448-450. Academic Press. New York.
28. Ogawa, H. & L.A. Goldsmith. 1976. J. Biol. Chem. **23:** 7281-7288.
29. Sun, T. & H. Green. 1976. Cell **9:** 511-521.

30. BUXMAN, M.M. & K.D. WUEPPER. 1976. Biochim. Biophys. Acta **452:** 356–369.
31. HASSELL, J., J. PENNYPACKER, H. KLEINMAN, R. PRATT & K. YAMADA. 1979. Cell **17:** 821–826.
32. O'BRIEN, T.G., R.C. SIMSIMAN & R.K. BOUTWELL. 1975. Cancer Res. **35:** 1662–1670.
33. O'BRIEN, T.G., R.C. SIMSIMAN & R.K. BOUTWELL. 1975. Cancer Res. **35:** 2426–2433.
34. LICHTI, U., S.H. YUSPA & H. HENNINGS. 1978. *In* Carcinogenesis: Mechanisms of Tumor Promotion and Carcinogenesis. T.J. Slaga, A. Sivak & R.K. Boutwell, Eds. Vol **2:** 221–232. Raven Press. New York.
35. SCHWARZ, J.A., A. VIAJE, T.J. SLAGA, S.H. YUSPA, H. HENNINGS & U. LICHTI. 1977. Chem. Biol. Interactions **17:** 331–347.
36. MUFSON, R.A., S.M. FISCHER, A.K. VERMA, G.L. GLEASON, T.J. SLAGA & R.K. BOUTWELL. 1979. Cancer Res. **39:** 4791–4795.
37. TODARO, G.J., J.E. DE LARCO & M.B. SPORN. 1978. Nature **276:** 272–274.
38. ADAMO, S., L.M. DE LUCA, I. AKALOVSKY & P.V. BHAT. 1979. J. Natl. Cancer Inst. **62:** 1473–1478.
39. WEINSTEIN, I.B., H. YAMASAKI, M. WIGLER, L.S. LEE, A. JEFFREY & D. GRUNBERGER. 1979. *In* Carcinogens: Identification and Mechanisms of Action. A.C. Griffin & G.R. Shaw, Eds.: 399–418. Raven Press. New York.
40. DRIEDGER, P.E. & P.M. BLUMBERG. 1980. Proc. Natl. Acad. Sci. USA **77:** 567–571.

THE INFLUENCE OF RETINOIDS ON POLYAMINE AND DNA SYNTHESIS IN MOUSE EPIDERMIS*

R.K. Boutwell and A.K. Verma

McArdle Laboratory for Cancer Research
University of Wisconsin
Madison, Wisconsin 53706

INTRODUCTION

A useful strategy for obtaining clues to the biochemical mechanism of chemical carcinogenesis is to investigate the role of factors that modify the process. As a part of this approach, we have investigated the effect of retinoic acid and other retinoids on skin carcinogenesis in mice using the initiation-promotion model system[1] as well as tumor formation caused by repeated applications of the carcinogenic hydrocarbon, 7,12-dimethylbenz[a]anthracene.

The typical initiation-promotion protocol for mouse skin consists of a single application of a carcinogen at a dose so that no tumors result (initiation), followed by twice-weekly applications of a noncarcinogenic promoting agent capable of eliciting appreciable numbers of tumors only in the initiated skin. Typically, between 1 and 50 μg of 7,12-dimethylbenz[a]anthracene in 0.2 ml of acetone is applied to the skin of the back of a mouse to accomplish initiation. The most effective tumor promoting agent is 12-O-tetradecanoylphorbol-13-acetate; in many strains of mice, as little as 6 μg of the phorbol ester applied twice weekly in 0.2 ml acetone produces a maximum tumor incidence.[1]

Mouse skin, treated with appropriate doses of the phorbol ester or a carcinogen, responds with a number of pleiotypic changes that mimic the tumor cell phenotype. Of these changes, only the induction of ornithine decarboxylase and the stimulation of the incorporation of [3H]thymidine into DNA will be considered herein.

Application of the powerful tumor promoter, 12-O-tetradecanoylphorbol-13-acetate to mouse skin causes the rapid induction of ornithine decarboxylase activity, the first enzyme in the polyamine biosynthetic pathway.[2] Peak induction is achieved within 5 hr, amounting to 200- to 300-fold above the control activity.[3] The duration of the increased activity is brief, so that a return to essentially control activity is achieved within 12 hr. The extent of induction is dependent on the dose of the phorbol ester in the range of 1 to 10 nmoles, which is the same range giving a dose-dependent tumor response in mouse skin.[3,4] The correlation observed between the dose required for the induction of ornithine decarboxylase activity and for tumor promotion is supporting evidence that the induction of the enzyme is an essential component of the mechanism of skin-tumor promotion. The second enzyme in the polyamine biosynthetic pathway, S-adenosylmethionine decarboxylase, is also induced in a dose-dependent manner, but peak activity is about 7-fold above control activity and is not reached until about 12 hr after exposure to the phorbol ester. Control activity is approached 4 days later.[3] The level in the epidermis of the polyamine products of these enzymes follows closely

* This research was supported by Grants CA-07175, CA-22484, CA-09135, and CA-09020 from the National Institutes of Health.

0077-8923/81/0359-0275 $01.75/0 © 1981, NYAS

the level of enzyme activity[5]; thus, ornithine decarboxylase activity is indicative of putrescine synthesis.

The incorporation of [³H]thymidine into the DNA of mouse epidermis is altered after treatment with the tumor-promoting phorbol ester in a dose-dependent manner. At optimal tumor-promoting doses, there is an initial decrease to about 50% of the control level of incorporation (based on 30-min incorporation times) until about 12 hr after treatment when incorporation increases rapidly to a peak at 18 hr that is 3-fold the control level. A second peak occurs at 24 hr and there is a third peak at 42 hr before the extent of incorporation returns to normal at 72 hr. In contrast, 7,12-dimethylbenz[a]anthracene at initiating doses of 12.5 μg causes only a brief inhibition of [³H]thymidine incorporation into DNA lasting less than 18 hr without a subsequent stimulation of incorporation. At doses of dimethylbenzantharacene (150 μg or greater), which when applied repetitively act as a complete carcinogen, there is a prolonged inhibition of thymidine incorporation lasting 2–4 days followed by an increase in apparent DNA synthesis at 6 days.[6] Because both the induction of ornithine decarboxylase activity and the resultant increase in putrescine level as well as an increase in DNA synthesis may be associated with tumor formation, the impact of retinoic acid on the response of these two parameters was correlated with the impact of retinoic acid on tumor formation by the initiation-promotion regimen and the multiple application of dimethylbenzanthracene regimen. The results will be presented herein.

As early as 1926, Fujimaki reported the appearance of carcinomas in the stomach of rats fed a vitamin A-deficient diet,[7] and reports of increased susceptibility of animals and man on diets low in vitamin A continue to appear.[8] A direct corollary of these reports is the fact that administration of supplemental vitamin A, particularly in the form of retinoic acid and its derivatives, protects against carcinogenesis in a variety of model systems.[8-10] Although in most systems retinoids protect against carcinogenesis, there are a few reports in which retinoids had no effect or even an enhancing effect on carcinogenesis.[11-19] In some of these cases, administration of excessive amounts of vitamin A might account for the effect, but in any case additional studies are needed to further define the conditions under which retinoids either inhibit or enhance carcinogenesis.

Therefore the effect of retinoic acid administered under identical conditions of dose, vehicle, route of administration, and timing was determined with respect to its effect on (1) tumor formation by the initiation-promotion regimen, (2) tumor formation by the multiple application of dimethylbenzanthracene, (3) the induction of ornithine decarboxylase activity by promoting doses of the phorbol esters and carcinogenic doses of dimethylbenzanthracene, and (4) the incorporation of [³H]thymidine into DNA under the same stimuli described in section (3) for ornithine decarboxylase activity. More extensive reviews of the effect of retinoids on the pleiotypic response of mouse skin have appeared.[20,21]

THE EFFECT OF RETINOIC ACID ON TUMOR FORMATION IN MOUSE SKIN

Retinoic acid, when applied to the skin of mice in conjunction with an initiating dose of dimethylbenzanthracene has no effect on the subsequent incidence of tumors elicited by multiple applications of the tumor-promoting phorbol ester.[22] In contrast, retinoic acid when applied to the skin of mice in conjunction with each of the multiple applications of the phorbol ester in the initiation-promotion regimen inhibits both papillomas and carcinoma formation.[22-24] The inhibitory effect of retinoic acid is dependent on the dose and time of application. In contrast to its inhibitory effect on tumor formation elicited by the phorbol ester, retinoic acid applied to the skin of mice in conjunction with a carcinogenic regimen consisting of multiple applications of dimethylbenzanthracene did not inhibit tumor formation but rather resulted in a small increment in tumors that has been repeatedly observed. Typical data are shown in TABLE 1. In this experiment, the effect of 17 nmoles of retinoic acid in 0.2 ml of acetone was determined concurrently on the papilloma incidence resulting from either an initiation-promotion regimen or multiple applications of dimethylbenzanthracene. Thus, there is no question of differerences in retinoic acid level, etc.; in both cases the same solution of retinoic acid was used. It is evident that retinoic acid inhibited the appearance of papillomas by the initiation-promotion regimen but not by the complete carcinogenesis regimen.

As is the case when retinoic acid is applied to the same area of skin as the carcinogen, retinoic acid administered by stomach tube also appeared to augment the carcinogenic action of dimethylbenzanthracene. Control mice, treated once each week with 0.2 μmole of dimethylbenzanthracene (and given 0.2 ml of corn oil intraperitoneally 30 min before each skin application of carcinogen) developed an average of 8.7 papillomas per mouse at 20 weeks. Those mice treated similarly except that 3.3 μmoles of retinoic acid were given in the corn oil, developed 14.8 papillomas per mouse at 20 weeks. In contrast, retinoic acid administered systemically inhibits ornithine decarboxylase induction by the phorbol ester[24] as well as tumor promotion.[10]

Therefore, it may be concluded that retinoic acid inhibits skin tumor formation in mice by the initiation-promotion regimen but not by the repetitive application of dimethylbenzanthracene.

THE EFFECT OF RETINOIC ACID ON THE INDUCTION OF ORNITHINE DECARBOXYLASE IN MOUSE EPIDERMIS

The ability of retinoic acid to inhibit the induction by phorbol esters of ornithine decarboxylase in mouse epidermis is firmly established.[22-24] In contrast,

TABLE 1

THE EFFECT OF RETINOIC ACID ON TUMOR FORMATION*

Treatment	Papillomas/ Mouse	% Papillomas
1. Acetone – 1 hr – phorbol ester	7.1	80
2. Retinoic acid – 1 hr – phorbol ester	1.3	40
3. Acetone – 1 hr – dimethylbenzanthracene	4.0	93
4. Retinoic acid – 1 hr – diemthylbenzanthracene	6.1	90

* The back of each mouse in all four groups was treated once with 0.2 μmole of dimethylbenzanthracene in 0.2 ml of acetone two weeks before the indicated treatments. The indicated treatments consisted of: group 1, 0.2 ml of acetone 1 hr before twice weekly applications of 5 nmoles of tetradecanoylphorbol acetate in 0.2 ml of acetone; group 2, the same as group 1 except that 17 nmoles of retinoic acid in 0.2 ml of acetone preceded each application of the phorbol ester; group 3, 0.2 ml of acetone, 1 hour before once weekly applications of 0.2 μmoles of dimethylbenzanthracene in 0.2 ml of acetone; group 4, the same as group 3 except that 17 nmoles of retnoic acid in 0.2 ml of acetone preceded each application of the carcinogen. Data at 20 weeks of treatment.

retinoic acid does not inhibit the induction in epidermis of ornithine decarboxylase by dimethylbenzanthracene. The results of a typical experiment are summarized in TABLE 2. The induction of ornithine decarboxylase activity by the
phorbol ester was reduced to 5.6% of the control value by retinoic acid pretreatment. In contrast, the carcinogen-induced level was increased to 155% of the control level by pretreatment with retinoic acid.

Thus the data on enzyme induction correlate with the data on the effect of
retinoic acid on tumor formation by the two regimens.

THE EFFECT OF RETINOIC ACID ON THE SYNTHESIS OF DNA IN MOUSE EPIDERMIS

As stated earlier, 12-O-tetradecanoylphorbol-13-acetate applied to the skin
of mice in a tumor-promoting dose causes an initial depression in the incorporation of [³H]thymidine into DNA. Incorporation is depressed to 40 to 50% of the
control level at 6 to 9 hr after pretreatment; incorporation returns to normal by 12
to 15 hr and reaches a first peak of incorporation 3-fold above the control value at
18 hr. Treatment with 17 nmoles of retinoic acid in 0.2 ml of acetone one hour
before treatment with the 17-nmole dose of the phorbol ester results in a greater
initial depression of incorporation, which falls to 30 to 40% of the control between 6 and 12 hr after the phorbol ester. Incorporation remains at the control
level at 18 hr; thus retinoic acid pretreatment eliminated the first peak in DNA
synthesis. However, there is an apparent compensatory increase in the later
phase of thymidine incorporation; normally the second and third peaks of
thymidine incorporation were 3 to 3.5-fold above the control at 24 and 42 hr after
phrobol ester treatment, whereas retinoic acid pretreatment results in only a
single large peak more than 4.5-fold greater than the control value at 42 hr after
phorbol ester treatment.

No clearly repeatable alteration by retinoic acid pretreatment was found in
the incorporation of thymidine following a carcinogenic dose of DMBA.

DISCUSSION AND CONCLUSIONS

The fact that retinoic acid enhances the formation of mouse skin tumors

TABLE 2

THE EFFECT OF RETINOIC ACID PRETREATMENT ON THE INDUCTION OF
ORNITHINE DECARBOXYLASE ACTIVITY BY TETRADECANOYLPHORBOL ACETATE AS WELL
AS BY DIMETHYLBENZANTHRACENE*

Treatment	Ornithine Decarboxylase Activity
Acetone - 1 hr - phorbol ester	7.2
Retinoic Acid - 1 hr - phorbol ester	0.4
Acetone - 1 hr - dimethylbenzanthracene	0.9
Retinoic Acid - 1 hr - dimethylbenzanthracene	1.4

* Ornithine decarboxylase activity shown is at the time of maximum induction: 4 hr
after the phorbol ester and 36 hr after the dimethylbenzanthracene. Activity is expressed as
nmoles of CO_2/60 minutes/mg protein. Groups of mice were treated with 17 nmoles of
retinoic acid or acetone 1 hr before the application of 3.6 μmoles of dimethylbenzanthracene or 5 nmoles of the phorbol ester.

elicited by multiple applications of dimethylbenzanthracene is of great practical as well as mechanistic importance. The reality of this observation is emphasized by its repeatability and the fact that the two different regimens were run concurrently so that the experiment was internally controlled. Furthermore, the dose of retinoic acid was the same in both regimens and the effect of dose level and schedule have been thoroughly studied.[23] The doses of dimethylbenzanthracene and phorbol ester were not excessive. One is led to the conclusion that the promoting component of skin carcinogenesis attributable to multiple applications of the carcinogenic hydrocarbon is not the same as that of the phorbol ester.

The conclusion is strengthened by the metabolic studies. Treatment of mouse skin with either agent induces ornithine decarboxylase activity,[3] but the induction by dimethylbenzanthracene is only just beginning at 24 hr after treatment, several hours after the induction by the phorbol ester has peaked and returned to the low, control value. Peak induction by the hydrocarbon is not reached until approximately 36 hr and the peak activity is severalfold less. The delay in the induction can not be entirely attributed to the time required for metabolic activation.

Strong evidence for a mechanistic difference between the two agents is revealed by the differing effects on the induction of ornithine decarboxylase after retinoic acid pretreatment: the induction by the phorbol ester is blocked; in contrast, the peak induction by hydrocarbon is augmented by about 50%. The modification of the metabolic response by retinoic acid correlates with the modification of tumor formation. Not only do these facts indicate that the mechanism of promotion by the two agents is different, the facts also indicate that hydrocarbon-induced ornithine decarboxylase activity may be an important component of the mechanism of dimethylbenzanthracene carcinogenesis.

Finally there are practical considerations. Forbes, Urbach, and Davies reported that topical applications of retinoic acid solutions greatly enhanced the tumor response of hairless mouse skin to a moderate dose of simulated sunlight,[19] confirming a preliminary finding by Epstein.[18] These and other observations,[11-17] together with the data reported herein that retinoic acid treatment increased the yield of tumors induced by skin applications of dimethylbenzanthracene, emphasize the need for further research before embarking on programs of cancer prophylaxis by retinoids in human populations.

REFERENCES

1. BOUTWELL, R. K. 1978. Biochemical Mechanism of Tumor Promotion. *In* Carcinogenesis, Mechanisms of Tumor Promotion and Cocarcinogenesis. T.J. Slaga, A. Sivak & R.K. Boutwell, Eds. Vol. **2:** 49-58. Raven Press. New York.

2. RUSSELL, D.H. & B.G.M. DURIE. 1978. Polyamines as markers of normal and malignant growth. Raven Press. New York.

3. O'BRIEN, T.G., R.C. SIMSIMAN & R.K. BOUTWELL. 1975. Induction of the polyamine biosynthetic enzymes in mouse epidermis by tumor-promoting agents. Cancer Res. **35:** 1662-1670.

4. VERMA, A.K. & R.K. BOUTWELL. 1980. Effects of dose and duration of treatment with the tumor-promoting agent, 12-0-tetradecanoylphorbol-13-acetate on mouse skin carcinogenesis. Carcinogenesis **1:** 271-276.

5. O'BRIEN, T.G. 1976. The Induction of ornithine decarboxylase as an early, possibly obligatory, event in mouse skin carcinogenesis. Cancer Res. **36:** 2644-2653.

6. SLAGA, T.J., G.T. BOWDEN, B.G. SHAPAS & R.K. BOUTWELL. 1974. Macromolecular synthesis following a single application of polycyclic hydrocarbons used as initiators of mouse skin tumorigenesis. Cancer Res. **34:** 771-777.

7. FUJIMAKI, Y. 1926. Formation of gastric carcinomas in albino rats. J. Cancer Res. **10:** 469–477.

8. SPORN, M.B., N.M. DUNLOP, D.L. NEWTON & J.M. SMITH. 1976. Prevention of chemical carcinogenesis by vitamin A and its synthetic analogs (retinoids). Fed. Proc. **35:** 1332–1338.

9. SPORN, M.B. & D.L. NEWTON. 1979. Chemoprevention of cancer with retinoids. Fed. Proc. **38:** 2528–2534.

10. MAYER, H., W. BOLLAG, R. HANNI & R. RUEGG. 1978. Retinoids, a new class of compounds with prophylactic and therapeutic activities in oncology and dermatology. Experentia **34:** 1105–1119.

11. MARCH, B.E. & J. BIELY. 1967. Increased incidence of avian leukosis in response to excess vitamin A. Nature **214:** 287–288.

12. PRUTKIN, L. 1968. The effect of vitamin A acid on tumorigenesis and protein production. Cancer Res. **28:**1021–1030.

13. LEVIJ, I.S. & S. POLLIACK. 1969. The effect of topical vitamin A on papillomas and intraepithelial carcinomas induced in hamster cheek pouches with 9, 10-dimethyll, 2-benzanthracene. Cancer Res. **29:** 327–332.

14. SCHMAAHL, D., C. KRUGER & P. PREISSLER, 1972. Experiments on neoplasm prevention by Vitamin A. Arzneimittenl. Forsch. **22:** 946–949.

15. SMITH, D.M., A.E. ROGERS, B.J. HERNDON & P.M. NEWBERNE. 1975. Vitamin A (retinyl acetate) and benzo[a]pyrene-induced respiratory tract carcinogenesis in hamsters fed a commercial diet. Cancer Res. **35:** 11–16.

16. SMITH, W.E., E. YAZDI & L. MILLER. 1972. Carcinogenesis in pulmonary epithelia in mice on different levels of vitamin A. Environ. Res. **5:**152–163.

17. COHEN, S.M., J.F. WITTENBERG & G.T. BRYAN. 1976. Effect of avitominosis A and hypervitaminosis A on urinary bladder carcinogenicity of N-[4-(5-nitro-2-furyl)-2-thiazoyl] formamide. Cancer Res. **36:** 2334–2339.

18. EPSTEIN, J.H. 1977. Chemicals and photocarcinogenesis. Australian J. Dermatol. **18:** 57–61.

19. FORBES, P.D., F. URBACH & R.E. DAVIES. 1979. Enhancement of experimental photocarcinogenesis by topical retinoic acid. Cancer Letters **7:** 85–90.

20. VERMA, A.K. & R.K. BOUTWELL. 1980. Inhibition of tumor promoter-induced mouse epidermal ornithine decarboxylase activity and prevention of skin carcinogenesis by vitamin A acid and its analogues (retinoids). *In* Polyamines in Biomedical Research. J.M. Gaugas, Ed. Chapter 12: 185–201.

21. BOUTWELL, R.K. & A.K. VERMA. 1979. Effects of vitamin A and related retinoids on the biochemical processes linked to carcinogenesis. Pure Appl. Chem. **51:** 857–866.

22. VERMA, A.K., B.G. SHAPAS, H. M. RICE & R.K. BOUTWELL. 1979. Correlation of the inhibition by retinoids of tumor promoter-induced mouse epidermal ornithine decarboxylase activity and of skin tumor promotion. Cancer Res. **39:** 419–425.

23. VERMA, A.K. & R.K. BOUTWELL. 1977. Vitamin A acid (retinoic acid) a potent inhibitor of 12-*O*-tetradecanoylphorbol-13-acetate-induced ornithine decarboxylase activity in mouse epidermis. Cancer Res. **37:**2196–2201.

24. VERMA, A.K., H. M. RICE, B.G. SHAPAS & R.K. BOUTWELL. 1978. Inhibition of 12-*O*-tetradecanoylphorbol-13-acetate-induced ornithine decarboxylase activity in mouse epidermis by vitamin A analogs (retinoids). Cancer Res. **38:** 793–801.

ANTIPROLIFERATIVE EFFECTS OF RETINOIDS RELATED TO THE CELL CYCLE-SPECIFIC INHIBITION OF ORNITHINE DECARBOXYLASE

Diane Haddock Russell and Mari K. Haddox

Department of Pharmacology
University of Arizona College of Medicine
Tucson, Arizona 85724

An enzyme shown to be induced in response to a wide variety of hormones and other trophic agents is ornithine decarboxylase (ODC), which is both the initial enzyme in polyamine biosynthesis and also may serve as an initiation factor for RNA polymerase I, the enzyme that regulates ribosomal RNA synthesis.[1-4] There is now substantial evidence in both normal and transformed cells that the induction of ODC is a G_1-specific transcriptional event, the magnitude of which is related to the magnitude of the growth stimulus.[5] TABLE 1 indicates the generality of the induction of ODC during the G_1 phase of the cell cycle in response to a variety of stimuli including exposure of the cells to fresh serum and media, growth factors, and synchronization techniques. The increase in enzyme activity in G_1 of cell cycle is often 100- to 500-fold above basal levels. The more complete studies reveal that progression through the entire cell cycle involves a biphasic pattern of increase in ODC activity.[6,28-30] The initial rise in ODC activity is generally maximal within 4 to 6 hr after the stimulus to initiate cell cycle, whether the progression is due to synchronous cell cycle traverse, the addition of serum, or the addition of growth factors. The second excursion of ODC activity that occurs during cell cycle progression is expressed late in S phase and reaches a maximum during the G_2 phase of the cell cycle.

An increase in ODC activity during G_1 is not only a universal feature, but is apparently essential for cell cycle progression. TABLE 2 lists those cell types in which the effects of the addition of specific inhibitors of ODC have been examined. In all cases, the inhibition of ODC activity was associated with an inhibition of cell replication. Most of the studies of inhibition of proliferation have indicated that the cells block prior to S phase with a G_1 content of DNA.[32-34] It was because of the sensitivity of ODC excursion as a marker of early G_1 cell cycle progression that we attempted to use it to pinpoint the site of the antiproliferative block of vitamin A analogs. Evidence has accumulated that leads us to postulate that retinoid analogs affect the transcription of messenger RNA for ODC and thus arrest cells in G_1 prior to the cell cycle-specific expression of ODC. This paper will review the major experimental evidence we have obtained in Chinese hamster ovary (CHO) cells to support this thesis[37-39] and will attempt to summarize possible new approaches in order to further understand growth-specific inhibitory properties of retinoids.

CONCENTRATION-DEPENDENT INHIBITION OF ASYNCHRONOUS CHO CELL GROWTH BY VARIOUS RETINOIDS

Retinoic acid has previously been identified as an antiproliferative agent in lymphocytes[148] and as a potent inhibitor of phorbol ester-induced ODC activity in

281

0077-8923/81/0359-0281 $01.75/0 © 1981, NYAS

TABLE 1

GENERALITY OF THE INDUCTION OF ORNITHINE DECARBOXYLASE
DURING THE G_1 PHASE OF THE CELL CYCLE

Stimulus	Cell Type	Reference
Fresh serum/media	HTC	6-8
	H35 hepatoma	43
	HeLa	10
	BHK	11-13
	3T3	14
	Neuroblastoma	15-17
	Glioma	16
	WI-38	18, 19
	L	20
	L1210	21
	Endothelial	22
Pituitary growth factors	3T3	23
Epidermal growth factor	Chick embryo epidermis	24
Insulin	BHK	11, 13
	HTC	8
	L	20
	Parenchymal	25
Polyoma virus	Mouse kidney	26
Mitotic selection	V79	27
	CHO	28
Colcemid synchronization	DonC	29
	CHO	30
Double TdR synchronization	BHK	31

mouse epidermis.[40] It was, therefore, rather surprising that both retinal and retinol inhibited the mitosis of asynchronous CHO cells at much lower concentrations than either retinoic acid or retinyl acetate (FIG. 1). Although retinal was the most potent inhibitor, this analog was not used since the addition of 5 μM retinal actually increased the cell number after 24 hr of incubation.[39] Therefore, the analog studied for its ability to inhibit cell doubling in CHO cells was retinol. This retinoid completely inhibited cell doubling at a concentration of 120 μM,

TABLE 2

INHIBITION OF CELL REPLICATION BY ORNITHINE DECARBOXYLASE INHIBITORS

Agent	Cell Type	Reference
α-Methylornithine	HTC	32
	WI-38	19
	Ehrlich ascites	33
α-Difluoromethylornithine	HTC	34
	L1210	34
1,3-Diaminopropane	Neuroblastoma	17
	CHO	35
Dehydro-ornithine	Chick embryo muscle	36

whereas concentrations of 200 μM retinyl acetate and 1000 μM retinoic acid were required to fully inhibit proliferation. In all cases, the retinoid solutions were prepared in dioxane under subdued light and used immediately. Control cell populations received an equivalent amount of dioxane (0.5%), which has been found to have no effect on growth parameters. It was important to ascertain whether the retinoid solutions were toxic to cells. Therefore, the survival of the cells after exposure to retinol or dioxane was determined by the ability of the cells to form colonies. Neither dioxane nor retinol had significant effects on the plating efficiency of the cells, suggesting the block was reversible. Therefore, in all further studies of the effects of retinoids on cell cycle progression in synchronized CHO cells, 120 μM retinol was used to inhibit proliferation. The efficacy of various retinoid analogs in different tissues is thought to be related to different

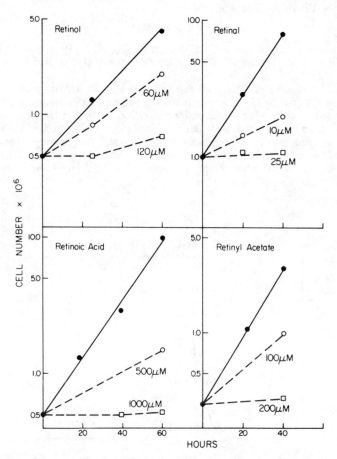

FIGURE 1. Concentration-dependent inhibition of asynchronous CHO cell growth by various retinoids. Asynchronous logarithmically growing CHO cells were plated in the presence of the indicated concentrations of the various retinoids or in 0.5% dioxane (control) (●). At the times indicated, cell samples were collected by scraping with a rubber policeman and counted by a Coulter electronic particle counter.

functional receptors for different forms of retinoids. Chytil and coworkers[41] have demonstrated alterations in levels of cellular retinol and retinoic acid-binding proteins in the liver and lung during perinatal development.

FLOW MICROFLUORIMETRY OF RETINOL INHIBITION IN ASYNCHRONOUS CHO CELLS

In order to find out whether the addition of retinol resulted in the arrest of cells at a particular point in the cell cycle, retinol-exposed asynchronous cell populations were analyzed by flow microfluorimetry. FIGURE 2 shows the relative DNA content of exponentially growing and of retinol-inhibited CHO cells as a function of cell number. Exposure to retinol, 120 μM, for 24 hr arrested the cells at some point in G_1 prior to an increase in cellular DNA content. Therefore, synchronous cells were studied in all subsequent experiments in an attempt to localize the site of vitamin A action.

DOSE-DEPENDENT INHIBITION OF ODC INDUCTION DURING G_1 PROGRESSION AND THE SUBSEQUENT INHIBITION OF THYMIDINE INCORPORATION INTO DNA

FIGURE 3 illustrates a tight correlation between the extent of inhibition of ODC induction during G_1 progression and the subsequent inhibition of DNA synthesis as assessed by [³H]thymidine incorporation. Note that the maximal ODC activity, which is expressed in mitotic CHO cells, decreases rapidly once the cells exit mitosis. Previous experiments have demonstrated that the rapid loss during the initial minutes of G_1 progression results in a minimal expressed activity of the enzyme within 1 hr. The loss of approximately 78% of the enzyme activity within

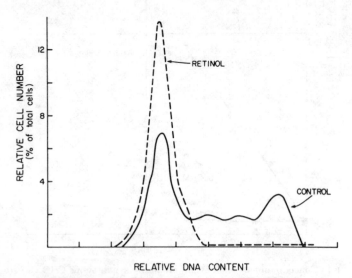

FIGURE 2. Relative DNA content of exponentially growing and retinol-inhibited CHO cells. Asynchronous, logarithmically growing CHO cells were incubated for 24 hr in the presence of 0.5% dioxane (control) or 120 μM retinol prior to harvesting and processing for flow microfluorimetric analysis.

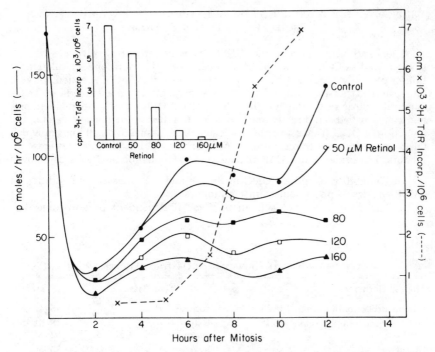

FIGURE 3. Concentration dependence of retinol inhibition of ODC induction and [³H]-thymidine incorporation into mitotically synchronized CHO cells. Mitotically synchronized cells were plated in the presence of the indicated concentration of retinol. The data presented in the concentration dependence curve represent the average of 4 experiments. Estimations of total cellular [³H]thymidine in cell cultures washed extensively after the short-term pulse showed comparable amounts in the control and in the 50 and 80 µM retinol-treated cells and 20 and 40% less amounts in the 120 and 160 µM retinol-treated cells. This effect of the vitamin to limit transport of the nucleoside into the cells is not sufficient to account for the total inhibition of incorporation seen after vitamin addition.

30 min, allowing the first 30 min of incubation for exit from mitosis, correlates well with the previously reported half-life of the enzyme (10–20 min).[42] The G_1 induction of ODC is maximal at 6 hr, a time corresponding to S phase transition as indicated by [³H]thymidine incorporation. As cells traverse S phase, the enzyme appears to increase again. The biphasic nature of the ODC increase probably reflects overlapping independent G_1 and G_2 phase expression of the enzyme as has been shown to occur in other cell types.[6,28] The same pattern of rapid post-mitotic loss of enzyme activity and G_1 and G_2 phase-dependent ODC induction is demonstrable in CHO cells that are synchronized either by mitotic shake-off and cold accumulation or by mitotic shake-off after colcemid treatment. The addition of retinol at the time of mitotic release has no effect on either cell exit from mitosis or progression into the original 60 min of G_1 phase as indicated by the lack of effect of the analog on either the rate of decrease in mitotic index or the rate of turnover of ODC activity. However, the presence of the retinoid totally inhibited the G_1 induction of the enzyme.

LACK OF EFFECT OF RETINOL ON THE ACTIVATION OF CYCLIC AMP-DEPENDENT
PROTEIN KINASE DURING G_1 PHASE

There is considerable evidence that ODC induction during cell cycle progression, as well as ODC induction in response to trophic hormone stimulation, is transcriptionally regulated by the activation of cyclic AMP-dependent protein kinase and its translocation to the nucleus where it affects genetic read-out. TABLE 3 indicates those systems in which cyclic AMP (cAMP) and cAMP-dependent protein kinase have been directly implicated in the action of the hormone and in the induction of ODC. TABLE 4 further indicates those tissues and cell lines in which ODC can be induced in response to cAMP analogs and/or phosphodiesterase inhibitors. The evidence of cAMP mediation of the induction of ODC is as follows:

1. The ability to induce ODC in tissues and cell lines by the addition of cAMP analogs or phosphodiesterase inhibitors.
2. The dose-dependent activation of cAMP-dependent protein kinase by

TABLE 3

CYCLIC AMP-MEDIATED INDUCTION OF ORNITHINE DECARBOXYLASE

Trophic Hormones	Target Tissue(s)	References
Adrenocorticotropin hormone (ACTH)	adrenal cortex	45–47
Follicle-stimulating hormone (FSH)	testis	48–51
	ovary	52–54
Glucagon	liver	55, 56
	liver cells	57
	perfused liver	58, 59
Growth hormone (GH)	liver	60–69
	kidney	70
	adrenal cortex	46, 63
Luteinizing hormone (LH)	testis	49
	ovary	54, 71–73
Parathyroid hormone	kidney	74
	chondrocytes	74
Relaxin	uterus, public symphysis	75
Thyroid-stimulating hormone (TSH)	thyroid	76–81
Thyroid-releasing hormone	anterior pituitary	82–84
Vasopressin	kidney	70
Amine Trophic Hormones		
Epinephrine, Isoproterenol	heart	85–89
Norepinephrine	salivary glands	90–92
Acetylcholine	adrenal medulla	93–95
Compensatory Hypertrophy		
Partial hepatectomy	liver	63, 96–100
Monolateral adrenalectomy	adrenal cortex	63
Unilateral nephrectomy	kidney	101
Stress-induced cardiac hypertrophy	right ventricle	86, 88
	left ventricle	85–87
Concanavalin A-stimulated lymphocytes	lymphocytes	102–104

TABLE 4

ORNITHINE DECARBOXYLASE INDUCTION IN RESPONSE TO
CYCLIC AMP ANALOGS AND/OR PHOSPHODIESTERASE INHIBITORS

Tissue	References
Adrenal cortex	45, 47, 94
Adrenal medulla	44, 93
Liver	94, 105–108
Kidney	94
Oviduct	109
Testis	48
Ventral prostate	110
Cell Lines	
Adrenal cell clones	111
BHK cells	11, 13
CHO cells	27, 112, 113
H35 Reuber cells	9
HTC cells	114
Glioma cells	15, 16
Neuroblastoma cells	15, 16

trophic hormones and the subsequent dose-dependent induction of ODC. In H35 Reuber cells in response to dibutyryl cAMP addition over a 3-log concentration range and in reserpine-stimulated adrenal medulla of the rat over a 2-log concentration range, the extent of the transcriptional excursion of ODC was directly proportional to the activation of cAMP-dependent protein kinase.[9,44]

3. After mitotic synchrony, the same tight sequential temporal relationship exists between cAMP elevation, activation of cAMP-dependent protein kinase and transcriptional induction of ODC during G_1 progression in a variety of cell lines that have been studied.[5]

4. The selective activation of type I cAMP-dependent protein kinase has been implicated in the transcriptional induction of ODC in lymphocytes stimulated to proliferate.[102–104] Increased specific activity of type I protein kinase also occurs after chronic growth stimulation of the rat heart and thyroid.[80,86] Further, adrenal cell clones deficient in cAMP-dependent protein kinase have an attenuated ability to induce ODC.[111]

Since an increase in cAMP and the activation of cAMP-dependent protein kinase is one of the earliest detectable events in G_1, we wished to know whether the inhibition of ODC induction was due to an alteration in the activation of cAMP-dependent protein kinase in retinol-treated cells. The retinol addition did not affect the increase in cAMP-dependent protein kinase activity, which occurred 2 hr after mitotic exit (TABLE 5). The ratio of active to total kinase increased twofold in both the control and the retinol-treated cultures. Therefore, the block in the cell cycle progression cascade as a result of the exposure of cells to retinol must occur after 2 hr.

ABILITY OF RETINOL TO INHIBIT ODC AND BLOCK CELL CYCLE PROGRESSION
RESTRICTED TO G_1 PHASE

As shown in TABLE 6, the blocking effect of retinol on the cell cycle-

TABLE 5

CYCLIC AMP-DEPENDENT PROTEIN KINASE ACTIVATION IN RETINOL-TREATED CELLS*

	Activated Kinase (cpm/5 min/10⁶ cells)		Activity ratio	
Time after mitosis (hr)	Untreated controls	Retinol-treated	Untreated controls	Retinol-treated
1	3550	3500	0.32	0.32
2	5980	6175	0.60	0.62
3	2500	2425	0.25	0.24

* Mitotically synchronized cells were incubated in the presence of 0.5% dioxane (untreated controls) or 120 μM retinol (retinol-treated) for 1, 2, or 3 hr after mitosis. Cells were harvested and assayed for protein kinase activity in the absence (activated) or presence (total) of cyclic AMP. The activity ratio is the ratio of ^{32}P incorporated into histone in the absence and in the presence of cAMP.

dependent increase in ODC activity was only apparent when the vitamin was added prior to hour 4 of the cell cycle. If retinol was added at the time of mitotic exit or after 2 hr of G_1 progression, the increase in ODC detectable in the control cells was inhibited. If retinol was added after 4 or 6 hr of progresion, the retinoid was without effect and ODC activity continued to increase as in the control cells. This lack of effect was not due to a time dependence for retinoid transport or action since only 2 hr were required for the inhibitory effect to become apparent after the addition at hour 2, while even 4 hr after the addition at hour 4 the control level of activity was maintained. The addition of retinol at zero or 2 hr totally blocked any increase in cell number, while cultures to which the retinoid was added after 4 or 6 hr of progression doubled as did the controls. Therefore, the retinol restriction point occurs between 2 and 4 hr in the G_1 phase of the cell cycle. However, previous studies have indicated that ODC is significantly elevated at 3 hr after release from mitosis, suggesting that the retinol inhibition is localized between 2 and 3 hr.[30]

TABLE 6

VITAMIN A INHIBITION OF GROWTH AS A FUNCTION OF CELL CYCLE POSITION*

	Ornithine Decarboxylase (pmol/hr/10⁶ cells)		Cell Number($\times$ 10⁶)	
Time of Retinol Addition (hr)	Control	Retinol	Control	Retinol
0 (M)	145	57	1.8	1.0
2 (early G_1)	200	89		1.0
4 (late G_1)	230	216		1.7
6 (early S)	218	206		1.8

* Retinol (120 μM) or dioxane (control) was added to synchronous cells at the times indicated after mitotic release. Ornithine decarboxylase activity was determined in control and retinol-treated cells 4 hr after the addition of the agent. Cell number was determined 24 hr after plating.

Effect of Retinol on RNA and Protein Synthesis in Synchronized CHO Cells

All of the effects of retinol on CHO cells that we have presented thus far could result from a general inhibitory effect on protein synthesis. Translation is required for the induction of ODC, as well as for the enzymes involved in DNA replication. Furthermore, protein synthesis inhibitors have previously been shown to inhibit G_1 progression.[115-118] Therefore, we examined the rate of protein synthesis after retinol addition. FIGURE 4 indicates that although 120 μM retinol resulted in the almost complete inhibition of ODC induction (FIG. 4A), protein synthesis as assessed by the rate of [³H]leucine incorporation (FIG. 4B) was only inhibited by approximately 20%. Therefore, it seems unlikely that the almost total inhibition of ODC expression at this retinol concentration was a result of the general inhibition of protein synthesis.

In contrast, the effect of retinol on RNA synthesis was marked and progressive (FIG. 4C). In the control cell cultures, the rate of RNA synthesis triples as the cells transit G_1. In the retinol-treated cells, there was no increase in RNA synthesis. The rate was reduced to 70% of control at 2 hr and was reduced further at 8 hr to approximately 30% that of the control cells.

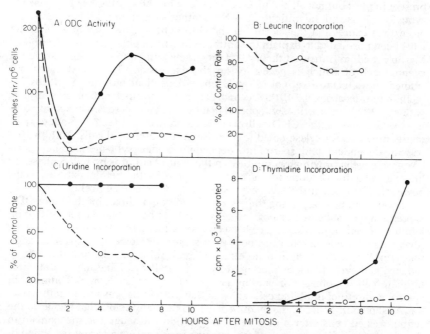

FIGURE 4. Retinol inhibition of A: ornithine decarboxylase activity; B: leucine incorporation; C: uridine incorporation; and D: thymidine incorporation as a function of cell cycle position. Control (●) or 120 μM retinol-treated (O) mitotically synchronized cells were assayed at various times after mitosis for the various components.

ORNITHINE DECARBOXYLASE EXPRESSION AFTER RETINOL REMOVAL IS BLOCKED BY
ACTINOMYCIN D

In order to assess whether transcription of messenger RNA for ODC was occurring in the presence of 120 μM retinol, cells were exposed to the retinoid for the first 4 hr of G_1 progression and then the monolayers were washed and supplemented with fresh media containing additional retinol, actinomycin D, or dioxane (control). Cells resupplemented with retinol retained the inhibition of ODC expression (FIG. 5A). However, those cells removed from the presence of the retinoid and placed in control media displayed increased ODC activity within 30 min which continued to progressively increase, lagging behind the activity of control cells by about 2 hr. This recovery paralleled and preceded the recovery of S phase transition after retinol removal (FIG 5B). However, cultures to which actinomycin D was added after removal of the retinol showed no increase in enzyme activity when tested from 30 min to 4 hr after media replacement. These data suggest that a specific effect of retinol is the inhibition of messenger RNA synthesis for ODC.

EFFECTS OF RETINOL ON OTHER PARAMETERS OF POLYAMINE BIOSYNTHESIS
AND ACCUMULATION

Substantial evidence suggests that the G_1 period of the cell cycle, which is present in most but not all cell lines, is necessary for the synthesis of key peak enzyme functions and the initiation of RNA synthesis required for the wide variety of enzyme expression that occurs at the G_1-S border. However, other theories have been postulated to explain the entrance into the S phase, such as Smith and Martin's random transition theory.[119] Using the assumption of a tight cascade of events, each of which is necessary for the expression of the next event, we studied the effects of retinol on an S phase-dependent enzyme, S-adenosyl-L-methionine decarboxylase, the second enzyme in the polyamine biosynthetic pathway. We have previously reported that this enzyme increases in activity during the S phase of the CHO cell cycle.[30] As shown in TABLE 7, S-adenosyl-L-methionine decarboxylase failed to increase in retinol-treated cells. Both the putrescine-dependent and spermidine-dependent S-adenosyl-L-methionine decarboxylase have approximately doubled in the control cultures by mid-S phase (10 hr). The activity of both forms of the enzyme in the retinol-exposed cells, however, remained at the level expressed in the G_1 phase control cultures.

Several studies examining the effects of addition of direct inhibitors of ODC expression (i.e., substrate analogs) to cells in culture have shown concomitant inhibition of cell proliferation (see TABLE 2). In some cases, this effect has been reversed by the addition of exogenous putrescine.[32, 120] However, putrescine addition (1mM) to CHO cells had no effect on preventing or relieving the retinol-induced cell cycle block as measured by either [³H]thymidine incorporation or ultimate cell doubling. Further, measurements of intracellular polyamines in control and retinol-inhibited cells showed that putrescine was not a limiting factor. As shown in TABLE 8, the diamine level was actually somewhat higher in the retinol-treated cells after 4 or 6 hr of progression. Although the mechanism in these cells for such an increase in putrescine in the absence of any induction of ODC is unknown, a similar phenomenon has been shown to occur in several other growing tissues.[121-123] In those studies, the biosynthetic pathway was shown to be reversed and the increased putrescine was synthesized from sper-

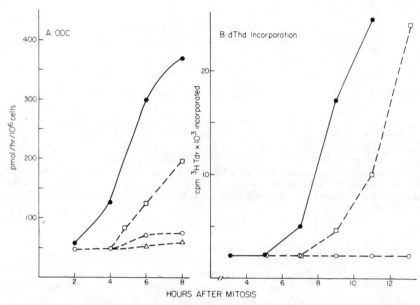

HOURS AFTER MITOSIS

FIGURE 5. Inhibition of recovery of ornithine decarboxylase activity after retinol removal by actinomycin D. Mitotically synchronized cells were plated in the presence of 0.5% dioxane (control) (●) or 120 μM retinol (O). After 4 hr of incubation, the monolayers were washed and resupplemented with prewarmed, pregassed fresh media containing 0.5% dioxane (●, □), 120 μM retinol (O) or 0.5% dioxane and 0.04 μg actinomycin D per ml (Δ). At the times indicated after mitosis, cells were harvested and assayed for ornithine decarboxylase activity (A) or incubated with [³H]thymidine to assess DNA synthetic rate (B).

midine and spermine. Similarly, the concentrations of the polyamines were significantly decreased in the retinol-treated cells. No significant amounts of any of the polyamines were detectable in the growth media from either the control or retinol-treated cells.

IMPLICATIONS OF RETINOL STUDIES OF SYNCHRONIZED CHO CELLS

We postulate, on the basis of the studies of retinol inhibition of cell cycle progression as well as those of direct inhibition of ODC by substrate analogs, that ODC expression is a key regulatory step during G_1 progression after which inhibition of cell cycle progression is less likely to occur. It should be noted that this pertains only to nontoxic blocking agents, since cells can be blocked in any phase of the cell cycle by agents that cause cell death within a prescribed period of time. We feel the key regulatory role played by ODC in the growth process is related to its ability to synthesize the organic cations of the cell, the polyamines, as well as the ability of ODC to serve as an initiation factor for RNA polymerase I resulting in the coordinate synthesis of rRNA and polyamines.[124,125] Therefore, it is interesting to note that the retinol block of cell cycle progression results in a marked inhibition of uridine incorporation into RNA. G_1 phase increase in RNA synthetic rate has been shown in several cell types to reflect an increased syn-

TABLE 7

INHIBITION BY RETINOL OF S PHASE-DEPENDENT
S-ADENOSYL-L-METHIONINE DECARBOXYLASE INDUCTION*

Time After Mitosis (h)	S-Adenosyl-L-Methionine Decarboxylase (pmol/hr/10⁶ cells)	
	Putrescine-dependent	Spermidine-dependent
2	200	40
6	250	30
10	530	80
10 + retinol	249	26

* Mitotically synchronized cells were incubated in the presence of 0.5% dioxane (control) or 120 μM retinol. At the times indicated, cells were harvested and soluble putrescine-dependent and spermidine-dependent S-adenosyl-L-methionine decarboxylase activities were determined.

thesis of rRNA rather than heterogeneous RNA.[126-128] Inhibitor studies in which low concentrations of actinomycin D were used to specifically block rRNA synthesis have shown that this G_1 phase event is essential for entry into S phase.[126,129,130] Baserga[131] has implicated the synthesis of specific RNA and enzymes as precursors to the initiation of DNA synthesis. The present demonstration, therefore, of the correlation between the block in ODC and the block in rRNA synthesis produced by retinol adds to the list of examples of the tight coupling of these two biochemical events. It is of further interest to quote the conclusion of Swann[132] in 1957, later quoted by Baserga,[131] "Differentiation during development is brought about by a process known as induction, the essence of which is that a short-lived stimulus of some sort produces a relatively long lasting effect on the pattern of synthesis. A number of lines of evidence suggest that stimulation of differentiated cells to divide is, in fact, an inductive process. . . . . ." We would go further and identify the initiation of this induction process as ornithine decarboxylase expression.

The specific inhibition of messenger RNA synthesis for ODC by retinol in CHO cells strongly suggests that the retinol is acting in the nucleus to exert its an-

TABLE 8

POLYAMINE CONCENTRATIONS IN RETINOL-TREATED CELLS*

Time after Mitosis (hr)	Putrescine		Spermidine		Spermine	
	Control	Retinol	Control	Retinol	Control	Retinol
2	0.71 ± 0.03†	0.64 ± 0.20				
4	0.71 ± 0.08	0.83 ± 0.07				
6	0.78 ± 0.01	1.18 ± 0.02	3.64 ± 0.21	2.96 ± 0.33	2.44 ± 0.08	1.82 ± 0.28

* Mitotically synchronized cells were incubated in the presence of 0.5% dioxane (control) or 120 μM retinol. At the time indicated, the cells were harvested, and TCA-extracted for analysis of polyamine concentrations, which are expressed as pmol/10⁶ cells.
† Mean ± S.D.

tiproliferative effects. Retinoids have been postulated to act like steroid hormones,[133-135] and under certain circumstances, the retinoid or its binding protein has been localized to the cell nucleus.[136-138] Since cAMP-dependent protein kinase after activation has now been demonstrated to translocate to the nucleus to affect genetic transcription, it is important to determine in future studies whether retinol inhibits the translocation of protein kinase, which could also result in the inhibition of messenger RNA synthesis for ODC. Retinoids and tumor-prevention studies of the antiproliferative properties of vitamin A analogs offer the long-term hope that nutritional agents that will decrease the incidence of certain common human tumors can be developed. These studies can be facilitated by the ability to rapidly evaluate the extent of growth inhibition of vitamin A analogs by the dose-dependent inhibition of ODC induction.[39] Vitamin A and several of its analogs have prophylactic and therapeutic effects on the chemical induction and growth of benign and malignant tumors in whole animals.[139-141] Previous studies of epithelial growth during retinoid deficiency[142,143] and of retinoid inhibition of tumor promoter action in epidermis[40,144,145] and in lymphocytes,[146,147] and of retinoid inhibition of the synchronous growth of a variety of cell lines in vitro[148,149] have suggested that at least part of the chemopreventive action of vitamin A involves the direct inhibition of cell proliferation. Boutwell and his coworkers[145] can inhibit skin papilloma formation in response to a tumor initiator and a tumor promoter with retinoic acid which also inhibits epidermal ODC induction specifically in a parallel dose-dependent manner. We are currently screening various analogs of vitamin A for their effects to inhibit proliferation of human melanoma cell cultures. Specific retinoid analogs may well find extensive use to control a variety of tumors. Chapman and Glant[150] have recently reported the ability to inhibit proliferation of neuroblastoma and glioma cells with retinoids. A correlation existed between the inhibition of growth and the inhibition of ODC. An earlier and more complete cytostatic response was observed in glioma cells treated with retinol and difluoromethylornithine, an irreversible inhibitor of ODC. Future attempts to use specific ODC substrate analogs as tumor inhibitors in conjunction with retinoid analogs may facilitate the rapid development of more effective cancer chemotherapy regimens.

Summary

The induction of ornithine decarboxylase (ODC) during G_1 phase of the cell cycle appears to be universal and essential for cell cycle progression. This induction has been demonstrated in at least 23 cell types in response to various growth stimuli. Further, specific inhibitors of ODC added to several of these cell lines resulted in inhibition of cell proliferation. The studies of the effects of retinoids to inhibit Chinese hamster ovary (CHO) cell growth indicate that the cells are blocked in G_1 of cell cycle, and that there is a concentration-dependent inhibition of ODC induction. Retinoids only inhibit the induction of ODC activity when added in the first 2-3 hr of G_1 progression. It is postulated that ODC induction is a requirement for G_1 progression and that the antiproliferative properties of retinoids are related to the specific ability to inhibit this expression. Since retinoids do not dramatically alter the rate of protein synthesis, their ability to inhibit ODC may be related to their ability to inhibit messenger RNA synthesis for ODC.

REFERENCES

1. COHEN, S.S. 1971. Introduction to the Polyamines. Prentice-Hall. Englewood Cliffs, NJ.
2. BACHRACH, U. 1973. Function of Naturally Occurring Polyamines. Academic Press. New York.
3. RUSSELL, D.H., Ed. 1973. Polyamines in Normal and Neoplastic Growth. Raven Press. New York.
4. RUSSELL, D.H. & B.G.M. DURIE. 1978. Polyamines as Biochemical Markers of Normal and Malignant Growth. Raven Press. New York.
5. RUSSELL, D.H. & M.K. HADDOX. 1979. Adv. Enzyme Reg. 17: 61-87.
6. McCANN, P.P., C. TARDIF, P.S. MAMONT & F. SCHUBER. 1975. Biochem. Biophys. Res. Commun. 64: 336-341.
7. HOGAN, B.L.M. 1971. Biochem. Biophys. Res. Commun. 45: 301-307.
8. HOGAN, B.L.M., A. McILHINNEY & S. MURDEN. 1974. J. Cell. Physiol. 83: 353-358.
9. BYUS, C.V., W.D. WICKS & D.H. RUSSELL. 1976. J. Cyclic Nucleotide Res. 2: 241-250.
10. HODGSON, J. & J.D. WILLIAMSON. 1975. Biochem. Biophys. Res. Commun. 63: 308-312.
11. HOGAN, B., R. SHIELDS & D. CURTIS. 1974. Cell 2: 229-233.
12. MELVIN, W.T., R.Y. THOMSON & J. HAY. 1972. Biochem. J. 130: 77P-78P.
13. HIBASAMI, H., M. TANAKA, J. NAGAI & T. IKEDA. 1976. MIE Med. J. Tsu. Japan 25: 223-230.
14. LEMBACH, K.J. 1974. Biochim. Biophys. Acta 354: 88-100.
15. BACHRACH, U. 1975. Proc. Natl. Acad. Sci. USA 72: 3087-3091.
16. BACHRACH, U. 1976. FEBS Lett. 68: 63-67.
17. CHAPMAN, S.K., M. MARTIN, M.S. HOOVER & C.Y. CHIOU. 1978. Biochem. Pharmacol. 27: 717-721.
18. HEBY, O., L.J. MARTON, L. ZARDI, D.H. RUSSELL & R. BASERGA. 1975. Exp. Cell Res. 90: 8-14.
19. DUFFY, P.E. & L.T. KREMZNER. 1977. Exp. Cell Res. 108: 435-440.
20. YAMASAKI, Y, & A. ICHIHARA. 1976. J. Biochem. 80: 557-562.
21. HELLER, J.S., W.E. FONG & E.S. CANELLAKIS. 1976. Proc. Natl. Acad. Sci. USA 73: 1858-1862.
22. D'AMORE, P.A. & D. SHEPRO. 1978. Life Sci. 22: 571-576.
23. CLARK, J.L. 1974. Biochemistry 13: 4668-4674.
24. STASTNY, M. & S. COHEN. 1970. Biochim. Biophys. Acta 204: 578-589.
25. PARIZA, M.W., J.E. BECKER, J.D. YAGER, R.J. BONNEY & V.R. POTTER. 1973. In Differentiation and Control of Malignancy of Tumor Cells. W. Nakahara, T. Ono, T. Sugimura & H. Sugano, Eds.: 267-285. University of Tokyo Press. Japan.
26. GOLDSTEIN, D.A., O. HEBY & L.J. MARTON. 1976. Proc. Natl. Acad. Sci. USA 73: 4022-4026.
27. RUSSELL, D.H. & P.J. STAMBROOK. 1975. Proc. Natl. Acad. Sci. USA 72: 1482-1486.
28. HEBY, O., J.W. GRAY, P.A. LINDL, L.J. MARTON & C.B. WILSON. 1976. Biochem. Biophys. Res. Commun. 71: 99-105.
29. FRIEDMAN, S.J., R.A. BELLANTONE & E.S. CANELLAKIS. 1972. Biochim. Biophys. Acta 261: 188-192.
30. FULLER, D.J.M., E.W GERNER & D.H. RUSSELL. 1977. J. Cell. Physiol. 93: 81-88.
31. HIBASAMI, H., M. TANAKA, J. NAGAI & T. IKEDA. 1977. Aust. J. Exp. Biol. Med. Sci. 55: 379-383.
32. MAMONT, P.S., P. BÖHLEN, P.P. McCANN, P. BEY, F. SCHUBER & C. TARDIF. 1976. Proc. Natl. Acad. Sci. USA 73: 1626-1630.
33. HEBY, O., G. ANDERSSON & J.W. GRAY. 1978. Exp.Cell Res. 111: 461-464.
34. MAMONT, P.S., M.C. DUCHESNE, J. GROVE & P. BEY. 1978. Biochem. Biophys. Res. Commun. 81: 58-66.
35. SUNKARA, P.S., P.N. RAO & K. NISHIOKA. 1977. Biochem. Biophys. Res. Commun. 74: 1125-1133.
36. RELYEA, N. & R.R. RANDO. 1975. Biochem. Biophys. Res. Commun. 67: 392-402.

37. HADDOX, M.K. & D.H. RUSSELL. 1978. Fed. Proc. **37:** 1432.
38. HADDOX, M.K. & D.H. RUSSELL. 1979. Cancer Res. **39:** 2476-2480.
39. HADDOX, M.K., K.F.F. SCOTT & D.H. RUSSELL. 1979. Cancer Res. **39:** 4930-4938.
40. VERMA, A.K. & R.K. BOUTWELL. 1977. Cancer Res. **37:** 2196-2201.
41. ONG, D.E. & F. CHYTIL. 1976. Proc. Natl. Acad. Sci. USA **73:** 3976-3978.
42. RUSSELL, D.H. & S.H. SNYDER. 1969. Molec. Pharmacol. **5:** 253-262.
43. FONG, W.F., J.S. HELLER & E.S. CANELLAKIS. 1976. Biochim. Biophys. Acta **428:** 456-465.
44. RUSSELL, D.H. & C.V. BYUS. 1976. Adv. Biochem. Psychopharmacol. **15:** 445-454.
45. LEVINE, J.H., W.E. NICHOLSON, A. PEYTREMANN & D.N. ORTH. 1975. Endocrinology **97:** 136-144.
46. LEVINE, J.H., W.E. NICHOLSON, A. PEYTREMANN & D.N. ORTH. 1973. Endocrinology **92:** 1090-1095.
47. RICHMAN, R., C. DOBBINS, S. VOINA, L. UNDERWOOD, D. MAHAFFEE, H.J. GITELMAN, J. VAN WYK & R.L. NEW. 1973. J. Clin. Invest. **52:** 2007-2015.
48. REDDY, R.P.K. & C.A. VILLEE. 1975. Biochem. Biophys. Res. Commun. **65:** 1350-1354.
49. HEINDEL, J.J., R. ROTHENBERG, G.A. ROBISON & A. STEINBERGER, J. Cyclic Nucleotide Res. **1:** 68-69.
50. MEANS, A.R., J.L. RADUNDING & D.J. TINDALL. 1976. Biol. Reprod. **14:** 54-63.
51. MEANS, A.R., E. MACDOUGALL, T.R. SODERLING & J.D. CORBIN. 1974. J. Biol. Chem. **249:** 1231-1238.
52. OSTERMAN, J., L.M. DEMERS & J.M. HAMMOND. 1978. Endocrinology **103:** 1718-1724.
53. OSTERMAN, J. & J.M. HAMMOND. 1978. Biochem. Biophys. Res. Commun. **83:** 794-799.
54. Osterman, J. & J.M. Hammond. 1977. Endocrinology **101:**1335-1338.
55. HÖLTTA, E. & A. RAINA. 1973. Acta Endocrinologica **73:**794-800.
56. PANKO, W.B. & F.T. KENNEY. 1971. Biochem. Biophys. Res. Commun. **43:** 346-350.
57. BYUS, C.V., J.S. HAYES, K. BRENDEL & D.H. RUSSELL. 1976. Life Sci. **19:** 329-335.
58. MALLETTE, L.E. & J.H. EXTON. 1973. Endocrinology **93:** 640-644.
59. MANEN, C.A., J.S. HAYES, K. BRENDEL & D.H. RUSSELL. 1977. Fed. Proc. **36:** 408.
60. FELDMAN, E.J., D. AURES & M.I. GROSSMAN. 1978. Proc. Soc. Exp. Biol. Med. **159:** 400-403.
61. RUSSELL, D.H. & S.H. SNYDER. 1969. Endocrinology **84:** 223-228.
62. RUSSELL, D.H., S.H. SNYDER & V.J. MEDINA. 1970. Endocrinology **86:** 1414-1419.
63. BYUS, C.V., G.A. HEDGE & D.H. RUSSELL. 1977. Biochim. Biophys. Acta **498:** 39-45.
64. FELLER, D.D., E.D. NEVILLE & S. ELLIS. 1977. Physiol. Chem. Phys. **9:** 55-61.
65. KOSTYO, J.L. 1966. Biochem. Biophys. Res. Commun. **23:** 150-155.
66. HÖLTTA, E. 1975. Biochim. Biophys. Acta **399:** 4209-427.
67. JÄNNE, J. & A. RAINA. 1969. Biochim. Biophys. Acta **174:** 769-772.
68. JÄNNE, J. & A. RAINA. 1968. Acta Chem. Scan. **22:** 1349-1351.
69. SUZUKI, F., H. INOUE & Y. TAKEDA. 1973. J. Biochem. **74:** 661-666.
70. SCALABRINO, G. & M.E. FERIOLI. 1976. Endocrinology **99:** 1085-1090.
71. KOBAYASHI, Y., J. KUPELIAN & D.V. MAUDSLEY. 1971. Science **172:** 379-380.
72. NUREDDIN, A. 1978. Proc. Natl. Acad. Sci. USA **75:** 2530-2534.
73. KAY, A.M., I. ICEKSON, S.A. LAMPRECHT, R. GRUSS, A. TSAFRIRI & H.R. LINDNER. 1973. Biochemistry **12:** 3072-3076.
74. TAKIGAWA, M., R. WATANABE, H. ISHIDA, A. ASADA & R. SUZUKI. 1979. J. Biochem. **85:** 311-314.
75. BRADDON, S.A. 1978. Biochem. Biophys. Res. Commun. **80:** 75-80.
76. MATSUZAKI, S. & M. SUZUKI. 1974. Endocrinol. Japon. **21:** 529-537.
77. MATSUZAKI, S. & M. SUZUKI. 1975. Endocrinol. Japon. **22:** 339-345.
78. MATSUZAKI, S., T. KAKEGAWA, M. SUZUKI & K. HAMANA. 1978. Endocrinol. Japon. **25:** 129-139.
79. SCHEINMAN, S.J., G.N. BURROW, T.C. THEOHARIDES & Z.N. CANELLAKIS. 1977. Life Sci. **23:** 1143-1148.
80. COMBEST, W., R.B. CHIASSON & D.H. RUSSELL. 1980. Gen. Comp. Endocrinol. **40:** 494-502.

81. COMBEST, W., R.B. CHIASSON, H. KLANDORF, G.A. HEDGE & D.H. RUSSELL. 1978. Gen. Comp. Endocrinol. **35:** 146–152.
82. SUNDBERG, D.K., C.P. FAWCETT & S.M. McCANN. 1976. Proc. Soc. Exp. Biol. Med. **151:** 149–154.
83. DANNIES, P.S., K.M. GAUTVIK & A.H. TASHJIAN. 1976. Endocrinology **98:** 1147–1149.
84. LABRIE, F., P. BORGEAT, A. LEMAY, S. LEMAIRE, N. BARDEN, J. DROUIN, I. LEMAIRE, P. JOLICOEUR & A. BELANGER. 1975. Adv. Cyclic Nucleotide Res. **5:** 787–801.
85. FULLER, R.W. & S.K. HEMRICK. 1978. Cell Cardiol. **10:** 1031–1036.
86. BYUS, C.V., J.M. CHUBB, R.J. HUXTABLE & D.H. RUSSELL. 1976. Biochem. Biophys. Res. Commun. **73:** 694–702.
87. FELDMAN, M.J. & D.H. RUSSELL. 1972. Am. J. Physiol. **222:** 1199–1203.
88. RUSSELL, D.H., K.T. SHIVERICK, B.B. HAMRELL & N.R. ALPERT. 1971. Am. J. Physiol. **221:** 1287–1291.
89. WOMBLE, J.R., M.K. HADDOX & D.H. RUSSELL. 1978. Life Sci. **23:** 1951–1958.
90. INOUE, H., H. TANIOKA, K. SHIBA, A. ADADA, Y. KATO & Y. TAKEDA. 1974. J. Biochem. **75:**679–687.
91. INOUE, H., Y. KATO, M. TAKIGAWA, K. ADACHI & Y. TAKEDA. 1975. J. Biochem. **77:** 879–893.
92. NELSON, N.F., B. BROWN, D.D. DOUTHIT, S. GHATAN & D.G. BROWN. 1979. J. Dental Res. **58:**1644–1651.
93. BYUS, C.V. & D.H. RUSSELL. 1975. Science **187:** 650–652.
94. BYUS, C.V. & D.H. RUSSELL. 1974. Life Sci. **15:** 1991–1997.
95. BYUS, C.V. & D.H. RUSSELL. 1976. Biochem. Pharmacol. **25:** 1595–1600.
96. MACMANUS, J.P., J.F. WHITFIELD, A.L. BOYNTON & R.H. RIXON. 1978. Adv. Cyclic Nucleotide Res. **9:** 719–734.
97. RUSSELL, D.H. & S.H. SNYDER. 1968. Proc. Natl. Acad. Sci. USA **60:** 1420–1427.
98. GAZA, D.J., J. SHORT & I. LIEBERMAN. 1973. Biochem. Biophys. Res. Commun. **54:**1483–1488.
99. HÖLTTA, E. & J. JÄNNE. 1972. FEBS Lett. **23:** 117–121.
100. RUSSELL, D.H. & T.A. McVICKER. 1971. Biochim. Biophys. Acta **244:** 85–93.
101. BRANDT, J.T., D.A. PIERCE & N. FAUSTO. 1972. Biochim. Biophys. Acta **279:** 184–193.
102. BYUS, C.V., G.R. KLIMPEL, D.O. LUCAS & D.H. RUSSELL. 1977. Nature **268:** 63–64.
103. BYUS, C.V., G.R. KLIMPEL, D.O. LUCAS & D.H. RUSSELL. 1977. Molec. Pharmacol. **14:** 431–441.
104. KLIMPEL, G.R., C.V. BYUS, D.H. RUSSELL & D.O. LUCAS. 1979. J. Immunology **123:** 817–823.
105. BECK, W.T., R.A. BELLANTONE & E.S. CANELLAKIS. 1972. Biochem. Biophys. Res. Commun. **48:** 1649–1655.
106. BECK, W.T. & E.S. CANELLAKIS. 1973. *In* Polyamines in Normal and Neoplastic Growth. D.H. Russell, Ed.: 261–275. Raven Press. New York.
107. ELORANTA, T. & A. RAINA. 1975. FEBS Lett. **55:** 22–24.
108. MANEN, C.A. & D.H. RUSSELL. 1975. Life Sci. **17:** 1769–1776.
109. PRESLOCK, J.P. & J.K. HAMPTON, JR. 1973. Am. J. Physiol. **225:** 903–907.
110. TSANG, B.K. & E.L. SINGHAL. 1976. Pharmacology **18:** 164.
111. KUDLOW, J.E., R.A. RAF, B.P. SCHIMMER & G.N. BURROW. 1978. Clin Res. **26:** 844A.
112. COSTA, M. & J.S. NYE. 1978. Biochem. Biophys. Res. Commun. **85:** 1156–1164.
113. COSTA, M. 1978. J. Cyclic Nucleotide Res. **5:** 375–387.
114. CANELLAKIS, Z.N. & T.C. THEOHARIDES. 1976. J. Biol. Chem. **251:** 4436–4441.
115. HARRIS, H. 1959. Biochem. J. **72:** 54–60.
116. MUELLER, G.C., K. KAJIWARA, E. STUBBLEFIELD & R.R. RUECKERT. 1962. Cancer Res. **22:** 1084–1090.
117. SCHNEIDERMAN, M.H., W.C. DEWEY & D.P. HIGHFIELD. 1971. Exp. Cell. Res. **67:** 147–155.
118. TERASIMA, T. & M. YASUKAWA. 1966. Exp. Cell Res. **44:** 669–672.
119. SMITH, J.A. & L. MARTIN. 1973. Proc. Natl. Acad. Sci. USA **70:** 1236–1267.
120. INOUE, H., Y. KATO, M. TAKIGAWA, K. ADACHI & Y. TAKEDA. 1975. J. Biochem. (Tokyo) **77:** 879–893.

121. HÖLTTA, E., R. SINERVIRTA & J. JÄNNE. 1973. Biochem. Biophys. Res. Commun. **54:** 350-357.
122. INOUE, H., A. ASADA, Y. KATO & Y. TAKEDA. 1978. J. Biochem. (Tokyo) **84:** 719-725.
123. SIIMES, M. 1967. Acta Physiol. Scand. Suppl. **298:** 1-66.
124. MANEN, C.A. & D.H. RUSSELL. 1977. Science **195:** 505-506.
125. MANEN, C.A. & D.H. RUSSELL. 1977. Biochem. Pharmacol. **26:** 2379-2384.
126. BASERGA, R., R.D. ESTENSEN & R.O. PETERSEN. 1965. Proc. Natl. Acad. Sci. USA **54:** 1141-1148.
127. ROSSINO, M. & R. BASERGA. 1978. Biochemistry **17:** 858-863.
128. TSUKADA, K. & I. LIEBERMAN. 1964. J. Biol. Chem. **239:** 1564-1568.
129. DOIDA, Y. & S. OKADA. 1972. Cell Tissue Kinet. **5:** 15-26.
130. EPIFANOVA, O.I., M.K. ABULADZE & A. ZOSIMOVSKAYA. 1975. Exp. Cell Res. **92:** 23-30.
131. BASERGA, R. 1965. Cancer Res. **25:** 581-595.
132. SWANN, M.M. 1957. Cancer Res. **17:** 727-757.
133. BASHOR, M.M., D.O. TOFT & F. CHYTIL. 1973. Proc. Natl. Acad. Sci. USA **70:** 3483-3487.
134. CHYTIL, R. & D.E. ONG. 1976. Nature **260:** 59-51.
135. LASNITZKI, I. 1976. Br. J. Cancer **34:** 239-248.
136. PRUTKIN, L. & B. BOGART. 1970. J. Invest. Dermatol. **55:** 249-255.
137. SANI, B.P. 1977. Biochem. Biophys. Res. Commun. **75:** 7-12.
138. SANI, B.P. & B.C. TITUS. 1977. Cancer Res. **37:** 4031-4034.
139. BOLLAG, W. 1971. Experientia (Basel) **27:** 90-92.
140. BOLLAG, W. 1972. Eur. J. Cancer **8:** 689-693.
141. SPORN, M.B., N.M. DUNLOP, D.L. NEWTON & W.R. HENDERSON. 1976. Nature **263:** 110-113.
142. HARRIS, C.C., T. SILVERMAN, J.M. SMITH, F. JACKSON & H.B. BOREN. 1973. J. Natl. Cancer Inst. **51:** 1059-1062.
143. HARRIS, C.C., M.B. SPORN, D.G. KAUFMAN, J.M. SMITH, F.E. JACKSON & U. SAFFIOTTI. 1972. J. Natl. Cancer Inst. **48:** 743-761.
144. VERMA, A.K., H.M. RICE, B.G. SHAPAS & R.K. BOUTWELL. 1978. Cancer Res. **38:** 793-801.
145. VERMA, A.K., B.G. SHAPAS, H.M. RICE & R.K. BOUTWELL. 1979. Cancer Res. **39:** 419-425.
146. KENSLER, T.W. & G.C. MUELLER. 1978. Cancer Res. **38:** 771-775.
147. KENSLER, T.W., A.K. VERMA, R.K. BOUTWELL & G.C. MUELLER. 1978. Cancer Res. **38:** 2896-2899.
148. LOTAN, R., G. GIOTTA, E. NORK & G.L. NICOLSON. 1978. J. Natl. Cancer Inst. **60:** 1035-1041.
149. LOTAN, R. & G.L. NICOLSON. 1977. J. Natl. Cancer Inst. **60:** 1035-1041.
150. CHAPMAN, S.K. 1980. Life Sci. **26:** 1359-1366.

IN VITRO VITAMIN A-MEDIATED GLYCOSYLATION: RECENT DEVELOPMENTS IN ENZYMATIC STUDIES

Jacques Frot-Coutaz, Robert Létoublon, and René Got

Laboratoire de Biologie et Technologie des Membranes
Université Claude Bernard
69622 Villeurbanne, France

In 1969, Dr. Morton considered for the first time that vitamin A could be involved in sugar transfer reactions, and, I quote, "in a manner akin to the carrier role recently discovered for the undecaprenol.[1]" Since then many observations have been published on this subject[2-8]; for instance it has been shown that vitamin A deficiency or excess results in a decrease or increase in glycoprotein biosynthesis, respectively,[3,8] but these results obtained in an *"in vivo"* situation do not tell if the observed effect is a side effect or if vitamin A is, as polyprenols,[9,10] directly involved according to the following scheme:

1. Retinol ⟶ retinylphosphate (RP);
2. RP + GDP-mannose ⟶ GDP + mannosylretinylphosphate (MRP);
3. MRP + acceptor ⟶ RP + acceptor-mannose.

To confirm this hypothesis, two basic different approaches have been used:

(a) Under *in vivo* conditions, attempts have been made to isolate RP and/or MRP.

(b) The developments of *in vitro* systems have been necessary at least to confirm the *in vivo* findings.

The results that I will present have been obtained in an *in vitro* situation and concern mainly the retinoic acid problem. This problem comes from the fact that retinoic acid is, with the exception of vision and reproduction, as active as retinol *in vivo*.[6,7] Even if retinoylphosphate (RyP) – which has been made chemically[11] – has never been identified, to my knowledge, as a naturally occurring metabolite of retinoic acid, it is interesting to reconsider the question of its ability to accept mannose.[12]

Reactions number 2 and number 3 are catalyzed by enzymes that are bound to microsomal membranes, and a more precise subcellular localization of the enzyme that forms MRP has been investigated.[13,14] MRP is synthesized from GDP-mannose and exogenous RP; in the absence of exogenous RP the main product that appears in the lower phase – the incubation mixtures are analyzed by a modification of the Folch extraction procedure[15] – is dolichylmannosylphosphate (DMP), and very little MRP-like material is made.

RESULTS

In a preliminary experiment (FIG. 1) we studied the influence of divalent cations on reactions number 2 and number 3. In this experiment rat liver microsomes were prepared in the absence of any divalent cation.[16] Although DMP does not require for its synthesis any exogenous cation, from endogenous DP, synthesis of MRP from exogenous RP is strictly dependent upon the presence of

0077-8923/81/0359-0298 $01.75/0 © 1981, NYAS

FIGURE 1. Effect of Mn⁺⁺ and Mg⁺⁺ on the formation of DMP and MRP (lipids) upon reactions of GDP-[¹⁴C] mannose and endogenous membrane acceptors (proteins). Assays (1 mg proteins for a final volume of 0.2 ml) for each data point contained: 50 mM Tris-HCl pH 7.8, 3 mM ATP (disodium salt), GDP-[¹⁴C] mannose 0.125 μCi (specific activity: 166 mCi/mmol., the Radiochemical Centre), 10 μl of DMSO with or without 25 μg of RP. Incubations were for 60 minutes at 22°C in presence of variable concentrations of Mn⁺⁺ and Mg⁺⁺. The reaction was stopped by adding 3 ml of chloroform/methanol (2/l, v/v) to the incubation mixture; DMP and MRP were determined by thin-layer chromatography as previously described.[15] The precipitate (interphase material) was layered on glass microfiber (GF/ C, Whatman) and washed free of GDP-[¹⁴C] mannose and [¹⁴C]mannolipids successively by 10 ml 5% phosphotungstic acid in 2 N HCl, 50 ml water, 10 ml chloroform/methanol (2/l, v/v), 10 ml chloroform/methanol/water (1/1/0.3, v/v), 10 ml ethanol; the filter was transferred to a scintillation vial and radioactivity measured in presence of 10 ml PPO/POPOP/toluene scintillation mixture.

N.B.: DMP synthesis is not modified by exogenously added RP[15]; this is the reason why only one set of curves is shown.

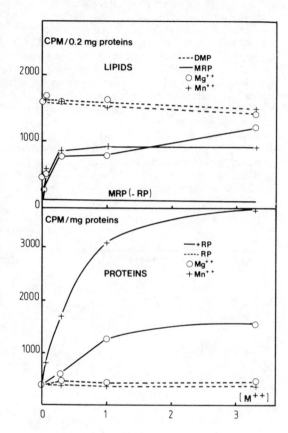

divalent cations, and Mg⁺⁺ is about as efficient as Mn⁺⁺. Analysis of the radioactivity contained in the insoluble material (considered as proteins[15]) shows that in the presence of exogenous RP the enhancement of glycoprotein labeling is more prominent with Mn⁺⁺ than with Mg⁺⁺ and that the optimal concentration is 1 mM. These results are not in full agreement with the observations made by Butler and Wolf,[17] but their conditions (microsome preparation and incubation mixtures) were different from ours.

In the previous experiment all the reactants were mixed at the same time in the test tube and RP was added as a solution prepared in dimethyl-sulfoxide (DMSO). If a 20 μM RyP solution in a 50 mM Tris-HC1 buffer pH 7.8 is made, the usual spectrum is obtained (FIG. 2).[11] When Mn^{++} or Mg^{++} is added so that the cation concentration is brought up to 2.5 mM the characteristic spectrum disappears very rapidly in the presence of Mn^{++} and less quickly in the presence of Mg^{++}. If we repeat the experiment, starting with a higher concentration of RyP and no cation and then progressively increase the concentration of divalent cation, the amount of "soluble" RyP that remains in the supernatant after centrifugation decreases (FIG. 3); in the presence of 3 mM Mn^{++} the concentration of soluble RyP drops very rapidly down to 5 μM (Fig. 3).

If RyP forms a stable and insoluble complex with Mn^{++} and to a lesser extent with Mg^{++}, we cannot expect RyP to interact with the enzyme responsible for its mannosylation. To give RyP a better chance to be mannosylated by delaying the interaction with the cation necessary for reaction number 2, we have achieved a controlled transfer of any substrate like RyP or RP or DP from liposomes to microsomal vesicles.[16,18]

Liposomes are phospholipid-containing vesicles that interact with microsomes under certain conditions; it has been shown that in our conditions, fusion between microsomes and liposomes reaches a plateau after 30 to 60 min of incubation and that about 40% of the liposomes have interacted with microsomes.[16] In other words, reaction number 2 is carried out in two steps:

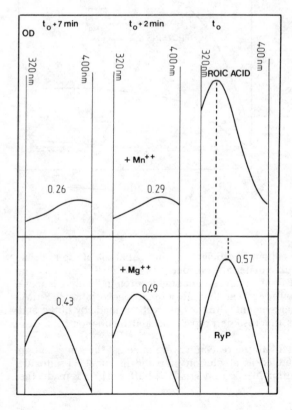

FIGURE 2. Behavior of RyP in presence of Mn^{++} and Mg^{++}.

The spectrum of RyP (20 μM solution in a 50 mM Tris-HCl pH 7.8 buffer – DMSO: 0.25%) was drawn in the absence or presence of Mn^{++} and Mg^{++} (2.5 mM). Roic acid stands for retinoic acid.

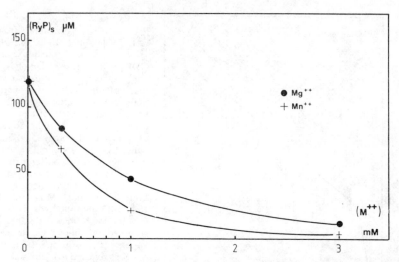

FIGURE 3. Evidence for complex formation between RyP and some divalent cations: Mn⁺⁺ and Mg⁺⁺.

RyP was dissolved (120 μM solution) in a 50 mM Tris-HCl, pH 7.8 buffer containing DMSO (3.3%). This solution is stable upon centrifugation at 150,000 × *g* for 2 min (air driven centrifuge). Increasing amounts of MgCl₂ and MnCl₂ were added and the mixture centrifuged for 2 min at 150,000 × *g*. 100 μl of the supernatant were diluted with 1.9 ml of methanol and the optical density at 360 nm measured ((RyP)s).

1. Microsomes are enriched in any of the lipophilic substrates that one wants to test for its ability to accept mannose: RyP, RP, or DP.

2. Transfer of mannose itself is initiated by addition of the necessary reactants, namely the divalent cation and GDP-[¹⁴C]mannose.

In this experiment (FIG. 4) we have used liposomes containing in addition to phosphatidylcholine (PC) and phosphatidylethanolamine (PE) either phosphatidic acid (PA) or RyP or DP; in the presence of Mn⁺⁺ or Mg⁺⁺ at a 1 mM concentration no mannosylretinoylphosphate-like material is made, while addition of exogenous DP results in a very important increase in the synthesis of DMP. It is interesting to remark that:

1. Liposomes do not modify the velocity of DMP synthesis (see control), which would mean that the enzymatic environment is not modified.

2. Exogenous RyP does not inhibit DMP synthesis from endogenous DP.

If the same experiment is repeated with replacement of RyP by RP, the following results are obtained (FIG. 5):

(a) as in the previous experiment DMP synthesis is increased in the presence of exogenous DP;

(b) MRP is made from exogenous RP and GDP-mannose in the presence of Mn⁺⁺;

(c) exogenous RP does not inhibit the synthesis of DMP from endogenous DP.

In this same experiment radioactivity in the insoluble material – considered as glycoproteins – has been measured (FIG. 6); we see that equivalent synthesis of DMP and MRP due to exogenously added DP and RP does not result in a propor-

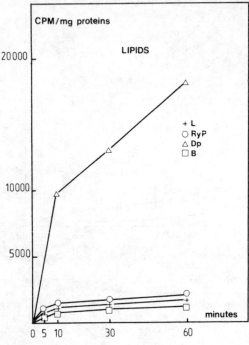

FIGURE 4. Time course of [¹⁴C]mannose transfer from GDP-[¹⁴C]mannose to DP or RyP.

[¹⁴C]mannose transfer from GDP-[¹⁴C]mannose to DP or RyP was studied in the presence of four different enzymatic preparations obtained after incubation for 30 min at 22°C of a microsomal suspension with liposomes as previously described.[16] Suspensions of phospholipid vesicles in 50 mM Tris-HCl buffer, pH 7.8 were prepared by sonicating for 4 min (at a 35 W setting microprobe, Branson sonifier, Model B-12) 18-30 mM phospholipids. Centrifugation for 20 min at 150,000 × g served to remove the largest vesicles; the resulting supernatant was referred to as liposomes.

The liposome composition was as follows: +: phosphatidylcholine: 5 mg; phosphatidylethanolamine: 2.5 mg; phosphatidic acid: 1 mg. ○: same as (+) but 0.45 mg of RyP an no phosphatidic acid. △: same as (+) but 0.6 mg of DP and 0.85 mg of phosphatidic acid. □: control: liposomes were replaced by the buffer solution used for the preparation of the lipid vesicles.

Incubation and analysis was as for FIGURE 1 with MgCl₂ 1 mM as divalent cation. Determination of mannolipids was performed as for FIGURE 1.

tional mannose transfer into glycoproteins; while DMP has little effect, a dramatic enhancement is obtained from MRP.

CONCLUSIONS

The absence of inhibition of DMP synthesis from endogenous DP by high amounts of exogenous RP and the fact that similar amounts of MRP and DMP are quantitatively unequally efficient in *in vitro* mannoslylation of glycoproteins favor:

1. a direct involvement of retinol in mannoprotein biosynthesis;
2. the existence of a double pathway one involving retinol, the other one dolichol.

Such a double pathway has already been considered as a possibility,[19] but its significance remains to be elucidated. To get back to the retinoic acid problem, one can say that RyP is not the active form of retinoic acid and the present results confirm those obtained in 1976.[12]

A shift in the maximum of absorption is observed when retinoic acid undergoes phosphorylation;[11] no such phenomenon occurs for retinol (325 nm for both

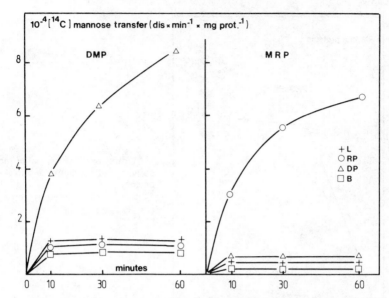

FIGURE 5. Time course of incorporation of [¹⁴C]mannose into DMP and MRP.
The experiment was conducted and analyzed as in FIGURE 4, except that RyP was replaced by RP (O) (0.450 mg) and MnCl₂ 1 mM was used instead of MgCl₂.

retinol and RP). Because of the presence of the carbonyl group, which can be considered as a sixth conjugated double bond, the phosphate group in the RyP molecule "interacts" with the other conjugated double bonds of the hydrocarbon chain; in other words a phosphate group is different when it belongs to retinoic acid or retinol. It is possible to imagine how retinoylphosphate can interact with Mn^{++} to form a stable complex and that in an aqueous medium as well as in a membranous environment:

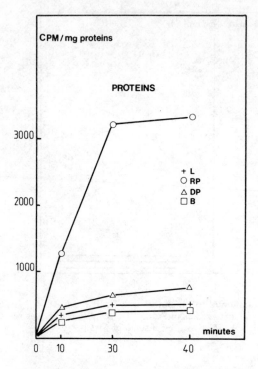

FIGURE 6. Time course of incorporation of [14C] mannose into glycoproteins.

For conditions and symbols see FIGURE 5.

Such a complex would hardly fit the catalytic site of the enzyme responsible for MRP synthesis and could explain why, according to unpublished preliminary results, RyP is a poor inhibitor for *in vitro* MRP synthesis.

Obviously retinoic acid must undergo some chemical modification, which is not a reduction of the carbonyl group since nobody has been able to show that retinoic acid is reduced into retinol.

De Luca has speculated on the formation of a compound X[6] which would be an alcohol, and this is in agreement with what Chen and Heller[20] have found in a preliminary report.

ACKNOWLEDGMENT

The authors wish to express their gratitude to Professor Jean Huet for helpful comments and suggestions.

REFERENCES

1. MORTON, R.A. 1969. Am. J. Clin. Nutr. **22:** 943–944.
2. ROSSO, G.C., L.M. DE LUCA, C.D. WARREN & G. WOLF. 1975. J. Lipid Res. **16:** 235–243.
3. DE LUCA, L.M., C.S. SILVERMAN-JONES & R.M. BARR. 1975. Biochim. Biophys. Acta **409:** 342–359.
4. FROT-COUTAZ, J.P., C.S. SILVERMAN-JONES & L.M. DE LUCA. 1976. J. Lipid Res. **17:** 220–230.

5. ROSSO, G.C., S. MASUSHIGE, H. QUILL & G. WOLF. 1977. Proc. Natl. Acad. Sci. USA **74** (9): 3762–3766.
6. DE LUCA, L.M. 1977. Vitam. Horm. **35**: 1–57.
7. SATO, M., L.M. DE LUCA. & Y. MUTO. 1978. J. Nutr. Sci. Vitaminol. **24**: 9–23.
8. KIORPES, T.C., S.J. MOLICA & G. WOLF. 1976. J. Nutr. **106**: 1659–1667.
9. LETOUBLON, R. & R. GOT. 1974. Febs. Letters **46**: 214–217.
10. PARODI, A.J. & L.F. LELOIR. 1979. Biochim. Biophys. Acta **559**: 1–37.
11. FROT-COUTAZ, J.P. & L.M. DE LUCA. 1976. Biochem. J. **159**: 799–801.
12. DE LUCA, L.M., J.P. FROT-COUTAZ, C.S. SILVERMAN-JONES & P.R. ROLLER. 1977. J. Biol. Chem. **252**: 2575–2579.
13. BERGMAN, A., T. MANKOWSKI, T. CHOJNACKI, L.M. DE LUCA, L.M. PETERSON & G. DALLNER. 1978. Biochem. J. **172**: 123–127.
14. SMITH, M.J., J.B. SCHREIBER & G. WOLF. 1979. Biochem. J. **180**: 449–453.
15. SILVERMAN-JONES, C.S., J.P. FROT-COUTAZ & L.M. DE LUCA. 1976. Analytical Biochem. **75**: 664–667.
16. FROT-COUTAZ, J.P., R. LETOUBLON & R. GOT. 1979. Febs Letters **107**: 375–378.
17. BUTLER, N.A. & G. WOLF. 1976. Biochem. Biophys. Res. Commun. **63**: 704–711.
18. BARENHOLZ, Y. D. GIBBES, B.J. LITMAN, J. GOLL, T.E. THOMPSON & F.D. CARLSON. 1977. Biochemistry **16**: 2806–2810.
19. ROSSO, C.G., S. MASUSHIGE, H. QUILL & G. WOLF. 1977. Proc. Natl. Acad. Sci. USA **74**: 3762–3766.
20. CHEN, C.C. & J. HELLER. 1977. J. Biol. Chem. **252**: 5216–5221.

MODULATION OF GLYCOSAMINOGLYCAN BIOSYNTHESIS BY RETINOIDS

Stanley S. Shapiro and Dante J. Mott

Clinical Nutrition
Hoffmann-La Roche, Inc.
Nutley, New Jersey 07110

The role of cell surface glycoconjugates in the specificity of biological recognition reactions is well known. In addition to the known effect of phenotypic expression, retinoids have been shown to modulate the synthesis and secretion of glycoconjugates such as glycoproteins,[1] glycolipids,[2] and glycosaminoglycans.[3] The work of DeLuca and Wolf[4-6] has extended our knowledge on the role of vitamin A in glycoprotein biosynthesis. The involvement of vitamin A in the biosynthesis of other glycoconjugates such as glycosaminoglycans (GAG) is obscure. Reports have appeared in the literature reporting that vitamin A either stimulates or inhibits GAG biosynthesis.

Recent reports have suggested a central role for GAG in cellular recognition and adhesion.[7-10] The GAG most often implicated is heparan sulfate. Heparan sulfate has been identified on the surface of every eukaryotic cell examined. It is a heteropolymer, possessing structural variation with respect to the sulfate position and component hexuronic acid. This structural diversification, presumably leads to functional diversification. Its large size allows for interaction between cells. Generally, the level of heparan sulfate and the degree of sulfation, depend on the state of differentiation of the cell. Cells undergoing regulated rates of growth have higher levels of heparan sulfate or more highly sulfated heparan sulfate.

In an attempt to clarify the role of vitamin A in GAG biosynthesis, we have investigated the modulation of GAG biosynthesis in a number of isolated cell types *in vitro*. We have attempted to determine if a relationship exists between modulation of phenotypic expression by retinoids and modulation of GAG biosynthesis by retinoids. In addition, if such a relationship exists, is it obligatory or casual?

RESULTS AND DISCUSSION

Modulation of Chondrocyte Phenotypic Expression by Retinoids

Rat costal cartilage was prepared from neonates by a previously described procedure.[11] Chondrocytes, when grown in the presence of increasing levels of retinoids, undergo a distinct change in morphology (FIG. 1). Control cells appear typically polygonal. With increasing concentrations of retinoids, the cells become elongated and fibroblastic. We have observed this with synthetic retinoids as well as retinoic acid and retinol. This is in agreement with Solursh and Meier[12] who reported on morphological changes in chondrocytes with retinol. At the level of retinoic acid tested, there was no observed effect on total protein, collagen, or cell number. There was a dramatic change in the amount and type of GAG produced. In a well-differentiated chondrocyte, much of the synthetic capacity is utilized to

0077-8923/81/0359-0306 $01.75/0 © 1981, NYAS

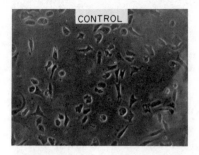

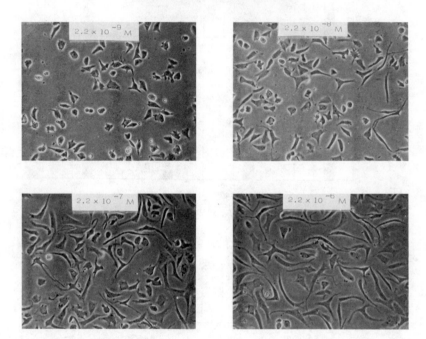

FIGURE 1. Morphological changes of chondrocytes grown in the presence of increasing levels of RO 10-1670.

produce the components of cartilage, namely collagen and proteoglycans. Retinoids have a major effect on one of these components, namely proteoglycans. At high levels of retinoic acid (10^{-7}M) GAG production is reduced by 80% (FIG. 2) with 50% of the GAG being heparan sulfate. The profile of the GAG produced by retinoid-treated cells resembles that of a fibroblast and not that of a chondrocyte. We could not detect any evidence for lysosomal enzyme release at the tested levels. It must be noted that the absolute level of heparan sulfate was not changed in the treated cells. The absolute level remained constant. The increase in heparan sulfate is a relative change, based on the absolute reduction in the other GAG.

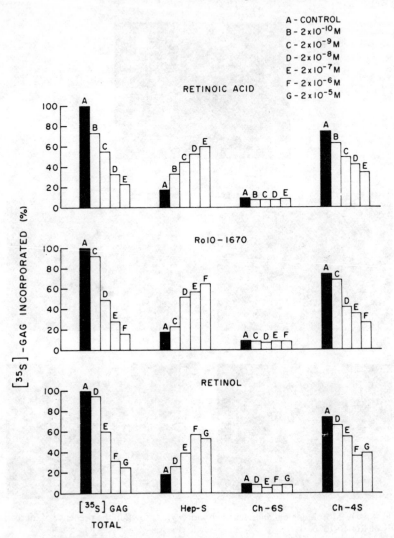

FIGURE 2. Effect of retinoids on $^{35}SO_4$ incorporation into chondrocyte matrix GAG. Matrix [^{35}S]-GAG was isolated from chondrocytes grown in the presence of increasing levels of retinoic acid. Total [^{35}S]-GAG was determined, and then digested with chondroitinase ABC. The ^{35}S fractions are represented as a percentage of the entire [^{35}S]-GAG.

Modulation of Epidermal and Dermal Phenotypic Expression

Epidermal and dermal primary cultures were prepared according to the method of Yuspa[13] and cultured as described by Shapiro and Poon.[14] GAG that were found in the medium are referred to as medium GAG. Detachment of the cells from the flasks by trypsin resulted in the release of pericellular GAG, referred to as matrix GAG. The GAG associated with the washed cells after trypsin release is referred to as cell GAG.

Modulation of Compartmental Dermal [^{35}S]-GAG

A representative experiment showing dividing dermal cultures exposed to retinyl acetate for 4 days is shown in TABLE 1. Except for the highest concentration of retinyl acetate (1.8 × 10^{-5}M), there is no effect on cell number, yet there is a concentration-dependent increase in cellular and matrix GAG. There is no significant increase in the medium GAG. At 1.8 × 10^{-5}M retinyl acetate, cell proliferation is inhibited with greater levels of cellular and matrix [^{35}S]-GAG produced per cell. The GAG levels in the three compartments with three retinoids are shown in FIGURE 3. All-*trans*-retinoic acid, RO 10–1670 (an aromatic retinoid), and retinyl acetate were compared. The three retinoids elicited the same general response. Medium levels of GAG are not changed, but cellular and matrix are stimulated.

Effect of Retinyl Acetate on the Relative Distribution of Individual GAG in Dermal Cells

The relative incorporation of ^{35}SO$_4$ into chondroitin 4-S (Ch 4-S), dermatan-S, and chondroitin 6-S (Ch 6-S) was determined in the medium, matrix, and cell associated GAG (FIG. 4). Retinyl acetate modulates specific GAG levels. The effect is different in each of the three GAG compartments. In the cell compartment, retinyl acetate stimulates ^{35}SO$_4$ fixation into Ch 4-S, concomitant with this increase is a less dramatic but consistent decrease in dermatan-S, and heparan sulfate. There was no apparent modification of individual GAG in the matrix (FIG. 4), although total incorporation of ^{35}SO$_4$ into GAG was stimulated 60% (FIG. 3). Thus, the levels of the individual matrix GAG increase proportionally. In contrast, the profile of the individual medium GAG is modified by retinyl acetate (FIG. 4). There is no net change in total medium GAG, yet there is a dose-dependent increase in medium Ch 4-S and possibly Hep-S. There is also a pronounced decrease in dermatan-S. Thus, the three GAG compartments analyzed were modified differently from each other by retinyl acetate.

TABLE 1

EFFECT OF RETINYL ACETATE ON THE COMPARTMENTAL DISTRIBUTION OF DERMAL [^{35}S]-GAG

Dosage (M)	Cell Number (10^6)	[^{35}S]-GAG (cpm/10^6 cells)			
		Cell	Matrix	Medium	Total
DMSO	1.36	13.2	40.0	214	267
1.8 × 10^{-8}	1.25	12.8	45.6	232	290
1.8 × 10^{-7}	1.32	16.6	47.0	223	287
0.6 × 10^{-6}	1.24	21.0	58.0	227	315
1.8 × 10^{-6}	1.40	20.7	59.0	194	274
0.6 × 10^{-5}	1.32	20.4	58.3	181	260
1.8 × 10^{-5}	0.79	24.0	86.0	227	337

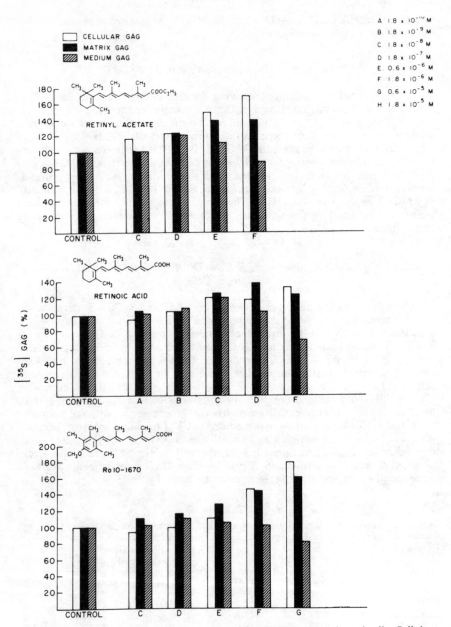

FIGURE 3. Retinoid modulation of compartmental [35S]-GAG in dermal cells. Cellular, matrix, and medium [35S]-GAG were isolated from dermal cells grown in the presence of the indicated retinoid. A, 1.8×10^{-10}M; B, 1.8×10^{-9}M; C, 1.8×10^{-8}M; D, 1.8×10^{-7}M; E, 0.6×10^{-6}M; F, 1.8×10^{-6}M; G, 0.6×10^{-5}M. The [35S]-GAG for each compartment is represented relative to its control compartments.

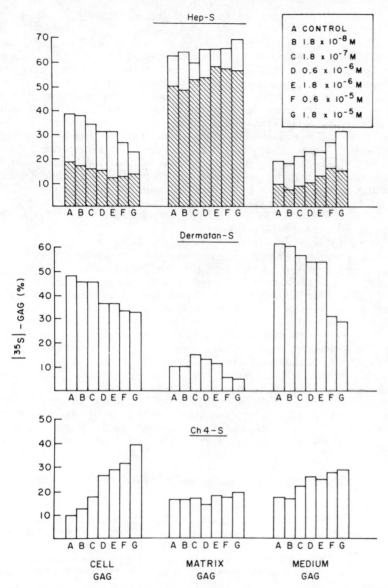

FIGURE 4. Retinyl acetate modulation of individual [^{35}S]-GAG in dermal cells. Cellular, matrix and medium [^{35}S]-GAG were isolated from dermal cells grown in the presence of increasing levels of retinyl acetate. The [^{35}S]-GAG was reacted with Ch ABCase, Ch ACase and nitrous acid. Concentrations of retinyl acetate employed are A, control; B, 1.8 × 10^{-8}M; C, 1.8 × 10^{-7}M, D, 0.6 × 10^{-6}M; E, 1.8 × 10^{-6}M; F, 0.6 × 10^{-5}M; G, 1.8 × 10^{-5}M. ABCase-resistant material is the percent of ^{35}S material remaining at the origin after Ch ABCase digestion. The slashed areas represent the amount of Ch ABCase-resistant material identified as heparin/heparan sulfate by nitrous acid degradation.

Modulation of Compartment Epidermal [^{35}S]-GAG

The effect of 3 retinoids; retinyl acetate, all-*trans*-retinoic acid, and RO 10-1670 (an aromatic retinoid) on the compartmental distribution of epidermal [^{35}S]-GAG, is compared (FIG. 5). The three retinoids elicit the same general response. The cellular and matrix GAG compartments are stimulated to the greatest extent. The medium GAG is also stimulated by retinoid treatment, in contrast with the dermal cells where medium GAG is not stimulated by retinoids.

The individual GAG were determined in all three compartments. The major GAG is Hep-S. Depending on the compartment analyzed, Hep-S constitutes approximately 70-85% of the total GAG. The cellular GAG compartment has the highest level of Ch ABCase-digestible material. Approximately 10% of the [^{35}S] macromolecular material precipitated by cetylpyridinium chloride cannot be identified by this treatment. In any event, although total synthesis of [^{35}S]-GAG is stimulated by retinoids, there is no change in the relative levels of the individual GAG. This is similar to the matrix compartment of the dermal cells (FIG. 4) where Hep-S is also the major GAG present.

Vitamin A effects phenotypic expression in "target" tissue, i.e., epithelium, cartilage, *etc.* Skin is a target tissue for vitamin A. Yuspa has described the morphological changes[13] of various dermal and epidermal cells in the presence of retinoids *in vitro*. *In vivo* vitamin A is necessary for the maintenance of skin. In addition, claims for therapeutic efficacy have been made for a number of dermatological lesions (acne,[15,16] psoriasis[17,18] and disorders of keratinization[19]) as well as actinic keratosis.

There are reports in the literature that vitamin A[20,22] promotes wound healing. This is consistent with the observation of both dermal and epidermal cells laying down more matrix GAG in the presence of retinoids. We have shown that retinoids stimulate cell and matrix heparan sulfate in dermal and epidermal cells. A current concept is that the heparan sulfate level is an index of the state of differentiation of the cell. Cells experiencing regulated rates of growth have higher levels of heparan sulfate. The possibilities exist for modulation of phenotype by intervention of Hep-S in psoriasis or other dermatological lesions where retinoid treatment results in a modulation of phenotypic expression.

Modulation of Phenotypic Expression in Established Fibroblasts

Attempts were made to correlate the changes in phenotypic expression of fibroblasts with changes in GAG content. 3T3 and 3T6 cells are sensitive to retinoid treatment. Jetten has shown that retinoids cause inhibition of cellular proliferation, increase adhesivesness and increase spreading of cells.[23] Interestingly, 3T3SV does not show any modulation of phenotypic expression and lacks the retinoic acid-binding protein, whereas 3T3, 3T6 cells have the retinoic acid-binding protein.

Incorporation of $^{35}SO_4$ into GAG was measured in cells grown in the absence and presence of $10^{-5}M$ retinoic acid. [^{35}S]-GAG was measured in the medium, matrix and cellular compartments (TABLE 2). 3T6 cells exhibit the greatest enhancement of $^{35}SO_4$ incorporation into GAG, although increases in [^{35}S]-GAG content in all three compartments of retinoic acid-treated 3T3 cells are also observed. The increase in GAG content is greatest in the cellular compartment, followed by the matrix, and least marked in the medium compartments. There is no increase in[^{35}S]-GAG in the three compartments of treated 3T3SV cells.

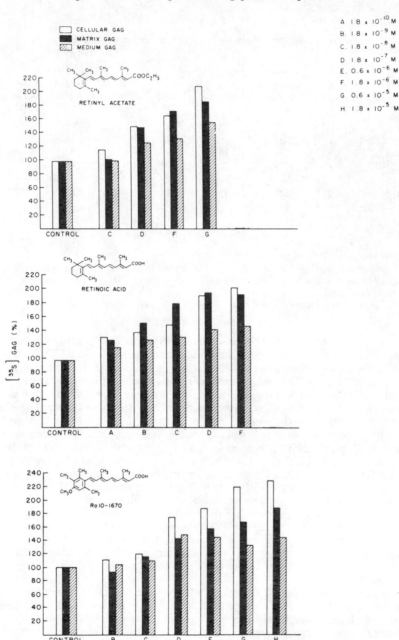

FIGURE 5. Retinoid modulation of compartmental [35S]-GAG in epidermal cells. Cellular, matrix, and medium [35S]-GAG were isolated from epidermal cells grown in the presence of increasing levels of the indicated retinoid. A, 1.8×10^{-10}M; B, 1.8×10^{-9}M; C, 1.8×10^{-8}M; D, 1.8×10^{-7}M; F, 1.8×10^{-6}M; G, 0.6×10^{-5}M; H, 1.8×10^{-5}M. The [35S]-GAG for each compartment is represented relative to the control compartments.

TABLE 2

EFFECT OF RETINOIC ACID ON $^{35}SO_4$ INCORPORATED INTO GAG*

Cell Line	Retinoic Acid 10^{-5} M	Medium GAG		Matrix GAG		Cell GAG	
		cpm/10^3 Cells	% Change	cpm/10^3 Cells	% Change	cpm/10^3 Cells	% Change
3T3SV							
Expt. 1†	0	102	− 15	59	+ 8	15	+ 7
	+	87		64		16	
Expt. 2†	0	269	− 15	136	+ 15	33	− 6
	+	229		155		31	
3T3							
Expt. 1	0	142	+ 15	62	+ 40	20	+ 30
	+	163		87		26	
3T6							
Expt. 2	0	169	+ 50	80	+ 81	30	+ 97
	+	253		145		59	

* Values are expressed as cpm $^{35}SO_4$ incorporated into GAG/10^3 cells. The percent change represents the difference in [^{35}S]-GAG produced in the absence and presence of 10^{-5} M retinoic acid.

† Expt. 1, cells were pulsed for 16 hr; Expt. 2, cells were pulsed for 24 hr.

　　The relative incorporation of $^{35}SO_4$ into Ch 4-S, dermatan sulfate and heparan sulfate was determined in the medium, matrix and cell GAG in 3T6, 3T3, and 3T3SV cells. In the case of 3T6 cells, the presence of retinoic acid results in alterations in specific GAG levels. In the cellular compartment, retinoic acid markedly stimulates $^{35}SO_4$ incorporation into chondroitin 4-sulfate. Concomitant with this increase is a consistent decrease in incorporation into dermatan sulfate. There is no observed change in heparan sulfate or chondroitin 6-sulfate (not shown). There is no apparent modification of the relative GAG profile in the matrix compartment, although total $^{35}SO_4$ fixed in GAG is stimulated (TABLE 2). Thus, the levels of the individual matrix GAG increase proportionally. The profile of the various GAG in the medium is modified by retinoic acid in a manner similar to that of the cellular compartment, namely, there is a dose-dependent increase in chondroitin 4-sulfate and a decrease in dermatan sulfate. Thus, medium and cellular compartments exhibit similar profiles, which are different from the matrix GAG profile. In the case of 3T3 cells, changes in GAG levels similar to those of 3T6 cells are observed. However, the relative changes for the GAG species are only about one half of that observed for 3T6 cells. In the case of 3T3SV, there are no changes in the GAG profiles in any of the three compartments analyzed.

　　Treatment of 3T6 and 3T3 fibroblasts with retinoic acid causes a moderate increase in secretion of sulfated glycosaminoglycans into the medium, while cell-associated glycosaminoglycans levels are greatly enhanced. Goto et al.[24] noted that addition of dextran sulfate can reduce the saturation density and cause flattening of 3T6 cells. Other investigators have shown that db-cAMP and theophylline treatment of 3T3SV cells decrease their saturation density,[25] enhance incorporation of SO_4 into glycosaminoglycans[26] and increase adhesion.[27] These observations may suggest that elevated glycosaminoglycan levels are also involved in the enhanced adhesiveness, the reduction in saturation density and the flattening of the cells that we observed following treatment with retinoic acid.

Recent studies have suggested a relationship between glycosaminoglycans and one or more external proteins.[28,29] Under certain conditions, cells can be detached by chelating agents, leaving a residue on the substratum that contains glycosaminoglycans as well as LETS glycoprotein.[30] This material has been called the Substrate Attached Material (SAM). The amount of sulfated glycosaminoglycans synthesized by cells is generally reduced following transformation[26,29] as is the amount of LETS glycoprotein at the cell surface.[31] Toole[32] has shown that chondroitin sulfate can form insoluble complexes with collagen. It is, therefore, conceivable that glucosaminoglycans and one or more cell surface proteins form an extra-cellular complex that is responsible for cell-to-substratum adhesiveness.

Retinoid Modulation of Heparan Sulfate Biosynthesis in Fibroblasts

It was important to determine if retinoids were effecting an increase in sulfate (and/or) an increase in backbone synthesis of heparan sulfate. Cells were grown in the presence of $^{35}SO_4$ and [^{14}C]glucosamine. The degree of sulfate as esters (O-Sulfate) and sulfamidos (N-Sulfate) was determined, as well as [^{3}H]glucosamine incorporation. As shown in (TABLE 3) in the medium GAG there is an increase in N-, and O-sulfation without an increase in glucosamine. In the matrix GAG, there is an increase in glucosamine as well as sulfation. In the cell GAG, backbone as well as sulfation is increased fourfold. If one looks at the change in N-Sulfate/O-Sulfate in the medium there is an increase of 30%. In the matrix there are changes in backbone synthesis, the increase in sulfate is greater than the increase in backbone.

Thus, retinoid treatment of fibroblast results in a greater amount of heparan sulfate per cell, and the heparan on the cell surface (matrix) is more highly sulfated. This is in total agreement with other cells, when one examines cells undergoing regulated vs. unregulated rates of growth.

Retinoid Modulation of Hyaluronic Acid in Fibroblasts

Retinoid acid (10^{-5}) also results in approximately an 80% increase of

TABLE 3

INCORPORATION OF $^{35}SO_4$ AND [^{3}H]GLUCOSAMINE INTO HEPARAN SULFATE BY 3T6 CELLS

Compartment	Retinoic Acid (10^{-5} M)	GAG	O-Sulfate	N-Sulfate (dpm/10^3 cells)	Glucosamine
Medium	0	48	4.7	5.3	6.4
	+	65	7.9	12.1	6.5
Matrix	0	30	7.6	9.4	8.8
	+	84	24.1	30.9	11.2
Cell	0	22	3.4	3.7	7.3
	+	65	13.2	15.1	29.8

hyaluronic acid into the medium, as measured by [³H]glucosamine incorporation (TABLE 4).

Effect of Retinoids on the Substrate-attached Material Glycosaminoglycan

Culp and his coworkers[33-35] have described the protein-protoglycan complex left on the plastic substratum after fibroblasts are detached with calcium chelators. SAM has been shown to effect attachment kinetics of cells, morphological spread, and mediate adhesions of cells to substratum. The material represents an enrichment of the cellular adhesion site. The major constituents are LETS protein, heparan sulfate, and actin. The heparan sulfate represents 52–82% of the total GAG in this complex and is not solubilized with trypsin. Electron microscopy of these sites after calcium chelation shows maintenance of structural integrity and the sites look like intact foot pads from wellspread cells.

Since retinoids increase cell surface GAG in fibroblasts (namely heparan sulfate), concomitantly with increased adhesion and LETS protein, we measured the increase in GAG in the SAM of retinoid-treated skin dermal fibroblasts. A 50% increase of heparan sulfate in SAM, as well as cell surface GAG is observed (FIG. 6). There are identical decreases in dermatan sulfate and Ch 4-S in the SAM and cell surface. Culp[33] has postulated that SAM is an extension of the cell surface. The identical changes in the GAG in these compartments tend to confirm this hypothesis. The retinoid-induced increase in heparan sulfate helps explain the increase in adhesion, spreading, and possibly inhibition of growth in fibroblasts.

Modulation of Glycosaminoglycans in an Epithelial Cell Line

We investigated the modifications of the GAG in an established human intestinal cell line (407 cells). The cells were grown under conditions described by Shapiro and Poon.[36] The cells, when grown in the presence of retinoic acid, exhibit distinct morphological changes. Control cells retain their typical epithelial-like morphology, while treated cells (10⁻⁵M retinoic acid) are elongated and fibroblastic (FIG. 7). Treated cells do not grow in close association with each other, as control cells do. Unlike fibroblasts, treated 407 cells do not have reduced saturation densities, and show enhanced detachability with trypsin treatment.

TABLE 4

STIMULATION OF MEDIUM HYALURONIC ACID BY RETINOIC ACID IN 3T6 CELLS

Retinoic Acid (10⁻⁵ M)	[³H]Glucosamine Incorporated (dpm/10⁶ cells)
0	5321
+	9547
Δ	79%

Ratio of Medium:Matrix:Cell hyaluronic Acid 1.0 : .14 : .01
 No detectable change in matrix hyaluronic acid.
 Incorporation into cells not significant for analysis.

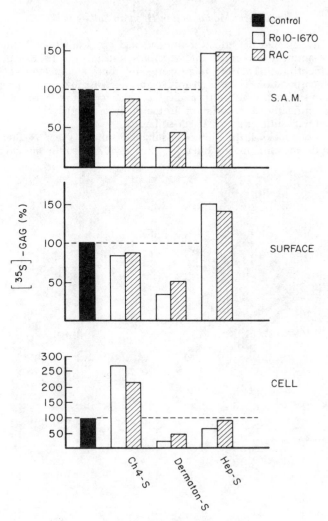

FIGURE 6. Glycosaminoglycans after EGTA treatment. Dermal cells were grown in the presence of retinyl acetate and RO 10-1670 (2.0×10^{-6}M). Cells were detached with EGTA and the washed isolated cells were treated with trypsin to liberate the surface GAG. SAM represents the substrate adhesive material. The individual GAG were determined with chondroitin ABCase and nitrous acid.

There is a reduction in total GAG found in the medium. In the matrix (TABLE 5) there are minor changes in the individual GAG, with heparan sulfate remaining constant, and dermatan-S, Ch6-S, and Ch4-S decreasing. This is consistent with the fact that there is not an observed increase in adhesion or flattening of treated cells. However, there is a decrease in the rate of cell growth.

Retinoic Acid Modulation of Heparan Sulfate in 407 Cells

We investigated the effect of retinoic acid on O-sulfation, N-sulfation and [³H]glucosamine incorporation into heparan sulfate in 407 cells. Except in the medium compartment (TABLE 6), there were only minor modifications of [³H]glucosamine incorporation. There is an appreciable decrease in the backbone synthesis of heparan sulfate. In the matrix and cell compartment, the degree of N-sulfation is increased relative to O-sulfation. In the medium compartment, O-sulfation is decreased with little effect on the N-sulfate.

When one looks at the ratio of N-sulfate/O-sulfate (TABLE 7), there is an increase in the medium, matrix and cells. Thus, in 407 cells retinoic acid modulates

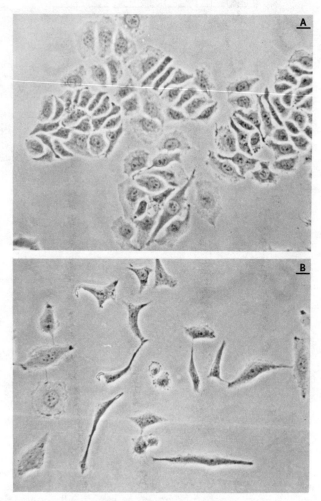

FIGURE 7. Intestinal 407 cells. A, control cells; B, retinoic acid-treated cells. Cells were grown for 3 days.

TABLE 5

EFFECT OF RETINOIC ACID ON $^{35}SO_4$ INCORPORATION INTO MATRIX GAG

Retinoic Acid (M)	[$^{35}SO_4$] GAG* (Total)	Hep-S*	CH6-S*	CH4-S*	Dermatan-Sulfate*	Other*
–	42.6	26	3.2	5.5	2.3	5.6
2.2 × 10^{-9}	34.0	22	2.3	3.8	1.9	4.2
2.2 × 10^{-8}	31.0	21	2.4	3.1	1.3	3.2
2.2 × 10^{-7}	34.6	24	2.2	3.3	1.5	3.8
2.2 × 10^{-6}	31.9	22	1.5	2.9	0.9	4.5
2.2 × 10^{-5}	37.0	26	2.0	4.0	0.4	5.4

* Values are expressed in counts per minute per 10^3 cells.

the ratio of N-sulfate/O-sulfate without a major change in total sulfate incorporation. Since there is a decreased adhesion and decreased cell volume, we would not expect to see an increase in total heparan sulfate, and in fact there is no increase in total heparan sulfate. What is significant is the change in N/O sulfate levels. Since initial growth of these cells is slower in the presence of retinoic acid, this may be a clue as to the role of heparan sulfate in cellular proliferation. It may be that the degree of N-sulfation is more important in this aspect than total heparan sulfate.

SUMMARY

In conclusion, retinoids modulate phenotypic changes such as morphology, adhesion, and growth rate. These changes also result in specific alterations of glycosaminoglycans. We have observed increases in the degree of sulfation in fibroblast matrix heparan sulfate and, a change in the ratio of sulfamido to ester sulfate in matrix heparan sulfate in 407 cell surface. Matrix glycosaminoglycans have been functionally implicated in cellular interactions, and have a specific role in adhesion and growth rates. Our results are consistent with the proposed role for heparan sulfate. It is possible that some of the modulation in cellular

TABLE 6

INCORPORATION OF $^{35}SO_4$ AND [^{3}H]GLUCOSAMINE INTO HEPARAN SULFATE BY 407 CELLS

Compartment	Retinoic Acid (10^{-5} M)	GAG	O-Sulfate	N-Sulfate	Glucosamine
			(dpm/10^4 cells)		
Medium	0	87.9	25.0	14.1	37.8
	+	80.2	18.2	15.3	25.0
Matrix	0	33.6	9.8	6.6	10.3
	+	39.3	9.5	9.1	9.1
Cells	0	3.45	1.6	1.2	6.9
	+	9.35	1.9	2.7	8.2

TABLE 7

MODULATION OF HEPARAN SULFATE BY RETINOIC ACID IN 407 CELLS

Compartment	Retinoic Acid (10⁻⁵ M)	N-³⁵ Sulfate / O-³⁵ Sulfate	Hep-³⁵ S [³H]Glucosamine
Medium	0	.56	1.03
	+	.84	1.34
	Δ%	50.0	30.1
Matrix	0	.67	1.59
	+	.96	2.04
	Δ%	43.3	28.3
Cell	0	.75	.41
	+	1.42	.56
	Δ%	89.3	36.6

behavior resulting from retinoid treatment may be mediated by cell surface and cellular changes in heparan sulfate and other glycosaminoglycans.

REFERENCES

1. DE LUCA, L.M., J.P. FROT-COUTAZ, C.S. SILVERMAN-JONES & P.R. ROLLER. 1977. J. Biol. Chem. 252: 2575-2579.
2. PATT, L.M., K. ITOYA & S. HAKOMORI. 1978. Nature. 273: 379-385.
3. SHAPIRO, S.S. & J.P. POON. 1978. Conn. Tissue Res. 6: 101-108.
4. DE LUCA, L.M. & G. WOLF. 1972. Agric. Food Chem. 20: 474-476.
5. DE LUCA, L.M., E.P. LITTLE & G. WOLF. 1969. J. Biol. Chem. 244: 701-708.
6. DE LUCA, L.M., M. SCHUMACHER, G. WOLF & P.M. NEWBERNE. 1970a. J. Biol. Chem. 245: 4551-4558.
7. JOHNSTON, L.S., K.L. KELLER & J.M. KELLER. 1979. Biochim. Biophys. Acta 583: 81-94.
8. DUNHAM, J.S. & R.O. HYNES. 1978. Biochim. Biophys. Acta 506: 242-255.
9. KELLER, K.L., C.B. UNDERHILL & J.M. KELLER. 1978. Biochim. Biophys. Acta 540: 431-442.
10. DIETRICH, C.P., L.O. SAMPAIO, D.M.S. TOLEDO & C.M.F. CASSARO. 1977. Biochem. Biophys. Res. Commun. 75: 329-336.
11. SHAPIRO, S.S. & J.P. POON. 1976. Arch. Biochem. Biophys. 174: 74-81.
12. SOLURSH, M. & S. MEIER. 1973. Cell Tissue Res. 13:131-142.
13. YUSPA, S.H. & C.C. HARRIS. 1974. Exp. Cell Res. 86: 95.
14. SHAPIRO, S.S. & J.P. POON. 1978. Conn. Tiss. Res. 78: 101-108.
15. ASHTON, H., C.J. STEVENSON & E. FRENK. 1971. Br. J. Dermatol. 85: 500-503.
16. PAPA, C.M. 1976. Postgrad. Med. 59: 61.
17. ORFANOS, C.E. & U. RUNNE. 1976. Br. J. Dermatol. 95: 101-103.
18. HODGSON, C. & E. HELL. 1976. Clin. Exp. Dermatol. 1: 215-220.
19. PECK, G.L. & F. YODER. 1977. Lancet : 1172-1192.
20. SEIFTER, E., L.V. CROWLEY, G. RETTURA, C. GRUBER, D. KAN & S.M. LEVENSON. 1975. Ann. Surg. 181: 836-841.
21. LEVENSON, S.M., E.F. GEEVER, L.V. CROWLEY, et al. 1965. Ann. Surg. 161: 293.
22. LEVENSON, S.M., G. RETTURA, L.V. CROWLEY & E. SEIFTER. 1972. Fed. Proc. 31: Abst. 2569.
23. JETTEN, A.M., M.E.R. JETTEN, S.S. SHAPIRO & J.P. POON. 1979. Exp. Cell Res. 119: 289-299.
24. GOTO, M., Y. KATAOKA, T. KIMURA, K. GOTO & H. SATO. 1973. Exp. Cell Res. 82: 367-374.

25. SHEPPARD, J. 1971. Proc. Natl. Acad. Sci. USA **68:** 1316.
26. GOGGINS, J., G. JOHNSON & I. PASTAN. 1972. J. Biol. Chem. **247:** 5759-5764.
27. JOHNSON, G. & I. PASTAN. 1972. Nature New Biol. **236:** 247-249.
28. DUNHAM, J.S. & R.O. HYNES. 1978. Biochim. Biophys. Acta **506:** 242-255.
29. ROBBIN, R., S. ALBERT, N. GELB & P.H. BLACK. 1975. Biochemistry **14:** 347-357.
30. TERRY, A.H. & L.A. CULP. 1974. Biochemistry **13:** 414-425.
31. HYNES, R.D. 1976. Biochim. Biophys. Acta **458:** 73-107.
32. TOOLE, B.P. 1969. Nature **222:** 872-873.
33. CULP, L.A. 1974. J. Cell Biol. **63:** 71-83.
34. ROSEN, J.J. & L.A. CULP. 1977. Exp. Cell Res. **107:** 139-149.
35. CULP, L.A., B.J. ROLLINS, J. BUNIEL & S. HITRI. 1978. J. Cell Biol. **79:** 788-801.
36. SHAPIRO, S.S. & J.P. POON. 1979. Exp. Cell Res. **119:** 349-359.

RETINOIC ACID-INDUCED ALTERATIONS OF GLYCOSAMINOGLYCAN SYNTHESIS AND DEPOSITION IN B16F10 MELANOMA CELLS*

Charles A. Maniglia and Alan C. Sartorelli

*Department of Pharmacology and
Developmental Therapeutics Program
Comprehensive Cancer Center
Yale University School of Medicine
New Haven, Connecticut 06510*

INTRODUCTION

The retinoids as a class consist of the synthetic and natural analogs of vitamin A. Among a variety of biological effects produced by these agents is their capacity to alter the synthesis of glycosaminoglycans (GAG).[1-3] The GAG are ubiquitous components of mammalian cells that appear to be of fundamental importance in phenomena such as cell-cell and cell-substratum interactions.[4,5] Thus, these macromolecules have been implicated in the attachment and migration of transformed[6] and embryonic cells,[7] and they have been reported to interfere with the growth of neoplastic cells.[8]

Since the study of retinoid-induced alterations of GAG synthesis and composition may provide an understanding of the complex role of these polymeric carbohydrates in the phenotypic behavior of cells and of the mechanism(s) by which the retinoids cause changes in the function of these macromolecules, we have investigated the effects of retinoic acid (RA) on the biosynthesis and processing of GAG during the attachment and spreading on the substratum of the murine melanoma B16F10. The results demonstrate that a concentration of 10^{-5} M RA is required to inhibit the replication of B16F10 cells, which accumulate in the G_1 phase of the cell cycle. This decrease in growth rate is accompanied by alterations in the synthesis and distribution of GAG during the process of cellular anchoring and spread on the tissue culture substratum. Initially, the incorporation of radioactive precursors of GAG into cetylpyridinium chloride (CPC)-precipitable material was decreased by treatment with RA; on the other hand, longer exposure to this agent led to apparent increased deposition of GAG into the medium.

MATERIALS AND METHODS

B16F10 melanoma cells were kindly provided by Dr. I. J. Fidler (Federick Cancer Research Center, Federick, MD). Cells were grown in Eagle's Minimal Essential Medium (Grand Island Biological Company, Grand Island, NY) supplemented with L-glutamine and 10% fetal bovine serum. All experiments were

* The research upon which this paper is based was supported in part by United States Public Health Service Grants CA-02817, CA-16359, and CA-09085 from the National Cancer Institute.

conducted on cells that were passed less than 15 times in tissue culture. Retinoic acid was kindly supplied by Dr. Beverly Pawson (Hoffmann-LaRoche, Inc., Nutley, NJ).

[³H]Glucosamine (38 Ci/mmole) and Na_2[³⁵S]sulfate (880 mCi/mmole) were purchased from New England Nuclear Corp. (Boston, MA). Incorporation of these radiolabeled precursors into GAG was monitored in these macromolecules present in pericellular (or matrix), cellular, and medium compartments, the latter representing GAG shed by cells into the culture medium. The pericellular material is representative of GAG associated with cells, but removed by exposure of cells to 0.05% trypsin for 3 min. The cellular fraction consists of those GAG present in washed cellular pellets after their removal from the tissue culture substratum by exposure to trypsin.

GAG were isolated from each of the above described compartments by a modification of the method of Cohen et al.[9] All fractions were digested with pro-teinase K (20 units/fraction) for 12 hr at 37°C, adjusted to pH 12 with 1 N NaOH to remove possible peptide residues from the linkage region,[10] neutralized and precipitated with 4 volumes of ethanol-5% potassium acetate at −20°C for 12 hr. The precipitate was collected by centrifugation, washed once with chloroform: methanol:ether (2:2:1, v/v) and dried under a stream of N_2. The dried residue of polysaccharides was resuspended in 0.2 M NaCl, clarified by centrifugation and stored at -20°C until analyzed.

[³H]Glucosamine- and [³⁵S]sulfate-labeled GAG in the various cell culture compartments were precipitated with 1% CPC in 40 mM Na_2SO_4 at 37°C for 1 hr.[11] Precipitates were collected on 0.45 μm Millipore HA membrane filters (Whatman, Clifton, NJ), and radioactivity therein determined in an ambient tem-perature scintillation spectrometer (Beckman LS 7500).

B16F10 melanoma cells were stained using acriflavin-Feulgen as described

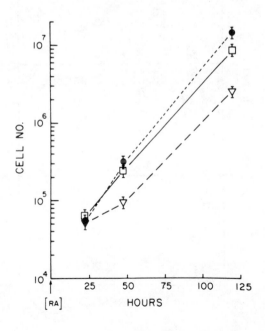

FIGURE 1. Effect of retinoic acid on the cellular proliferation of B16F10 melanoma cells. Each point represents the average of 3 flasks. ●, control; □, 10⁻⁹ M RA; ∇, 10⁻⁵ M RA. Bars indicate the deviation from the mean.

by Gill and Jotz,[12] and the cell cycle distribution of the stained cells was analyzed with a Becton-Dickinson FACS IV flow cytometer.

Exposure of B16F10 melanoma cells to RA caused a marked decrease in the rate of cellular proliferation (FIG. 1). Thus, 120 hr after incubation in the presence of RA, inhibition of cellular growth of 40 and 90% occurred at levels of RA of 10^{-9} and 10^{-5} M, respectively. The RA-induced inhibition of cellular replication was examined further by analyzing the cell cycle distribution from DNA histograms generated by flow cytometry. As can be seen from the data presented in FIGURE 2, RA appeared to induce the accumulation of B16F10 cells in the G_1 phase of the cell cycle. This observation is consistent with the observed inhibition of cellular proliferation by this agent, and has been reported in other cell systems.[13]

The capacity of RA to induce changes in the biosynthesis of GAG was determined, and the results are depicted in FIGURE 3. Logarithmically growing B16F10 cells were pretreated with 10^{-5} M RA for 48 hr. After removal of cells from the tissue culture flasks by treatment with trypsin, control and RA pretreated cells were reseeded in the presence of either [³H]glucosamine or [³⁵S]sulfate for 3, 6, 15, and 44 hr. All cell cultures were seeded in a manner that resulted in equivalent control and experimental cell densities at the end of the labeling period. The incorporation of radioactive precursors into GAG was decreased at 3

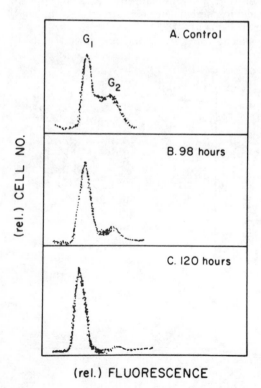

FIGURE 2. Cell cycle distribution of B16F10 cells exposed to retinoic acid. Logarithmically growing B16F10 cells were treated with 10^{-5} M retinoic acid for 0 hr (*panel A*), 98 hr, (*panel B*) and 120 hr (*panel C*). Cells were fixed and stained and DNA histograms were generated by flow cytometry as described in the METHODS section.

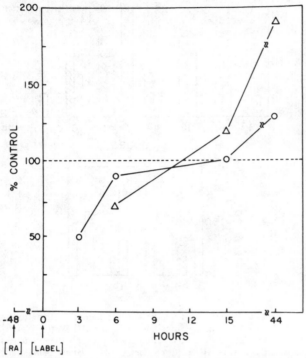

FIGURE 3. Effects of retinoic acid on total GAG synthesis. Logarithmically growing B16F10 cells were pretreated for 48 hr with 10^{-5} M retinoic acid, exposed to a radioactive precursor of GAG at 0 time, and incorporation was allowed for the indicated times. O, [³H]-glucosamine-labeled GAG; Δ, [³⁵S]sulfate-labeled GAG. Each point represents the average of 2 to 5 flasks, and variation between flasks was <10%.

and 6 hr; this period reflects the time during which newly seeded cells actively begin to attach and spread on the tissue culture substratum. At 3 hr, [³H]glucosamine incorporation into GAG was inhibited by approximately 50%. This degree of inhibition decreased by 6 hr to only 10% for [³H]glucosamine; at this time, 25% inhibition of [³⁵S]sulfate incorporation into GAG occurred. By 15 hr, cells were attached and spread uniformly over the tissue culture substratum; precursor incorporation into GAG of RA-treated cells under these conditions was equal to or slightly elevated over that of untreated control cells. After almost 2 days (44 hr) in culture, cells exposed to RA exhibited a substantial increase in the degree of incorporation of radiolabeled precursors into GAG; thus, the total incorporation of [³H]glucosamine and [³⁵S]sulfate into GAG was 190 and 130% of control values, respectively.

The relative deposition of CPC-precipitable GAG into the medium, cellular and pericellular compartments was measured following labeling with [³H]glucosamine; the results are shown in FIGURE 4. The percentage of the total [³H]glucosamine-labeled GAG excreted into the medium increased with time for the first 15 hr from about 25 to 60% for control untreated cells and from approximately 10 to 75% for RA-treated cultures. However, after an extended period in

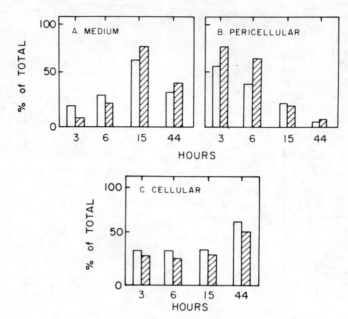

FIGURE 4. Effects of retinoic acid on the compartmental distribution of [³H]glucosamine labeled GAG. Medium, pericellular and cellular GAG were isolated from B16F10 cells after the indicated labeling periods. Each point represents the average of 2 to 5 flasks. Variation between flasks was <10%. (*Open bars*, control; *hatched bars*, cells treated with 10⁻⁵ M RA).

culture (44 hr), the GAG shed into the medium for control and experimental cultures represented only 25 and 35%, respectively, of the total labeled GAG.

The relative decrease in incorporation of glucosamine into GAG shed into the medium exhibited at early time points by RA-treated cultures was accompanied by a concomitant increase in the amount of labeled material present in the pericellular compartment. Thus, following a labeling period of 3 hr, treatment with trypsin removed 65 and 85%, respectively, of the total labeled GAG from control and RA-treated cells. A time-dependent decrease in the amount of radioactive GAG found in the pericellular (matrix) compartment in both control and RA-treated cultures is a reflection of the progressive shedding of surface GAG into the medium.

At 3 to 15 hr after growth in the presence of [³H]glucosamine, RA-treated and control cultures consistently had 25 to 30% of their labeled GAG associated with the cellular compartment. However, after a labeling period of 44 hr, the cellular compartment of control and RA-treated cultures contained approximately 50% of the total labeled GAG.

Although the percentage distribution of labeled GAG of control and RA treated cultures appeared to be similar (FIG. 4), the actual amount of [³H]glucosamine and [³⁵S]sulfate incorporated into the GAG present in the various compartments was altered considerably by exposure to RA (FIG. 5). Thus, after a 3-hr period of incorporation of [³H]glucosamine, the quantity of GAG present in the medium was markedly depressed by RA. During this period of attachment (i.e., 3 hr), cells exposed to RA shed only 25% of the labeled GAG into the medium than did untreated control cultures. At 6 hr, the amount of radioactive GAG present in the medium was decreased by treatment with RA by 50 and 35% for [³H]glucosamine and [³⁵S]sulfate, respectively. As cells became firmly attached and began to spread on the substratum (15–44 hr), an increase in the quantity of labeled GAG found in the medium was observed, and after a 44-hr labeling period in the presence of RA, [³H]glucosamine and [³⁵S]sulfate incorporation into GAG present in the medium were 150 and 203% of untreated control values, respectively.

RA produced inhibition of GAG deposition into pericellular material during the initial 3-hr labeling period; however, the results obtained at subsequent times suggest that the treatment of B16F10 cells exposed to RA with trypsin resulted in the removal of somewhat greater amounts of labeled GAG from the surface of the cells, since radioactivity in the pericellular fraction of RA-treated cells was somewhat higher than that of the corresponding untreated controls. This finding was particularly evident at 44 hr, where [³H]glucosamine incorporation into GAG was 155% of the control value.

The utilization of [³H]glucosamine and [³⁵S]sulfate for the biosynthesis of cellular GAG was markedly altered by RA during the 3- to 15-hr labeling period. This phenomenon was particularly evident for [³⁵S]sulfate-labeled GAG, which in RA-treated cells were only 25 to 30% of control values at 6 and 15 hr, respec-

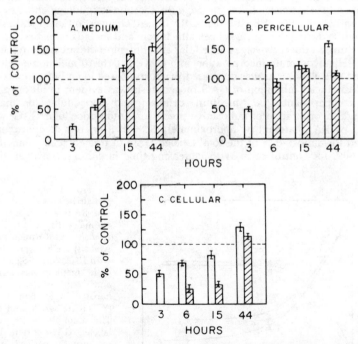

FIGURE 5. The effects of retinoic acid on the incorporation of [³H]glucosamine and [³⁵S]sulfate into CPC-precipitable GAG of B16F10 melanoma cells. Labeled GAG were isolated from medium, pericellular and cellular compartments. (Open bars, [³H]glucosamine; hatched bars, [³⁵S]sulfate incorporation into GAG after treatment with 10⁻⁵ M RA). Each point represents the average of 2 to 5 flasks; bars represent the mean deviation.

tively. However, the RA-induced inhibition of the formation of cellular GAG was not observed after a prolonged labeling period (44 hr), at which time the utilization of [³H]glucosamine and [³⁵S]sulfate for the biosynthesis of GAG was 125 and 110% of control values, respectively.

To ascertain whether the observed increase in the amount of radioactive precursors incorporated into GAG of RA-treated cells after 44 hr of exposure was the result of a decrease in the rate of degradation of these macromolecules, control and RA-treated cells were labeled with 10 μCi/ml of [³⁵S]sulfate. After 44 hr, the medium was removed and the cell monolayer was washed repeatedly to remove unincorporated [³⁵S]sulfate. Unlabeled medium was added and cultures were reincubated for 24 and 55 hr, at which times [³⁵S]sulfate-labeled GAG present in the various compartments were isolated and analyzed. The results shown in FIGURE 6 demonstrate that both untreated control and RA-treated cultures exhibited similar turnover rates of labeled GAG. Approximately 50% of the cell-associated GAG were shed into the medium by 24 hr in both situations, with a concomitant decrease in GAG present in pericellular and cellular compartments.

DISCUSSION

RA at a concentration of 10^{-5} M markedly inhibited the replication of B16F10 melanoma cells; this decrease in proliferation was expressed as an accumulation of cells in the G_1 phase of the cell cycle. In addition to inducing changes in the proliferative capacity of B16F10 cells, RA caused changes in GAG synthesis and distribution during the process of cell attachment and spread on the tissue culture substratum. In the early stages of cellular attachment to the substratum (i.e., 0 to 3 hr), [³H]glucosamine incorporation into GAG of B16F10 melanoma cells pre-exposed to RA for 48 hr was decreased when compared to an untreated control. The RA-induced inhibition of GAG biosynthesis was evident in all of the analyzed compartments (i.e., medium, cellular, and pericellular (or matrix)). Although incorporation of radioactive precursors into pericellular GAG was inhibited by RA treatment by approximately 50% at 3 hr, this compartment accounted for almost 75% of the total labeled GAG in treated cells, compared to about 50% for control cells. With increasing time in culture, however, during

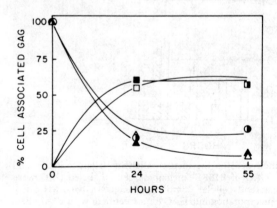

FIGURE 6. Glycosamino-glycan turnover in untreated and RA-treated B16F10 melanoma cells. Control (open symbols) and RA treated (closed symbols) cells were labeled with 10 μCi/mL [³⁵S]sulfate for 44 hr, medium was decanted, and cultures were reincubated in medium without [³⁵S]sulfate for 24 and 55 hr. The amounts of [³⁵S]sulfate-labeled GAG present in the medium (□), pericellular, (△), and cellular (○) compartments were determined as described in the METHODS section.

which initiation of cellular spreading on the tissue culture substratum occurred, the observed inhibition of GAG synthesis by RA diminished, and after 44 hr of labeling, cultures exposed to RA were found to have shed approximately twice as much labeled GAG into the extracellular matrix as untreated control cells. At this time, an increase in the incorporation of radioactive precursors into GAG occurred in all compartments of cells exposed to RA. The increase in the shedding of labeled GAG into the medium of RA-treated B16F10 cells was not a reflection of a decrease in the rate of degradation of these macromolecules, since labeled GAG were removed from the cellular compartment of treated and control cells at similar rates. These findings suggest that exposure to RA alters B16F10 melanoma cell GAG synthesis differently during the initial expression of cellular attachment and subsequent spread onto the tissue culture substratum, and is consistent with the concept that these polymeric carbohydrates are of importance in cellular communication. That cell-substratum interaction is one of the principal aspects of cellular communication in which GAG are implicated was shown for example by Kraemer and Barnhart,[14] who reported that during the anchorage period extensive GAG synthesis occurred, and by Barnhart et al.[15] who demonstrated that CHO cell detachment variants had an altered GAG composition. Furthermore, it has been shown that cellular substrate adhesion sites have a specific GAG composition that changes as these sites mature.[16]

Cell-cell or cell-tissue interactions have also been demonstrated to be responsive to GAG content and composition. In this regard, Underhill and Dorfman[17] have demonstrated that treatment of cells with enzymes that degrade surface GAG leads to alterations in cellular aggregation, which presumably result from the steric exclusion properties of the GAG,[18] and Toole et al.[19] have reported that an invasive line of the V_2 carcinoma grown in rabbits had a different GAG content than these cells propagated in the athymic mouse, a host in which the V_2 carcinoma is not invasive.

Another important aspect of cellular communication is the phenotypic expression of saturation density. The observation that RA-treated B16F10 cells show an increase in medium GAG content concomitant with the accumulation of cells in the G_1 phase of the cell cycle is consistent with the concept that GAG regulate in part the phenomenon of contact inhibition in tissue culture.[20] Increases in medium GAG concentration have been correlated in several cell lines with reduced saturation density, both in cultures induced to synthesize increased levels of GAG[21,22] and in cultures in which GAG were added exogenously.[8,23] Consistent with these findings is the observation in a human intestinal epithelial cell line, that in a situation in which RA failed to decrease the saturation density, the biosynthesis of GAG was inhibited.[24]

Thus, the kind of RA induced alterations of GAG synthesis and processing that occur may be a reflection of changes in the phenotypic response of the cell to its environment, and may be responsible in part for the altered cell-cell and cell-substratum interactions reported for the B16F10 melanoma and other cell lines exposed to this metabolite of vitamin A.

REFERENCES

1. SHAPIRO, S. 1976. Cancer Res. **36:** 3702–3706.
2. SHAPIRO, S. & J. POON. 1976. Arch. Biochem. Biophys. **174:** 74–81.
3. SHAPIRO, S. & J. POON. 1979. Exp. Cell Res. **119:** 349–357.
4. ROBBINS, J.C. & G.L. NICHOLSON. 1976. Surfaces of Normal and Transformed Cells. *In*

Cancer, Vol. 4, Biology of Tumors, Surfaces, Immunology and Comparative Pathology. F.F. Becker, Ed.: 3–53. Plenum Press. New York.

5. ATHERLY, A.C., B.J. BARNHART & P.M. KRAEMER. 1977. J. Cell Physiol. **90:** 375–386.
6. TURLEY, E. & S. ROTH. 1979. Cell **17:** 109–115.
7. TOOLE, B. 1969. Nature **222:** 872–873.
8. OHNISHI, T., E. OHSIMA & M. OHTSUKA. 1975. Exp. Cell Res. **93:** 136–142.
9. COHEN, R., J. CASSIMAN & M. BERNFIELD. 1976. J. Cell Biol. **71:** 280–294.
10. HEINEGARD, D. 1972. Biochim. Biophys. Acta **285:**193–207.
11. GLIMELIUS, B., B. NORLING, B. WESTERMARK & A. WASTESON. 1978. Biochem. J. **172:** 443–456.
12. GILL, J.E. & M. M. JOTZ. 1974. J. Histochem. Cytochem. **22:** 470–476.
13. HADDOX, M. K., K.F. FRASIER-SCOTT & D. HADDOCK-RUSSELL. 1979. Cancer Res. **39:** 4930–4938.
14. KRAEMER, P.M. & B.J. BARNHART. 1978. Exp. Cell Res. **114:** 153–157.
15. BARNHART, B.J., S.H. COX & P.M. KRAEMER. 1979. Exp. Cell Res. **119:** 327–332.
16. ROLLINS, B.J. & L.A. CULP. 1979. Biochemistry **18:** 141–148.
17. UNDERHILL, C. & A. DORFMAN. 1978. Exp. Cell Res. **117:** 155–164.
18. MORRIS, J.E. 1979. Exp. Cell Res. **120:** 141–153.
19. TOOLE, B., C. BISWAS & J. GROSS. 1979. Proc. Natl. Acad. Sci. USA **76:** 6299–6303.
20. ROBLIN, R., S.O. ALBERT, N.A. GELB & P.H. BLACK. 1975. Biochemistry **14:** 347–357.
21. GOGGINS, J., G. JOHNSON & I. PASTAN. 1972. J. Biol. Chem. **247:** 5759–5764.
22. SHEPPARD, J. 1971. Proc. Natl. Acad. Sci. USA **68:** 1316–1320.
23. MONTAGNIER, L. 1971. Ciba Found. Symp. :33–44.
24. SHAPIRO,S. & J. POON. 1979. Exp. Cell Res. **119:** 349–357.

FORMATION OF α-1,2- AND α-1,3-LINKED MANNOSE DISACCHARIDES FROM MANNOSYL RETINYL PHOSPHATE BY RAT LIVER MEMBRANE ENZYMES*,†

Helen Quill‡ and George Wolf

Department of Nutrition and Food Science
Massachusetts Institute of Technology
Cambridge, Massachusetts 02139

INTRODUCTION

The initial glycosylation of mammalian aspargine-linked glycoproteins is believed to occur by transfer of an oligosaccharide unit from a lipid-bound oligosaccharide intermediate to protein acceptors.[1-3] The protein-bound oligosaccharide may then be processed by removal of some sugar residues and addition of others.[4-6] The lipid-bound oligosaccharide contains several α-linked mannose residues,[7,8] and dolichyl mannosyl phosphate (DMP) is a substrate *in vitro* for the addition of some of these mannose units[9,10]; GDP-mannose may also be a direct donor.[10] DMP also acts as a substrate for mannose transfer by an α-1, 2-linkage to exogenously supplied simple mannose glycosides[11] and free mannose.[12]

A role for vitamin A in mammalian glycoprotein biosynthesis has been indicated by several studies,[13-15] and a metabolite of retinol, mannosyl retinyl phosphate (MRP), has been found *in vivo* in rat liver and intestine,[16] hamster liver,[17] and mouse epidermal cell cultures.[18] We have investigated the possibility that MRP functions directly as a substrate for mannosyltransferases of rat liver microsomal membranes.

EXPERIMENTAL PROCEDURES

Enzyme Preparation

Male albino rats (100–150 g, Holtzman strain) were killed by decapitation. All further procedures were done at 0–4°C. Livers were removed, rinsed with 0.25 M sucrose and 50 mM Tris-Cl (pH 7.5; sucrose-Tris buffer), and homogenized by 3-4 strokes of a Teflon-pestle, motor-driven homogenizer in three volumes (ml/g wet weight) of the same buffer. Homogenates were centrifuged at 20,000 × *g* for 10 min, and the resulting supernatant was centrifuged at 105,000 × *g* for 1 hr. The pellet was suspended in sucrose-Tris buffer and stored at –20°. Microsomes were thawed just before use, washed with 50 mM Tris-Cl (pH 7.5) by centrifugation at 105,000 × *g* for 1 hr and resuspended in 50 mM Tris-Cl (pH 7.5).

* In partial fulfillment of the requirements for the Ph.D. degree (H.Q.)

† We thank the National Institutes of Health for Grant No. Arg. 20476, which provided partial support for this work.

‡ *Present Address:* Division of Rheumatology, Washington University School of Medicine, Box 8045, 660 S. Euclid Ave., St. Louis, MO 63110.

Synthesis and Isolation of MRP

Retinol was prepared by reducing retinal with NaBH$_4$, as described by Heller and Horwitz.[19] Retinyl phosphate was synthesized and isolated by preparative thin-layer chromatography as previously described.[20] Incubations for MRP synthesis contained, at final concentrations: 50 mM [^{14}C]-GDP-mannose (10μCi/ml), 1 mM retinyl phosphate, 50 mM Tris-Cl (pH 8.0), 0.5% Triton X-100 (adjusted to pH 7.5), 2.5 mM EDTA (pH 7.5), 5 mM ATP, 10 mM MnCl$_2$, and microsomal protein at a concentration of 15–20 mg/ml. Incubations were done at 37°C for 30 min. The reaction was stopped by adding 100 volumes of methanol at room temperature. Samples were mixed well and filtered to collect the methanol extract, which was applied to a column of DEAE-cellulose (approximately 1.5 × 7 cm), previously converted to the acetate form and equilibrated with 99% methanol.[21] The column was washed with 3–4 column volumes of 99% methanol and MRP was eluted with 10 mM NH$_4$-acetate in 99% methanol. Fractions (5 ml) were assayed for radioactivity and peak fractions were pooled. The NH$_4$-acetate was removed either by lyophilizing the dried sample for 4 hr or by repeated (10 times) flash-evaporation with methanol. Samples were dissolved in a small volume of methanol and portions were assayed by thin-layer chromatography on silica gel plates to determine the amount of [^{14}C]-DMP present, and on Whatman KC$_{18}$ plates to determine the amount and purity of MRP (see below, under *Reversed-Phase Thin-Layer Chromatography*). No GDP-mannose was present in MRP samples. DMP was present as 1–5% of the total radioactivity. Small amounts of [^{14}C]mannose phosphate were also present as a result of MRP breakdown. MRP was generally present as 85–90% of the total radioactivity.

Synthesis and Isolation of DMP

Incubations included, at final concentrations: 5 mM [^{14}C]-GDP-mannose (1 μCi/ml), 50 mM Tris-Cl (pH 7.0), 0.5% Triton X-100 (adjusted to pH 7.5), 2.5 mM EDTA (pH 7.5), 5 mM ATP, 10 mM MnCl$_2$, and 5–10 mg microsomal protein/ml. After 5 min incubation at 37°, 15 volumes of chloroform:methanol (C:M, 2:1, v/v) and 0.2 volumes of H$_2$O were added, mixed thoroughly, and centrifuged to separate the phases. The organic phase was dried, redissolved in a minimal volume of C:M (2:1, v/v) diluted with 99% methanol, and eluted from DEAE-cellulose acetate columns, as for MRP samples. Fractions containing DMP were pooled, dried, redissolved in C:M (2:1, v/v), washed with H$_2$O to remove NH$_4$-acetate, dried, and redissolved in a small volume of C:M (2:1, v/v). Portions were assayed by thin-layer chromatography on silica gel plates before use. All DMP samples contained only a single peak of [^{14}C]-DMP at an R$_f$ of 0.5–0.6.

Assay of Mannose Transfer from DMP and MRP to Endogenous Microsomal Acceptors

Portions of MRP or DMP solutions were placed in glass test tubes and the solvent was removed by a stream of N$_2$. Detergent solutions and microsomes were added and mixed gently. Other reagents were added in the order given. Incubations included, at final concentrations: approximately 50,000 dpm/ml MRP or DMP, 0.15% Zonyl A (adjusted to pH 7.0) or 0.5% Triton X-100 (adjusted to pH 7.0), 10 mg microsomal protein/ml, 100 mM Tris-Cl (pH 7.0), 1 mM ATP, and 10 mM MnCl$_2$. Assays were incubated at 30° for 2 hr and were stopped by adding

C:M (1:2, v/v). After mixing and centrifugation, the pellets were extracted twice with C:M (2:1, v/v), dried, and resuspended by sonication in H_2O. Particulate material was washed three times with H_2O and then three times with chloroform:methanol:water (C:M:W, 10:10:3). All extracts and washes were saved and radioactivity counted. The final pellet (protein fraction) was dissolved in 0.2 N NaOH at 80°C. Samples were neutralized with acetic acid and assayed for radioactivity and protein.

Assay of Mannose Transfer from DMP and MRP to Exogenous Acceptors

Incubations included, at final concentrations: 100 mM Tris-Cl (pH 7.5); 0.5% Triton X-100 (adjusted to pH 7.5); 5 mM ATP; 10 mM $MnCl_2$; 5-10 mg microsomal protein/ml; 20 mM CH_3-α-man, 20 mM p-nitrophenyl-α-D-mannose (PNP-α-man), or 400 mM mannose; and 3-6 × 10^6 dpm/ml [^{14}C]-MRP, 5-10 × 10^5 dpm/ml [14C]-DMP, or 1-2 × 10^6 dpm/ml [14C]-GDP-man. Assay mixtures (0.1 ml) were incubated at 30° for 2 hr, stopped by adding 2 ml of cold H_2O, and frozen. After thawing and mixing, the samples were centrifuged and super-natants were applied to coupled columns of Dowex 50W-X4 (H^+ form) and Dowex 1-X8 (formate form), containing 1 ml of each gel in H_2O.[22] The columns were washed with 6-8 volumes of H_2O or 30% methanol. Total eluates were collected, lyophilized, and redissolved in 0.05-0.10 ml H_2O. The desalted samples were applied to Whatman 3 MM paper for descending chromatography (see *Paper Chromatography*, below) in Solvent C for products formed with pNP-α-man, in Solvent D for products formed with CH_3-α-man, and in Solvent E for products formed with free mannose as acceptor.[12,22] An alternative isolation method was used in some experiments when CH_3-α-man was the acceptor. The desalted samples were applied to 1 ml columns of charcoal:Celite (1:1, g/g, previously washed with concentrated HCl and H_2O), washed with H_2O to remove free [^{14}C]mannose, and eluted with 10% ethanol to remove the CH_3-α-disaccharide product.

Paper Chromatography

Samples were applied to Whatman 3 MM or Whatman #1 paper for descending chromatography in the following solvents: (C) 1-butanol, saturated with H_2O, 2 days; (D) 1-butanol:ethanol:H_2O (10:1:2), 4-5 days; (E) 1-propanol:ethyl acetate:H_2O (7:1:2) 2 days; (F) pyridine:ethyl acetate:H_2O:acetic acid (5:5:3:1), 20 hr. Dried papers were cut in 0.25-1.0 cm fractions and counted either directly or after elution with 1 ml H_2O. Hexose and disaccharide standards were detected by the alkaline-$AgNO_3$ method.[23]

Thin-Layer Chromatography

Analytical (0.25 mm thick) silica gel 60 F-254 plates (EM Laboratories, Elmsford, NY) were used to assay for retinol, in toluene:chloroform:methanol (4:1:1; Solvent A), and for retinyl phosphate, MRP, and DMP, in C:M:W (60:35:6; Solvent B).

Retinol and retinyl phosphate were detected by fluorescence under UV light, and retinyl phosphate was also identified by spraying with molybdate-H_2SO_4 reagent.[24] After chromatography of MRP and DMP samples, the plates (2.5 × 9 cm) were scaped in 0.25-cm fractions and counted in 0.5% diphenyloxazole (PPO) in toluene.

Reversed-Phase Thin-Layer Chromatography

Whatman KC_{18} thin-layer plates were used for assay of MRP in Solvent B. We have found that very little degradation of MRP resulted when this reversed-phase thin-layer system was used. This method was, therefore, applied routinely for the assay of [^{14}C]mannose-labeled MRP synthesized in vitro, as described above. After thin-layer chromatography on silica gel, by contrast, the MRP peak contained only 58.6% of the total label. The remainder was found as mannose phosphate at the origin and also in the area between the origin and the MRP peak, probably as a result of continued breakdown during chromatography. When the same MRP sample was run on KC_{18} plates, 88.5% of the label was seen in the MRP peak ($R_f = 0.84$). The amount of degradation was usually 5 to 10%, seen as mannose phosphate at the origin, and as a constant low level of radioactivity in all fractions between the origin and the MRP peak. Only 2 to 5% of the labeled products was present as DMP ($R_f = 0.70$).

Repeated chromatography on KC_{18} plates of aliquots of the same MRP sample gave reproducible results. MRP samples that had spontaneously broken down during storage showed most of the label as mannose phosphate at the origin.

The MRP region of a KC_{18} chromatogram ($R_f = 0.75$-0.95) was scraped from the plate, eluted with methanol, concentrated and reapplied to a second KC_{18} plate. Most of the label was found in the MRP peak (86%), but some breakdown was again observed. It is not known whether this breakdown occurred during elution and concentration or during re-application of the sample and chromatography. Rechromatography after elution of the origin material, and of the DMP peak, resulted in migration of 100% of the label to the original positions of these compounds.

Retinyl phosphate co-chromatographed with MRP in both systems. While it is not eluted from DEAE-cellulose with 10 mM NH_4 acetate and therefore is not present in the MRP samples, it can be used as a guide to locate MRP on chromatograms.

Thus, reversed-phase TLC provides a rapid, reproducible assay for identification and quantitation of MRP, and may also prove to be a useful system for separating other possible inpurities while isolating MRP from tissue extracts.

High-Voltage Paper Electrophoresis

Samples were applied to Whatman 3 MM paper for electrophoresis in 0.1 M Na molybdate (pH 5.0, adjusted with H_2SO_4) at 1150 V (20 V/cm) for 60 min.[12] Sample strips, when dry, were cut into 0.5-1.0 cm fractions, eluted with 1 ml H_2O, and counted. Samples were applied to Whatman #1 paper for electrophoresis in 0.06 M Na borate (pH 9.0) at 1700 V (30 V/cm) for 3 hr. The dried paper was cut into 0.25-cm fractions, eluted with 1 ml H_2O, and counted.

Treatment with Pronase

The extracted protein fractions from endogenous acceptor incubations with

MRP or DMP were solubilized in sodium dodecyl sulfate and treated with pronase as described previously.[25]

TREATMENT WITH α-MANNOSIDASE

Enzyme activity (Sigma Chemical Co., St. Louis, MO; type III, suspension in $[NH_4]_2SO_4$, 0.1 mM zinc acetate, pH 7.5) with 10 mM pNP-α-man was 14 units/mg; with 10 mM pNP-β-man, no activity could be detected. The extracted protein fractions from endogenous acceptor incubations with MRP or DMP were solubilized by pronase digestion and incubated with α-mannosidase at a final concentration of 10 units/ml, in 0.15 M Na acetate (pH 4.5) and 1 mM $ZnCl_2$, for 20 hr at 37° under a toluene atmosphere. The reaction was stopped by boiling and the supernatants were applied to Whatman 3 MM paper for chromatography in Solvent E. The products from exogenous acceptor assays with CH_3-α-man and free mannose were isolated by paper chromatography, eluted from the paper, lyophilized, and incubated with α-mannosidase at a concentration of 10 units/ml in 0.15 M Na citrate (pH 4.0) for 3 hr at 37°. Hydrolysis was demonstrated by paper chromatography in Solvent D for CH_3-α-man products and in Solvent E for products formed from mannose. The product of α-mannosidase treatment was identified as [14C]mannose by chromatography on Whatman #1 paper in Solvent F with standard mannose.

Partial acid hydrolysis of the products formed in exogenous acceptor assays with CH_3-α-man or free mannose was done by incubating the isolated products with either 0.1 N H_2SO_4 at 100° for 60 min, or with 0.5 N HCl at 100° for 10 min.

Products from exogenous acceptor assays were isolated by paper chromatography, eluted from the paper with H_2O, lyophilized, and redissolved in 0.2 ml H_2O. NaBH_4 (0.1 ml, 0.5 M) was added and samples were incubated at room temperature for 16-18 hr.[12] Glacial acetic acid was then added to reach pH 5.0. Samples were diluted to 1.0 ml with H_2O and applied to 1.5 ml columns of cation exchanger (Biorad AG 50W X4, 200-400 mesh, hydrogen form). Columns were washed with 15 ml of 30% methanol and eluates were dried by flash-evaporation. Samples were redissolved in methanol and redried 8-10 times, to remove boric acid.

Protein concentrations were determined by the method of Lowry et al.,[26] using bovine serum albumin as the standard. Radioactivity was measured in a scintillation counter (Model LS-250, Beckman Instruments, Fullerton, CA). Lipid samples were counted in 0.5% PPO in toluene, and aqueous samples in a solution of 1 ml H_2O/10 ml of 0.27% PPO in toluene:Triton X-100 (1:1, v/v).

[14C]GDP-mannose, prepared by the method of Braell et al.,[27] was supplied by Dr. P.W. Robbins (Department of Biology, Massachusetts Institute of Technology, Cambridge, MA). Darco G-60-activated carbon was obtained from Fisher Scientific Co. (Fairlawn, NJ) and Celite 545 from Johns-Manville (New York, NY). Mannose was obtained from Aldrich Chemical Co., Inc. (Milwaukee, WI), CH_3-α-man (Grade III), pNP-β-GlcNAc, and pNP-α-Glc from Sigma Chemical Co. (St. Louis, MO), pNP-α-man from Pierce Chemical Co. (Rockford, IL), and pNP-β-man from Calbiochem (La Jolla, CA). All-trans-β-retinol was purchased from Sigma. All other reagents were from usual commercial sources. All procedures with retinol compounds were done in a nitrogen atmosphere when possible, and in yellow light.

Transfer of Mannose to Exogenous Acceptors

MRP was an active substrate in the transfer of mannose to exogenously supplied pNP-α-man, CH_3-α-man, and free mannose. The products formed migrated during paper chromatography to the positions relative to free mannose that have been reported by others.[12,22] No product was formed in assays without the exogenous acceptor, or when boiled microsomes were used in the presence of acceptors. No transfer was seen when pNP-β-GlcNAc (20mM), pNP-α-Glc (20 mM), or free glucose (400 mM) were tested as acceptors. To demonstrate that lipid-phosphate-mannose (lipid-P-man) was the immediate substrate in reactions with MRP, and that significant conversion to [^{14}C]-GDP-mannose did not occur during incubation, an experiment was done with unlabeled GDP-mannose (10 μM) incubated with MRP and CH_3-α-man. The K_m reported for GDP-mannose in the reaction with CH_3-α-man is 1.36 μM.[11] The same amount of labeled product from MRP was formed both in the presence and the absence of unlabeled GDP-mannose, indicating that [^{14}C]-GDP-mannose was not the substrate in these reactions.

Total Product Formation with Exogenous Acceptors

Some conditions for optimal transfer from MRP to exogenous acceptors were determined. Transfer activity varied somewhat between assays, as did the observed effects of adding other reagents to the incubation. This finding may reflect changes in enzyme activity during storage of the microsomes, or may be due to variable contamination of the MRP substrates with unlabeled impurities. However, replicate incubations within an experiment had the same amount of product formation (within 10%); therefore, comparisons were made using data from assays done at the same time.

In experiments using CH_3-α-man as acceptor, transfer activity for both mannose donor substrates was linear with incubation time at 30°, up to at least 2 hr, and was proportional to the enzyme concentration, up to 5 mg/ml for MRP assays. There was no absolute requirement for detergent, and the effect of Triton X-100 was variable, but usually a two- to threefold stimulation was found at the optimal concentration of 0.5%.

Product formation increased when increasing amounts of MRP were used (FIG. 1). MRP preparations contained 1–5% of the total ^{14}C-label as DMP. This substance could also act as mannose donor under similar conditions; however, this level of contamination by DMP was not sufficient to account for the activity seen with MRP (FIG. 1, curve 2). Furthermore, for one experiment MRP was prepared by taking only the very latest-eluting portion of the MRP peak from DEAE-cellulose. This MRP sample contained no detectable DMP (<0.05% of total dpm), and, when incubated with CH_3-α-man, the same amount of product was formed from this MRP as from MRP with 5% DMP contamination.

Addition of divalent cations was not required for transferase activity, but 10 mM $MnCl_2$ usually stimulated product formation by 20–100%, and 10 mM EDTA inhibited activity by 30–80%. Addition of 5 mM ATP inceased activity. A small inhibition (10%) was seen with 2.5 mM 2-mercaptoethanol; 5 mM p-chloromercuribenzoate completely inhibited transfer. These results were similar for assays done with CH_3-α-man, pNP-α-man, or mannose as acceptor.

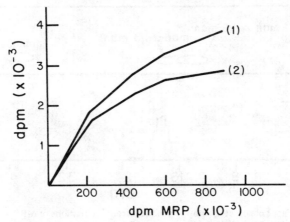

FIGURE 1. Product formation after incubation of MRP with CH_3-α-man: dependence on lipid-P-man concentration. Incubations were done as described in the text. Products were isolated by paper chromatography in solvent D. *Curve 1*, total incorporation; *curve 2*, after subtraction of possible DMP contribution to total incorporation.

Product Identification

Products from large-scale incubations of CH_3-α-man or free mannose with MRP were isolated by paper chromatography and incubated with α-mannosidase. This treatment caused complete conversion of the labeled disaccharides to free [^{14}C]mannose, identified by chromatography with standard monosaccharides on paper in Solvent F.

Partial acid hydrolysis of the pNP-α-man products released only 15-25% as free disaccharide, with significant free mannose production. To identify further the α-glycosidic linkages in the products, we used chromatographic and electrophoretic methods which have been described for separating the four possible α-linked mannose disaccharides.[12,22] Because these methods require free disaccharides for analysis, and because acid hydrolysis generated insufficient amounts of disaccharide, we analyzed the products from incubations using free mannose as acceptor.

FIGURE 2 shows that man-α-1, 6-man was absent in products formed from MRP. In this solvent system, the α-1,2-, α-1,3-, and α1, 4-linked mannose disaccharides comigrate to the position indicated by the α1,3-linked disaccharide standard.[12] When chromatographed in a second solvent system, the product peaks moved to the position corresponding to the man-α-1,2-man and man-α-1,3-man standards, and again no man-α-1,6-man was seen (FIG.3). Although the man-α-1,4-man standard was not available to us, it has been reported[22] to migrate faster than the other three disaccharides in this solvent, and we found no labeled product in the α-1,4 area of the chromatogram.

Results of high-voltage paper electrophoresis in borate buffer confirmed the absence of α-1,6- and α-1,4-linked products and the presence of α-1,2- and α-1,3-linked disaccharides (FIG. 4). Assays done in the absence of Triton X-100 showed double peaks for products from MRP, corresponding to the α-1,2 and α-1,3 standards (FIG. 4). These two products were well separated after reduction

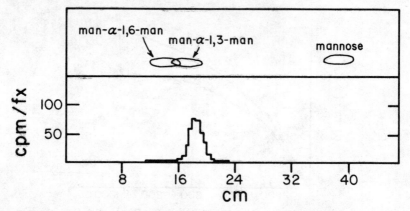

FIGURE 2. Paper chromatography of products from incubations of MRP with mannose. Incubations were done as described in the text. Products were isolated by paper chromatography in Solvent E, eluted from the paper, and lyophilized, then applied to Whatman 3 MM paper for rechromatography in Solvent E.

by NaBH$_4$ and electrophoresis in a molybdate buffer (FIG. 5). Nonreduced product also moved to the position of the α-1,3 standard in this system. However, the α-1,3 peak seen in FIGURE 5 did not indicate incomplete reduction of the labeled products. When the reduced product was chromatographed on paper in Solvent E, all of the label moved as a peak to a position corresponding to reduced α-1,2 and α-1,3 disaccharides; these moved more slowly than the nonreduced product, and we found no labeled peaks corresponding to the nonreduced product.

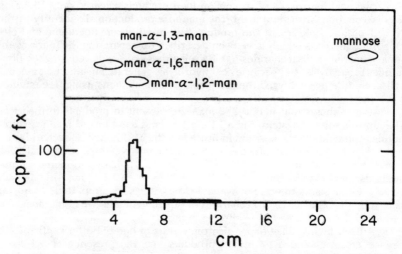

FIGURE 3. Paper chromatography of products from incubations of MRP with mannose. Products were prepared as in FIGURE 2 and rechromatographed in Solvent D on Whatman #1 paper for 7 days.

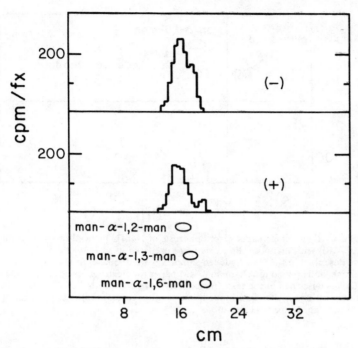

FIGURE 4. High-voltage paper electrophoresis of products from incubations of MRP with mannose. Products were prepared as in FIGURE 2 and applied to Whatman #1 paper for electrophoresis in borate buffer (pH 9.0) as described in the text. (−), Incubated in the absence of Triton X-100; (+), incubated with 0.5% Triton X-100. Man-α-1,4-man should be to the right of the man-α-1,3-man standard (ref. 12). The small peak in the MRP(+) panel that moved like man-α-1,6-man was not found in other MRP samples.

Only a very small amount of α-1,3-linked disaccharide product was found when incubations were done in the presence of Triton X-100. When detergent was omitted, the α-1,3 peak after molybdate electrophoresis represented about 20% of the total product. The results in TABLE 1 demonstrate the effects of 0.5% Triton X-100 on both α-1,2- and α-1,3-linked product formation from MRP. Synthesis of the α-1,3-linked product was severely inhibited by 0.5% Triton X-100. Formation of α-1,2-linked disaccharide from MRP approximately doubled when Triton X-100 was included in the assay.

TABLE 2 gives the effects of divalent cations on synthesis of the two products from MRP and DMP in the absence of detergent. EDTA at 10 mM had only a small effect on transfer activity. The divalent cations tested at a concentration of 10 mM inhibited synthesis of both products, the order of inhibition being Zn^{++} > Ni^{++} > Mn^{++}.

Preincubating microsomes at 60° for 5 min completely inhibited enzyme activity (TABLE 3). When microsomes were incubated at 40° for 15 min before assay, approximately 15% of α-1,2-linked and 45% of α-1,3-linked product synthesis were lost.

The data in TABLES 2 and 3 were obtained from single experiments; the differences in activities seen with DMP and MRP may not be significant.

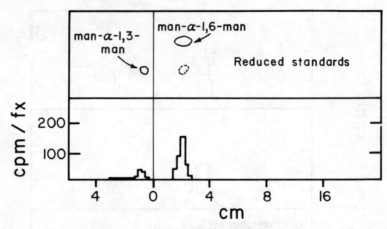

FIGURE 5. High-voltage paper electrophoresis of NaBH$_4$-reduced products from incubations of MRP with mannose. Products were prepared as in FIGURE 2 and treated with NaBH$_4$ as described in the text. Reduced samples were dissolved in H$_2$O, lyophilized to a small volume, and applied to Whatman 3 MM paper for electrophoresis in molybdate buffer (pH 5.0) as described in the text. Incubations were done with 0.5% Triton X-100. The reduced man-α-1,2-man standard moved to a position corresponding to the major peaks, slightly to the right of man-α-1,6-man.

Transfer of Mannose to Endogenous Membrane Acceptors

DMP was an active substrate with rat liver microsomes for the transfer of mannose to endogenous lipid-oligosaccharide and protein acceptors, as reported by others.[9,10] Product synthesis was proportional to DMP concentration, enzyme concentration, and incubation time. The reaction was dependent on the presence of MnCl$_2$ and was stimulated by 5 mM ATP and the addition of detergent. The labeled product soluble in C:M:W (10:10:3) contained a compound of oligosaccharide size, after treatment with mild acid and chromatography on Biogel P-6. The labeled protein fraction was converted by pronase treatment to smaller molecular weight material as assayed by Sephadex G-100 chromatography. α-Mannosidase treatment completely released [^{14}C]mannose from the glycopeptides.

In contrast, incubation of microsomes with MRP did not result in enzymatic transfer of mannose to endogenous acceptors. No incorporation of label above background levels was seen in the C:M:W (10:10:3) soluble fraction. Label was incorporated into the protein fraction, but this evidently occurred by a nonenzymatic reaction of MRP with the microsomes, since significant labeling also

TABLE 1

EFFECT OF 0.5% TRITON X-100 ON PRODUCT FORMATION
FROM MRP WITH MANNOSE AS ACCEPTOR

Incubation Conditions	Man-α-1,2-man (cpm)	Man-α-1,3-man (cpm)
Without Triton X-100	3415	685
With Triton X-100	7319	81

TABLE 2

EFFECTS OF EDTA AND DIVALENT CATIONS ON PRODUCT FORMATION
WITH MANNOSE AS ACCEPTOR

| | MRP as Substrate | | | | DMP as Substrate | | | |
| | Man-α-1,2-man | | Man-α-1,3-man | | Man-α-1,2-man | | Man-α-1,3-man | |
Additions to Incubation*	cpm	%†	cpm	%	cpm	%	cpm	%
Experiment 1								
None	1299		210		2158		747	
EDTA 10 mM	977	75.2	263	125.2	1927	89.3	649	86.9
MnCl₂ 10 mM	812	62.5	153	72.9	943	43.7	567	75.9
MnCl₂ 20 mM	577	44.4	66	31.4	648	30.0	307	41.1
Experiment 2								
None	2404		105		1021		81	
NiCl₂ 10 mM	977	40.6	41	39.0	387	37.9	0	
ZnCl₂ 10 mM	422	17.6	0		0		0	

* Assayed as described in text, except that Triton X-100 and MnCl₂ were omitted from the incubation unless indicated in the table.
† Percent of activity found with no additions.

resulted when boiled microsomes were used as control, and no true enzymatic activity could be detected either by changing the incubation conditions or by analyzing the products formed.

DISCUSSION

These results demonstrate that rat liver membrane mannosyltransferases are active with MRP as substrate. MRP was found to be a substrate for both α-1,2- and α-1,3-linked disaccharide synthesis when free mannose was the acceptor. The products were identified by comparison with standard disaccharides in

TABLE 3

EFFECTS OF PREINCUBATION OF MICROSOMES AT 40° AND 60° ON PRODUCT FORMATION
WITH MANNOSE AS ACCEPTOR

| | MRP as Substrate | | | | DMP as Substrate | | | |
| | Man-α-1,2-man | | Man-α-1,3-man | | Man-α-1,2-man | | Man-α-1,3-man | |
Preincubation*	cpm	%†	cpm	%	cpm	%	cpm	%
None	965		95		658		250	
40°, 5 min	854	88.5	49	51.6	606	92.1	200	80.0
40°, 15 min	803	83.2	53	55.8	555	84.3	135	54.0
60°, 5 min	0		0		0		0	

* Assayed as described in the text, except that Triton X-100 and MnCl₂ were omitted from the incubation. Microsomes were preincubated at the temperature and times indicated and cooled to 0° before addition of other reagents.
† Percent of activity found without preincubation of microsomes.

several chromatographic systems, since this approach required less time and smaller amounts of the disaccharide products than the more rigorous methylation analysis and periodate degradation methods.

In both reactions, DMP and GDP-mannose were also substrates, forming man-α-1,2-man and man-α-1,3-man, under conditions very similar to those for MRP. Maximal activity was found for DMP and GDP-mannose as substrates at about 1/10 the concentration of MRP, at least when based on dpm per milliliter of each compound incubated. Since endogenous concentrations of MRP, DMP, or GDP-mannose were not determined, the K_m for none of the substrates could be calculated.

In the absence of Triton X-100, the α-1,3-linked disaccharide formed from both MRP and DMP (data not shown for DMP). Until now, only an α-1,2-linked mannose donation has been reported from DMP, especially when mannose or methylmannoside was used as acceptor.[12,22] Since α-1,3-linked mannose certainly occurs in oligosaccharide-lipids and the core region of glycoproteins, mannosyltransferases must exist to form this bond. In the present work, rat liver membrane mannosyltransferase catalyzed the formation of α-1,3-linked mannose both from MRP and DMP, when incubated in the absence of detergent.

Since inhibition of man-α-1,3-man synthesis by Triton X-100 occurred regardless of which mannose donor was used, the detergent probably affects the enzyme itself. The largest stimulation by Triton X-100 of man-α-1,2-man synthesis was seen in DMP incubations. A smaller increase in activity with MRP and a decrease with GDP-mannose were observed. This result parallels the order of aqueous solubility of the substrates, and therefore may indicate a detergent effect on the donor substrates.

Attempts to separate the mannosyltransferase activities into one for MRP and another for DMP, by use of EDTA and variation in divalent cations (TABLE 2), failed to reveal significant differences, except that the inhibition of activity with Zn^{++} was not as severe for MRP as for DMP. With either DMP or MRP, formation of the man-α-1,3-man product was more sensitive to inactivation by incubation at 40° than was the synthesis of man-α-1,2-man (TABLE 3).

Although the data presented do not show that MRP is a specific substrate in the reactions studied, the results do not exclude this possibility. The effects of various reagents and treatments on product synthesis were much the same when either DMP or MRP was the substrate, but enzymes that perform similar functions may not be distinguished by these methods. In studies with simple exogenous acceptors, products can be isolated and characterized rather easily. However, the physiological relevance of reactions using artificial acceptors must be demonstrated, and further investigations are in progress.

No enzymatic transfer of mannose from MRP to endogenous acceptors was found. Control incubations of MRP with heat-killed enzyme incorporated label into the protein fraction to much the same extent as did incubations with non-boiled microsomes. No enzymatic transfer could be detected, either after modification of incubation conditions or after the analysis of the labeled products. In contrast, under conditions used here, transfer of mannose from DMP to endogenous lipid-oligosaccharide and protein was similar to results found by others,[9,10] except that a divalent cation was required for transfer activity. These results have altered our previous conclusions,[25] and contrast with those reported by Sasak and De Luca[28] and De Luca[13] who found that control incubations with boiled microsomes incorporated very little label from MRP, compared to incubations with non-boiled microsomes. We have not yet resolved this difference.

No labeling of products soluble in C.M.W. (10:10:3) was found after MRP incubations. Since MRP was an active substrate for the enzymatic transfer of mannose to exogenous acceptors, it is possible that there were no suitable endogenous acceptors of mannose from MRP in the membranes. This could be the case if MRP were a substrate for the addition of internal mannose residues to lipid-oligosaccharide, and if most of the endogenous lipid-oligosaccharide were present in a nearly complete form.

SUMMARY

Mannosyl retinyl phosphate (MRP) was an active substrate for the transfer of mannose to methyl-α-D-mannose (CH$_3$-α-man), p-nitrophenyl-α-D-mannose, and free mannose. The products formed during MRP incubation with CH$_3$-α-man or with mannose were α-linked. The disaccharides formed by incubation of MRP with mannose were identified by paper chromatography and electrophoresis as mannose-α-1,2-mannose and mannose-α-1,3-mannose. Triton X-100 greatly inhibited mannose-α-1,3-mannose synthesis. In the absence of detergent, MnCl$_2$, NiCl$_2$, and ZnCl$_2$ inhibited synthesis of both products. Formation of mannose-α-1,3-mannose was more sensitive to preincubation of the enzyme at 40°C then was synthesis of mannose-α-1,2-mannose. No differences in membrane mannosyltransferase activity with MRP, compared to DMP, could be demonstrated.

ACKNOWLEDGMENTS

Gifts of standard mannose disaccharide samples from Drs. J.S. Schutzbach and R.G. Spiro are gratefully acknowledged.

REFERENCES

1. ROBBINS, P.W., S.C. HUBBARD, S.J. TURCO & D.F. WIRTH. 1979. Cell **12:** 893–900.
2. TABAS, I., S. SCHLESINGER & S. KORNFELD. 1978. J. Biol. Chem. **253:** 716–722.
3. SCHER, M.G. & G.J. WAECHTER. 1979. J. Biol. Chem. **254:** 2630–2637.
4. TURCO, S.J. & P.W. ROBBINS. 1979. J. Biol. Chem. **254:** 4560–4567.
5. HUBBARD, S.C. & P.W. ROBBINS. 1979. J. Biol. Chem. **254:** 4568–4576.
6. KORNFELD, S., E. LI, & I. TABAS. 1978. J. Biol. Chem. **253:** 7771–7778.
7. LI, E., I. TABAS & S. KORNFELD, 1978. J. Biol. Chem. **253:** 7762–7770.
8. SPIRO, R.G., M.J. SPIRO & V.D. BHOYROO. 1976. J. Biol. Chem. **251:** 6409–6419.
9. HERSCOVICS, A., A.M. GOLOVTCHENKO, C.D. WARREN, B. BUGGE & R.W. JEANLOZ. 1977. J. Biol. Chem. **252:** 224–234.
10. CHAMBERS, J., W.T. FORSEE & A.D. ELBEIN. 1977. J. Biol. Chem. **252:** 2498–2506.
11. ADAMANY, A.M. & R.G. SPIRO. 1975. J. Biol. Chem. **250:** 2842–2854.
12. VERMA, A.K., M.K. RAIZADA & J.S. SCHUTZBACH 1977. J. Biol. Chem. **252:** 7235–7242.
13. DE LUCA, L.M. 1977. Vitam. Horm. **35:** 1–57.
14. WOLF, G. 1977. Nutr. Rev. **35:** 97–99.
15. WOLF, G., T.C. KIORPES, S. MASUSHIGE, J.B. SCHREIBER, M.J. SMITH, & R.S. ANDERSON. 1979. Fed. Proc. **38:** 2540–2543.
16. MASUSHIGE, S., J. SCHREIBER & G. WOLF. 1978. J. Lipid Res. **19:** 619–627.
17. BARR, R.M. & L.M. DE LUCA. 1974. Biochem. Biophys. Res. Commun. **60:** 355–363.
18. ADAMO, S., L.M. DE LUCA, C.S. SILVERMAN-JONES & S.H. YUSPA. 1979. J. Biol. Chem. **254:** 3279–3287.
19. HELLER, J. & J. HORWITZ. 1973. J. Biol. Chem. **248:** 6308–6316.

20. Rosso, G.C., L. De Luca, C.D. Warren. & G. Wolf. 1975. J. Lipid Res. **16**: 235–243.
21. Dankert, M., A. Wright, W.S. Kelley & P.W. Robbins. 1966. Arch. Biochem. Biophys. **116**: 425–435.
22. Adamany, A.M. & R.G. Spiro. 1975. J. Biol. Chem. **250**: 2830–2841.
23. Trevelyan, N.E., D.P. Procter & J.S. Harrison. 1960. Nature (London) **166**: 444–445.
24. Dittmer, J.C. & R.L. Lester. 1964. J. Lipid Res. **5**: 126–127.
25. Rosso, G.C., S. Masushige, H. Quill, & G. Wolf. 1977. Proc. Natl. Acad. Sci. USA **74**: 3762–3766.
26. Lowry, O.H. N.J. Rosebrough, A.L. Farr & R.J. Randall. 1951. J. Biol. Chem. **193**: 265–275.
27. Braell, W.A., M.A. Tyo, S.S. Krag & P.W. Robbins. 1976. Anal. Biochem. **74**: 484–487.
28. Sasak, W. L.M. De Luca. 1977. Fed. Proc. **36**: 1103 (Abstract).

RECENT STUDIES ON THE INVOLVEMENT OF RETINYL PHOSPHATE AS A CARRIER OF MANNOSE IN BIOLOGICAL MEMBRANES

Yoshihiro Shidoji, Wlodzimierz Sasak, Carol S. Silverman-Jones, and Luigi M. De Luca*

National Cancer Institute
National Institutes of Health
Bethesda, Maryland 20205

INTRODUCTION

It was the consensus of the participants to the International Symposium on vitamin A, convened by George Wolf in 1968, that no specific molecular involvement of the vitamin had been shown to explain its systemic function.[1] Considerable evidence has now gathered that retinyl phosphate functions as a carrier of mannosyl residues in mammalian membranes.[2]

The initial report that mannosylretinylphosphate (MRP) is a biosynthetic product of mammalian cells[3] was simultaneous with Leloir's findings[4] that dolichol, the polyisoprenoid alcohol of longer chain length, was also involved as a carrier of glycosyl residues. Some distinctive characteristics for the glycosyl acceptor activities of retinyl phosphate (RP) and dolichylphosphate (Dol-P) soon emerged. It was found that Dol-P is a carrier for glucose, mannose and glucosamine,[5] whereas RP appeared highly specific for mannose.[6] Moreover, phosphorylated metabolic derivatives of retinol and/or retinoic acid may play a role as sugar carriers for galactose[7] and mannose.[8] Such compounds may be referred to as glycosyl*retinoid* phosphates.

RESULTS

In this report we address two major questions.

1. *Are two mannosyl transferases involved in the biosynthesis of mannosylretinylphosphate (MRP) and dolichylmannosylphosphate (DMP)?*

Ever since two lipid intermediates for mannose MRP and DMP (FIG. 1), were found,[9] the importance of establishing whether one or two mannosyl transferase(s) are responsible for the two products was recognized. So far, no clear-cut evidence for one or two enzymes has appeared. Here, evidence for two separate enzyme activities for MRP and DMP synthesis is presented.

FIGURE 2A shows the time course for the synthesis of MRP and DMP from GDP-[14C]mannose in incubations containing 0.15 mM RP and Dol-P. Maximum accumulation of product was reached at 2 min. Therefore, we took 1-min incubations to measure the initial rate of the reactions.

The initial reaction rate was found to depend linearly upon the amount of microsomal protein for MRP synthesis (FIG. 2B). DMP synthesis, however, showed linearity up to 2.8 mg of protein, followed by a decline up to 5.35 mg of microso-

---

*To whom requests for reprints should be addressed at Building 37, Room 2B26.

0077–8923/81/0359–0345 $01.75/0 © 1981, NYAS

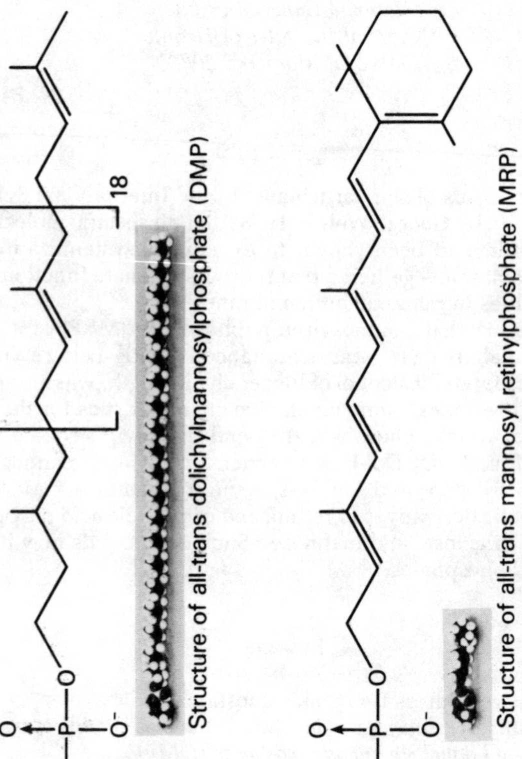

FIGURE 1. Molecular models of dolichylmannosylphosphate and of mannosyl retinylphosphate. In the fully extended all-*trans* configuration MRP is approximately 25A° and DMP approximately 108A°. Structures of MRP and DMP, reflecting the molecular models, are also shown.

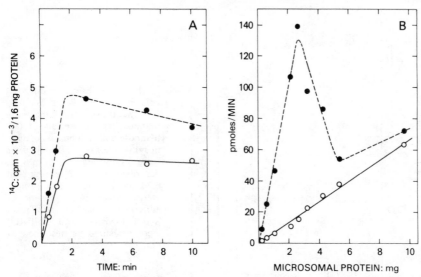

FIGURE 2A. Time course(s) of mannosylretinylphosphate and dolichylmannosylphosphate formation by rat liver microsomes. Incubations were carried out at 37°C for in indicated times. The incubation mixtures contained: 25 μM GDP-[^{14}C]mannose (0.5 μCi), 10 μg retinylphosphate (.15 mM), 50 μg dolichylphosphate (.15 mM), 0.5% Triton X-100, 30 mM Tris HCl buffer (pH 8.0), 10 mM MnCl$_2$, 8 mM NaF, 2 mM ATP, 5 mM AMP and 1.6 mg rat liver microsomal protein in a final volume of 200 μl. After incubation, mannolipids were extracted in 15 volume of chloroform:methanol (2:1). After removing the insoluble materials by centrifugation, the C:M (2:1) extracts were flash-evaporated and redissolved in 200 μl of methanol prior to thin-layer chromatographic (tlc) analysis. The two mannolipids were separated on tlc of Silica gel F257 (Merck) with a developing solvent of chloroform: methanol:water = 45:35:6 (v/v/v), R$_f$ for MRP was 0.5, DMP 0.9. All procedures were done under a dim light. The recovery of MRP from all these procedures was estimated at 60% by adding purified [^{14}C]MRP[21] and carrying it through the procedure. DMP (●----●), MRP (O——O).

FIGURE 2B. Effect of protein concentration on initial rates of the reactions. Incubations were carried out at 37°C for 1 min. Incubation mixtures were the same as in (A), except that the protein concentrations were varied from 0.27 mg/200 μl up to 9.63 mg/200 μl. MRP (O——O) and DMP (●----●) were measured as described in (A).

mal protein and a subsequent increase at higher microsomal protein concentration.

FIGURE 3 shows that the initial rate for DMP synthesis increased from 70 picomoles per min per 5.35 mg of protein at 0.5% Triton X-100 to 510 picomoles per min at 1.0% Triton X-100, suggesting that the detergent to protein ratio may influence the initial velocity of the reaction. Under the same conditions MRP synthesis was inhibited 50% by 1% Triton X-100. Thus, the detergent requirements for the two reactions appear to be different.

FIGURE 4 shows the Lineweaver-Burk plot of the dependence on GDP-mannose concentration for the synthesis of MRP and DMP. From these data a higher affinity activity was shown to catalyze DMP synthesis, enzyme activity I (EA I) (K$_m$ 1.7 μM) and a lower affinity activity to catalyze MRP synthesis (K$_m$ 12.5 μM)

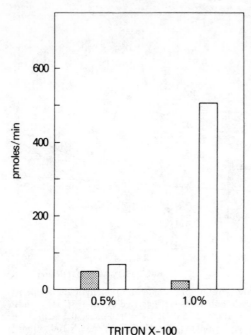

FIGURE 3. Effects of different concentrations of Triton X-100 on GDP-mannose:retinylphosphate mannosyltransferase and GDP-mannose:dolichylphosphate mannosyltransferase. Incubations were performed for 1 min as described in FIG. 2, except that 5.35 mg of microsomal protein were incubated in the presence of either 0.5% or 1.0% of Triton X-100. MRP (▩) and DMP (☐) were measured as described in FIG. 2.

(EA II). The same K_m (12.5 μM) was found for EA II when the assay was performed in the absence of exogenous Dol-P.

Inasmuch as EA II is particulate at 0.5% Triton X-100 and it can be recovered in the pellet by centrifugation (shown later), the question was asked as to whether the solubilized form of EA II would have the same K_m as the particulate form. FIGURE 5 shows that the K_m values for the two enzyme activities did not change after solubilization with 1% Triton X-100. In these experiments the final concentration of Triton X-100 was adjusted to 0.5%.

A direct approach to show two different enzyme activities was to solubilize them with Triton X-100 from rat liver membranes. The enzyme activities were assayed in the presence of exogenous RP and Dol-P. The GDP- mannose: retinylphosphate mannosyl transferase was solubilized at a higher concentration of Triton X-100 than the GDP-mannose:dolichylphosphate mannosyl transferase. The enzymes had high specificity for their substrates and entirely different solubilization characteristics (FIG. 6).

2. *Does mannosylretinylphosphate function as a mannosyl donor?*

Previous studies have demonstrated that radioactivity derived from [⁴C]mannosylretinylphosphate is found associated with macromolecular acceptors[10-12] or that MRP can function as donor of mannose to exogenous acceptors, such as mannose, mannose-methyl mannoside and paranitrophenolmannoside.[13] But it is unclear in systems utilizing endogenous acceptors whether mannose alone or mannose phosphate, or the entire MRP becomes conjugated to endogenous proteins.

The problem was addressed here with triple labeled [¹⁴C]mannosyl[³H]

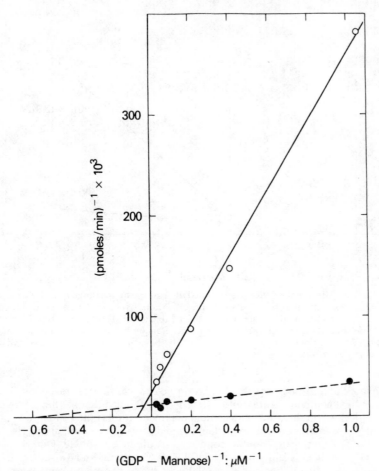

FIGURE 4. Effect of GDP-mannose concentration on the initial rate of the mannosyl transfer reactions. Incubations were carried out for 1 min in the presence of exogenous retinylphosphate (.15 mM) and dolichylphosphate (.15 mM), and 2.5 mg of microsomal protein. Double reciprocal plots for the two reactions were drawn from the data obtained from the same incubations. MRP O———O, DMP ●----●.

retinyl[32P]phosphate. The ratio of 3H/32P/14C labels in triple labeled MRP was 1/1.4/4.4. FIGURE 7A shows the tlc pattern of the mannolipid used for the transfer studies. FIGURE 7B shows the Biogel elution pattern after incubation of triple-labeled MRP with rat liver membranes. The ratio of 3H/32P/14C labels associated with the macromolecular material is 1/1.4/20 (FIG. 7B) instead of the original 1/1.4/4.4 (FIG. 7A), thus strongly suggesting that only mannose is transferred to macromolecules.

DISCUSSION

In 1970, it was proposed that two mammalian polyisoprenoids, dolichyl-

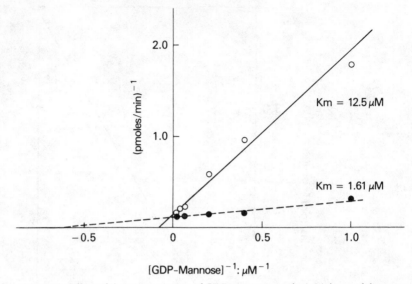

FIGURE 5. Effect of the concentration of GDP-mannose on the initial rate of the manno-syl transfer reactions after solubilization with 1% Triton X-100. The same as FIG. 4, except that 3.0 mg of microsomal protein, which was solubilized by 1% Triton X-100, were used as enzyme source, separated from the particulate fraction by centrifugation at 105,000 × g/60 min. The final concentration of Triton X-100 in the incubation mixtures (0.5%) was the same as in FIG. 4 MRP O——O, DMP ● - - - - ●.

phosphate[14] and retinyl phosphate,[3] play a role in sugar transfer reactions. Structurally, these compounds are quite different (FIG. 1), even though they share certain similarities, in that they both contain polymeric forms of the isoprenoid unit. Retinol (C_{20}) contains an additional double-bond per isoprene unit, giving rise to a system of five conjugated double bonds and an allylic phosphate (FIG. 1).

Pig liver dolichols contain from 85 to 110 carbon atoms and a α-saturated iso-prenoid unit, which gives rise to a relatively stable phosphate ester (FIG. 1).[14] Moreover FIGURE 1 shows the extended (all-*trans*) configuration for DMP, even though dolichol contains mostly *cis* double bonds.[14] This is done here for the purpose of an easy comparison between the length of DMP (about 108A°) and that of MRP (about 25A°). It should also be noted that previous estimates of the length of MRP were in error.[15]

At least four groups of researchers[14,16-18] have conducted in-depth investiga-tions, utilizing different chain length polyisoprenylphosphates, containing from 3 (C15) to 22 (C110) isoprenoid units, and have shown that dolichylphosphate has the greatest activity, by far, as an acceptor of mannosyl residues from GDP-mannose in a reaction catalyzed by microsomes from pig liver,[14] calf pancreas,[16] bovine retina,[18] and human lymphocytes.[17] Retinyl phosphate was found to be either totally inactive[17] or to possess very little activity.[16,18]

In all these studies, the concentration of GDP-mannose used was in the neighborhood of 1.5 μM, a value very close to the K_m we find (1.7 μM) for the higher affinity GDP-mannose:dolichylphosphate mannosyl transferase, EA I, in rat liver membranes. The conclusions from the studies were that dolichylphos-phate was the natural acceptor for mannose and that shorter polisoprenylphosphates were competing for the same enzyme site. However, incubation mixtures used in our investigations for mannosylretinylphosphate synthesis contained concentrations of GDP-mannose of 5.6μM,[6] 7μM,[9,11,19] 22.6μM[15] with most studies conducted at about 50 μM[20-22],i.e. close or above the K_m now found for GDP-mannose (12.5 μM) in the GDP-mannose:retinylphosphate mannosyl transferase reaction (EA II). Under these incubation conditions[20] no inhibition of DMP formation by exogenous RP could be observed.

In general, in a reaction involving two substrates, the K_m for one substrate is dependent on the concentration of the other substrate. However, the exact concentrations of dolichylphosphate and retinylphosphate are difficult to determine because these lipophilic compounds form complex micelles with Triton X-100; for example, retinylphosphate in a Triton X-100 solution forms micellar aggregates of MW 90,000 (data not shown). Moreover, specific and precise methods for determination of the endogenous levels of these polyisoprenoid phosphates have not been published. Therefore, we measured K_m values for GDP-mannose at constant concentrations of exogenous polyisoprenoid phosphates, using 0.15 mM dolichylphosphate and/or 0.15 mM retinylphosphate, i.e., at saturation for these substrates of the mannosyltransferase reactions (data not shown).

Even though the concentrations of lipid acceptors, which we used in this work, are different from those used by others[23-26] the rat liver membrane EA I had a K_m for GDP-mannose (1.7 μM) similar to that (0.25 μM) found by Carlo and Villemez in *Acanthamoeba Castellani*[23]; to that (0.56 μM) found by Lucas *et al.*[24] for rabbit erythrocyte membranes; to that (0.2 μM) reported by Harford and Waechter[25] for brain microsomes of both myelinating and adult pigs, and to that (0.4 μM) obtained by Heifetz and Elbein for the enzyme from porcine aorta.[26] However, the K_m (12.5 μM) for EA II is obviously distinct from those obtained for EA I.

FIGURE 6. Enzyme solubilizations studies. Rat liver microsomes (3 mg) in 50 μliters were treated with Triton X-100 at the concentrations shown in the abscissa for 20' at 0°C at pH 7.5. Particles and solubilized enzyme were separated by centrifugation at 105,000 × *g* for 60 minutes. The supernatant was tested for MRP and DMP synthetase activity after adjusting the detergent concentration at 0.5% Triton X-100. The incubation mixture contained, in addition to the enzyme, 0.3 mM retinylphosphate and dolichylphosphate, [14C] GDP-mannose (9.6 × 10⁻⁷M) 0.2 μCi; 0.008 M NaF; 0.01 M MnCl₂; 2 mM ATP; 5 mM AMP; 0.5% Triton X-100 in a final volume of 100 μl. Incubation proceeded at 37°C for 7 minutes. Tubes were cooled to 0°C, and lipids were extracted with 15 volumes of chloroform/methanol (2/1). They were then analyzed by tlc in C/M/W 60/35/6.

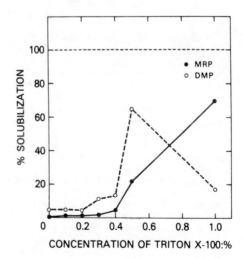

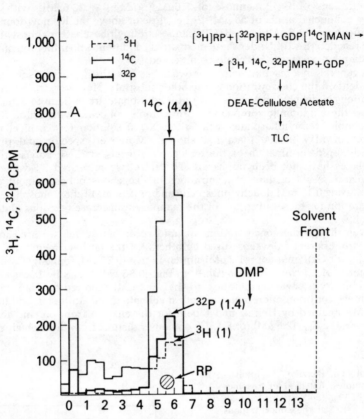

FIGURE 7A. Thin-layer chromatography of triple-labeled MRP. [14C]Mannosyl-[3H]
retinyl[32P]phosphate was prepared as follows: 0.5 ml of a solution of retinyl [32P]phosphate
726,000 CPM (0.1 μMole) were mixed with 2.1 ml of a methanolic solution of [1-3H]retinyl-
phosphate (4.5 × 10⁶ cpm or 0.13 μ Mole). These were prepared from their precursors as
described previously.[48] To this mixture, (86.2 μg of RP 0.5 mM final concentration) was
added 4 μCi of GDP-[14C]mannose (specific radioactivity 886,000 cpm/0.019 μ Mole). This
mixture was dried and incubated with rat liver microsomal enzyme for the synthesis of
MRP after the following additions: 0.5% Triton X-100; 0.02 M MnCl₂; 0.03 M Tris-HCl pH
8; 2 mM ATP and 7.4 mg of protein in a final volume of 400 μliters. This was incubated for
20 min at 37°C. The UV absorption spectrum of labeled RP was checked before the incubation and gave a typical maximum at 325 nm in 99% methanol. The reaction was stopped
with 40 ml of methanol and the mixture was applied on a DEAE-cellulose-acetate (1 × 8
cm) column, which was eluted first with 60 ml of 99% methanol and then with 60 ml of 10
mM ammonium acetate. 10 ml fractions were collected and 100 μl was used for counting.
Under these conditions, i.e. 0.5 mM RP in the incubation and methanol extraction procedure (2) only MRP is detected as seen by thin-layer chromatography in chloroform/
methanol/water (60/35/6). Counting conditions were standardized throughout and gave a
ratio of 3H/32P/14C of 1/1.4/4.46 in the triple-labeled MRP.

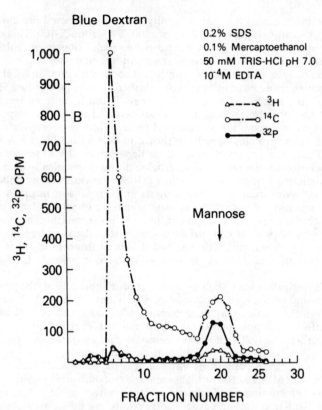

FIGURE 7B. Biogel P-150 column chromatography of acceptors from triple-labeled MRP. [^{3}H, ^{32}P, ^{14}C]-Labeled MRP was obtained from DEAE-cellulose-acetate at 10 mM ammonium acetate as described under FIGURE 7A. The equivalent of 0.0007 μMoles (22,400 cpm of ^{14}C) was evaporated to dryness and incubated with rat liver membranes (425 μg of protein) in a mixture containing 0.06 M Tris pH 8; 0.5% Triton X-100; 0.01 M MnCl$_2$ in a final volume of 50 μliters. Incubation proceeded for two hours at 27°C. It was stopped with 3 ml of C/M (2/1). The mixture was allowed to stand at room temperature for 15 minutes and then centrifuged at 1000 × *g* for 20 min. The pellet was washed three times with 1 ml each of the following solvents:chloroform/methanol (2/1); water; and chloroform/methanol/water (1/1/0.3). The residue was solubilized with 800 μl of 1% SDS containing 5 mM Tris-HCl buffer, pH 7.0. This extract was applied to a column (1.5 × 30 cm) of Biogel P-150 and eluted in the equilibrating buffer containing 0.2% SDS; 0.1% mercaptoethanol; 50 mM Tris-HCl, pH 7.0 and 10^{-4} M EDTA. Fraction of 2.5 ml were collected. The elution positions of Blue-dextran and mannose are shown. The ratio of ^{3}H/^{32}P/^{14}C in the peak at the void volume was 1/1.4/20.

The data presented in this manuscript show for the first time that two distinct enzyme activities are responsible for mannosylretinylphosphate and dolichylmannosylphosphate synthesis. The lower affinity enzyme utilizes retinylphosphate (EA II) whereas the higher affinity enzyme utilizes dolichylphosphate (EA I).

The protein concentration dependence of the reaction deserves comment. The lower affinity enzyme is not affected appreciably by changes in the detergent to protein ratio, whereas the higher affinity enzyme is affected profoundly at a protein concentration higher than 2.8 mg/ml at .5% Triton X-100. This different detergent requirement may indicate distinct functional sites in the microsomal membranes for the two mannosyltransferases. In this context it is also of interest that EA I can be solubilized at a lower detergent concentration than EA II (FIG. 6).

Even though many basic questions obviously remain to be clarified, it is clear from studies in vitamin A deficiency,[27,28] excess,[29] and in cultured transformed cells[30] that the biochemical parameter so far detected to be most responsive to vitamin A is the incorporation of mannosyl residues into glycoconjugates. Moreover, specific glycoproteins have been shown to depend on vitamin A for their synthesis. Thus, in a system of cultured rat hepatocytes, it was shown recently that incorporation of mannose in α_2-microglobulin was specifically decreased in vitamin A-deficient hepatocytes from the rat.[31] Similar results were obtained by Kiorpes et al.[32] who studied the biosynthesis and levels of α_1-macroglobulin in normal and vitamin A-depleted rats in vivo, though the effect was less pronounced.[32] In another interesting development, Jetten[33] has shown that the availability of EGF-receptor sites at the cell surface is greatly stimulated by treatment of the cells with biologically active retinoids and that tunicamycin, an antibiotic that blocks glycosylation, also blocks the retinoid-induced increase in EGF-receptor sites.[34]

Other investigators have shown[35] an effect of retinoic acid on the production of interferon and on the level of plasminogen activator activities.[36] However, the mechanism in these cases may be different, and Blalock and Gifford have suggested an effect of retinoic acid at the transcriptional level.[35]

In rat corneas Hassell et al.[37] have demonstrated an immediate response to vitamin A in the biosynthesis of epithelial glycoproteins from the conjunctival epithelium of cultured corneas of vitamin A-depleted rats. These responsive glycoproteins had MW 180,000 or higher and the response was specific for the incorporation of glucosamine and mannose, without effect on the incorporation of aminoacids. Similar effects on sugar incorporation into epithelial glycopeptides have been reported for rat corneal epithelium,[38] in tracheal epithelium,[39] cultured mouse epidermal cells,[40] and for rat intestinal mucosa.[41]

Specific effects of biologically active retinoids on cell surface adhesion had been reported for transformed[42,43] and nontransformed[44] cell lines and these effects have been correlated with an increase in the biosynthesis of glycoproteins at the cell surface[30,45] or the attachment of fibronectin to the cell surface, in the case of chondrocytes.[46]

Therefore, it seems reasonable to propose that vitamin A and its phosphorylated derivatives may function as modulators of cellular interactions through their direct involvement in the biosynthesis of specific glycoproteins, which modify the cell surface. Such biosynthetic mechanism may well be the regulatory step in the expression of specific cell-surface traits, which determine the behavior of the cell.

It is also of interest that the neoplastic cell seems to resist the modification from an asocial to a more social behavior as induced by retinoids: such resistance may be expressed in the ability of the cell to dispose of retinol; Bhat et al.[47] have reported that 3T12 and 3T3 cells, but not primary mouse dermal fibroblasts, convert all-trans-retinol to anhydroretinol, a compound without biological activity.

In conclusion, having established that biologically active retinoids modify cell surface glycoprotein synthesis and cell adhesion, it remains to be clarified which is the specialized glycosylating function of MRP distinct from that of DMP and whether differentiation effects depend on this function.

SUMMARY

Rat liver microsomes synthesized [^{14}C]mannosylretinylphosphate and dolichyl [^{14}C]mannosylphosphate from guanosinedisphosphate [^{14}C]mannose, retinylphosphate and dolichylphosphate. Two distinct enzyme activities were shown to be responsible for the biosynthesis of the two mannolipids. A higher affinity mannosyl transferase (EA I), responsible for dolichylmannosylphosphate synthesis, displayed a K_m for GDP-mannose of 1.7 μM; while a lower affinity enzyme (EA II), responsible for mannosylretinylphosphate synthesis, displayed a K_m for GDP-mannose of 12.5 μM. These K_m values were unaffected by the addition of either dolichylphosphate for EA II, or retinylphosphate for EA I. The same K_m values were found before and after solubilization of the enzyme activity with 1% Triton X-100. Differential solubilization of EA I and EA II was demonstrated, utilizing different concentrations of Triton X-100. Triple-labeled mannosylretinylphosphate was prepared from [^{3}H]retinylphosphate, retinyl[^{32}P]phosphate and GDP-[^{14}C]mannose from incubations containing rat liver microsomes. This compound was shown to donate [^{14}C]mannose to endogenous acceptors of rat liver microsomes.

REFERENCES

1. DINGLE, J.T. 1969. Discussion and Summary. Am. J. Clin. Nutr. **22**(18): 1047.
2. DE LUCA. L.M. 1977. The direct involvement of vitamin A in glycosyltransfer reactions of mammalian membranes. Vitam. Horm. **35**: 1-57.
3. DE LUCA, L.M., G.C. ROSSO & G. WOLF. 1970. The biosynthesis of a mannolipid that contains a polar metabolite of [15-^{4}C]retinol. Biochem. Biophys. Res. Commun. **41**: 615-620.
4. BEHRENS, N.H. & L.F. LELOIR. 1970. Dolichol-monophosphate-glucose: An intermediate in glucose transfer in liver. Proc. Natl. Acad. Sci. USA **66**: 153-159.
5. WAECHTER, C.J. & W.J. LENNARZ. 1976. The role of polyprenol-linked sugars in glycoprotein synthesis. Annu. Rev. Biochem. **45**: 95-112.
6. BERGMAN, A., T. MANKOWSKI, T. CHOJNACKI, L.M. DE LUCA, E. PETERSON & G. DALLNER. 1978. Glycosyl transfer from nucleotide sugars to C$_{85}$- and C$_{55}$-polyprenyl and retinyl phosphates by microsomal subfractions and Golgi membranes of rat liver. Biochem. J. **172**: 123-127.
7. PETERSON, P.A., L. RASK, T. HELTING, L. OSTBERG & Y. FERNSTEDT. 1976. Formation and properties of retinyl phosphate galactose. J. Biol. Chem. **251**: 4986-4995.
8. BHAT, P.V. & L.M. DE LUCA. 1981. The biosynthesis of a mannolipid containing a metabolite of retinoic acid by 3T12 mouse fibroblasts. Ann. N.Y. Acad. Sci. **359**:
9. DE LUCA, L.M. N. MAESTRI, G. ROSSO & G. WOLF. 1973. Retinol glycolipids. J. Biol. Chem. **248**: 641-648.
10. ROSSO, G.C., S. MASUSHIGE, H. QUILL & G. WOLF. 1977. Transfer of mannose from mannosylretinolphosphate to protein. Proc. Natl. Acad. Sci. USA **74**: 3762-3766.
11. SASAK, W. & L.M. DE LUCA. 1980. Mannosyl transfer from mannosylretinylphosphate to glycoconjugates of rat liver membranes. FEBS Lett. **114**: 313-318.
12. FROT-COUTAZ, J.P., R. LETOUBLON & R. GOT. 1979. Comparative effects of exogenous retinyl phosphate and dolichyl phosphate on the in vitro mannosylation of glycoproteins. FEBS Lett. **107**: 375-378.
13. QUILL, H. & G. WOLF. 1981. Formation of α-1,2- and α-1,3-linked mannose disaccharides from mannosyl retinyl phosphate by rat liver membrane enzymes. Ann. N.Y. Acad. Sci. **359**:
14. HEMMING, F.W. 1977. Dolicholphosphate, a coenzyme in the glycosylation of animal membrane-bound glycoproteins. Biochem. Soc. Trans. **5**: 1223-1231.
15. DE LUCA, L.M., P.V. BHAT, W. SASAK & S. ADAMO. 1979. Biosynthesis of phosphoryl and glycosyl phosphoryl derivatives of vitamin A in biological membranes. Fed. Proc. **38**: 2535-2539.

16. TKACZ, J.S., A. HERSCOVICS, C.D. WARREN, & R.W. JEANLOZ. 1974. Mannosyl transferase activity in calf pancreas microsomes. J. Biol. Chem. **249:** 6372–6381.
17. WEDGWOOD, J.F., J. STROMINGER, & C.D. WARREN. 1974. Transfer of sugars from nucleoside diphosphosugar compounds to endogenous and synthetic dolichylphosphate in human lymphocytes. J. Biol. Chem. **249:** 6316–6324.
18. KEAN, E.L. 1977. GDP-mannose-polyprenyl phosphate mannosyl transferases of the retina. J. Biol. Chem. **252:** 5622–5629.
19. FROT-COUTAZ, J.P., C.S. SILVERMAN-JONES & L.M. DE LUCA. 1976. Isolation, characterization and biological activity of retinylphosphate from hamster intestinal epithelium. J. Lipid Res. **17:** 220–230.
20. SILVERMAN-JONES, C.S., J.P. FROT-COUTAZ & L.M. DE LUCA. 1976. Separation of mannosylretinylphosphate from dolichylmannosylphosphate by solvent extraction. Anal. Biochem. **75:** 664–667.
21. SASAK, W., C.S. SILVERMAN-JONES & L.M. DE LUCA. 1979. Separation of mannosylretinyl- phosphate from dolichylmannosylphosphate by chromatography on columns of DEAE-Sephacel. Anal. Biochem. **97:** 298–301.
22. DE LUCA, L.M., J.P. FROT-COUTAZ, C.S. SILVERMAN-JONES & P.R. ROLLER. 1977. Chemical synthesis of phosphorylated retinoids: Their mannosyl acceptor activity in rat liver membranes. J. Biol. Chem. **252:** 2575–2579.
23. CARLO, P.L. & C.L. VILLEMEZ. 1979. Solubilization and properties of polyprenylphosphate: GDP-D-mannose mannosyl transferase. Arch. Biochem. Biophys. **198:** 117–123.
24. LUCAS, J.J. & NEVAR, C. 1978. Loss of mannosyl phosphoryl polyisoprenol synthesis upon conversion of reticulocytes to erythrocytes. Biochim. Biophys. Acta **528:** 475–482.
25. HARFORD, J.B. & C.J. WAECHTER. 1980. A developmental change in dolichylphosphate mannose synthase activity in pig brain. Biochem. J. **188:** 481–490.
26. HEIFETZ, A. & A.D. ELBEIN. 1977. Solubilization and properties of mannose and N-acetylglucosamine transferases involved in formation of polyprenyl-sugar intermediates. J. Biol. Chem. **252:** 3057–3063.
27. DE LUCA, L.M., C.S. SILVERMAN-JONES & R.M. BARR. 1975 Biosynthetic studies on mannolipids and mannoproteins of normal and vitamin A depleted hamster livers. Biochim. Biophys. Acta **409:** 342–359.
28. SATO, M., L.M. DE LUCA & Y. MUTO. 1978. Effects of exogenous retinol and retinoic acid on the biosynthesis of [^{14}C]mannose-labeled glycolipids and glycoproteins in rat liver. J. Nutr. Sci. Vitamin. (Tokyo). **24:** 9–23.
29. HASSELL, J.R., C.S. SILVERMAN-JONES & L.M. DE LUCA. 1978. Stimulation of mannose incorporation into specific glycolipids and glycopeptides of rat liver by high doses of retinyl palmitate. J. Biol. Chem. **253:** 1627–1631.
30. SASAK, W., S. ADAMO, I. AKALOVSKY & L.M. DE LUCA. 1978. Role of Retinoids in the induction of adhesion and mannosylation of glycoconjugates of cultured spontaneously-transformed mouse fibroblasts (Balb/c 3T12-3 cells). J. Cell Biol. **79:** 41a.
31. HAARS, L.J. & H.C. PITOT. 1979. α_2-Microglobulin in the rat. J. Biol. Chem. **254:** 9401–9407.
32. KIORPES, T.C., S.J. MOLICA & G. WOLF. 1976. A plasma glycoprotein depressed in vitamin A deficiency in the rat: α_1 macroglobulin. J. Nutr. **106:** 1659–1667.
33. JETTEN, A. 1980. Retinoids enhance specifically the number of epidermal growth factor receptors. Nature **278:** 180–182.
34. JETTEN, A. 1981. Action of retinoids and phorbol esters on growth and the binding of epidermal growth factor. Ann. N.Y. Acad. Sci. **359:**
35. BLALOCK, J.E. & G.E. GIFFORD. 1977. Retinoic acid induced transcriptional control of interferon production. Proc. Natl. Acad. Sci. USA **74:** 5382–5386.
36. WILSON, E.L. & E. REICH. 1978. Plasminogen activator in chick fibroblasts: Induction of synthesis by retinoic acid; synergism with viral transformation and phorbol ester. Cell **15:** 385–392.
37. HASSELL, J.R., D.A. NEWSOME & L.M. DE LUCA. 1980. Increased biosynthesis of specific

glycoconjugates in rat corneal epithelium following treatment with vitamin A. Invest. Ophthal. **19:** 642–647.

38. KIORPES, T.R., Y.L. KIM & G. WOLF. 1979. Stimulation of the synthesis glycoproteins in corneal epithelium by vitamin A. Exp. Eye Res. **28:** 23–35.

39. CLARK, J.N. & A.C. MARCHOK. 1979. The effect of vitamin A on cellular differentiation and mucous glycoprotein synthesis in longterm rat tracheal organ culture. Differentiation **14:** 175–183.

40. ADAMO, S., L.M. DE LUCA, C.S. SILVERMAN-JONES & S.H. YUSPA. 1979. Mode of action of retinol; involvement in glycosylation reactions of cultured mouse epidermal cells. J. Biol. Chem. **254:** 3279–3287.

41. DE LUCA, L.M., M. SCHUMACHER, G. WOLF & P.M. NEWBERNE. 1970. Biosynthesis of a fucose-containing glycopeptide from rat small intestine in normal and vitamin A-deficient conditions. J. Biol. Chem. **245:** 4551–4558.

42. ADAMO, S., I. AKALOVSKY & L.M. DE LUCA. 1978. Retinoic acid-induced changes in saturation density and adhesion of transformed mouse fibroblasts. Am. Assoc. Cancer Res. Proc. **19:** 107a.

43. ADAMO, S., L.M. DE LUCA, I. AKALOVSKY & P.V. BHAT. 1979. Retinoid-induced adhesion in cultured transformed mouse fibroblast. J. Natl. Cancer Inst. **62** 1473–1478.

44. JETTEN, A.M., M.E.R. JETTEN, S. SHAPIRO & J. POON. 1979. Characterization of the action of retinoids on mouse fibroblast cell lines. Exp. Cell Res. **119:** 289–299.

45. SASAK, W., L.M. DE LUCA, L.D. DION & C.S. SILVERMAN-JONES. 1980. Effect of retinoic acid on cell-surface glycopeptides of cultured spontaneously-transformed mouse fibroblast (Balb/c 3T12-3 cells). Cancer Res. **40:** 1944–1949.

46. HASSELL, J.R., J.P. PENNYPACKER, H.K. KLEINMAN, R.M. PRATT & K.M. YAMADA. 1979. Enhanced cellular fibronectin accumulation in chondrocytes treated with vitamin A. Cell **17:** 821–826.

47. BHAT, P.V., L.M. DE LUCA, S. ADAMO, I. AKALOVSKY, C.S. SILVERMAN-JONES & G.L. PECK. 1979. Retinoid metabolism in spontaneously-transformed mouse fibroblasts (Balb/c 3T12-3 cells): Enzymatic conversion of retinol to anhydroretinol. J. Lipid Res. **20:** 357–362.

48. BHAT, P.V., L.M. DE LUCA & M. WIND. 1980. Reverse phase high pressure liquid chromatography separation of retinoids, including retinyl phosphate and mannosylretinylphosphate. Anal. Biochem. **102:** 243–248.

VITAMIN A-INDUCED ALTERATIONS IN CORNEAL AND CONJUNCTIVAL EPITHELIAL GLYCOPROTEIN BIOSYNTHESIS

John R. Hassell* and David A. Newsome

*Section on Retinal and Ocular Connective Tissue Diseases
Clinical Branch, National Eye Institute
National Institutes of Health
Bethesda, Maryland 20205*

INTRODUCTION

Vitamin A may regulate the synthesis or glycosylation of certain epithelial glycoproteins. Experimental vitamin A deficiency has been found to reduce radioactive glucosamine incorporation into certain glycoprotein fragments of a variety of epithelia. The epithelial tissues so affected include the intestinal mucosa,[1,2] corneal epithelium,[3-5] and tracheal respiratory epithelium.[6,7] Administration of vitamin A to the deficient animals restores glucosamine incorporation into the glycoprotein fragments. Furthermore, administration of excess vitamin A to either deficient or normal rats increases glucosamine incorporation into glycoproteins or glycoprotein fragments to above normal levels.[5,6]

Vitamin A deficiency is also associated with a reduction in the number of goblet cells in the intestinal mucosa,[1] ocular conjunctiva,[8] and tracheal respiratory epithelium.[9] Goblet cells are restored in these tissues after the administration of vitamin A. The major product of goblet cells is mucins.[10,11] Mucins are high molecular weight glycoproteins that consist mostly of carbohydrate and probably play a role in epithelial surface function. Antibodies against the vitamin A-regulated glycopeptide fragment isolated from intestinal mucosa react specifically with the goblet cells of intestinal mucosa, tracheal epithelium, and conjunctival epithelium.[9,12] These observations suggest that vitamin A regulates the synthesis of mucins.

There are several possible mechanisms by which vitamin A may regulate mucin production. Vitamin A may act in a manner similar to steroid hormones to regulate directly the transcription or translation of the mucin protein core.[13] Glycosylation would then follow to produce a functional mucin. On the other hand, there is evidence that glycosylated derivatives of vitamin A may act themselves to glycosylate proteins.[14,15] Therefore, it is possible that one of these derivatives may be involved in the addition of some or all of the carbohydrate side chains to mucin precursors and thereby regulate the synthesis of the intact mucin. The results of this study suggest that vitamin A controls the glycosylation of mucins.

MATERIALS AND METHODS

The procedures used for producing vitamin A-deficient rats, radioactively

---

* Current address: Laboratory of Developmental Biology and Anomalies, National Institute for Dental Research, National Institutes of Health, Bethesda, MD 20205.

0077-8923/81/0359-0358 $01.75/0 © 1981, NYAS

labeling the corneas and harvesting the epithelium have been described in a previous report.[5] In brief, vitamin A-deficient rats were divided into three groups of three rats each when the weights of the animals had reached the plateau stage. One group remained "deficient" (D), a second group was "repleted" with 300 μg retinoic acid/animal (R) and a third group was repleted with "excess" (3 mg/animal) retinoic acid (XR). The "normal" rats used in this study were raised on standard chow.

The animals were sacrificed 18 hr after administration of the retinoic acid. The corneas were excised whole, pooled by group and incubated in tissue culture medium containing either 150μCi [6-³H]glucosamine/ml, 50μCi [U-¹⁴C]glucosamine/ml, or 150μCi [6-³H]glucosamine plus 500μCi [³⁵S]Na SO₄/ml. The conjunctival tissue overlying the sclera was also removed and incubated in medium containing radioisotopes. In some cases retinoic acid was added to the labeling media at a final concentration of 3 μg/ml. Vitamin A was added to the media in ethanol solution. Media of controls received an equivalent amount of ethanol.

The labeled epithelia were scraped off the corneas in phosphate-buffered saline, harvested by centrifugation, and stored frozen at −20°C. The corneal epithelium and conjunctiva were extracted or solubilized in 2% sodium dodecyl sulfate (SDS) as previously described.[5] Protein measurements[16] were made on aliquots of the extract and the remainder of the extract stored frozen (−20°). The extracts were prepared and electrophoresed in polyacrylamide gels containing SDS as previously described.[5] After electrophoresis, the gel was fixed in 50% trichloroacetic acid, stained with Coomassie blue, destained, embedded with 2.5 diphenyloxazole, dried and exposed to Kodak X-Omat film at −76°C. Liquid scintillation spectrophotometry of acrylamide gels was accomplished by cutting the

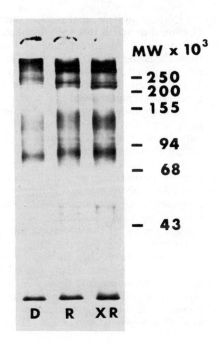

FIGURE 1. Autofluorograph of corneal epithelial glycoconjugates. Corneas from vitamin A-deficient rats (D), deficient rats repleted with 3 mg retinoic acid (R), and deficient rats repleted with 3 mg retinoic acid (XR) were labeled in media containing [³H]glucosamine. The epithelia were harvested, electrophoresed in acrylamide gels and the ³H-containing synthetic products evaluated by autofluorography. Equal amounts of protein were applied to each track. Vitamin A repletion increased ³H incorporation into a 220,000 molecular weight glycoconjugate and two glycoconjugates greater than 250,000 molecular weight. The radioactivity represents a portion of the pooled epithelia from 6 corneas.

MW x 10³

− 250
− 200
− 155

− 94

− 68

− 43

D   R   XR

gel into 1 mm slices and soaking the slices overnight in 0.5 ml of NCS (Amersham) prior to the addition of 10 ml of ACS scintillant (Amsersham).

Corneal epithelium was also solubilized by sonication in 8M urea buffered with O.05M Tris, pH 6.8. The buffered urea was prepared from a stock solution of 9M urea treated with a mixture of resins (Biorad AG 501 × 8) to remove ionic substances. The sonicated epithelium was dialyzed against 8M urea, 0.05M Tris, pH 6.8 to remove unincorporated radioactivity and centrifuged at 12,000 RPM for 20 min to remove insoluble material. Aliquots of the extract and residue were assayed for radioactivity. The extract was applied to a column (1.6 × 6 m) of DEAE-cellulose (Whatman DE52) equilibrated with 8M urea, 0.05M Tris, pH 6.8, and bound material was eluted from the column with a linear gradient of 0-0.75M NaCl in 8M urea, 0.05M Tris, pH 6.8.[17] Aliquots of each tube were assayed for radioactivity and the tubes containing the peak fractions were pooled, dialyzed against distilled water and lyophilized to dryness. The fractions were electrophoresed on acrylamide gels and the gels assayed for radioactivity by either fluorography or by slicing and direct liquid scintillation spectrophotometry as described above.

In some cases, the individual acrylamide gel slices were incubated at 45° for 36 hr in 1.0 ml of 1M Na borohydride containing 0.01N NaOH to release O-linked oligosaccharides. The slices were removed and assayed for radioactivity after incubation in NCS as described above. Aliquots of 0.01 ml were also removed from the extract and assayed for radioactivity. The radioactivity extracted from a single slice was then chromatographed on a column (0.6 × 150 cm), packed with P-10 resin (Biorad) equilibrated and eluted with 1.0M pyridine, pH 6.5. The entire contents of each tube were assayed for radioactivity.

Results

Corneal and conjunctival specimens from three groups (3 animals/group) of vitamin A-deficient rats were incubated with [³H]glucosamine, pooled by group and analyzed for incorporated ³H-activity by SDS polyacrylamide gel electrophoresis and autofluorography. The three groups were: (1) vitamin A-deficient rats (D); (2) vitamin A-deficient rats repleted with 300 μg retinoic acid/animal (R); and (3) vitamin A-deficient rats repleted with 3 mg retinoic acid/animal (XR). The autofluorographs showed that treatment with 300 μg retinoic acid (R) increased ³H incorporation into a 220,000 molecular weight glycoconjugate and into two glycoconjugates greater than 250,000 molecular weight (FIG. 1). Repletion with 3 mg retinoic acid/rat (XR) increased ³H incorporation into these 3 high molecular weight glycoconjugates even further. Autofluorographs of polyacrylamide gels of conjunctival epithelium (FIG. 2) showed that this tissue also synthesized these three high molecular weight glycoconjugates and that retinoic acid repletion increased ³H incorporation into three cellular products. Thus, Vitamin A repletion increases ³H incorporation into three high molecular weight glycogonjugates synthesized by both the corneal and conjunctival epithelium. Furthermore, the stimulation of ³H incorporation into these glycoconjugates is vitamin A dose dependent.

Previous work[5] has shown that adding retinoic acid (3 μg/ml) directly to media containing normal corneas and [³H]glucosamine also produced an increase in ³H incorporation into these 3 high molecular weight glycoconjugates. Therefore, organ culture of normal corneas was used to help determine the composition of these three high molecular weight glycoconjugates and the basis for the vitamin A-mediated increase in ³H incorporation.

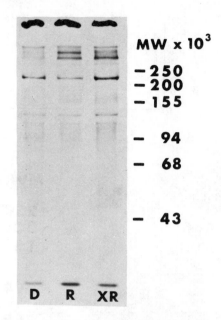

FIGURE 2. Autofluorograph of conjunctival epithelial glycoconjugates. Conjunctiva from vitamin A-deficient rats (D), deficient rats repleted with 300 μg retinoic acid (R), and deficient rats repleted with 3 mg retinoic acid (XR) were incubated in media containing ^{3}H glucosamine. The conjunctiva were solubilized, electrophoresed in acrylamide gels and the ^{3}H-containing synthetic products evaluated by autofluorography. Equal amounts of protein were applied to each track. Vitamin A repletion increased ^{3}H incorporation into the same 3 high molecular weight glycoconjugates observed in the corneal epithelium (FIG. 1). The radioactivity represents a portion of 6 pooled conjunctival specimens.

MW x 10^3

—250
—200
—155

— 94

— 68

— 43

D   R   XR

The epithelium from 12 corneas labeled with [^{3}H]glucosamine and Na$_2$ ^{35}SO$_4$ was extracted in buffered urea (8M urea, 0.05M Tris, pH 6.8) and the insoluble material removed by centrifugation. This procedure extracted 90% of the incorporated ^{3}H and 88% of the incorporated ^{35}S-labeled material. The extract was then applied to a column of DEAE cellulose and eluted with a linear NaCl gradient (FIG. 3, *upper panel*) to separate the intact glycoconjugates according to their charge. Four peaks of radioactively labeled material were obtained. Peaks 1, 2, and 3 contained only ^{3}H-activity. Peak 4 contained both ^{3}H- and ^{35}S-activity and was therefore designated the proteoglycan peak. The tubes containing the radioactivity in each of the four peaks were pooled as shown by the brackets in FIGURE 1 (*upper panel*). Equal amounts of radioactivity from each of these peaks were then electrophoresed in polyacrylamide gels to separate the glycoconjugates according to size. An autofluorograph of the gel (FIG. 1, *lower panel*) showed that peak 3 contained most of the radioactivity incorporated into the high molecular weight glycoconjugates. The ^{3}H-activity in peak 3 was found to be resistant to chondroitinase ABC (not shown). Peak 4, the proteoglycan peak, contained little or no radioactivity incorporated into high molecular weight material. Hyaluronic acid elutes midway between peaks 3 and 4 in this system (not shown). These observations indicate that the high molecular weight epithelial glycoconjugates are glycoproteins.

Another set of experiments were conducted to determine whether the vitamin A-mediated increased ^{3}H incorporated into the high molecular weight glycoproteins was due to increased glycosylation of the protein core. Corneas from 12 normal rats were divided into two equal groups. One group was incubated in medium containing [^{14}C]glucosamine (here termed control) and the other group incubated in medium containing [^{3}H]glucosamine plus 3 μg retinoic acid/ml (here termed retinoic acid). The epithelium in each group was extracted in buffered urea, the extracts mixed together and chromatographed on a column

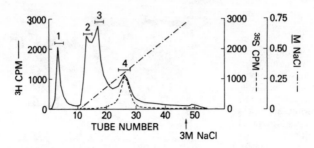

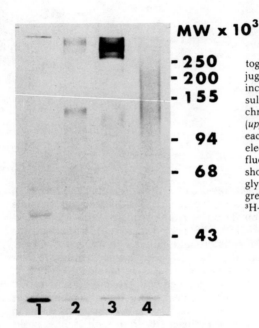

MW x 10³

- 250
- 200
- 155

- 94

- 68

- 43

1 2 3 4

FIGURE 3. DEAE Cellulose chromatography of corneal epithelial glycoconjugates. Corneas from normal rats were
incubated in [³H]glucosamine and [³⁵S]
sulfate. The harvested epithelium was
chromatographed on DEAE cellulose
(*upper panel*). The material eluting in
each of the 4 radioactive peaks was
electrophoresed and evaluated by autofluorography (*lower panel*). The results
showed that peak 3 contained the 2
glycoconjugates with molecular weights
greater than 250,000. Equal amounts of
³H-activity were applied to each track.

of DEAE cellulose (FIG. 4). Four peaks containing both ³H- and ¹⁴C-activity were
obtained. The third peak exhibited an increased ³H/¹⁴C ratio when compared to
peaks 1 and 2. This was expected since peak 3 was found to contain most of the
high molecular weight glycoproteins (FIG. 3). The tubes containing peak 3 were
pooled, as shown by the bracket in FIGURE 4, and electrophoresed on a
polyacrylamide gel. The radioactivity of the gel (FIG. 5) showed that most of the
radioactive label was contained in the 3 peaks which migrated into the top part of
the gel. The peak at slice 17 corresponds to the 220,000 MW glycoprotein and the
peaks at slices 7 and 10 correspond to the two glycoproteins with molecular
weights greater than 250,000. The upper portion of a similar gel was also sliced
and each slice incubated in 0.01N NaOH containing 1M Na borohydride to
release O-linked oligosaccharides from the protein core. More than 98% of the
incorporated ³H- and ¹⁴C- label was released from the slices by this treatment.
The radioactivity released from the tenth slice (bracketed region, FIG. 5) was fractionated on a P-10 column (FIG. 6) to separate the oligosaccharides according to

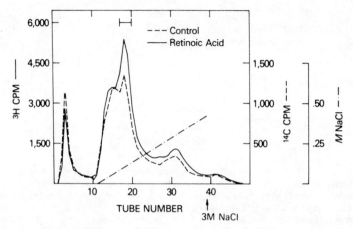

FIGURE 4. DEAE-cellulose chromatography of corneal epithelium glycoconjugates. Corneas from 12 normal rats were divided into 2 equal groups. One group was incubated in medium containing [¹⁴C]glucosamine (control) and the other group in medium containing [³H]glucosamine plus 3 μg retinoic acid/ml (Retinoic Acid). The epithelia in each group were harvested, extracted in urea and the extracts chromatographed on a column of DEAE-cellulose. The results showed that peak 3 contained a higher ³H/¹⁴C ratio than peaks 1 or 2.

size. Four peaks of radioactively labeled material were obtained. This indicates that the glycoprotein in slice 10 contained 4 different sizes of oligosaccharide side chains. In general, the ³H/¹⁴C ratio was similar for 3 of the peaks but the peak at tube 70 exhibited a greater ³H/¹⁴C ratio than the other 3 peaks. The results suggest that the increased incorporation of ³H-activity seen with vitamin A treatment is due to an increase in the amount of a particular size oligosaccharide side chain added to the protein core of the glycoprotein.

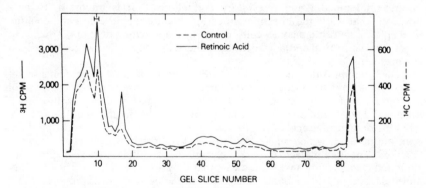

FIGURE 5. Acrylamide gel electrophoresis of peak 3 material obtained from DEAE chromotography. The tubes containing the radioactivity in peak 3 were pooled as shown in FIGURE 4 and electrophoresed on acrylamide gels. The gel was cut into 1 mm slices, the radioactivity eluted with NCS and measured by liquid scintiliation spectrophotometry. The results show that peak 3 contains 3 high molecular weight glycoproteins which migrated to slices 7, 10, and 17.

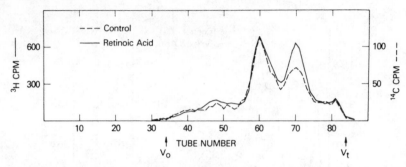

FIGURE 6. P-10 chromatography of oligosacchardies of a high molecular weight glycoprotein isolated by DEAE chromatography and acrylamide gel electrophoresis. An acrylamide gel, identical to that shown in FIGURE 5, was sliced and the slices incubated in dilute base. The radioactivity that eluted from the 10th slice of the gel (FIG. 5) by the action of the base was chromatographed on P-10. Four peaks of radioactivity were obtained. The $^3H/^{14}C$ ratio was increased in the 3rd peak (tube 70). The results indicate that the glycoprotein contained 4 different size oligosaccharides and vitamin A treatment increased the amount of one of the oligosaccharides on the protein core.

DISCUSSION

Numerous studies have shown that vitamin A treatment increases the incorporation of radioactive glucosamine into specific glycoproteins of mucoussecreting epithelium.[1-7] Antibodies prepared against these glycoproteins localize to the goblet cell of tracheal epithelium, intestinal mucosa and conjunctival epithelium.[9,12] In the present study, we found that vitamin A treatment increased [^3H]glucosamine incorporation into several distinct glycoproteins synthesized by both the corneal epithelium and conjunctival epithelium. These glycoproteins are probably similar to those "vitamin A-dependent" glycoproteins found previously in intestinal mucosa and respiratory epithelium.[1-7] It is important to note, however, that while the intestinal mucosa, respiratory epithelium and conjunctival epithelium contain goblet cells, the corneal epithelium does not. Thus, it appears that the corneal epithelial cells have the ability to synthesize goblet cell-like glycoproteins.

The "vitamin A-dependent" glycoproteins synthesized by the mucous-secreting epithelia have been isolated and characterized.[1,6] Based on their composition and their site of synthesis, they would belong to a class of glycoproteins termed mucins.[10] They contain 80-90% carbohydrate, are rich in glucosamine and contain little or no uronic acid or sulfate. They also contain threonine as the predominant amino acid, which suggests that the oligosaccharide side chains may be O-linked. The high molecular weight glycoproteins of the rat corneal epithelium exhibited characteristics which indicate that they are also mucins. They are high molecular weight, they labeled intensely with radioactive glucosamine, and they labeled poorly with leucine.[5] Their oligosaccharide side chains were released with dilute base, suggesting that they are O-linked.

The results of this study may also provide an explanation for the observed increase in mucin synthesis that occurs with vitamin A treatment. We found that one of the high molecular weight glycoproteins, which exhibited increased glucosamine incorporation as a result of vitamin A treatment, contained 4 different sized oligosaccharide side chains. Vitamin A treatment increased [^3H]glucosamine incorporation into one of the oligosaccharide side chains. These observations could be interpreted to mean that vitamin A acts to stimulate the synthesis of a mucin which contains a different proportion of various sized oligosaccharide side chains. Alternatively, the mucin protein core may be the same and vitamin A or derivatives of the vitamin may be acting to increase the number of a particular oligosaccharide side chain attached to the mucin protein core by a glycosylation-type mechanism. In support of this later hypothesis, we previously[5] observed that while vitamin A increased [³H]glucosamine incorporation into these high molecular glycoproteins, it did not alter [¹⁴C]leucine incorporation. These studies were conducted with high levels of vitamin A and, although the high doses appear to increase further the heightened [³H]glucosamine incorporation seen with low doses of the vitamin, the exact relationship between the mechanism of action of low and high dose effects remains to be determined.

REFERENCES

1. DE LUCA, L., M. SCHUMACHER & G. WOLF. 1970. Biosynthesis of a fucose containing glycopeptide from rat small intestine in normal and vitamin A-deficient conditions. J. Biol. Chem. **245:** 4551-4558.
2. KLEINMAN, H.K. & G. WOLF. 1874. Extraction and characterization of a "native" vitamin A-sensitive glycoprotein from rat intestine. Biochim. Biophys. Acta **359:** 90-100.
3. KIM, Y.L. & G. WOLF. 1974. Vitamin A deficiency and the glycoproteins of rat corneal epithelium. J. Nutr. **104:** 710-718.
4. KIORPES, T.C., Y.L. KIM & G. WOLF. 1979. Stimulation of the synthesis of specific glycoproteins in corneal epithelium by vitamin A. Exp. Eye Res. **28:** 23-35.
5. HASSELL, J.R., D.A. NEWSOME & L.M. DE LUCA. 1980. Increased biosynthesis of specific glycoconjugates in rat corneal epithelium following treatment with vitamin A. Invest. Ophthalmol. In press.
6. BONANNI, F. S.S. LEVINSON, G. WOLF & L.M. DE LUCA. 1973. Glycoproteins from the hamster respiratory tract and their response to vitamin A. Biochim. Biophys. Acta **297:** 441-451.
7. CLARK, J.M. & A.C. MARCHOK. 1979. The effect of vitamin A on cellular differentiation and mucous glycoprotein synthesis in long-term tracheal organ cultures. Differentiation **14:** 175-183.
8. PFISTER, R. R. & M.E. RENNER. 1978. The corneal and conjunctival surface in vitamin A deficiency: A scanning electron microscope study. Invest. Ophthalmol. **17:** 874-890.
9. DE LUCA, L.M. N. MAESTRI, F. BONANNI & D. NELSON. 1972. Maintenance of epithelial cell differentiation: The mode of action of vitamin A. Cancer. **30:** 1326-1331.
10. FORSTNER, J.F., I. JABBAL & G. FORSTNER. 1973. Goblet cell mucin of rat small intestine. Chemical and physical characterization. Can. J. Biochem. **51:** 1154-1166.
11. MOORE, J.C. & J.M. TIFFANY. 1979. Human Ocular Mucins. Origins and preliminary characterization. Exp. Eye Res. **29:** 291-301.
12. DE LUCA, L., M. SCHUMACHER & D.P. NELSON. 1971. Localization of the retinol dependent fucose-glycopeptide in the goblet cell of the rat small intestine. J. Biol. Chem. **246:** 5762-5765.
13. SONI. B.P. 1977. Localization of retinoic acid binding protein in nuclei. Biochem. Biophys. Res. Commun. **75:** 7-12.
14. WOLF, G. 1977. Retinal-linked sugars in glycoprotein synthesis. Nutr. Rev. **35:** 97-99.
15. DE LUCA, L.M. 1977. The direct involvement of vitamin A in glycosyl transfer reactions of mammalian membranes. Vitam. Horm. **35:** 1-57. Academic Press Inc. New York.
16. LOWRY, O.H., N.J. ROSEBROUGH, A.L. FARR & R.J. RANDALL. 1951. Protein measurement with the Folin phenol reagent. J. Biol. Chem. **193:** 265-275.
17. ANTONOPOULOS, C.A., I. AXELSSON, D. HEINEGÅRD & S. GARDELL. 1974. Extraction and purification of proteoglycans from various types of connective tissue. Biochim. Biophys. Acta **174:** 108-119.

RETINOIDS IN HUMAN EPIDERMIS

A. Vahlquist

Department of Dermatology
University Hospital, Uppsala University
Uppsala, Sweden

Retinoids are essential for a normal epidermal differentiation, and a deficiency may cause hyperkeratotic metaplasia.[1] A quantitative analysis of the normally occurring retinoids in human epidermis was attempted in a search for abnormalities related to skin diseases responsive to vitamin A therapy.[2] For this purpose, epidermal shave biopsies were obtained from controls and patients with psoriasis and Darier's disease (keratosis follicularis). The samples were hydrolyzed in KOH-ethanol and extracted with light petroleum. High-performance liquid chromatography (HPLC) showed at least two reproducible peaks in normal skin extracts, the last of which was conclusively identified as all-*trans*-retinol.[2] The other peak was markedly increased in hyperkeratotic skin lesions. A partial characterization of this material revealed a compound with a MW of 284 daltons and an absorption maximum at 352 nm. Its identity was subsequently established as 3,4-dehydroretinol (vitamin A_2).[3] The mean concentration of dehydroretinol in extracts of normal epidermis and of the uninvolved skin of the patients was 0.26 μg/g protein. The corresponding values were 1.25 and 1.8 μg/g protein, respectively, for skin lesions of patients with psoriasis and Darier's disease. At present the true nature of this compound in unhydrolyzed skin remains to be determined. The possibility that it represents a hydrolytic product of, for example, some hydroxylated or conjugated retinoid cannot be excluded. The reason for the accumulation of this retinoid in dyskeratotic skin lesions is also obscure. One possibility is that its further metabolization to other retinoids is defective.

REFERENCES

1. WOLBACH, S.B. & O.A. BESSY. 1942. Tissue changes in vitamin deficiencies. Physiol. Rev. **22**:233.
2. VAHLQUIST, A., J.B. LEE & G. MICHAËLSSON. 1979. Vitamin A in normal and diseased human skin. Invest. Dermatol. **72**: 271.
3. VAHLQUIST, A. 1980. The identification of dehydroretinol (vitamin A_2) in human skin. Experientia **36**: 317.

GLYCOSYLATION REACTIONS AND TUMOR ESTABLISHMENT: MODULATION BY VITAMIN A*

D. James Morré,[†,‡] Kim E. Creek,[‡] Dorothy M. Morré,[§]
and Carol L. Richardson[‡]

Departments of [†] *Medicinal Chemistry,*
[‡] *Biological Sciences, and* [§] *Foods and Nutrition*
and Purdue Cancer Center
Purdue University
West Lafayette, Indiana 47907

Vitamin A is important in maintaining and inducing differentiated functions of epithelial tissues caused by a deficiency of vitamin A. Alterations include a decrease in the number of mucus-secreting cells and the occurrence of squamous metaplasia[1] similar to that induced by chemical carcinogens.[2] Mucus membranes of mucus epithelia change to a single layer of epithelial cells with overlying layers of keratin, resembling those of the skin. Conversely, excess amounts of vitamin A cause keratinizing tissues to become mucus-secreting.[3-5]

Studies with experimental animals exposed to carcinogenic polycyclic aromatic hydrocarbons have shown the value of vitamin A in protecting against squamous metaplasia. Saffiotti *et al.*[6] demonstrated that intratracheal administration of benzo(a)pyrene to Syrian golden hamsters induced squamous metaplasia in the tracheobronchial mucosa. However, vitamin A palmitate administered orally following the carcinogen, markedly inhibited both squamous metaplasia and development of squamous tumors. Squamous metaplasia induced by benzo(a)pyrene was inhibited in organ transplants of hamster trachea by vitamin A.[7] Additionally, supplemental vitamin A prevented cancer of the forestomach and cervix in hamsters treated with polycyclic aromatic hydrocarbons,[8] and Davis[9] found that papillomas induced by 7, 12-dimethylbenz(a)anthracene in mice were delayed for 2 weeks and papillomas disappeared at a high rate in vitamin A-supplemented animals. Thus, many reports point to the effectiveness of vitamin A in inhibiting or preventing development of epithelial cancer.

The molecular mechanism of how vitamin A controls growth and differentiation of epithelial tissue or the basis of its antitumor action are still unknown. The action of retinoids appears to be opposite to that of tumor promoters. Verma *et al.*[10] have shown that vitamin A inhibits the activity of a phorbol ester (TPA) in promotion of skin papilloma formation as well as the TPA-induced epidermal ornithine decarboxylase, an activity consistently elevated following administration of the promoter. Thus, it might be argued that vitamin A may not in itself prevent cancer but may decrease the rate of tumorigenesis through some sort of antipromoter activity.

Hepatoma lines are generally unresponsive to retinoids. Nevertheless, over the past several years, we have investigated effects of vitamin A administered to rodents on various cell surface parameters of livers of animals bearing transplantable hepatocellular carcinomas. Vitamin A was found to alter glycolipid metabolism, especially the activities of several glycolipid and glycoprotein

* This work was supported in part by grants from the American Cancer Society and National Institutes of Health CA 18801.

367

TABLE 1

PERCENT OF RATS WITH TUMORS AT 42 DAYS POST-INJECTION OF TRANSPLANTABLE
HEPATOMAS WHEN DIETARY REGIMENS WERE INITIATED ON DAY OF TRANSPLANT*

Dietary Group	Percent of Animals with Tumors
Deficient	80
Adequate	80
Excess	60

* The tumor line was a nonmetastatic, poorly differentiated hepatoma designated
RLT-2. Results are from 10 animals per dietary group. From Morré et al.[22].

glycosyltransferases in normal liver and to exert a variable but discernible effect
on establishment of transplantable hepatomas. Subsequent investigations have
revealed a more reproducible effect of the vitamin on establishment of secondary
metastatic foci with hepatoma lines that are metastatic to the lung. The findings
suggest one mechanism whereby vitamin A may exert a chemopreventative action that is consistent with vitamin A effects on normal liver, but which may differ from other effects including the antipromoter activity.

MATERIALS AND METHODS

Experimental Animals, Tumor Growth Studies, and Hepatoma Lines

Weanling male inbred rats (CDF; Charles River Breeding Laboratories) were
randomly divided into three groups and fed diets containing no, adequate (4000
IU/kg diet), or excessive amounts of vitamin A (400,000 IU/kg diet). Vitamin A
was in the form of retinyl acetate. The rats were housed individually in suspended mesh galvanized cages in a room thermostatically maintained at 21° C and
40% relative humidity with alternating 12-hr periods of light and dark. Food intake and weight gain were recorded weekly.

The primary hepatocellular carcinomas from which transplantable hepatocellular carcinomas were derived were induced in male CDF rats by acetyl-
aminofluorene according to Merritt et al.[11] Tumor transplantations were as
follows. Viable tumor tissue of syngeneic donor rats was dissected free of connective tissue and hemorrhagic areas under balanced salt solution at room

TABLE 2

PERCENT OF RATS WITH TUMORS WHEN DIETARY REGIMENS WERE INITIATED
TWO WEEKS PRIOR TO DAY OF TRANSPLANT*

Dietary Group	Days Post-transplant (% Animals with Tumors)			
	21	28	35	42
Deficient	0	10	40	50
Adequate	10	90	90	90
Excess	0	10	20	40

* The tumor line was a nonmetastatic, poorly differentiated hepatoma designated RLT-2.
Results are from 10 animals per dietary group. From Morré et al.[22]

temperature. The tumor tissue was then transferred to a second aliquot of balanced salt solution and finely minced. Approximately 10^6 cells were injected by means of a trocar into the subcutaneous scapular region of the recipient animal.

Animals were examined daily for external manifestations of tumor presence. Tumor mass was estimated from measurements with a vernier caliper of two tumor dimensions. The following mathematical formula was used to determine approximate tumor mass: $M = 4/3 \, \pi(a^2/4)b/2$[12] where a and b are two dimensions (perpendicular axes) measured and M = tumor mass. At the termination of the study, animals were killed and tumor tissues and livers removed. Pulmonary metastases were confirmed by observing tumor foci on the surface of the lung and from histological analyses. Vitamin A concentration of liver and tumor mass was determined according to the procedure of Bayfield.[13] Protein was determined according to Bradford[14] or Lowry *et al.*[15]

Extraction and Analyses of Gangliosides

Gangliosides were isolated either by chloroform-methanol extraction[16] or by

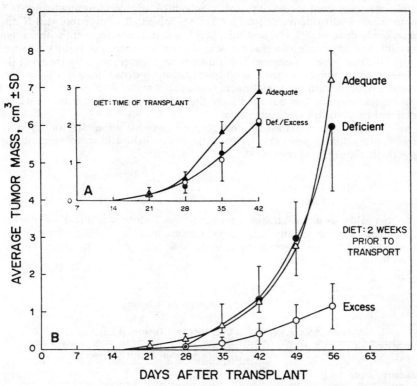

FIGURE 1. Effect of vitamin A on tumor mass. Rats were injected with poorly differentiated but nonmetastatic transplantable hepatocellular carcinoma cells (RLT-2) at the time of initiation of the dietary regimens (A) or two weeks post-initiation of the dietary regimens (B). Results are average tumor mass ± standard deviation for 10 animals. (From Morré *et al.*[22] Used with permission.)

TABLE 3

EFFECT OF DIETARY VITAMIN A ON METASTATIC SPREAD OF HEPATOCELLULAR CARCINOMAS
IN RATS AT 100 DAYS POST-INJECTION*

Dietary Group	Animals with Pulmonary Metastases (%)
Deficient	60
Adequate	75
Excess	0

* Dietary regimens were initiated two weeks prior to transplant with a metastatic hepatocellular carcinoma line designated H-2. Results are from 10 to 12 animals per dietary treatment group. From Morré et al.[22].

the method of Ledeen et al.,[17] the latter appropriately modified to guard against losses of gangliosides during extraction and purification. Individual ganglioside components of extracts of known sialic acid content were isolated and identified by thin-layer chromatography on silica gel G plates. Three different solvent combinations were used to develop plates: Solvent A = chloroform-methanol-28% ammonium hydroxide-water (60:35:7:3, v/v), Solvent B = propanol -1.0 N ammonium hydroxide (7:3, v/v) and Solvent AA = double development with solvent system A. Ganglioside composition was determined from the results obtained with all three solvent systems. The amounts were determined by spraying the plates with resorcinol reagent[18] with quantitation by densitometry. Values were corrected for the number of sialic acid residues per molecule of ganglioside. Total ganglioside content was obtained from the same tissue as that from which individual gangliosides were separated.

Chromatographic standards and glycosphingolipid acceptors for glycosyltransferase activities were prepared as described.[19] Sialic acid was determined by the thiobarbituric acid method.[20]

Neutral Lipids

Neutral lipids were extracted as described by Ledeen et al.[17] and analyzed by thin-layer chromatography with development in chloroform-methanol-water (70:22:3, v/v). Plates were sprayed with 50% sulfuric acid to detect neutral glycolipids.

TABLE 4

VITAMIN A CONCENTRATION IN LIVERS AND TUMORS (RLT-2) OF RATS

	Vitamin A (μg/mg Protein)*	
Dietary Group	Liver	Tumor
Deficient	0.08 ± 0.03	0.06 ± 0.03
Adequate	1.73 ± 0.25	0.15 ± 0.06
Excess	170.11 ± 30.52	1.90 ± 0.18

* Mean ± standard error of six rats per dietary group after 8 weeks. From Morré et al.[22]

TABLE 5

EFFECT OF DIETARY VITAMIN A ON TOTAL GANGLIOSIDES OF RAT LIVER AND OF A
TRANSPLANTABLE METASTATIC HEPATOMA LINE (H-2)

| Dietary Group | Ganglioside Sialic acid, nmoles/mg Protein | |
	Liver*	Hepatomas†
Deficient	0.26 ± 0.02	1.55
Adequate	0.33 ± 0.02	1.70
Excess	0.26 ± 0.02	1.80

* Mean ± standard deviation of 8 animals per dietary group after 12 weeks.
† Average of duplicate determinations from pooled tumors of 8 animals after 8 weeks.

RESULTS

With the transplantable hepatocellular carcinomas under investigation, vitamin A had little effect on tumor establishment when rats were subcutaneously injected with hepatoma cells on the initial day of the dietary regimen (TABLE 1, FIG. 1). However, when rats were started on the dietary regimens 2 weeks prior to the injection of hepatoma cells, tumors were fewer and appeared later under conditions of either vitamin A deficiency or excess in some (TABLE 2) but not all experiments. In this particular experiment, by day 21 post-injection, 10% of the animals in the group fed adequate amounts of vitamin A had tumors and by day 28, 90% of the animals in this group exhibited palpable tumors. In both the deficient and excess vitamin A groups, there were no signs of tumors at day 21 with only 10% of the animals in both groups having tumors at day 28 post-injection. Similar results were obtained with transplantable mammary carcinomas.[21] In general, there were no inhibitory effects of the vitamin on growth of tumors once established (FIG. 1).

Based on these preliminary findings, studies were extended to metastatic hepatoma lines to determine if a similar effect of the vitamin might be observed on establishment of metastases at sites distant from the primary tumor mass. These studies involved the H-2 line derived from RLT-1 in tissue culture, a hepatoma line metastatic to the lung. Cells were again injected 2 weeks following the initiation of the dietary vitamin A regimen. We were encouraged to find that animals fed excess vitamin A had no metastases to the lung while 75% of the

TABLE 6

EFFECT OF DIETARY VITAMIN A ON THE RELATIVE PERCENT OF CONSTITUENT GANGLIOSIDES
OF RAT LIVER AFTER 3 MONTHS

| Dietary Group | Percent of Total Ganglioside Sialic Acid | | | | | Ratio $\frac{G_{M1} + G_{D1a}}{G_{D1b} + G_T}$ |
	G_{M3}	G_{M2}	$G_{M1} + G_{D1a}$	G_{D3}	$G_{D1a} + G_T$	
Deficient*	48	1	24	9	19	1.3
Adequate†	42	1	11	0	38	0.3
Excess†	41	3	20	17	19	1.1

* Average of 5 determinations.
† Average of 10 determinations.

TABLE 7

EFFECT OF DIETARY VITAMIN A ON THE RELATIVE PERCENT OF DIFFERENT GANGLIOSIDES OF
A TRANSPLANTABLE METASTATIC HEPATOMA LINE H-2 AFTER 8 WEEKS*

| | Hepatomas from Animals Fed: | | | | | | | | | | | | Control Liver | | | |
| | Adequate Vitamin A | | | | No Vitamin A | | | | Excess Vitamin A | | | | | | | |
Ganglioside	A	B	AA	Mean	A	B	AA	Mean	A	B	AA	Mean	A	B	AA	Mean
G_M3	51	46	45	47	52	40	46	46	51	47	45	47	47	44	50	47
G_M2	6	18	6	10	3	22	8	11	8	13	8	10	6	16	10	10
G_D3	3	6	3	4	4	5	3	4	3	5	3	4	2	7		4
G_M1	18	[18	17	17	18	[18	14	15	21	[23	23	22	15	[17	12	12
G_D2	4	5	5	4	7		7	6	6		7	6	3		6	4
G_D1a	11	5	11	9	11	8	9	9	8	4	9	7	11	7	10	9
G_D1b	4	8	8	5	3		8	5.5	[2		2	2	3		3	3
G_T	3	[7	5	4	2	[7	5	3.5	[2	[4	3	2	13	[9	9	11
G_D2:G_D1b + G_T		0.3				0.7				1.5				0.3		
G_M1 + G_D1a:G_D1b + G_T		2.9				2.7				7.3				1.5		

* Values were corrected for numbers of sialic acid residues/molecule of ganglioside. Brackets indicate incompletely resolved components. Letters A, B and AA refer to different chromatographic systems (see text).

animals in the adequate group showed pulmonary metastases (TABLE 3). Unlike the results on establishment of primary tumors, vitamin A deficiency had little or no effect on establishment of metastases, with 60% of the animals in the deficient group developing lung involvement. Hepatocellular growth in the lungs was verified by histological analyses with all three dietary groups. Primary tumors of animals fed excess vitamin A were generally much more friable than those of animals fed adequate vitamin A or of those fed diets deficient in vitamin A. Vitamin A content of livers paralleled intake while that in tumors reflected but did not parallel the amounts fed (TABLE 4).

To relate loss of metastatic ability (ability for metastases to establish at distant sites), we investigated the status of putative receptors for fibronectin, proteins that bind cells to an underlying substrate or stroma. These receptors are thought to be principally di- and trisialogangliosides.

Dietary vitamin A had little or no effect on total ganglioside content of either liver or hepatocellular carcinomas (TABLE 5). However alterations were observed in ganglioside composition. In livers of animals of both the vitamin A-deficient and excess groups there was a marked decrease in $G_{DIb} + G_T$ (TABLE 6).

When tumors were analyzed, similarly altered ganglioside patterns were obtained. Primary tumors of animals fed excess vitamin A showed decreased levels of G_{DIb} and G_T and an almost complete absence of higher homologs (TABLE 7; FIGS. 2-4). A similar result was obtained with control and vitamin A-treated (10^{-5} M) BALB/c 3T12-3 cells obtained from Dr. L. De Luca, National Cancer Institutes (TABLE 8; FIG. 5). The pattern of ganglioside change was in the direction of reductions (approximately 50%) in the putative fibronectin receptors, G_{DIb} and G_T.

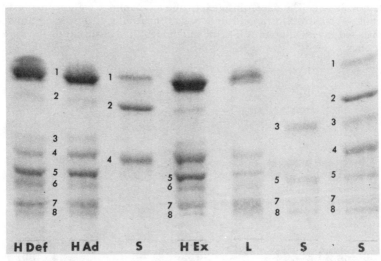

FIGURE 2. Thin-layer chromatogram of gangliosides for hepatomas (H) of animals fed no (Def), adequate (Ad) and excess (Ex) vitamin A levels in the diet in comparison to normal liver (L). Gangliosides for which standards (S) were available were 1 = G_{M3}, 2 = G_{M2}, 3 = G_{D3}, 4 = G_{M1}, 5 = G_{D1a}, 7 = G_{DIb} and 8 = G_T. Standard gangliosides (10-20 nmoles) and approximately 80 nmoles of ganglioside sialic acid from each tissue source were separated on silica gel G plates with double development system A and visualized with resorcinol reagent.[18] 6 = G_{D2}.

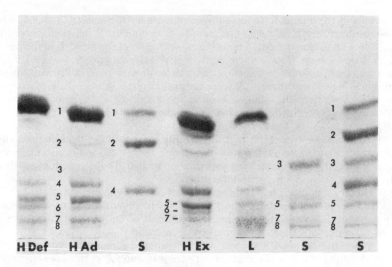

FIGURE 3. As in FIGURE 2 except single development with solvent system A.

These vitamin A-treated cells also showed reduced levels of bound fibronectin as evidenced from analyses of profiles of radioiodinated surface proteins (L. De Luca, personal communication).

Neutral lipids were elevated above those in normal livers in the hepatomas (data not shown). The major differences due to vitamin A were reduction in the amount of trihexosylceramide and higher neutral glycolipids in tumors of animals fed excess vitamin A (FIG. 6) and unidentified changes due to vitamin A deficiency.

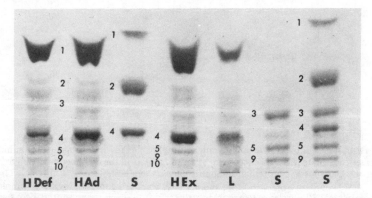

FIGURE 4. As in FIGURE 2 except solvent system B. 9 = G_{D1b} + G_T, 10 = higher ganglioside homologs more complex than G_T.

TABLE 8

EFFECT OF 10^{-5} M RETINOIC ACID ON DIFFERENT GANGLIOSIDES OF BALB/c 3T12-3 CELLS

	% of Total	
Ganglioside	No Retinoic Acid	Plus Retinoic Acid
G_{M3}	50	52
G_{M2}	18	20
G_{M1}	6	12
G_{D1a}	8	7
G_{D3}	4	4
G_{D2}	2	2
G_{D1b}	11	3
G_T	1	0
$G_{D2}{:}G_{D1b} + G_T$	0.2	0.7
$G_{M1} + G_{D1a}{:}G_{D1b} + G_T$	1.2	6.3
$G_{D1a} + G_{D1b} + G_T$ (nmoles/mg protein)*	1.6	0.9

    * Based on a total ganglioside content of 8.0 nmoles/mg protein for cells in the absence of retinoic acid and 8.9 nmoles/mg protein for cells treated with retinoic acid.

DISCUSSION

In clinical cancer the formation of metastases most often seems to defeat therapeutic efforts. There is increasing evidence that metastases result from sub-populations of tumor cells with specific phenotypic characteristics that enable them to invade surrounding host tissues, penetrate into the lymphatics and/or the

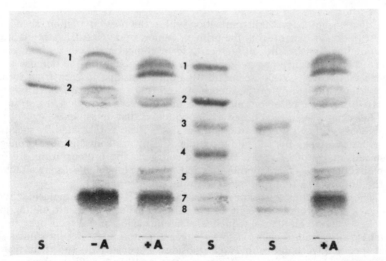

FIGURE 5. Thin-layer chromatogram of ganglioside of BALB/c 3T12-3 cells obtained through the courtesy of Dr. L. M. De Luca. Labeling and solvent system as for FIGURE 2. The comparison is between control cells (− A) and cell treated with 10^{-5} M retinoic acid (+ A).

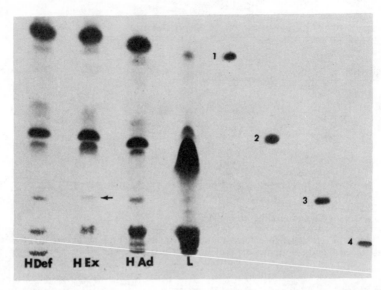

FIGURE 6. Thin-layer chromatogram of neutral lipids of a transplanted metastatic hepatoma line H-2 obtained from animals fed different dietary vitamin A regimens as in FIGURE 2. The solvent system was chloroform-methanol-water (70:20:3, v/v). 1 = glucosylceramide, 2 = lactosylceramide, 3 = digalactosylglucosylceramide, 4 = N-acetylgalactosaminylgalactosylgalactosylglucosylceramide (globoside). Spots were visualized by spraying with H_2SO_4 and charring. Arrow indicates the reduction in trihexosylceramide observed in tumors of animals fed diets containing excess vitamin A.

vascular system, survive dissemination within the host circulation, successfully arrest in organs distant from the primary tumor, undergo extravasation into the surrounding tissues, and proliferate to form clinical metastases.[23,24] At each of these stages, the invading cells must survive assault from the defense mechanisms of the host. What seems to separate metastatic disease from localized neoplasia is the ability of the metastatic cell to leave the primary tumor mass, break through the basement membrane, and attach to an underlying stroma.

Reasonably well-established evidence shows that invasiveness or lack of invasiveness of a cell within an organized tissue mass is regulated by specific interactions between the cell and a complex meshwork consisting of fibronectins, collagens and proteoglycans. While the collagens and proteoglycans are major constituents of basement membranes and substrata to which cells are attached, it is the fibronectins that link the cells to the collagen (FIG 7).

The fibronectins (also known as CPS or LETS) are high molecular weight adhesive glycoproteins present on the cell surface as well as circulating in the blood.[25-27] They bind to a sequence of amino acids of collagen near the collagenase site[28] and to cells via specific receptor molecules. Recent studies show that specific glycosphingolipids (gangliosides), especially di- and trisialogangliosides, are able to interact with fibronectins and block cell attachment to the fibronectin-collagen complex.[29] These and other lines of evidence suggest that the fibronectin receptors at the cell surface are glycolipids and that these glycolipids (or other glycoconjugates with similar oligosaccharide chains) are involved in the binding sites for fibronectins.

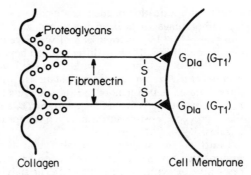

FIGURE 7. Diagrammatic representation of the fibronectin links that bind cells to a collagen-rich substratum.

The absence or reduction in amount of fibronectin at the surface of transformed cells is a reproducible correlate of metastatic ability.[30-32] The reductions are due in part to decreased biosynthesis and increased turnover but result in large measure from the failure of the cells to bind either fibronectin they produce or that already present in the medium. Once no longer bound to the collagen substratum via fibronectin links, the cells gain mobility and the freedom of movement associated with metastasis.

A second reproducible correlate of malignancy is a reduction or loss of di- and trisialogangliosides,[33-37] the putative fibronectin receptors. The same phenome-

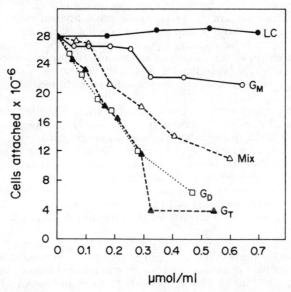

FIGURE 8. Effect of gangliosides and ceramides on cell adhesion. Gangliosides and ceramides were dissolved at 10 mg/ml in Eagle's medium and different amounts were added to collagen-coated culture dishes containing serum. After 1 hr, the cells were added and cell adhesion was assayed. Values represent duplicate measurements. The source of cells was freshly trypsinized Chinese hamster ovary cells. (From Kleinman *et al.*[29] Used with permission.)

non of a simplification of ganglioside patterns and loss of higher gangliosides during tumorigenesis has been found for solid tumors induced by chemical carcinogens.[19,38-40] In a comparison of well-circumscribed (PDH_{wc}) and poorly circumscribed (PDH_{pc}) poorly differentiated hepatomas, we found major reductions in contents of G_{D1a} and G_{T1} with the more invasive phenotype.[19] More recently, Kloppel *et al.*[41] reported that metastatic isolates of poorly circumscribed, poorly differentiated hepatomas of the rat show even further reductions in G_{D1a} and a nearly complete absence of G_{T1}. A return to a more normal ganglioside composition may occur post-metastasis with a reappearance of both di- and trisialogangliosides.

Further investigations revealed that these glycolipid alterations during tumorigenesis were a direct reflection of alterations in the activities of their respective biosynthetic enzymes.[39,43] The sialyltransferase responsible for the formation of G_{D1a} from its immediate precursor ganglioside in PDH_{pc} was 0.3 the level found in PDH_{wc} and correlated with reduced levels of G_{D1a}. Similarly, the entry enzyme into the pathway for formation of G_{T1} and higher homologs was reduced to about 0.1 normal levels.

Thus, the following hypothesis, summarized in FIGURE 9, is proposed to account for the ability of cells to metastasize.

(1) As a relatively late event in the tumorigenic cascade, the glycosyltransferases responsible for the continued formation of fibronectin receptors are repressed or rendered defective.

(2) As a result of altered glycosyltransferase activities, the cells' membranes become deficient in the fibronectin receptors G_{D1a}, G_{D1b} and G_{T1} (or other glycoconjugates with similar oligosaccharide chains).

(3) In the absence of fibronectin receptors on the cell surface, the cells no longer bind fibronectin, are freed from existing mobility restraints, and are able to migrate as an essential first step toward successful metastasis.

(4) Once the cells have gained metastatic potential and are free to migrate from the primary mass, these enzymes and pathways may be restored at a later time prior to or during establishment of secondary foci.

(5) Finally, the cells once again may be able to bind fibronectin and grow as a solid tissue mass.

Presumably, this course of events could be repeated in successive cycles to permit invasion by cells from secondary foci in highly disseminated disease.

At least with the transplantable hepatomas investigated here, the effect of vitamin A may be to prevent step 4 or step 5 – the establishment of metastases at distant sites. Glycolipid analyses reveal that vitamin A appears to prevent the reappearance of the putative fibronectin receptors, the di- and trisialogangliosides. These findings would account for the friable texture observed with hepatomas of animals receiving vitamin A excess. The inability of such cells to bind fibronectin might well account for their inability to establish as secondary metastatic foci.

The hope is that vitamin A might be used experimentally to prevent metastatic establishment in disseminated disease where metastatic cells are present in the circulation or as small foci but prior to major secondary involvement. Under these conditions, it may be possible to surgically remove the primary tumor and then use hypervitamin A therapy to prevent establishment of already circulating cells.

The mechanism by which vitamin A reduces the amount of fibronectin receptor is unknown, but an action by blocking the galactosyltransferase of G_{D1b} formation is indicated (FIGURE 10). This is evidenced by a decrease in both G_{D1b} and

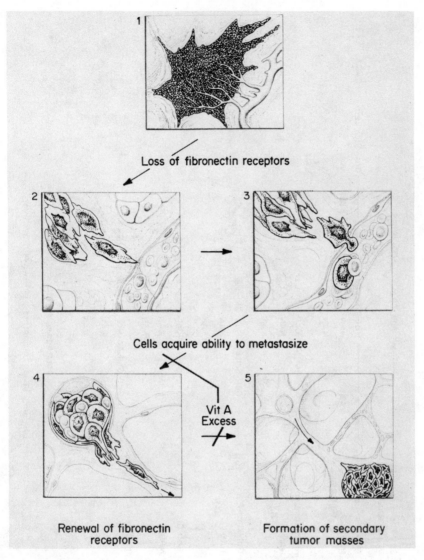

1

Loss of fibronectin receptors

2 3

Cells acquire ability to metastasize

4 5

Vit A
Excess

Renewal of fibronectin
receptors

Formation of secondary
tumor masses

FIGURE 9. Hypothetical scheme to account for the ability of cells to metastasize (adapted from Nicolson *et al.*[45]) and steps that may be blocked by vitamin A.

higher homologs as well as a build-up of the precursors to G_{Dlb} This particular galactosyltransferase has been little studied principally due to the lack of ready availability of its substrate G_{D2}. Few tissues accumulate G_{D2}, so isolation from natural sources has not been possible. Merritt *et al.*[39] prepared small amounts of G_{D2} by removal of the terminal galactose of G_{Dlb} from bovine brain with a β-galactosidase from rat liver lysosomes. In order to pursue the possibility that the galactosyltransferase of G_{Dlb} formation is blocked, it will be necessary to

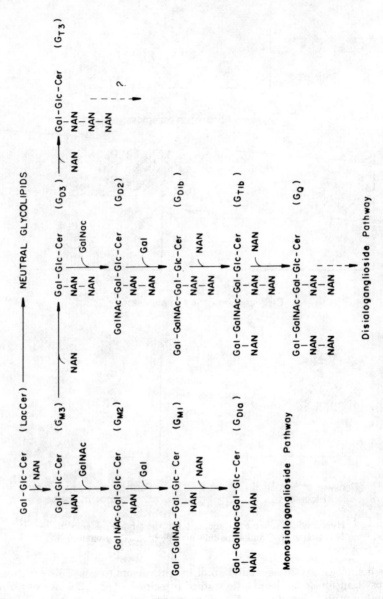

FIGURE 10. Ganglioside biosynthetic pathways of rat liver.

secure substantial amounts of G_{D2} substrate. This is currently under investigation.

The overall increase in neutral lipids and reduced trihexosylceramide is a characteristic of rat hepatomas.[42] The significance of a further reduction in trihexosylceramide by excess vitamin A is uncertain. A role for neutral glycolipids in regulating cell function has been suggested. The addition of globoside to transformed hamster cells produced a reduction in saturation density and growth rate, as well as increased adhesion between cells.[44]

SUMMARY

The ability of retinoids to prevent or alter the course of experimental tumorigenesis is well established. We have extended these observations to include effects on establishment of tumors and tumor metastases. A diet containing excess retinyl acetate fed to rats prior to injection of a metastatic line of transplantable hepatoma, prevented establishment of secondary tumor foci while 75% of the animals fed adequate retinyl acetate showed pulmonary metastases. Metastatic ability may be related to the ability to bind fibronectins, proteins that link cells to an underlying stroma. Findings suggest involvement of higher gangliosides in the attachment of cells to a fibronectin-collagen complex. Prior to metastasis, hepatoma lines become depleted in the putative fibronectin receptor gangliosides as an end result of a complex cascade of altered glycosyltransferase activities. After metastasis, fibronectin receptors are apparently restored in those secondary tumor foci that become established. Analyses suggest that excess vitamin A may prevent the reappearance of fibronectin receptor gangliosides so that secondary tumor foci do not establish.

REFERENCES

1. MOORE, T. 1967. *In* The Vitamins. W.H. Sebrell & R.S. Harris, Eds. Vol. 1:245–266, 280–294. Academic Press, New York.
2. HARRIS, C. C., M.B. SPORN, D.G. KAUFMAN, J.M. SMITH, F.E. JACKSON & U. SAFFIOTTI. 1972. J. Natl. Cancer Inst. **48**: 743–761.
3. MARCHOK, A.C., M.V. CONE & P. NETTESHEIM. 1975. Lab. Invest. **33**: 451–460.
4. DELUCA, L.M., M. SCHUMACHER & G. WOLF. 1970. J. Biol. Chem. **245**: 4551–4558.
5. WOLF, G. & L. DELUCA. 1969. *In* Fat-Soluble Vitamins. H.F. DeLuca & J. W. Suttie, Eds.: 257–265. University of Wisconsin Press. Madison, WI.
6. SAFFIOTTI, U., A. MONTESANO, R. SELLAKUMAR & S.A. BORG. 1967. Cancer **20**: 857–863.
7. CROCKER, T. T & H. M. SANDERS. 1970. Cancer Res. **30**: 1312–1318.
8. CHU, E.W. & R. A. MALMGREN. 1965. Cancer Res. **25**: 884–895.
9. DAVIES, R.E. 1967. Cancer Res. **27**: 237–241.
10. VERMA, A. K., B.G. SHAPAS, H.M. RICE & R.K. BOUTWELL. 1979. Cancer Res. **39**: 419–425.
11. MERRITT, W.D., T.W. KEENAN & D.J. MORRÉ. 1976. Cancer Biochem. Biophys. **1**: 179–185.
12. SEDLACEK, H.H., MESSMAN, H. & SEILER, R.D. 1975. Int. J. Cancer **15**: 409–416.
13. BAYFIELD, R.F. 1975. Anal. Biochem. **64**: 403–413.
14. BRADFORD, M.M. 1976. Anal. Biochem. **72**:248–254.
15. LOWRY, O.H., N.J. ROSEBROUGH, A.L. FARR & R.J. RANDALL. 1951. J. Biol. Chem. **193**: 265–275.

16. FOLCH, J., M. LEES & G.H. SLOANE STANLEY. 1957. J. Biol. Chem. **226:** 497–509.
17. LEDEEN, R. W., R.K. YU & L.F. ENG. 1973. J. Neurochem. **21:** 820–839.
18. SVENNERHOLM, L. 1957. Biochim. Biophys. Acta **24:** 604–611.
19. MERRITT, W.D., C.L. RICHARDSON, T.W. KEENAN & D.J. MORRÉ. 1978. J. Natl. Cancer Inst. **60:** 1313–1327.
20. WARREN, L. 1959. J. Biol. Chem. **234:** 1971–1975.
21. RICHARDSON, C.L. 1976. Doctoral Thesis. Purdue University.
22. MORRÉ, D.M., T.M. KLOPPEL, A.L. ROSENTHAL & P.C. FINK, J. Nutr. **110:** 1629–1634.
23. FIDLER, I. J. 1979. J. Supramol. Struct. Suppl. **3:** 165.
24. POSTE, G. 1979. J. Supramol. Struct. Suppl. **3:** 165.
25. HYNES, R.O. 1973. Proc. Natl. Acad. Sci. USA **70:** 3170–3174.
26. GAHMBERG, C. G. & S. HAKOMORI. 1973. J. Biol. Chem. **248:** 4311–4317.
27. YAMADA, K.M. & J.A. WESTON. 1975. Cell **5:** 75–81.
28. YAMADA, K.M., E.H. LIANG-HSIEN & K. OLDEN. 1979. J. Supramol. Struct. Suppl. **3:** 167.
29. KLEINMAN, H.K., G.R. MARTIN & P.H. FISHMAN. 1979. Proc. Natl. Acad. Sci. USA **76:** 3367–3371.
30. HYNES, R.O. 1976. Biochim. Biophys. Acta **458:** 73–107.
31. YAMADA, K.M. & K. OLDEN. 1978. Nature **275:** 179–184.
32. VAHERI, A. & D.F. MOSHER. 1978. Biochim. Biophys. Acta **516:** 1–25.
33. HAKOMORI, S. 1973. Adv. Cancer Res. **18:** 265–315.
34. HAKOMORI, S. 1975. Biochim. Biophys. Acta **417:** 55–89.
35. BRADY, R.O. & P.H. FISHMAN. 1974. Biochim. Biophys. Acta **355:** 121–148.
36. FISHMAN, P.H. & R.O. BRADY. 1976. Science **194:** 906–915.
37. RICHARDSON, C.L., S. BAKER, D.J. MORRÉ & T.W. KEENAN. 1975. Biochim. Biophys. Acta **417:** 175–186.
38. KEENAN, T.W. & D.J. MORRÉ. 1973. Science **182:** 935–937.
39. MERRITT, W.D. J. MORRÉ & T.W. KEENAN. 1978. J. Natl. Cancer Inst. **60:** 1329–1337.
40. MORRÉ, D.J., T.M. KLOPPEL, W.D. MERRITT & T.W. KEENAN. 1978. J. Supramol. Struct. **9:** 157–177.
41. KLOPPEL, T.M., D.J. MORRÉ & L.B. JACOBSEN. J. Supramol. Struct. In press.
42. WALTER, V.P., T.M. KLOPPEL, I.G. DEUMLING & D.J. MORRÉ. Cancer Biochem. Biophys. In press.
43. MERRITT, W.D., D.J. MORRÉ, R. L. DOAK & T.W. KEENAN. Cancer Biochem. Biophys. In press.
44. LAINE, R.A. & S. HAKOMORI. 1973. Biochem. Biophys. Res. Commun. **54:** 1039–1045.
45. NICOLSON, G.T. 1979. Sci. Am. **240:** 66–93.

BIOCHEMICAL SYSTEMS: SUMMARY AND FUTURE

James Allen Olson

Department of Biochemistry and Biophysics
Iowa State University
Ames, Iowa 50011

The conference has been like a dinner party – a successful dinner party, I might add. The hosts were wise in inviting a mixed group of people, so that the individual guest both encountered many new people with refreshingly different views and approaches as well as relaxed with a comforting number of old friends and colleagues. The intellectual repast has been interesting and challenging, the conversation bright, the personal interaction joyful; now all that remains is to blow out the dinner-table candles, or perhaps more pragmatically, to load the dishwasher.

My charge is to summarize the more biochemical papers in the conference and, rather presumptuously I feel, to talk of the future. Although I shall address these matters to some degree, I wish to start by musing about the nature of the conference. I was struck first of all by its vitality, and particularly by the extent of interaction among participants in the broad spectrum of fields represented. Five years ago such a conference would not have been called, and if called, would probably not have been successful. The biochemists would have been bored by papers on the gross effects of huge doses of innumerable synthetic drugs, chemically but not physiologically related to vitamin A, on the induction of tumors, all expressed in an incomprehensible jargon. For their part, cancer researchers would have spent more and more time talking to colleagues in the hall rather than listening to a dreary sequence of papers on protein purification, enzyme kinetics, and the chemical and physical characterization of retinol metabolites. What relevance could that possibly have to cancer research? But that situation has now changed; the fields have significant overlap, and in all probability this overlap will increase in coming years.

But what indeed is responsible for this change of attitude, this growing interrelationship between two such disparate groups? First of all, with the increased sophistication of model systems in cancer research, the availability of new retinoids that act at very low concentrations, the identification of biochemical markers of carcinogen and promoter action, and the selective effects of retinoids on these actions, the realization has grown in both groups that we are dealing, at least in some cases, with relatively specific biochemical events, and not solely with the irreversible flattening of tumor cells, literally bashed by a sledgehammer-like dose of retinoids. The second converging interest has been the growing attention paid by biochemists to the molecular role of vitamin A in cellular differentiation. That is *The Big Question* in pure vitamin A research, and all of us would love to find the answer. Indeed, I am sure we all nurture lovely but tender ideas, some engendered by this meeting, which we are going to rush back to our laboratories and test. But differentiation, or the lack of it, has always been a central issue in the cancer field, and the thought that retinoids might act by stimulating the differentiation of stem cells into some innocuous terminally differentiated form, draws the concepts and approaches of biochemists and cell biologists together. And then, these dreary cellular proteins that specifically bind vitamin A have not only been elegantly characterized in recent years, but also it appears that they may be either diagnostic for cancer or directly involved in the protective action of retinoids against neoplastic change. But we are not quite through in our litany of happy interactions.

The only extant hypothesis for the molecular role of retinol in cellular differentiation is that of L. DeLuca and Wolf, namely that retinol serves as a carrier for the incorporation of mannose into specific glycoproteins. Now whether or not that hypothesis ultimately proves to be correct, the fact that cell-surfaces interactions, which undoubtedly involve glycoproteins, both change during transformation and are affected by retinoids has focused the attention of both groups on this important class of substances. Finally, biochemists and nutritionists, long content with their vitamin A-deficient rats, liver homogenates, and separatory funnels, have become increasingly interested in simplifying their models by using tissue and cell culture techniques, procedures that have long been employed most skillfully by our cancer research colleagues. Thus we finally are starting to talk each other's language.

But what of the biochemistry of vitamin A? Where are we and where are we going? The first observation, if one compares now with the past, is the general use of improved instrumentation, e.g. high pressure liquid chromatography (HPLC), mass spectrometry, and nuclear magnetic resonance, with resonance Raman spectroscopy waiting in the wings. These methods are of course not new, but present-day instrumentation has become extraordinarily sensitive and easy to use. A laboratory without HPLC these days, for example, is a real research pariah. The careful use of this improved methodology, so evident in the many papers presented here, has allowed the ready elucidation of several metabolic problems and a feasible approach to many others. On another tack, the specific intracellular carrier proteins for retinol and retinoic acid have been elegantly characterized and now studied in a large variety of tissues and cells. It is interesting and undoubtedly important that vitamin A is constantly chaperoned by specific proteins both in the plasma and within cells. But we still do not know the role played by these intracellular binding proteins. It is to keep vitamin A safe from outside dangers, such as oxidation, to protect other structures from the toxic ravages of vitamin A, or to direct the vitamin's action to some specific intracellular site? Does vitamin A serve as a derepressor of the genome? And if so, how? Biochemists brood about these questions, and some of us work actively in this important but difficult area.

The age-old concern about the active form of vitamin A in promoting cellular differentiation is alive and well in modern research activity. Retinol itself remains popular, particularly among conservatives, mannosylretinylphosphate has its strong adherents, and more recently a growing band of supporters wave flags for retinoic acid. Even in an election year, however, it is unlikely that the active form of vitamin A will be determined by vote. In all likelihood we will need to know more about the molecular function of vitamin A before the question of the active form can be resolved. Nonetheless it is safe to say that the active form will probably *not* be vitamin A alone, but rather a complex – presumably with protein – which lends stability and specificity to the molecule.

In its well-defined function in photoreception, vitamin A is active as a specific isomer, namely as 11-*cis*-retinal in rhodopsin and as 13-*cis*-retinal in bacteriorhodopsin. Growing attention is now being given to the process of vitamin A isomerization outside of the eye, and mainly to the 13-*cis*: all *trans* interconversion. Although the impetus for this interest derives mainly from the efficacious use of 13-*cis*-retinoic acid against some types of cancer, the problem is of fundamental biochemical importance. Further studies on the mechanism of isomerization, both in the eye and elsewhere, seem well warranted.

But now let me express some notes of caution, particularly for those participants studying phenotypic changes in cells as a result of retinoid administration. Biochemists working with vitamin A are well aware of the instability of these compounds, and particularly when they are exposed to air and light. So it would be comforting to be assured that the retinoids added to tissue culture systems are both pure and chemically stable under the selected conditions of culture. And it would also be of interest to know both if the retinoids are rapidly metabolized by the culture cells and where they are localized within sensitive cells. In trying to define a unified molecular hypothesis of retinoid action in cultured cells, the observation that each cell line has its own characteristic and reacts differently to added retinoids is disquieting. Although such a variety of responses stuns one into silence relative to a possible molecular role, there must exist some underlying thread of consistency among this jungle of observations. Finally, we should note the difference between the *pharmacological* action of vitamin A, of which hypervitaminosis A is one expression, and its *physiological* action at low concentrations within epithelial cells. Quite possibly some effects of large and physiological doses may be similar, just as we know that some effects are quite different. The danger is in forgetting the distinction, i.e. in presuming that pharmacological actions are *necessarily* an extension of physiological roles.

But now, as the final candle flickers, we wish to thank our able and hard-working hosts, Luigi DeLuca and Stanley Shapiro, for putting together a fine conference, and our sponsor, the New York Academy of Sciences, for its expert and congenial arrangements.

ALTERED METABOLISM OF α-TOCOPHEROL BY LOW DIETARY LEVELS OF RETINOIC ACID

John G. Bieri and Teresa J. Tolliver

Laboratory of Nutrition and Endocrinology
National Institute of Arthritis, Metabolism and Digestive Diseases
National Institutes of Health
Bethesda, Maryland 20205

In the course of checking by high performance liquid chromatography the decline in plasma retinol when weanling rats were fed retinoic acid as the only form of vitamin A, we noted incidentally that the plasma α-tocopherol (α-T) of rats fed retinoic acid was only one-half the value of rats fed retinol. In subsequent experiments male weanling rats or day-old chicks (mixed sex) were fed purified diets with retinol or retinoic acid at 4-6 mg/kg diet, and dl-α-tocopheryl acetate varying from 20 to 150 mg/kg diet in different experiments.

In the first experiment with rats, after 2 weeks the tissue α-tocopherol levels (mean ± SE) for rats fed retinol or retinoic acid, respectively, were: plasma, 1184 ± 36 vs. 800 ± 69 μg/dl; liver, 318 ± 23 vs. 152 ± 31 μg/liver; adipose, 130 ± 5 vs. 69 ± 5 μg/fat pad (all differences, p<.01). Thus, the depressed plasma concentration was reflected in the liver and adipose contents.

In a second rat experiment, in addition to groups fed retinol or retinoic acid, a third group was fed both compounds, each at 4 mg/kg diet; α-T was 20 mg/kg. After 4 weeks, plasma α-tocopherol (μg/dl) for each group, respectively, was: 326 ± 24; 225 ± 20; 199 ± 24 (both retinoic groups significantly lower than the retinol group). Thus, dietary retinoic acid depressed plasma α-tocopherol even in the presence of dietary retinol. Plasma total lipids (mg/dl) were: 685 ± 60, 614 ± 52, and 579 ± 43, and plasma triglycerides were: 89 ± 10, 81 ± 11, and 83 ± 9.5 In this as in all experiments, there was no significant alteration of plasma lipids by retinoic acid.

In a third study, male and female weanling rats were fed the same diets with retinol or retinoic acid and their blood analyzed after 4 and 5 weeks. Females fed retinoic acid had a smaller decrease in plasma tocopherol at 4 weeks than did males, and by 5 weeks females showed no difference between retinol and retinoic acid groups. The twofold difference in males fed the two forms of vitamin A persisted.

In a 21 day chick experiment, the values for groups fed retinol or retinoic acid, respectively, were: plasma α-T (μg/dl) 2660 ± 158 vs. 662 ± 54; liver α-T (μg/g) 22.5 ± 2.1 vs. 5.6 ± 1.7 (p<0.01 for both comparisons). The chick thus also demonstrates the effect of retinoic acid, perhaps more so than the rat. When chicks were given a single oral dose of ^{3}H-α-tocopherol and killed after 2.5 hr, the values for retinol and retinoic acid birds were respectively (percent of dose in entire tissue): blood, 1.41 ± 0.06 vs. 0.31 ± 0.08; liver, 2.45 ± 0.29 vs 0.43 ± 0.13 (both p's<0.01).

To determine if retinoic acid may cause an increased turnover of tissue tocopherol, two groups of 160 g rats with adequate stores of α-tocopherol and retinol were fed a tocopherol-free diet containing retinoic acid or no form of vitamin A. The decrease in plasma α-tocopherol was determined after 8, 15, and 22 days. At each period, there was no difference between rats fed retinoic acid or no vitamin A, and liver contents of α-tocopherol were similar. Thus, dietary retinoic acid did not accelerate the loss of endogenous tocopherol.

A preliminary absorption study with ^{3}H-α-tocopherol was conducted with rats in which the mesenteric lymph duct was cannulated. Collection of lymph hourly for 6 hr after an intraduodenal dose of an aqueous dispersion of labeled α-tocopherol gave $19.0 \pm 3.0\%$ absorption for rats fed retinol and $13.8 \pm 2.5\%$ for rats fed retinoic acid. On the basis of the chick and rat labeling studies, we postulate that low dietary levels of retinoic acid in some unknown manner decrease the absorption of α-tocopherol.

VITAMIN A-INDUCED MODULATION OF THE TRANSFORMED CELL PHENOTYPE *IN VITRO*

L. David Dion

Laboratory of Viral Carcinogenesis
National Cancer Institute
Bethesda, Maryland 20205

George E. Gifford

Department of Immunology and Medical Microbiology
University of Florida
Gainesville, Florida 32610

Our interest in vitamin A-induced modification of the transformed cell phenotype began several years ago while studying substances thought to be modifiers of interferon synthesis. It was eventually determined that vitamin A inhibition of interferon synthesis in L-929 cells was a consequence of the induction of a controlling protein.[1] During these studies, it was determined that retinoic acid (RA) also restored density-dependent inhibition of L-929 cell proliferation.[2] Two other cell lines (SVA31, B16C3) were studied to determine if this was a general phenomenon, but only the L-929 cell showed a density-dependent inhibition. Nevertheless, this observation suggested that retinoic acid might also affect other phenotypic markers of transformation in the L-929 cell line. RA treatment of L-929 cells did not prevent growth in low serum (1.0%) but did inhibit the growth of cells suspended in semi-solid media. Restoration of anchorage-dependent growth by RA was found to be neither unique to L-929 cells nor universal among the other cell lines tested. L-929, B16C3, and HeLa cells were identified as being susceptible to RA-induced inhibition of colony formation in semi-solid media. AV3, L132, CHO and SVA31 cells were identified as being resistant to RA when assayed in a similar manner. The inhibition of L-929 cell colony formation was specific for RA. Other natural analogs of vitamin A were at least 100 times less active. Synthetic vitamin A analogs demonstrated that the terminal group was important for activity. It is also shown that the ring structure can be modified substantially without significant loss of activity. The RA-induced inhibition of cell proliferation in semi-solid media was shown to be reversible in both the L-929 and HeLa cell lines.[3] In an effort to better characterize the RA-induced inhibition of anchorage-independent growth, experiments were conducted using HeLa cell spinner cultures. This technique has allowed us to investigate the RA-induced block with respect to the cell cycle. Spinner cultures of RA-inhibited cells were blocked in the G_1 phase, and this block was reversible by simultaneous removal of RA and attachment of the cells to a plastic tissue-culture surface. Studies with a synchronized cell population demonstrated that the RA had to be added during or before late S phase if the cells were to be blocked in the subsequent G_1 phase. Since the normal resting state of eukaryotic cells is usually in a portion of the G_1 phase, these observations strengthen the possibility that vitamin A may play a role in maintaining normal growth controls although, perhaps, under very specific conditons.

REFERENCES

1. BLALOCK, J.E. & G.E. GIFFORD. 1977. Retinoic acid (vitamin A acid) induced transcriptional control of interferon production. Proc. Natl. Acad. Sci. USA **74:** 5382–5386.
2. DION, L.D., J.E. BLALOCK & G.E. GIFFORD. 1977. Vitamin A-induced density-dependent inhibition of L-cell proliferation. J. Natl. Cancer Inst. **58:** 795–801.
3. DION, L.D., J.E. BLALOCK & G.E. GIFFORD. 1978. Retinoic acid and the restoration of anchorage dependent growth to transformed mammalian cells. Exp. Cell Res. **117:** 15–22.

RETINOIC ACID AND HYPERTRIGLYCERIDEMIA

Leonard E. Gerber and John W. Erdman, Jr.

Department of Food Science
University of Illinois
Urbana, Illinois 61801

Previous feeding experiments performed in our lab[1,2] have shown that hypertriglyceridemia was induced by vitamin A in cholesterol- or non-cholesterol-fed rats. All-*trans*-retinoic acid (RA) was more potent than retinyl acetate in eliciting this response. A series of experiments have been subsequently performed to further investigate the effects of RA administration on lipid metabolism in the rat.

Initially, the effects of all-*trans*-and 13-*cis*-RA were compared.[3] Rats were intraperitoneally injected or fed, for up to 8 days, either 1500, 3000, or 4500 μg/day of either all-*trans* or 13-*cis*-RA. All levels of all-*trans*-RA induced hypertriglyceridemia; however, only the highest intake of the 13-*cis* form was effective. Injection of the all-*trans* form consistently increased serum triglycerides. Retinoid-fed rats fasted for 6 hr prior to blood sampling demonstrated similar increases in serum triglycerides compared to their non-fasted controls, suggesting that the hypertriglyceridemia was unrelated to altered intestinal metabolism. Additionally, retinoid administration was found to reduce serum retinol at all levels tested with the all-*trans* form appearing to be more potent than the 13-*cis* isomer.

Three types of experiments were performed to characterize the hyperlipidemia. After feeding young adult male Sprague-Dawley rats supplemental retinoic acid (100 μg/g dry diet) for 3 days, and fasting them for 6–8 hr, the triglyceride, cholesterol, and phospholipid content of various serum lipoprotein fractions was determined. When compared to unsupplemented controls, both the VLDL and HDL fractions were found to harbor an elevated triglyceride content. While VLDL cholesterol and phospholipid content were also elevated in retinoic acid-fed rats, total serum cholesterol and phospholipids were not statistically altered. Serum triglyceride accumulation was measured in an *in vivo* system, employing Triton WR 1339 blockade of serum lipoprotein clearance. RA feeding resulted in greater serum triglyceride accumulation compared to controls, suggesting increased triglyceride secretion from the liver. *In vitro* experiments have shown increased incorporation of lipid precursors into fatty acids and glycerides in rat liver isolates incubated with retinoic acid.[4]

Since VLDL triglyceride is broken down by the lipoprotein lipase of extrahepatic tissues, the activity of the enzyme in several of these tissues was determined. Although perirenal adipose tissue lipoprotein lipase activity decreased by about 15% as a result of the intake of RA, more dramatic depressions of 76% and 64% were observed in red and white gastrocnemius muscle, respectively. Cardiac ventricular muscle lipoprotein lipase activity was not affected by retinoic acid feeding.

In conclusion, triglyceride metabolism is altered in rats administered excess vitamin A in cholesterol-free or cholesterol-containing diets. Hypertriglyceridemia is evident in both the fasted and fed state. All-*trans*-retinoic acid appears to be more potent than either retinyl acetate or 13-*cis*-retinoic acid in elevating serum triglycerides. Depression of serum retinol was noted with RA feeding. The results suggest an increased rate of VLDL triglyceride release from liver and a decreased capacity for tissue uptake in the vitamin A-fed rat.

REFERENCES

1. ERDMAN, J.W., JR. & L.W. SOLOMON. 1980. Lipids **15:** 157–162.
2. GERBER, L.E. & J.W. ERDMAN, JR. 1979. J. Nutr. **109:** 580–589.
3. GERBER, L.E. & J.W. ERDMAN, JR. 1980. J. Nutr. **110:**343–351.
4. ERDMAN, J.W., JR., J.G. ELLIOT & P.A. LACHANCE. 1977. Nutr. Rep. Int. **16:** 37–46.

METABOLITES OF RETINOL IN CULTURED HUMAN DERMAL FIBROBLASTS

Thomas D. Gindhart, Pangala V. Bhat, and Carol Silverman-Jones

National Cancer Institute
National Institutes of Health
Bethesda, Maryland 20205

Human individual variations in responsiveness to and metabolism of biologically active materials have been most extensively studied in cultured dermal fibroblasts. The effects of retinoids on mouse (Exp. Cell. Res. **119**: 289–299, 1979; J. Lip. Res. **20**: 357–362, 1979) and rat (Nature **276**: 272–274, 1978) fibroblasts have been well characterized, especially in terms of parameters relating to malignant transformation. Spontaneously transformed mouse fibroblasts (3T12-3 cells) have been shown to actively metabolize retinol to the hydrocarbon anhydroretinol as well as retinyl esters (J. Lip. Res. **20**: 357–362, 1979). Previous studies of cultured human dermal fibroblasts have demonstrated differential responses to retinol by cells from patients with Hurler's Syndrome (J. Exp. Med. **124**: 1181–1198, 1966). Cellular retinoic acid binding has recently been identified in human fibroblasts (Lacroix, Á., Anderson, G.D., and Lippman, M.E. Poster Paper, this volume), but two independent studies have failed to find in human fibroblasts cellular retinol-binding protein (Invest. Ophthalmal. **15**: 1017–1022, 1976; Lacroix, Á., et al. Poster Paper, this volume). Accordingly the present study was designed to identify the metabolites of retinol in dermal fibroblasts from four individuals.

Cells were cultured with [15¹⁴C]retinol in Ham's F-12 medium containing 15% FCS for 72 hr. Cell pellets were extracted with absolute methanol and the lipid extract analyzed by thin-layer chromatography on silica gel in toluene/chloroform/methanol (4/1/1) yielding three main peaks of radioactivity: one at R_fO, constituted less than 10%, one in the area of retinol constituted ∼ 40% and a main peak in the area of retinyl esters (∼ 50% of total). The identity of the various metabolities was verified by an improved reverse phase HPLC procedure (Anal. Biochem. **102**: 243–248, 1980).

Retinyl fatty acid esters represented 40–50% of the total lipid-extracted radioactivity. Retinol, the second most abundant species, represented 30–40% of the total. A third peak of highly polar metabolite(s) eluted in the area of mannosylretinylphosphate represented ∼ 4–5% of the radioactivity. The 13-*cis*-retinol isomer of retinol detected by HPLC accounted for 4–5% of the label. No form of retinoic acid was detected. Comparative studies of the metabolism of retinoids by fibroblasts from patients with genetically determined skin cancer are now in progress.

SCALES INTO FEATHERS—AN EFFECT OF RETINOIC ACID ON TISSUE INTERACTIONS IN THE DEVELOPING CHICK

Margaret H. Hardy

Department of Biomedical Sciences
University of Guelph
Guelph, Ontario, Canada

Danielle Dhouailly and Philippe Sengel

Laboratoire de Zoologie et de Biologie Animale
Université Scientifique et Médicale de Grenoble
Grenoble, France

Most domestic breeds of chicken have scales, but no feathers, on their feet. Large scales (*scuta*) form on days 9 to 11 on the anterior face of the shank and the upper surface of the toes; smaller scales (*scutella*) appear on day 11 on the posterior face of the shank; most of the smallest scales (*reticula*) form on days 12 and 13 on the plantar surface of the foot.

A single injection of 125 µg of retinoic acid (RA) into the amniotic cavity of F2 cross Wyandotte × Rhode Island Red chick embryos caused the formation of feathers on the foot scales by 17 days of incubation, in locations and percentages differing according to the age of embryos at the time of treatment. Injection at 10 days caused feathers to form on the feet in 57% of the embryos, almost all of which bore feathers on their scuta and scutella; a few reticula were occasionally affected. When treated at 11 days, 48% of embryos had feathered feet, the tarsometatarsal scutella and digital reticula being most frequently affected. Treatment at 12 days resulted in feathers on the feet of 15% of the embryos, all of which bore feathers on the reticula only, while the scuta and scutella were not affected.

It was concluded that the foot skin regions that were affected by RA treatment were those in which scale morphogenesis was starting or about to start at the time of injection. These regions contained preplacodal or placodal stages of scuta and scutella, and the pre-elevation or elevation states of reticula. The results of preliminary experiments with multiple injections[1] could be explained in a similar manner.

It is known from the tissue recombination work of Sengel, Dhouailly and others[2] that at these stages of development the dermis of the foot has already interacted with the epidermis, instructing it to "make appendages." The epidermis has not yet received from the dermis the second, specific instruction to "make scales and only scales." It appears that retinoic acid interferes with the second tissue interaction, and feather formation is no longer blocked. Although retinoic acid was probably degraded within one or two days after injection, feather development continued beyond hatching. In that this action of the retinoid was stage-dependent and perhaps irreversible, and permitted the unfolding of a new morphogenetic program on top of one already commencing, it resembles the transformation of developing mouse whisker follicles into mucus-secreting glands[3,4] rather than the retinoid-induced modulation of chick skin or other epithelia.

REFERENCES

1. DHOUAILLY, D. & M.H. HARDY 1978. Retinoic acid causes the development of feathers in the scale-forming integument of the chick embryo. Wilhelm Roux Arch. **185:** 195-201.
2. DHOUAILLY, D. 1978. Feather-forming capacities of the avian extraembryonic somatopleure. J. Emb. Exp. Morphol. **43:** 279-287.
3. HARDY, M.H. 1968. Glandular metaplasia of hair follicles and other responses to vitamin A excess in cultures of rodent skin. J. Emb. Exp. Morphol. **19:** 157-180.
4. HARDY, M.H. & C.G. BELLOWS 1978 The stability of vitamin A-induced metaplasia of mouse vibrissa follicles *in vitro.* J. Invest. Dermatol. **71:** 236-241.

DISPOSITION OF ORALLY ADMINISTERED
13-cis RETINOIC ACID IN MICE

D.L. Hill, J.R. Kalin, and M.E. Starling

Kettering–Meyer Laboratory
Southern Research Institute
Birmingham, Alabama 35250

The disposition of 13-cis retinoic acid (10 mg/kg, p.o.) was examined in male DBA mice using reversed-phase high pressure liquid chromatography (HPLC). Starved mice weighing 18–24 g were dosed by oral intubation with a 2 mg/ml solution of the drug in 0.9% saline containing 3% ethanol and 0.5% Tween 80, restrained for various periods of time, then sacrificed by cardiac puncture. Their tissues were removed, frozen on dry ice, and stored at $-20°C$. These tissues were then homogenized at $0°C$ in 2 ml/g of a solution containing 0.5 mg/ml each of EDTA and ascorbic acid using a Brinkman Polytron homogenizer. Homogenates were immediately extracted with 3 volumes of n-butanol-methanol (95:5, v/v) by occasional shaking for 30 min at $0°C$. Samples were centrifuged for 30 min at $5°C$ and the upper phases of the supernatant were analyzed by HPLC. Chromatography was performed using a Waters model 6000 pump, Model 440 UV detector (340 nm), and Model 710 automatic sample injector (WISP®). A Spectra-Physics Spherisorb ODS 5 μ column was used. Samples were eluted at ambient temperature with acetonitrile-1% ammonium acetate (5:3, v/v) at a flow rate of 1 ml/min. 13-cis Retinoic acid had a retention time of approximately 12 min in this system and was quantitated by measuring the recorded peak area (height × width at ½ height). A plot of peak area versus the amount of retinoic injected was linear from 1-40 ng, the range encountered in this study. All work involving dosing and dissection of the animals, extraction of the tissues, and manipulation of the samples during HPLC was performed under subdued light.

The serum concentration of 13-cis retinoic acid reached 7.3 μ ug/ml within 15

TABLE 1

ELIMINATION OF 13-cis RETINOIC ACID FROM TISSUES

Tissue	Peak Drug Concentration (μg + S.D., n = 3)	$t_{\frac{1}{2}}$ (min)
Serum	7.3 ± 1.3*	16
Liver	6.5 ± 1.8	18
Lung	3.6 ± 1.1	15
Small intestine	12.5 ± 4.4	17
Kidney	1.9 ± 0.1	17
Spleen	1.0 ± 0.3	20
Large intestine	0.8 ± 0.3	16
Fat	4.1 ± 1.1	28
Heart	2.6 ± 0.8	16
Brain	1.1 ± 0.2	30
Muscle	0.9 ± 0.1	21
Testes	0.5 ± 0.1	34

* μg/ml.

min then declined with a t½ of 16 min (TABLE 1). Maximum drug concentrations were reached in liver, lung, heart, and small intestines within 5 min and in other tissues within 15 min. Except in small intestines and liver, the maximum tissue levels were 2-to 15-fold lower than that in serum (TABLE 1). The drug disappeared from most tissues with t½ of 15-20 min. However, disappearance from adipose tissue, brain, and testes had t½'s of 28-34 min.

Following administration of 13-*cis* retinoic acid, a product with the retention time on HPLC characteristic of all-*trans* retinoic acid (14.5 min) was observed, being first detected in the gastrointestinal tract contents and tissues. This product was detected in the serum and other tissues examined within 15-30 min. The possibility that this material may have been made within the gut then absorbed and distributed was supported by its appearance *in vitro* upon incubation of 13-*cis* retinoic acid with digestive tract contents and tissue homogenates. This product, however, was accumulated by and subsequently cleared from most tissues more slowly than it was from serum. This suggests that the gut may not be the sole source of this product. Neither this product nor 13-*cis* retinoic acid was detected in appreciable levels in urine or bile.

In addition, a more polar component with an as yet unidentified structure was observed in liver, small intestines and contents, and bile within 5 min and in kidney and serum within 15 min. This material, although observed *in vivo*, could not be generated *in vitro* upon incubation of 13-*cis* retinoic acid with the appropriate biological samples.

SPECIFIC AND NONSPECIFIC ALTERATIONS IN MEMBRANE MICROVISCOSITY INDUCED BY RETINOIDS IN EMBRYONAL CARCINOMA AND FIBROBLAST CELLS

Anton M. Jetten, Robert G. Meeks,* and Luigi M. De Luca

Laboratory of Experimental Pathology
National Cancer Institute
National Institutes of Health
Bethesda, Maryland 20205

Retinoids can induce structural changes in erythrocyte and lysosomal membranes.[1,2] These alterations may also effect lipid-protein interactions and the fluid state of the membrane. Membrane microviscosity can be monitored quantitatively by fluorescence polarization analysis[3] with the aid of the fluorescent probe 1,6-diphenyl 1,3,5-hexatriene (DPH). In this study this technique was used to determine the effect of retinoids on the membrane microviscosity of some eukaryotic cells.

FIGURE 1 shows the effect of various concentrations of retinoic acid (RA) on membrane microviscosity of 3T6 cells. RA up to 10^{-7}M had no influence on microviscosity; at higher concentrations microviscosity dropped rapidly and leveled off at 5.10^{-6}M. A decrease in microviscosity (increase in fluidity) could be observed even after short treatments (2 hr) with RA. Similar results had been obtained previously with red blood cells.[4]

* Present address: Southern Research Institute, Birmingham, AL 35255.

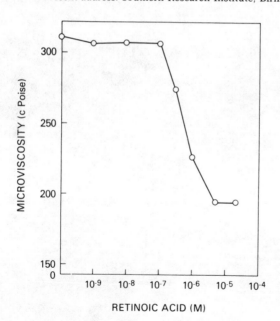

FIGURE 1. Effect of retinoic acid on the membrane microviscosity of 3T6 cells. 3T6 fibroblasts were grown in Dulbecco's modified Eagle's (DME) medium containing 10% calf serum in the presence and absence of various concentrations of retinoic acid. After three days of incubation DPH, dissolved in tetrahydrofuran, was added to a final concentration of 10^{-6}M. Membrane microviscosity was measured 1 hr later in a Cary 219 spectrophotometer as described previously.[1] The microviscosity was plotted against the concentration of retinoic acid.

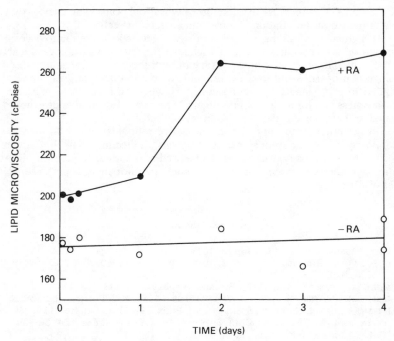

FIGURE 2. Increase in microviscosity during differentiation of embryonal carcinoma cells induced by retinoic acid. Embryonal carcinoma cells were grown in DME/Ham's F12 (1:1) medium containing 10% fetal calf serum. Cells were treated with 10^{-7}M retinoic acid and at different time intervals microviscosity was determined. ●, RA-treated; ○, control cells.

The reduction in microviscosity could be induced by various retinoids, among them retinol, the 13-*cis*-analog, and the pyrimidyl-analog of RA. The pyrimidyl-analog is not biologically active since it does not inhibit growth or increase adhesiveness of 3T6 cells,[5] indicating that retinoids decrease membrane microviscosity whether the analog is biologically active or not.

Retinoids decreased the microviscosity of mouse fibroblast 3T6, 3T12 and 3T3 cells and even in 3T3 SV cells, in which growth and adhesiveness were unaffected by retinoid treatment. These results confirm the nonspecific nature of the action of retinoids on microviscosity.

Retinoids can induce differentiation of embryonal carcinoma cells[6,7] the undifferentiated stem cells present in teratocarcinomas. Embryonal carcinoma cells OC15S1 can differentiate into a fibroblast-like cell type after treatment with RA. Embryonal carcinoma cells appeared to have a relatively higher fluid state of the membrane than some of their differentiated derivatives; this may be due to a difference in lipid composition of the cell types. Therefore, differentiation can be monitored by measurement of the lipid microviscosity as shown in FIGURE 2. After 24 hr of treatment with RA (10^{-7}M), membrane microviscosity increased steadily, concomitantly with the appearance of cells with a fibroblastic morphology. This increase also followed the enhancement of the binding of epidermal growth factor, which has been used as a marker for differentiation of

OC15S1 cells. This increase in microviscosity was only caused by analogs that are able to induce differentiation of embryonal carcinoma cells.[7]

At high concentrations, retinoids caused a decrease in the microviscosity of the membrane. This change occurred whether the analog was biologically active or not, which indicates the nonspecific nature of this action. Some alterations in biological properties induced by retinoids at high concentrations may be attributed to this change in microviscosity. However, the observed increased in adhesiveness and inhibition of growth are highly specific[5,8] and appear not to be related to these nonspecific changes in microviscosity.

On the other hand only biologically active retinoids caused an increase in microviscosity of embryonal carcinoma cells, indicating that this action is specific. Microviscosity, therefore, can be used as a marker to monitor differentiation of embryonal carcinoma cells, but not to monitor changes in the adhesiveness of fibroblasts.

REFERENCES

1. LUCY, J. 1969. Am. J. Clin. Nutr. **22:** 1033–1044.
2. ROELS, O., O. ANDERSON, N. LUI, D. SHAH & M. TROUT. 1969. Am. J. Clin. Nutr. **22:** 1020–1032.
3. SHINITZKY, M. & M. INBAR. 1976. Biochim. Biophys. Acta **433:** 133–149.
4. MEEKS, R., R. CHEN, D. ZAHAREWITZ & M. SPORN. 1980. Mol. Pharmacol. In press.
5. JETTEN, A.M., M.E.R. JETTEN, S. SHAPIRO & J. POON. 1979. Exp. Cell Res. **119:** 289–299.
6. JETTEN, A.M., M.E.R. JETTEN & M.I. SHERMAN. 1979. Exp. Cell Res. **124:** 381–391.
7. JETTEN, A.M. & M.E.R. JETTEN. 1979. Nature **278:** 180–182.
8. ADAMO, S., L.M. DE LUCA, I. AKALOVSKY & P. BHAT. 1979. J. Natl. Cancer Inst. **62:** 1473–1478.

UNDERGLYCOSYLATION OF RAT SERUM α_1-MACROGLOBULIN IN VITAMIN A DEFICIENCY*

Timothy C. Kiorpes

Department of Cornea Research
Eye Research Institute of Retina Foundation
Boston, Massachusetts 02114

Roger S. Anderson

Department of Nutrition and Food Science
Massachusetts Institute of Technology
Cambridge, Massachusetts 02139

A comparative study of the *in vivo* synthesis of α_1-macroglobulin (α_1-M) in vitamin A-deficient and pair-fed control rats has shown that the initial change in deficiency is in the glycosylation of α_1-M and not in its synthesis as had been previously reported by Kiorpes *et al.*[1]

Eight deficient-control pairs were given intraperitoneal injections of 20 μCI [^{3}H] or [^{14}C]glucosamine, and their blood collected 3 hr later by cardiac puncture. The deficient rats ranged from 0 to 11 days past the onset of weight plateau. The labeled serum obtained from these rats was analyzed by immunoprecipitation, radial immunodiffusion, and trichloroacetic acid precipitation, to calculate the specific activity of total serum protein (A) and of α_1-M (B), the radioactivity in α_1-M per weight of total serum protein (C), and the concentration of α_1-M in serum (D). The results are shown in TABLE 1.

The radioactivity in α_1-M per weight of total serum protein (C) is the parameter that was assessed in our original report,[1] and it was similarly depressed (30%). While such a depression could be the result of a lower rate of synthesis, there was no change in α_1-M concentration (D). Instead, this depression can be entirely accounted for by the decrease in the amount of label in α_1-M itself (B), which most likely reflects an underglycosylation.

* Most of the work reported here is from T.C.K.'s Ph.D. thesis.[2] A preliminary report of some of this work has appeared.[3]

TABLE 1

GLUCOSAMINE INCORPORATION INTO TOTAL SERUM PROTEIN AND α_1-MACROGLOBULIN*

	A dpm/mg Protein $(p > 0.1)$†	B dpm/mg α_1-M $(p < 0.05)$	C dpm α_1-M/ mg Protein $(p < 0.05)$	D μg α_1-M/ mg Protein
Deficient	$9,190 \pm 1,540$	$5,490 \pm 770$	366 ± 53	68.8 ± 5.1
Control	$11,160 \pm 1,110$	$8,180 \pm 1,040$	518 ± 54	65.4 ± 5.2
Ratio‡	0.823	0.671	0.707	1.052

* Data expressed as mean $\pm$ standard error of the mean.
† Probabilities determined using Student's t-test (one-tailed).
‡ Deficient mean to control mean.

0077-8923/81/0359-0401 $01.75/0 © 1981, NYAS

TABLE 2

GLUCOSAMINE INCORPORATION INTO TOTAL SERUM PROTEIN AND α_1-MACROGLOBULIN:
INDIVIDUAL PAIR RATIOS*

Pair Number	Days after Onset of Weight Plateau	A dpm/mg protein	B dpm/mg α_1-M	B/A
1	0	1.060	1.130	1.070
2	1	1.060	0.866	0.817
3	3	0.331	0.295	0.891
4	6	0.698	0.622	0.891
5	6	0.650	0.578	0.889
6	9	0.699	0.540	0.773
7	10	1.010	0.791	0.783
8	11	1.130	0.730	0.646
Average	5.8	0.830	0.694	0.845
Less than 1.000?†		p < 0.1	p < 0.01	p < 0.005

* Deficient to its pair-fed control.
† Probabilities determined using Student's t-test (one-tailed).

TABLE 3

COMPARISON OF CHANGES CAUSED BY SYNTHETIC AND GLYCOSYLATION LESIONS
TO THOSE DUE TO PRECURSOR SPECIFIC ACTIVITY CHANGE*

Parameter Compared	Type of Lesion		
	Synthesis	Glycosylation	Specific Activity
A. µg GlcN/mg α_1-M†	1.000	0.894	1.000
B. dpm/µg GlcN	0.801	0.801	0.700
C. dpm/mg α_1-M	0.801	0.716	0.700
D. dpm α_1-M/mg protein	0.716	0.716	0.700
E. µg α_1-M/mg protein	0.894	1.000	1.000

* Results are expressed as the ratio of the experimental to the control.
† Abbreviation used (GlcN) is for glucosamine.

TABLE 4

MEASURED CHANGES IN α_1-MACROGLOBULIN FROM
DEFICIENT RATS AS COMPARED TO THEIR CONTROLS*

Parameter Compared	Ratio
A. µg GlcN/mg α_1-M	0.912†
B. dpm/µg GlcN	0.831
C. dpm/mg α_1-M	0.766‡
D. dpm α_1-M/mg protein	0.766
E. µg α_1-M/mg protein	1.060

* Results are expressed as the ratio of the deficient to the control.
† Significantly less than 1.000 (p < 0.025).
‡ Significantly less than B (paired analysis, p < 0.05).

TABLE 5

COMPARATIVE CARBOHYDRATE COMPOSITION OF α_1-MACROGLOBULIN
FROM VITAMIN A-DEFICIENT AND CONTROL RATS*

	Percent by Weight		
	Control	Deficient	p <
Mannose	2.85 ± 0.06	2.56 ± 0.13	0.05
Galactose	1.89 ± 0.01	1.69 ± 0.01	0.005
N-acetylglucosamine	2.93 ± 0.05	2.62 ± 0.10	0.025
N-acetylneuraminic acid	2.88 ± 0.07	2.17 ± 0.55	0.1
Total	10.55 ± 0.15	9.04 ± 0.78	0.05

* Results are presented as mean ± standard error of the mean with the probabilities obtained using Student's t-test (one-tailed).

Looking at the results expressed as a ratio (deficient:control) for each deficient-control pair (TABLE 2), it can be seen that the decline in the labeling of α_1-M was not simply reflecting changes in total serum label uptake. Instead, examination of the corrected data (B/A) reveals a progressive decline in the apparent glycosylation of α_1-M with increasing duration of the deficiency that is independent of total serum labeling.

When a change occurs in the rate of synthesis or degree of glycosylation of a serum glycoprotein, it is not immediately reflected in the serum because of the presence of material synthesized prior to the change. If one performs a labeling study under such circumstances, the effect of this "lag" is to decrease the measured specific activity of the labeled components in the product relative to that in a control. Examination of the magnitude and pattern of these alterations in specific activity and other parameters allows one to clearly differentiate between the three possible explanations for the observed labeling depression: a decreased rate of synthesis and secretion, an underglycosylation, and a lowered specific activity of the precursor at the time of synthesis. As an example, TABLE 3 compares the pattern of changes one would observe if the rate of synthesis or degree of glycosylation linearly decreased 30% over the 24-hr period preceding the collection of serum (glucosamine injection 3 hr before collection) with those from a change in precursor specific activity.

To determine these parameters experimentally, the serum of 2 pairs from the preceeding experiment was pooled (deficient and controls separately), and the labeled α_1-M purified and analyzed. This procedure was repeated a total of three times, thereby using the serum of 6 of the 8 pairs. The results (TABLE 4) were consistent only with a progressive glycosylation lesion in deficiency.

As final proof, the carbohydrate composition of α_1-M purified from 3 separate groups of control and vitamin A-deficient rats (1-3 weeks past the onset of weight plateau) was determined by gas-liquid chromatography (TABLE 5). It is impossible to determine from these results whether the missing carbohydrate reflects the absence of entire sugar side-chains or the presence of incomplete chains.

REFERENCES

1. KIORPES, T.C., S.J. MOLICA & G. WOLF. 1976. J. Nutr. 106: 1659–1667.

2. KIORPES, T.C. 1978. Ph.D. Thesis. Massachusetts Institute of Technology. Cambridge, MA.
3. WOLF, G., T.C. KIORPES, S. MASUSHIGE, J.B. SCHREIBER, M.J. SMITH & R.S. ANDERSON. 1979. Fed. Proc. **38:** 2540–2543.

BINDING OF RETINOIDS TO HUMAN FIBROBLAST CELL LINES AND THEIR EFFECTS ON CELL GROWTH

André Lacroix, Gregory D. Anderson, and Marc E. Lippman

Medicine Branch
National Cancer Institute
National Institutes of Health
Bethesda, Maryland 20205

Recent investigations from several laboratories have indicated that retinoids can modulate the growth and influence specific cellular processes of certain fibroblast cell lines from various animal species. In several lines, retinoids produce a density-dependent growth inhibition, often associated with morphological changes and increased cell-to-substratum adhesiveness. In other cell lines, no effects on growth were noted, whereas recently, Dicker and Rozengurt (Biochem. Biophys. Res. Commun. **91:** 1203, 1979) found that retinoids stimulate the growth of 3T3 and NIL-8 cells when grown in low concentrations of serum. A cytoplasmic retinoic acid binding protein (cRABP) has been identified in retinoid-inhibited cell lines 3T6 and 3T3, but not in the retinoid-insensitive 3T3SV line. (Jetten *et al.* Exp. Cell. Res. **119:** 289, 1979). Few studies on the effects of retinoids on human fibroblasts have been performed: Danes and Bearn (J. Exp. Med. **124:** 1181, 1966) did not find effects of retinoids on morphology or growth of normal human fibroblasts and Swanson *et al.* (Invest. Ophthalmol **15:** 1017, 1976) did not detect cytoplasmic retinol binding protein (cRBP) or cRABP in human cultured fibroblasts.

In this study, we have examined skin fibroblast cell lines from four normal individuals for the presence of cRBP and cRABP, and for effects of retinoids on cell growth. Fibroblasts were grown in medium with 10% FCS with or without various concentrations of retinoids. When cells reached confluency in control dishes, cell numbers were decreased 10–25% by 10nM and 44–68% by 10μM retinoic acid, and 10–57% by 10μM retinol. No alterations of cell morphology were noted, and cell viability was not affected by the retinoid concentrations utilized. The plating efficiency of human fibroblasts was not modified by retinoic acid. The growth inhibition did not reach significance before the third day of treatment with retinoic acid, and was characterized by a decrease in the exponential growth rate. The time to onset and the percentage of growth inhibition were not influenced by cell density. The growth inhibition was reversible by retinoic acid washout. After prolonged exposure of the fibroblasts to retinoic acid, the final saturation density reached was similar to that of control cells. The inhibitory effects of 1μM retinoic acid on human fibroblasts grown in either 1, 2.5, 5, or 10% FCS were similar and no stimulation of growth was noted at any concentration of FCS. Treatment of human fibroblasts with various concentrations of retinoic acid or retinol did not modify their cell-to-substratum adhesiveness. In all four lines examined, a 2S peak of [³H]retinoic acid binding to cytosol was detectable by sucrose density gradient centrifugation. This binding was displaced by the addition of a 200-fold excess of unlabeled retinoic acid, but not by a 200-fold excess of unlabeled retinol. No binding of [³H]retinol was demonstrable in the cytosol of the four cell lines.

CONCLUSION

Retinoids decrease the growth rate of human skin fibroblast cell lines in a non-density-dependent mode; specific cRABP, but no cRBP is detectable in human fibroblasts.

CHANGES IN HeLa CELL PROLIFERATION RATE AND CELL SURFACE COMPONENTS

Reuben Lotan, Randall H. Kramer, and Garth L. Nicolson

Department of Developmental and Cell Biology
University of California
Irvine, California 92717

Retinoids have been shown to inhibit the growth of various untransformed and tumor cells in liquid medium[1-4] and reduce the ability of different tumor cells to form colonies in semi-solid medium.[5,6] Although the mechanism of retinoid action has yet to be elucidated, several possibilities have been suggested. One of these proposes that they bind to specific cellular retinoid-binding proteins, found in numerous normal and neoplastic cells,[7] with subsequent translocation of the complex to the nucleus[7-9] resulting in alteration of gene expression. Another suggestion is based on the demonstrated involvement of certain retinoids as sugar donors in glycosyl transfer reactions resulting in modification of cellular glycoproteins.[10,11] Thus, retinoids have the potential of altering the structure of cell membrane glycoconjugates in a way that could explain their effects on cell growth.

The finding that retinoids restore anchorage-dependent growth control to HeLa cells prompted us to employ this well-characterized cervical carcinoma cell line to investigate biochemical changes induced by retinoic acid and their possible involvement in growth control of epithelial cells. We found that the addition of retinoic acid to cultures of HeLa-S3 cells caused a reduction in cell proliferation rate which became apparent after 72 hr and was linearly dependent on retinoic acid concentration in the range 10^{-9}-10^{-5}M. After 72 hr of exposure to

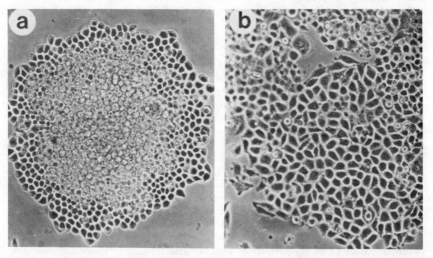

FIGURE 1. Phase-contrast photomicrographs of HeLa-S3 cells cultured for 8 days in the absence (A) or presence (B) of 10^{-5} retinoic acid.

407

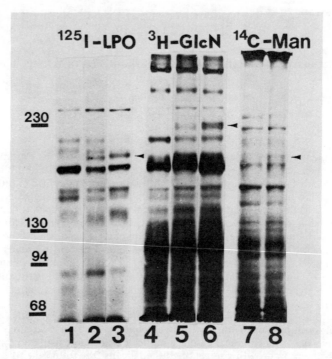

FIGURE 2. Retinoic acid-induced alterations in HeLa cell glycoproteins. Cell surface proteins were labeled by lactoperoxidase-catalyzed iodination (1–3) and cellular glycoproteins by a 48-hr metabolic labeling with either [6-^{3}H]glucosamine (4–6) or (1-^{14}C]mannose (7, 8). Growth conditions were as follows: 1, 4 and 7 – control growth medium 8 days; 2 and 5 – 2 days in the presence of 10^{-5}M retinoic acid; 3, 6 and 8 – 8 days in the presence of 10^{-5}M retinoic acid. After labeling the cells were washed, solubilized in detergent, and subjected to polyacrylamide gel electrophoresis. After electrophoresis the radiolabeled components were detected by autoradiography (1–3) or fluorography (4–8).

retinoic acid, the cells assumed a flattened appearance and no longer formed multilayers (FIG. 1). These changes were reversed within 48 hr after removal of retinoic acid from the medium. Structural analogs of retinoic acid with a free -COOH group at C-15 were usually more potent in growth inhibition than compounds with an alcohol, aldehyde, ether or ester group. A cellular retinoic acid-binding protein was detected in cell homogenates and the binding of [^{3}H]retinoic acid to the binding protein was inhibited by most, but not all, analogs that possess a free terminal -COOH group.

Analysis of cell surface and cellular glycoproteins by lactoperoxidase-catalyzed ^{125}I-iodination (FIG. 2, gels 1–3) and by metabolic labeling with [^{3}H]glucosamine (FIG. 2, gels 4–6) revealed that a 190,000-dalton glycoprotein which was labeled by both methods and a 230,000-dalton glycoprotein which was labeled only with [^{3}H]glucosamine were labeled more intensely in retinoic acid-treated compared to untreated cells. These changes could be observed clearly already after 48 hr of exposure to retinoic acid (FIG. 2, gels 2 and 5). Labeling with [^{14}C]mannose gave a pattern of labeling which was distinct from that with [^{3}H]glucosamine and also demonstrated an increase in labeling of a

190,000-dalton glycoprotein. The electrophoretic mobility of the 230,000-dalton glycoprotein could be modified by treatment of intact cells with either neuraminidase or proteolytic enzymes suggesting that this glycoprotein is also exposed on the cell surface. Although it comigrates with human fibronectin in gel electrophoresis, the 230,000-dalton glycoprotein is not recognized by anti-human fibronectin antiserum, which suggests that it is not fibronectin.

These results demonstrated that retinoic acid can modify HeLa-S3 cell proliferation, morphology, and cellular glycoprotein structure. Further studies will investigate the possible relationships among the diverse effects.

REFERENCES

1. LOTAN, R. & G.L. NICOLSON. 1977. J. Natl. Cancer Inst. **59:** 1717.
2. DION, L.D., J.E. BLALOCK & G.E. GIFFORD. 1977. J. Natl. Cancer Inst. **58:** 795.
3. PATT, L.M., K. ITAYA & S.I. HAKOMORI. 1978. Nature **273:** 379.
4. JETTEN, A.M., M.E.R. JETTEN, S.S. SHAPIRO & J.P. POON. 1979. Exp. Cell Res. **119:** 289.
5. DION, L.D., J.E. BLALOCK & G.E. GIFFORD. 1978. Exp. Cell Res. **117:** 15.
6. MEYSKENS, F.L. & S.E. SALMON. 1979. Cancer Res. **39:** 4055.
7. CHYTIL, F. & D. ONG. 1979. Fed Proc. **38:** 4055.
8. WIGGERT, B., P. RUSSELL, M. LEWIS & G. CHADER. 1977. Biochem. Biophys. Res. Commun. **79:** 218.
9. JETTEN, A.M. & M.E.R. JETTEN. 1979. Nature **278:** 180.
10. DeLUCA, L.M. 1977. Vitam. Horm. **35:** 1.
11. DeLUCA, L.M. 1978. *In* Handbook of Lipid Research. H.F. DeLuca, Ed. Vol. 2: 1. Plenum Publishing Corp. New York.

MODULATION OF DIFFERENTIATION AND MUCOUS GLYCOPROTEIN SYNTHESIS IN CLONED TRACHEAL EPITHELIAL TUMOR CELLS EXPOSED TO RETINYL ACETATE *IN VITRO**

Ann C. Marchok, Jeffrey N. Clark, and Andres Klein-Szanto

Biology Division, Oak Ridge National Laboratory and
University of Tennessee
Oak Ridge Graduate School of Biomedical Sciences
Oak Ridge, Tennessee 37830

It has long been known that glycoprotein synthesis and cellular differentiation of epithelial tissues such as the trachea are greatly influenced by vitamin A both *in vivo* and *in vitro*. We wanted to determine whether cell lines derived from two types of tumors originating from tracheal epithelial cells can also respond to vitamin A *in vitro*. Cell lines 1000 WT and T-8 were cloned from a keratinizing squamous cell carcinoma and an adenocarcinoma, respectively. Both cell lines keratinize *in vitro* when cultured in an enriched Waymouth's MB 752/1 + 10% fetal bovine serum. Cell line 1000 WT formed a continuous stratified epithelium while T-8 was mainly a monolayer with occasional multilayered papillae. After culture for 7 days in 2 or 10 μg retinyl acetate (RAc)/ml, both cell lines were essentially monolayers. There was significant growth inhibition (a 50% decrease in total cell number) only in the 10 μg RAc/ml for both cell lines.

Epon sections of cell line T-8 cultured in 0, 2, or 10 μg RAc/ml all showed cytoplasmic inclusions that stained positive with Periodic acid-Ag-methenamine (PAM); however, the number was greatly enhanced in the vitamin A-treated cultures. Cell line 1000 WT exhibited these inclusions only after culture in RAc. Those cultures that stained positively with PAM also exhibited secretory droplets and hypertrophy of the Golgi apparatus in electron micrographs. This suggests that differentiation is shifted toward a secretory epithelium in both cell lines.

The change in mucin glycoprotein synthesis was quantitatively measured by labeling the cell cultures for 24 hr with [^{3}H]glucosamine (GlcN) + [^{14}C]serine (Ser) in serum-free medium. After labeling, the cell cytosol was extracted and the secretions in the culture medium collected. Both were solubilized and fractionated as described by Clark and Marchok (Biochim. Biophys. Acta **588:** 357, 1979). Briefly, the unpurified, high-molecular weight mucin fraction was collected in the void volume after chromatography of the solubilized material on a Sepharose C1-6B column eluted with a phosphate buffer containing 0.1 M NaC1, 5mM 2-mercaptoethanol and 0.59 mM EDTA. This unpurified mucin fraction was digested with hyaluronidase, treated to reductive alkylation and then rechromatographed on a Sepharose C1-4B column. The purified, high-molecular weight mucin fraction was collected in the void volume.

A 7-day exposure of 1000 WT cells to 2 or 10 μg RAc/ml resulted in an increase in uptake of [^{3}H]GlcN of 4- to 8-fold and [^{14}C]Ser of 3- to 7-fold in the

* Supported by National Cancer Institute (Agreement no. Y01 CP 90207), National Institute of Environmental Health Sciences, National Heart, Lung and Blood Institute (Grant HL 21369–02), and the Office of Health and Environmental Research, U.S. DOE, under contract W–7405–eng–26 with the Union Carbide Corporation.

purified mucin fraction isolated from the cytosol. [³H]G1cN was increased 2- to 5-fold and the [¹⁴C]Ser 1- to 4-fold in the mucin fraction isolated from the secretions. In contrast, the increase in incorporation of [³H]G1cN was 133- to 147-fold and the [¹⁴C]Ser was 12- to 20-fold in the purified mucin fractions isolated from the cytosol of T-8 cells cultured for 7 days in the presence of 2 or 10 μg RAc/ml, respectively. Uptake of [³H]G1cN was increased 68- to 81-fold and [¹⁴C]Ser was increased 13- to 14-fold in the purified mucin fraction isolated from the secretions of T-8 cells. These results indicate that, although epithelial cells from a squamous cell carcinoma retain the capacity to respond to vitamin A *in vitro,* a cell line derived from an adenocarcinoma has a far greater capacity to produce mucin glycoproteins upon vitamin A stimulation.

VITAMIN A RESPONSE OF TESTICULAR CELLS IN CULTURE

J.P. Mather

The Population Council
The Rockefeller University
New York, New York 10021

Vitamin A deficiency leads to sterility in the male. It has been shown that the testis contains cytoplasmic receptors for both retinoic acid (RA) and retinal (R-ol). To date, there is little known about the cell type or types primarily affected or the mode of action in the testis.

Two nontumorigenic, clonal testicular cell lines have been isolated from immature (10 day) BALB/c mice. These cells have been tentatively identified as being of Leydig (TM3) and Sertoli (TM4) origin. In addition, there is a transformed variant (TM4-T) one of the lines. These cell lines can be grown in a serum-free medium supplemented with insulin (5 μg/ml) transferrin (5 μg/ml) and EGF (1 ng/ml). The availability of these cell lines and the hormone-supplemented serum-free medium[2] provide a defined culture system in which the action of retinoids on two different testicular cell types (Leydig and Sertoli) can be studied. In addition, comparisons can be made between the responses of a nontumorigenic line (TM4) and its transformed counterpart (TM4-T).

The TM4 cell line shows an increased cell number (265% of control on day 5) in the presence of both RA and R-ol (50–100 ng/ml). This increase in growth rate is first apparent on the 3rd or 4th day after the addition of the retinoids. There is also a 30% increase in cell volume in cells grown with (50 ng/ml) R.A. Growth of the TM3 cell line is inhibited by RA. Again this effect is not seen during the first 48 hr after addition of the RA. The decrease in cell number is accompanied by a decreased percentage of cells in mitosis on the 3rd to 6th days. This decrease in mitotic figures, like the decreased cell number, is dose dependent.

The transformed Sertoli cell line (TM4-T) is inhibited by RA in contrast to

TABLE 1

GROWTH STIMULATION OF TM$_4$ CELLS BY FSH: EFFECT OF RA

FSH ng/ml	Cell Number, % of Control*	
	– RA	+ RA†
0	100 ± 6%	100 ± 4%
0.1	99	100
2.5	90	102
5.0	218	103
10.0	220	96

* Control: Cells were grown in Ins, tf, EGF and α tocopherol.

† +RA cells were pre-incubated for 4 days prior to plating with 50ng/ml RA, 25ng/ml RA was added on day 0.

Cells were counted on day 3.

TABLE 2

EFFECT OF RA ON ^{125}I-BINDING IN CULTURES OF PORCINE LEYDIG CELLS

	Cell Number on Day 5	cpm ^{125}I hCG Bound/10^6 Cells
Control	3.1×10^5	19,935
+ RA	3.2×10^5	7,900

* Control cultures were supplemented with Ins, tf, EGF, α-tocopherol and 0.05% bovine serum.

stimulation seen in the nontumorigenic line. This growth inhibition is seen within 24 hr after addition of the vitamin and at concentrations as low as 5 ng/ml.

An influence of retinoids on gonadotropin response can be seen in 2 different model systems. The growth of the TM4 cell line, like that of primary cultures of immature Sertoli cells, is stimulated by follicle-stimulating hormone (FSH). This growth stimulation by FSH is entirely eliminated in the presence of 50 ng/ml RA (TABLE 1). Primary cultures of porcine Leydig cells contain high numbers of leuteinizing hormone (LH) receptors (40,000 receptors/cell). The receptor levels were measured directly by the binding of 125 I-hCG (human chorionic gonadotropin) to Leydig cells grown in Ins, tf, EGF, vitamin E 200 ng/ml and 0.05% calf serum. Under these conditions cell numbers and hCG receptor levels can be maintained for more than 3 weeks in culture. The addition of RA (25 ng/ml) causes a significant decrease in hCG receptor levels (40% of control on day 5) without altering cell number (TABLE 2). The hCG stimulated testosterone production is higher in the presence of RA. The decrease in receptor number cannot, therefore, be due to a specific loss of Leydig cells from the cultures.

It can be concluded that Vitamin A plays a role in the function of both Leydig and Sertoli cells in the testis. A possible mode of action may be to modulate gonadotropin receptor levels and/or the response of these cells to their respective gonadotropins.

REFERENCES

1. MATHER, J.P. 1980. Biol Reprod. **23:** 243.
2. MATHER, J.P. & G.H. SATO. 1979. Exp. Cell Res. **124:** 215.

INHIBITION OF HUMAN TUMOR COLONY FORMATION BY RETINOIDS

Frank L. Meyskens, Jr. and Sydney E. Salmon

Cancer Center Division
University of Arizona
Tucson, Arizona 85724

The effect of a 1.0-hr exposure of four retinoids (β-*trans*-retinol, RO; β-*all-trans*-retinoic acid, tRA; 13-*cis*-retinoic acid, cRA; and aromatic retinoic acid ethyl ester analog (RO 10-9359), aRA, on tumor colony-forming units (TCFU) was assessed in fresh biopsies of melanoma tissue from 16 patients. Reduction in TCFU was seen. At 10^{-5}M retinoid:

	RO	tRA	cRA	aRA
<40% reduction	5/14	6/13	10/14	8/9
40–70% reduction	6/14	5/13	2/14	1/9
>70% reduction	3/14	2/13	2/14	1/9

The specific retinoid causing a decrease in TCFU varied from patient to patient and differential sensitivities to the different retinoids in individual patients were present. The effect of 1 hr and continuous exposure of melanoma TCFU to RO and cRA was investigated in 4 samples. The reduction of TCFU with continous 1 hr exposure to cRA was similar in all 4 patients. In 2 of 4 patients, reduction of TCFU with RO corresponded. In 2 patients no effect on TCFU was noted with 1 hr exposure to RO, but continuous exposure to RO enhanced TCFU 400 and 500%. The increase in clonogenicity appeared to be a relatively selective expansion of one (light, large cells and not dark, small cells) of the two pigmentary colony variants in melanoma that can be morphologically identified.

The effects of retinoids on TCFU from a series of patients with other malignancies was also assessed. At 10^{-7}M retinoid:

	RO	cRA
<40% reduction		
bladder cancer	1/1	3/4
ovarian cancer	1/7	0/5
40–70% reduction		
bladder cancer	0/1	0/4
ovarian cancer	4/7	4/5
>70% reduction		
bladder cancer	0/1	1/4
ovarian cancer	2/7	1/5

These investigations demonstrate that retinoids affect human tumor clonogenicity in soft agar.

IMMUNOCHEMICAL STUDIES ON CELLULAR VITAMIN A-BINDING PROTEINS*

David E. Ong and Frank Chytil

Department of Biochemistry
Vanderbilt University School of Medicine
Nashville, Tennessee 37232

INTRODUCTION

Cellular retinol-binding protein (CRBP) as well as cellular retinoic-acid-binding protein (CRABP) both putative mediators of vitamin A action have been recently purified to homogeneity from rat liver and testis.[1,2] These proteins have almost the same molecular weight of 14,600. Each protein possesses a striking ability to discriminate between retinol and retinoic acid. Organs of numerous species also contain these binding proteins with physical properties (size, binding affinity for ligands) quite similar to those determined for the binding proteins for rat. Here we have examined CRBP from various sources as well as CRABP and serum retinol-binding protein (RBP) for immunochemical similarities.

MATERIALS AND METHODS

After isolating cellular retinol binding protein (CRBP) from rat liver,[1] attempts were made to produce antibodies against the homogeneous preparation in rabbit, goat and chicken. Attempts to immunize with (1) pure CRBP, (2) CRBP conjugated with bovine serum albumin, or (3) CRBP conjugated with bovine thyroglobulin were unsuccessful. Antibodies were finally obtained by immunizing rabbit and goat with glutaraldehyde-treated CRBP.[3]

Rat livers and testes for isolation of CRBP[1] as well as livers of other species were brought from Pel-Freez. A sample of human liver was obtained from Dr. Page. The liver cytosols were prepared as described earlier.[1] Cellular retinoic acid binding protein (CRABP) was purified as described.[2] Rat serum RBP was purified by B. McGuire.[4] Quantitation of CRBP by sucrose gradient centrifugation was performed as described elsewhere.[5] The radioimmunoassay (RIA) employed CRBP labeled with tritium by reductive methylation.[3] Antibody-bound CRBP was separated from free CRBP by ammonium sulfate precipitation.[3]

RESULTS AND DISCUSSION

The antiserum against rat liver CRBP obtained in rabbit was used to check the antigenicity of pure rat testis CRABP and rat serum RBP. As can be seen from FIGURE 1 pure CRABP as well as RBP were ineffective in competing with CRBP for antibody. Increasing the amount of CRABP and RBP to 1000 pmoles did not decrease binding of CRBP, indicating no immunochemical similarity for these

* This investigation was supported by Grants Number HD 05384, HD 09195, HL 15341 and CA20850 awarded by the National Institutes of Health.

415

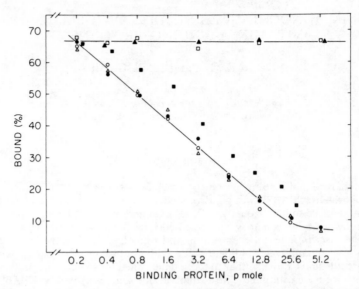

FIGURE 1. Comparison of the immunoreactivity of vitamin A-binding proteins (rabbit antibody). Pure CRBP from rat liver (O) and testis (●); rat liver cytosol (Δ); pure CRABP from rat testis (□); pure rat serum RBP (▲); and mouse liver cytosol (■).

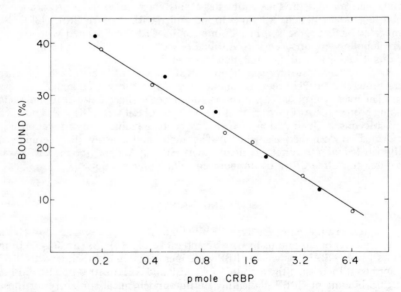

FIGURE 2. Standard RIA curve with antibody against pure rat liver CRBP (goat antibody). Pure rat liver CRBP (O); cytosol from hamster liver (●).

TABLE 1

COMPARISON OF ANTIGENICITIES OF LIVER CRBPs USING
A GOAT ANTI-RAT LIVER CRBP SERUM

Species	CRBP/g Liver* (pmole)	Relative Ability to Displace [³H]CRBP in RIA Compared to Rat CRBP (= 100)	
		2 pmole	4 pmole
Hamster	72	100	100
Rabbit	110	10	10
Cow	144	10	10
Guinea pig	240	4	4
Swine	88	5	4
Human	380	0	3
Sheep	250	0	0
Chick	200	0	0

* Determined by sucrose gradient centrifugation assay.

two proteins with CRBP. When CRBP purified from rat testis was tested in the RIA it was indistinguishable from that purified from rat liver (FIG. 1). In addition a cytosol from rat liver reacted as expected for its content of CRBP as determined by sucrose gradient centrifugation. Comparison with a cytosol of mouse liver showed similar but not identical immunoreactivity to rat CRBP (FIG. 1).

In the next experiments antiserum against rat liver CRBP raised in goat was used. FIGURE 2 shows the RIA curve.

The amount of CRBP in liver extracts of various species was quantitated by sucrose gradient centrifugation and the antigenicity assessed by determining the ability of the CRBP in these extracts to displace methylated CRBP. The potency of rat CRBP was set at 100%. As can be seen from TABLE 1 only hamster cytosol CRBP showed a displacement equal to rat (also shown in FIG. 2). The liver cytosols of rabbit and cow showed 10% potency, followed by guinea pig and swine. Human CRBP showed some antigenic similarity but no reaction with the antibody was found in sheep and chick.

Taken together the rodents mouse and hamster showed considerable similarity of antigenic structures of CRBP when compared with rat, whereas the CRBP in other species tested exhibited significantly less or no similarity in antigenicity.

REFERENCES

1. ONG, D.E. & F. CHYTIL. 1978. Cellular retinol-binding protein from rat liver. Purification and characterization. J. Biol. Chem. 253:828.
2. ONG, D.E. & F. CHYTIL. 1978. Cellular retinoic acid-binding protein from rat testis. Purification and characterization. J. Biol. Chem. 253: 4551.
3. ONG, D.E. & F. CHYTIL. 1979. Immunochemical comparison of vitamin A binding proteins of rat. Biol. Chem. 254:8733.
4. McGUIRE, B.W. & F. CHYTIL. 1980. Three step purification of retinol-binding protein from rat serum. Biochem. Biophys. Acta 621: 342.
5. ONG, D.E. & F. CHYTIL. 1976. Changes in levels of cellular retinol- and retinoic-acid-binding proteins of liver and lung during perinatal development of rat. Proc. Natl. Acad. Sci. USA 73: 3976.

SYNTHESIS OF LIPID-LINKED OLIGOSACCHARIDES IN VITAMIN A-DEFICIENT RAT LIVER *IN VIVO*

Gloria Chi Rosso and George Wolf

Department of Nutrition and Food Science
Massachusetts Institute of Technology
Cambridge, Massachusetts 02139

Labeled [1-^{14}C]glucosamine or [2-^{3}H]mannose was injected into vitamin A-deficient (D) and pair-fed control (N) rats, at an early stage of deficiency. The liver was homogenized in 0.15 M Tris HCl (pH 7.4) buffer containing 4 mM MgCl$_2$ (5 ml buffer/g liver). After centrifugation at 100,000 × g for 35 min, the supernatant fraction was decanted and the pellet resuspended in cold Tris buffer at a volume of 1.5 ml/g of original tissue. Extraction was carried out 3 times with chloroform:methanol:H$_2$O (3:2:1) to remove most of the lipids, followed by chloroform:methanol:H$_2$O (10:10:3) to preferentially extract the oligosaccharide-lipid.

This fraction when labeled with glucosamine, reached a maximum at 35 min after injection, and remained constant to 110 min. The fraction was chromatographed on DEAE-cellulose in chloroform:methanol:water (10:10:3), and was eluted at an ammonium acetate concentration of approximately 20 mM, as would be expected of oligosaccharide bound to dolichylpyrophosphate. Under these conditions of chromatography, dolichylmannosyl phosphate, prepared by liver enzyme, eluted at the much lower concentration of 7 mM.

Fractionation of the oligosaccharide produced after mild acid hydrolysis (0.02 M HCl in 100°C for 20 min) of the oligosaccharide-lipid, on a Bio-gel P4 column (1.4 × 113 cm), gave a major peak (pk I) followed by a heterogeneous broad minor peak (pk II) of smaller molecular weight. Peak II from deficient liver was always much greater than from normal liver (10–32% for D and 2–10% for N of total oligosaccharide).

Rechromatography of peak II on a Bio-gel P-4 (1 × 200) column, yielded several distinct peaks of smaller molecular weight than peak I with the principal peak having a K$_d$ of 0.486 corresponding to standard Man$_5$GlcNac$_2$. Peak I has a K$_d$ of 0.285, corresponding to Glc$_3$Man$_9$GlcNac$_2$ (S.C. Hubbard and P.W. Robbins, personal communication).

Both peaks were α-mannosidase digestible, peak I (labeled with [2-^{3}H]mannose) yielding 48% mannose and peak II with K$_d$ of 0.486 yielding 79% mannose. The Man$_5$GlcNac$_2$ component of peak II was resistant to endo-β-N-acetylglucosaminidase-H hydrolysis and peak I was sensitive to the enzyme under the same condition of treatment. The endo-H specificity requires the linking of mannose to man-1,6-man-β-1-4-(GlcNac)$_2$.* From the size of the molecule (Man$_5$GlcNac$_2$) and its resistance to endo-H hydrolysis, we concluded that vitamin A deficiency causes an increased pool of small molecular weight oligosaccharide-lipids, the predominant one being Man$_5$GlcNac$_2$ with structure:

---

* Trimble, R.B., A.L. Tarentino, T.H. Plummer, and F. Maley. 1978. Asparaginyl glycopeptides with a low mannose content are hydrolyzed by endo-β-N-acetylglucosaminidase-H. J. Biol. Chem. **253**: 4506–4511.

$$\begin{array}{l} \text{Man} \\ \qquad \diagdown \\ \qquad\qquad \text{Man-GlcNac}_2\text{-P-P-Dol} \\ \text{Man-Man-Man} \diagup \end{array}$$

CELLULAR AND SUBCELLULAR UPTAKE OF RETINOIC ACID AND ITS MEDIATION BY RETINOIC ACID-BINDING PROTEIN

Brahma P. Sani and Chandra K. Banerjee

Kettering-Meyer Laboratory
Southern Research Institute
Birmingham, Alabama 35205

Specific retinoic acid-binding protein (RABP), which has an S_{20} value of 2.0 and an isoelectric pH of 4.6, has been detected in the cytosol, nuclei and plasma membrane of chick embryo skin, and experimental murine tumors. The cytosol-binding protein from different tissues has been purified and partially characterized in different laboratories.

Twelve- to thirteen-day-old chick embryo skin segments were incubated in Eagles' modified medium containing 1 μM [^{3}H] retinoic acid for 2 hr at 0°, 20°, or 37°C. The incubation was terminated by quick chilling and immediate centrifugation followed by washings with phosphate-buffered saline, pH 7.2. At 37°, about 7% of the retinoic acid present in the medium appeared in the cytosol whereas at 20° and 0°, the uptake was 3.2% and 1.5% respectively. The relative efficiency of complex formation by cytosol RABP and retinoic acid under the above conditions was 1, 3, and 10 at 0°, 20°, and 37°, respectively. Time dependence of retinoic acid incorporation by cytosol RABP was studied after incubating the chick embryo skin with 1 μM [^{3}H]retinoic acid in Eagles' modified medium at 37°. As evidenced from the size of 2S RABP peaks after sucrose gradient sedimentation, retinoic acid incorporation increased linearly up to 120 min. A 240-min incubation resulted in 50% reduction of the RABP-[^{3}H]retinoic acid complex compared to a 120-min incubation.

Incubation of chick embryo skin in the presence of 5 μM or 10 μM [^{3}H]retinoic acid for 2 hr at 37° in Eagles' medium, subsequent isolation of the skin nuclei, and analysis for RABP-[^{3}H]retinoic acid complex in the nuclear extract revealed distinct 2S RABP peaks. Presence of 10-fold molar excess of unlabeled retinoic acid in the initial incubation mixture showed competition for the [^{3}H]retinoic acid binding sites on RABP. The binding of the radiolabeled ligand to the protein under the conditions of these experiments was loose inasmuch as dialysis of the complex resulted in dissociation of 90% of the complex.

The cellular recognition and transport of retinoic acid across the plasma membrane is not well understood. In the course of a study of the special surface membrane properties of epithelial cells, we have located and partially characterized a specific retinoic acid-binding component in the plasma membrane of chick embryo skin and of transplantable mouse colon tumor 26. Radioactivity profiles of the plasma membrane extract-[^{3}H]retinoic acid complex, after sucrose density sedimentation, revealed a distinct peak with an S_{20} value of 2.0, which is the same as that for cytosol RABP. Unextracted plasma membrane, under similar conditions, did now show any detectable 2S binding peak, and the [^{3}H]retinoic acid bound to the membrane sedimented to the bottom of the gradient tube. The protein nature of the binding component in the extracts was assessed by treatment with pronase, which completely abolished the 2S peak. The physicochemical characteristics including the ligand specificity of plasma membrane RABP was similar to cytosol RABP. Biologically active analogs of retinoic acid, such as trimethylmethoxyphenyl analog and 13-*cis*-retinoic acid, exhibited competition as efficiently as did retinoic acid for the binding sites. Like cytosol RABP, the plasma membrane-binding component is also present in large quantities in the embryonic tissues, marginally detectable in adult tissues, but evident after neoplastic transformations. The plasma membrane RABP also exhibited mercurial-sensitive thiol functions in ligand binding. The inhibition was reversed by thiol compounds. The plasma membrane RABP may facilitate the cellular recognition and selective transport of retinoic acid by epithelial cells.

APPLICATION OF A HPLC METHOD OF ANALYSIS OF RETINOIDS TO METABOLIC STUDIES

P. Ramnathan Sundaresan and Andrija Kornhauser

Division of Toxicology
Food and Drug Administration
Washington, D.C. 20204

Pangala V. Bhat

National Cancer Institute
Bethesda, Maryland 20014

In a previous publication Bhat *et al.* (Anal. Biochem. **102:** 243–248, 1980) described a reverse phase high-pressure liquid chromatographic (HPLC) method for the separation of naturally occurring retinoids. We modified this method in the present study to achieve base line separation of 13–*cis*– and all–*trans*–retinoic acid (RA) by employing reverse phase ion pair HPLC. In addition, we employed this method to investigate the interconversion of 13–*cis*– and all–*trans*-RA and their metabolism in normal rats.

The separation of naturally occurring retinoids was achieved by reverse phase HPLC on a octadecylsilane column eluted with acetonitrile-phosphate buffer, pH 7.2 mixtures. The order of elution from a mixture of 200–250 ng of each of the following standard retinoids was mannosyl retinyl phosphate (MRP), 4-oxoRA, 5,6-epoxyRA, retinyl phosphate, 13-*cis*-RA, all-*trans*-RA, retinol, retinal, retinyl acetate, anhydroretinol and retinyl palmitate. All the standards were in the all-*trans* configuration except 13-*cis*-RA. The column was eluted with acetonitrile-phosphate buffer, pH 7.2 (37:63), at an initial flow rate of 2.2 ml/min for the first 30 min to elute MRP, 4-oxoRA, 5,6-epoxyRA, 13-*cis*-RA and all-*trans*-RA and with acetonitrile-phosphate buffer, pH 7.2 (54:46), at a flow rate of 3.5 ml/min for the following 15 min to elute retinol, retinal, retinyl acetate, and anhydroretinol. The solvent composition was then altered to acetonitrile-water (98.2) and the flow rate adjusted to 1.5 ml/min for an additional 15 min to elute retinyl palmitate.

Metabolic studies on retinoic acid were carried out in normal male rats (200 g) of the Sprague-Dawley strain. Each rat was injected intraperitoneally with 50 μCi of either [10-³H]-all-*trans* (5.4 μg) or [11-³H]-13-*cis*-RA (8.8 μg) in 50 μl of ethanol and sacrificed after 0.5 and 3 hr. Blood, liver and testes were removed and lyophilized. The tissues were extracted in 99% methanol and an aliquot of the extract in absolute methanol was used for HPLC analysis. A small amount of all-*trans*-RA was converted 0.5 hr after injection to 13-*cis*-RA in all the tissues studied, the conversion being 2.4% (testes), 3.1% (liver) and 6.9% (blood) of the total recovered radioactivity. In addition, all-*trans*-RA was also transformed to highly polar metabolites. At 0.5 hr after injection, these constituted 17.5% for liver, 47.7% for testes and 37% for blood. At 3 hr after injection, most of the radioactivity was located in the highly polar metabolites (blood 81%, liver 87% and testes 75%). These metabolites were more polar than 5,6-epoxy-all-*trans*-RA and 4-oxoRA.

13-*cis*-RA was also found to be partially converted to the all-*trans* isomer at 0.5 hr after injection in the tissues examined (blood 21%, liver 12% and testes 3%)

and to the highly polar metabolites represented by Peak I (blood 8.3%, liver 14% and testes 30%). However, a second peak (Peak II) representing a compound of greater polarity than 5,6-epoxy-all-*trans* RA, but less polar than 4-oxoRA, was also observed in all the three tissues (blood 9.9%, liver 22% and testes 12.4%). At 3 hr after injection, there was still appreciable radioactivity in the 13-*cis*-RA fraction (blood 41%, liver 12.5% and testes 10%), indicating that the conversion of 13-*cis*-RA to highly polar compounds is not as rapid as in the case of all-*trans*-RA. In addition, both the peaks representing highly polar metabolites (Peaks I and II) indicated substantial increments in radioactivity (blood: peak I 15%, peak II 30%; liver: peak I 40%, peak II 33%; and testes: peak I 47%, peak II 23%).

These results demonstrate that there is interconversion of all-*trans*-RA to 13-*cis*-RA in the tissues studied and that all-*trans*-RA is rapidly converted to highly polar metabolites. The conversion of 13-*cis*-RA to the highly polar metabolites, however, is not as rapid as in the case of the all-*trans* isomer, as indicated by the retention of appreciable radioactivity in the 13-*cis* fraction even at 3 hr after injection.

We thank Dr. Luigi M. DeLuca for stimulating discussions during this study.

IN VITRO METABOLISM OF 13-*cis*-RETINOIC ACID BY 9,000 ×*g* RAT LIVER SUPERNATANT

Floie M. Vane and Christopher J.L. Bugge

Department of Biochemistry and Drug Metabolism
Hoffmann-La Roche Inc.
Nutley, New Jersey 07110

13-*cis*-Retinoic acid (RA) was incubated for 1 hr at 37°C with 9,000 ×*g* liver supernatant prepared from normal rats and fortified with an NADPH-generating system. Extracts of the incubation mixture were analyzed by reverse-phase high pressure liquid chromatography (HPLC). Metabolites isolated by HPLC were converted to methyl esters (ME) for mass spectrometry (MS) and nuclear magnetic resonance (NMR) studies.

A typical HPLC profile is shown in FIGURE 1. The major peak was shown by MS and NMR to be intact 13-*cis*-RA. The MS and NMR of the methyl esters of I, II, and IIIc were identical to the spectra of the reference compounds: methyl all-*trans*-retinoate, methyl 4-oxo-13-*cis*-retinoate and methyl 4-oxo-all-*trans*-retinoate, respectively. IIIb-ME was shown by MS to have a molecular weight of 330, which suggested a hydroxy metabolite. The NMR of IIIb-ME was very similar to

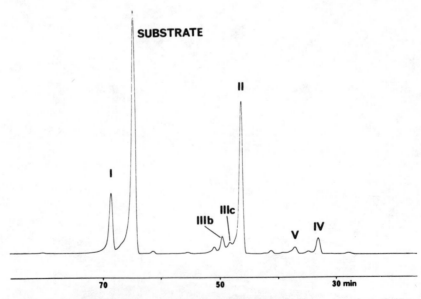

FIGURE 1. Partial chromatogram from the HPLC analysis of an extract from the incubation of 13-*cis*-retinoic acid with 9,000 × *g* rat liver supernatant. A reverse-phase column (Whatman Partisil Magnum 9 10/25 ODS) was used with a gradient solvent system (methanol/water: 33/67 →80/20; the solvents contained 0.01 M ammonium acetate and the final pH was 6) at a flow rate of 3 ml min⁻¹. Absorption at 365 nm was measured.

424

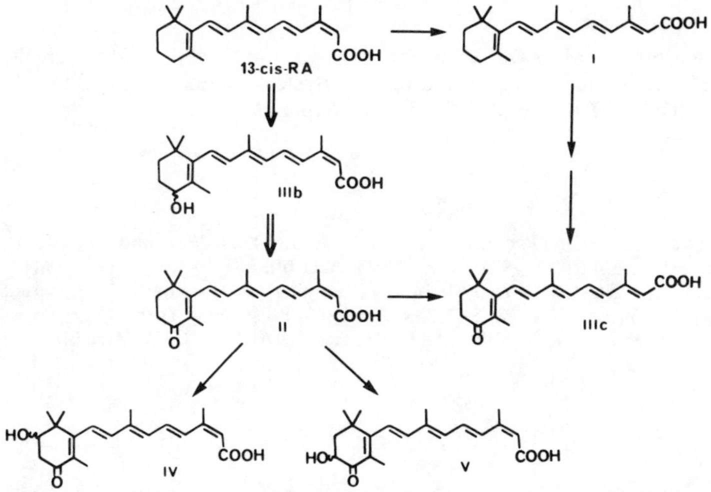

FIGURE 2. Metabolism of 13-*cis*-retinoic acid by 9,000 × g rat liver supernatant.

that of 4-hydroxy-all-*trans*-RA except that IIIb-ME contained an intact 13-*cis* side chain. Therefore, IIIB is very likely 4-hydroxy-13-*cis*-RA. The MS of IV-ME and V-ME both showed molecular ions at m/e 344, which suggested hydroxy, keto structures. NMR showed that the 13-*cis* side chains and methyl groups at C1 and C5 of the two metabolites were unchanged. A multiplet was observed at δ3.87 (doublet of doublets, J = 5,9 Hz) in the NMR of IV-ME which suggested that IV was 2-hydroxy-4-oxo-13-*cis*-RA. A similar multiplet was observed at δ4.32 (J = 6, 14 Hz) in the NMR of V-ME which is compatible with V being 3-hydroxy-4-oxo-13-*cis*-RA.

The presence of keto groups in II, IIIc, IV and V was confirmed by reaction of these metabolites with methoxyamine to form methoxime derivatives, which eluted later than the underivatized metabolites.

Individual incubations of all-*trans*-RA, 4-oxo-13-*cis*-RA, 4-oxo-all-*trans*-RA, and 4-hydroxy-all-*trans*-RA helped define the following sequence for the metabolism of 13-*cis*-RA by rat liver supernatant. The initial step is hydroxylation at C4 (FIG. 2) to form IIIb which is rapidly oxidized to the 4-oxo metabolite II. Metabolite II is further metabolized by hydroxylation at C2 (IV) and at C3 (V). In addition, 13-*cis*-RA and II are enzymatically converted to the corresponding all-*trans* isomers I and IIIc, respectively. 13-*cis*-RA and the other reference retinoids were stable to the incubation and isolation procedures when the rat liver supernatant was deleted.

The conversion of 13-*cis*-RA to 4-oxo metabolites by 9,000 × g rat liver supernatant is similar to that reported for the metabolism of all-*trans*-RA and 13-*cis*-RA in *in vivo*[1-3] and other *in vitro*[1] systems. The 2-hydroxy-4-oxo and 3-hydroxy-4-oxo metabolites appear to be novel. Metabolites of all-*trans*-RA containing a 4-keto group and a hydroxy on one of the C1 methyl groups have been identified in rat urine[4] and postulated for human urine[3]. Metabolites containing a hydroxy group on the C5 methyl group, but no keto group, were found in the feces of rats receiving all-*trans*-RA.[2]

ACKNOWLEDGMENTS

We are grateful to Dr. M. Rosenberger of the Chemical Research Dept. for providing reference retinoids and to the Physical Chemistry Dept. for obtaining the MS (Dr. W. Benz) and NMR (Dr. T. Williams) data.

REFERENCES

1. ROBERTS, A.B. & C.A. FROLIK. 1979. Fed. Proc. **38:** 2524–2527, and references therein.
2. HANNI, R. & F. BIGLER. 1977. Helv. Chim. Acta **60:** 881–887.
3. RIETZ, P.,O. WISS & F. WEBER. 1974. *In* Vitamins and Hormones. R.S. Harris & K.V. Thomann, Eds. Vol. **32:** 237–249. Academic Press. New York.
4. HANNI, R., F. BIGLER, W. MEISTER & G. ENGLERT. 1976. Helv. Chim. Acta **59:** 2221–2227.

CYTOSOL BINDING OF RETINYL PALMITATE AND PALMITIC ACID IN PIGMENT EPITHELIUM (PE) AND RETINA

Barbara Wiggert and Gerald J. Chader

Laboratory of Vision Research,
National Eye Institute
National Institutes of Health,
Bethesda, Maryland 20205

Retinyl palmitate is the major storage form of retinol in the pigment epithelium-choroid unit of the retina. We have previously demonstrated a specific soluble receptor for [³H]retinol in the cytosol fraction of the chick embryo PE that sediments at 2S on 5–20% sucrose gradient. Nonradiolabeled retinyl palmitate was found to compete with [³H]retinol for binding to the 2S retinol receptor, but this is probably due to release of free retinol by esterase action during the incubation period. Radiolabeled retinyl palmitate (palmitic-1-¹⁴C) did not bind in the 2S region. Instead, a single peak of radiolabel was observed sedimenting at about 6S on sucrose gradients. This peak is distinct from the 5S peak observed after [¹⁴C]retinyl palmitate is incubated with chick serum. Incubation with pronase substantially decreased 6S binding, indicating the protein nature of the 6S cellular receptor. A 50-fold excess of nonradiolabeled retinyl palmitate greatly diminished binding; thus only a limited number of binding sites are available in the cytosol preparation. A specific 6S protein thus appeared to be present in PE-choroid which could bind [¹⁴C]retinyl palmitate.

We next wished to determine if the 6S binding was truly binding of the intact [¹⁴C]retinyl palmitate moiety or possibly only of [¹⁴C]palmitate after esterase action. Incubation of [¹⁴C]palmitate with chick PE-choroid cytosol resulted in a discrete 6S binding peak. A 200-fold excess of nonradiolabeled palmitic acid substantially reduced [¹⁴C]palmitate binding. Thin-layer chromatography of extracts of the 6S peak after cytosol incubation with [¹⁴C]retinyl palmitate demonstrated that both [¹⁴C]retinyl palmitate and [¹⁴C]palmitic acid were bound in the 6S region. This indicates (1) that there is substantial esterase activity in the cytosol preparation and (2) that both the ester and the free fatty acid are bound in the 6S region. After incubation with [¹⁴C]palmitic acid, only the free acid was observed by TLC with no evidence of esterification with retinol. In parallel studies, cytosol fractions from chick embryo brain, liver, lung and intestine as well as bovine PE all demonstrated binding of both [¹⁴C]retinyl palmitate and [¹⁴C]palmitic acid at 6S. There was no detectable binding to a 2S peak in any of these tissues.

In the retina, there is no detectable binding of [¹⁴C]retinyl palmitate in either chick or bovine cytosol preparations. [¹⁴C]Palmitic acid was bound in peaks at both 6S and 2S, however. There is substantially more binding of the acid at 6S than at 2S. Thus, in contrast to PE and several other tissues, the 6S retinyl palmitate-binding species but not the palmitic acid-binding species appears to be missing in retina.

One of the major roles of the pigment epithelium is the uptake of vitamin A from the circulation and its storage in the ester form. The 6S protein might fulfill the role of a retinyl ester-binding protein, which mobilizes the ester, transporting it to the retina. It also might have a specific enzymic activity, e.g. esterase. Further studies on the nature of this protein and on its binding specificity (e.g. whether the same or different proteins bind retinyl palmitate and palmitic acid) will help to clarify its role in cell metabolism.

INDEX OF CONTRIBUTORS

429